Aug 17, 1971   50¢

The Holt Series in
High-School Literature

OUR READING HERITAGE

Exploring Life

Ourselves and Others

This Is America

England and the World

OUR READING

HERITAGE

Exploring Life

SELECTED AND EDITED BY

Harold H. Wagenheim
Principal, Mabel Dean Bacon Vocational High School
New York City

Elizabeth Voris Brattig
Teacher of English, Williamsburgh Vocational High School
Brooklyn, New York

Matthew Dolkey
Assistant Professor of English, New Jersey State Teachers College
Newark, New Jersey

NEW YORK   HENRY HOLT AND COMPANY

COPYRIGHT

We wish to thank the following authors, publishers, and other holders of copyright for permission to use and adapt copyrighted materials:

George Allen and Unwin Ltd. for permission to reprint in Canada: "Kon-Tiki" from *Kon-Tiki* by Thor Heyerdahl.

The Bobbs-Merrill Company, Inc. for "Modern Ode to the Modern School" from *Sonata and Other Poems* by John Erskine, copyright, 1925, 1953. Used by special permission of the publishers.

Brandt & Brandt for "The Most Dangerous Game," copyright, 1924, 1952, by Richard Connell; for "Ah Love! Ah Me!" by Max Steele, copyright, 1945, by Max Steele; for "I'm in a Hurry" by William Hazlett Upson, copyright, 1925, 1953, by William Hazlett Upson; for "Doc Mellhorn and the Pearly Gates" from *Selected Works of Stephen Vincent Benét,* published by Rinehart & Company, Inc., copyright, 1938, by Stephen Vincent Benét; and for "Indian" from *A Book of Americans* by Rosemary and Stephen Vincent Benét, copyright, 1933, by Rosemary and Stephen Vincent Benét.

Curtis Brown Ltd. for "All Yankees Are Liars" by Eric Knight, copyright, 1938, by Curtis Publishing Company. Reprinted by permission of the author's estate.

Paul Burlin for "We Are All One People" by Hiamovi from *The Indians' Book* edited by Natalie Curtis.

Burton Publishing Company, Inc. for "These Things I Love" from *Moments of Mood* by Annette Wildman.

The Christian Science Publishing Society for "Post Early for Space" by Peter J. Henniker-Heaton, originally published in *The Christian Science Monitor.*

Coward-McCann, Inc. for "Counters" from *Compass Rose* by Elizabeth Coatsworth, copyright, 1929, by Coward-McCann, Inc. Reprinted by permission.

Dodd, Mead & Company, Inc. for "How We Kept Mother's Day" from *Laugh with Leacock* by Stephen Leacock, copyright, 1930, by Dodd, Mead & Company, Inc. Reprinted by permission.

Doubleday & Company, Inc. for "Learning to Speak" from *The Story of My Life* by Helen Keller, copyright, 1903, by Helen Keller, reprinted by permission of Doubleday & Company, Inc.; for "The Rich Man" from *Column Book of F.P.A.* by Franklin P. Adams, copyright, 1928, by Doubleday & Company, Inc.; and for "The Ransom of Red Chief" from *Whirligigs* by O. Henry, copyright, 1910, by Doubleday & Company, Inc.

Louise Driscoll for "Hold Fast Your Dreams."

E. P. Dutton & Co., Inc. for "We Are the Young" ("Cief Didway") from *Album of Destiny* by Jesse Stuart, copyright, 1944, by Jesse Stuart; and for "Hills" from *Death*

The illustrations for this book were done by the following artists:

Leonard Everett Fisher
Douglas Gorsline
John Polgreen
Sideo Fromboluti
Mircea Vasiliu

Don Lynch
James Thurber
Clifford H. Schule
Lionel Reiss
George Pay

ACKNOWLEDGMENTS

and *General Putnam and 101 Other Poems* by Arthur Guiterman, copyright, 1935, by E. P. Dutton & Co., Inc.

Frederick and Pauline Gilsdorf for "The Ghost of Benjamin Sweet."

Carl Glick and *This Week* magazine for "My Song Yankee Doodle" by Carl Glick, copyright, 1938, by the United Magazine Corporation.

Harcourt, Brace and Company, Inc. for "The Most Beautiful Pagoda" from *North to the Orient* by Anne Morrow Lindbergh, copyright, 1935, by Anne Morrow Lindbergh; for "The Fifty-first Dragon" from *Seeing Things at Night* by Heywood Broun, copyright, 1921, by Harcourt, Brace and Company, Inc., renewed, 1949, by Heywood Hale Broun; for "The Pheasant Hunter" from *The Assyrian and Other Stories* by William Saroyan, copyright, 1949, 1950, by William Saroyan; for "Mama and Her Bank Account" from *Mama's Bank Account* by Kathryn Forbes, copyright, 1943, by Kathryn Forbes; for "Song of the Settlers" from *A Mirror for the Sky* by Jessamyn West, copyright, 1946, 1948, by Jessamyn West; for "Oh, the Swift Plunge . . . ," a part of "Swimmers" from *Selected Poems and Parodies of Louis Untermeyer,* copyright, 1935, by Harcourt, Brace and Company, Inc.; and for "My Kingdom for Jones" ("The Horse That Played Third Base for Brooklyn") copyright, 1944, by The Curtis Publishing Company, from *Wind-wagon Smith And Other Yarns* by Wilbur Schramm. All reprinted by permission of Harcourt, Brace and Company, Inc.

Harper & Brothers for "The First Day" from *Anything Can Happen* by George and Helen Papashvily, copyright, 1945, by George and Helen Papashvily; for "Kid Sister" from *Seventeen* by Booth Tarkington, copyright, 1932, by Harper & Brothers; for "The Victory" from *Of Men and Mountains* by William O. Douglas, copyright, 1950, by William O. Douglas; and for the use of the name Mark Twain (registered trade mark) for the selections from *Huckleberry Finn* and *The Autobiography of Mark Twain.*

Henry Holt and Company, Inc. for "The Road Not Taken" and "The Death of the Hired Man" from *Complete Poems of Robert Frost,* copyright, 1930, 1949, by Henry Holt and Company, Inc., 1936, 1948, by Robert Frost; and for "The Listeners" from *Collected Poems* by Walter de la Mare, copyright, 1941, by Walter de la Mare. All reprinted by permission of the publishers.

Agnes Newton Keith for "The Story of Saudin" as told by Saudin to Agnes Newton Keith. Originally published in *The Atlantic Monthly.*

Ladies Home Journal for "The Indian Swing" by Roma Rose, copyright, 1948. Reprinted by special permission of The Curtis Publishing Company.

John Lane The Bodley Head Ltd. for permission to reprint in Canada: "The Open Window" from *The Complete Short Stories of Saki* by H. H. Munro.

v

COPYRIGHT ACKNOWLEDGMENTS

Elias Lieberman for "I Am an American" from *Paved Streets* by Elias Lieberman.

J. B. Lippincott Company for "Camel Boy" from *Children of North Africa* by Louise A. Stinetorf, copyright, 1943, by Louise A. Stinetorf; and for "Song of a Little House" from *Chimneysmoke* by Christopher Morley, copyright, 1921, 1949, by Christopher Morley. Reprinted by permission of the publisher, J. B. Lippincott Company.

Little, Brown & Company for "Goody for Our Side and for Your Side, Too," "The Adventures of Isabel," and "Fragonard" from *Many Long Years Ago* by Ogden Nash, copyright, 1935, 1936, 1940, by Ogden Nash; for "I Turn Pearl Diver" from *The Pearl Lagoon* by Charles Nordhoff, copyright, 1924, by The Atlantic Monthly Press, 1952, by Mrs. Laura Dann, reprinted by permission of Little, Brown & Company and The Atlantic Monthly Press; and for "A Bird Came Down the Walk" from *Poems* by Emily Dickinson, edited by Martha Dickinson Bianchi and Alfred Leete Hampson.

Estate of Charmian K. London for "That Spot" by Jack London.

McClelland and Stewart, Ltd. for permission to reprint in Canada: "How We Kept Mother's Day" from *Winnowed Wisdom* by Stephen Leacock.

Macmillan & Company of Canada, Ltd. and Mrs. James Stephens for permission to reprint in Canada: "Little Things" from *Collected Poems* by James Stephens.

The Macmillan Company for "My Father Loved the Jumping-off Places" from *Primer for Americans* by Robert P. Tristram Coffin, copyright, 1934, by The Macmillan Company; for "Cargoes" from *Collected Poems* by John Masefield, copyright, 1953, by The Macmillan Company; for "Little Things" from *Collected Poems* by James Stephens, copyright, 1909, by The Macmillan Company; and for "For Anne Gregory" from *Collected Poems of William Butler Yeats,* copyright, 1951, by The Macmillan Company. All reprinted by permission of The Macmillan Company.

Harold Matson for "That's What Happened to Me" by Michael Fessier, copyright, 1935, by Story Magazine, Inc.; and for "Old Holy Joe" by James Street, copyright, 1943, by The Crowell-Collier Publishing Company. Both reprinted by permission of Harold Matson.

Angela Morgan for "Work" from *Gold on Your Pillow* by Angela Morgan. By permission of the author and the publisher, De Vorss and Company, Los Angeles.

William Morrow and Company, Inc. for "The Wish Books" from *The Nine Brides and Granny Hite* by Neill C. Wilson, copyright, 1948, 1949, 1950, 1951, 1952, by The Curtis Publishing Company, 1952, by Neill C. Wilson. Reprinted by permission of William Morrow and Company, Inc.

Robert Murphy for "You've Got to Learn" by Robert Murphy. Originally published in *The Saturday Evening Post.*

The *New York Times* and Anne Sutherland Brooks for "Poverty" by Anne Sutherland.

Harold Ober Associates for "Judge" by Walter D. Edmonds, copyright, 1935, by Walter D. Edmonds; and for "Bombardier" by Paul Gallico, copyright, 1942, by The Curtis Publishing Company. Both reprinted by permission of Harold Ober Associates.

Oxford University Press, London, for "How Much Land Does a Man Need?" from *Twenty-three Tales* by Leo Tolstoy, translated by Aylmer Maude.

Willard Price for "The Reluctant Tiger" by Willard Price. Originally published in *Outdoor Life.*

G. P. Putnam's Sons for "The Blow" from *Alone* by Richard E. Byrd, copyright, 1938. Used by courtesy of G. P. Putnam's Sons.

Rand McNally & Company for "Kon-Tiki" from *Kon-Tiki: Across the Pacific by Raft* by Thor Heyerdahl, copyright, 1950, by Thor Heyerdahl. Published in the United States by Rand McNally & Company.

COPYRIGHT ACKNOWLEDGMENTS

IN APPRECIATION

We wish to express our gratitude to Miss Helen Hanlon, Supervisor of Language Education, Detroit Public Schools, and to Miss Edith Bell, Chairman of the English Department, San Francisco Polytechnic High School, who undertook the labor of reading the manuscript of this book and whose criticisms and comments were most helpful.

We also wish to thank the many teachers and students in schools all over the country, from small towns to large cities, and from dominantly college-preparatory schools to those specializing in non-academic education, who cooperated so enthusiastically in evaluating the selections and instructional materials in this book.

PREFACE

In this age of easy entertainment, many boys and girls are unaware of the pleasure and personal satisfaction to be found in good reading. They may even ask, "Why should I read? What does literature have for me?" The only truly convincing answers to these questions must come, not from teachers and parents, but from the young people themselves. This anthology is designed to make the discovery of these answers an enjoyable and rewarding experience. Here boys and girls will find a wealth of reading which courts their interest, reflects their concerns, and invites them to look beyond their own small world and the immediate present.

The editors of this anthology believe that if they can awaken in young readers an immediate interest in the pleasure, understanding, and personal growth to be found in a single book, this interest will continue to grow and will extend to many books. From this immediate interest will develop a lasting interest. Therefore, this book is designed—both in appearance and content—to make a direct and positive impression on its readers. In appearance it has the appeal of a richly illustrated collection of stories, poems, plays, and essays and so creates a fresh and motivating atmosphere for the study of literature. In content it speaks to young people "where they live" and with the honesty, imagination, and insight found only in writing of the highest quality. The titles of the several parts of this book will persuade boys and girls that their interests and common concerns have not been overlooked. Nor have their varying abilities and tastes been forgotten. In each part there are selections for hesitant readers and ambitious readers, as well as for those who set an even pace. There is also a variety of types of literature so that young readers can see how ideas often find expression in different ways.

As young people discuss the selections in this book, they will discover that the study of literature is not a meaningless memorization of names, dates, and definitions. Rather, it is a study of people and experiences as they have been interpreted by men and women of literary standing. It is also an opportunity for growth in the understanding and appreciation of the form and manner in which these interpretations are presented. In this book young readers can acquire this understanding easily because new terms are handled in relation to a particular selection and reviewed again and again. In the same way these readers can acquire new reading skills and added confidence because they are led gradually from fairly simple selections to more difficult and more mature selections. Yet at no time is the sheer pleasure to be found in good reading destroyed by undue emphasis on the discussion of literary techniques or the development of skills.

This anthology will serve its purpose if it provides boys and girls with convincing and affirmative answers to the questions, "Why should I read? What does literature have for me?" These answers may mark the beginning of a life-time of satisfying and discriminating reading.

TABLE OF CONTENTS

TABLE OF CONTENTS

TABLE OF CONTENTS

SIDELIGHTS ON AMERICA—PART SIX

PEOPLE WHO DARED—PART SEVEN

ON THE LIGHTER SIDE—PART EIGHT

TABLE OF CONTENTS

THE THINGS THAT COUNT—PART NINE

PEOPLE LIKE YOU

Everyone enjoys hearing about other people. You want to know what other teen-age boys and girls are saying and doing. And you probably find it reassuring to learn that many young people face the same difficulties that perplex you.

Willie Baxter, Huck Finn, and Jasmine Griffith are teenagers like you. All belong to the same age group, and yet, they are not exactly alike. Willie's idea of a good time is certainly different from Huck's. And for a while Jasmine and Artie think they will never understand each other. Yet all these young people have at least one thing in common with one another and with you. All are trying to grow up in the best way they know how.

PART ONE

PEOPLE LIKE YOU

The Indian Swing

ROMA ROSE

Artie thought to himself, "What have they got that's so wonderful? Their father is a loafer, and their mother hasn't any pride, and they bring their groceries home in a goat wagon." Yet when Artie was with these "irresponsible" newcomers, everything seemed to be just right.

My father heard through the Bank that they were going to reopen the Warrenby house, and when he told my mother she was all excited and pleased. "Let me see," she said, shaking back her sleeve ruffles and putting her forearms on the table, "that will be Cecelia, the granddaughter, won't it? I remember the time I saw her— she was ten and I was eight, and they served green ices. I've heard she has several children now. Arthur," she said to me, "I want you to be very nice to them. We'll have them over soon to a nice party on the lawn."

"How old are they—big enough to play baseball?" I asked, but my mother didn't know.

The Warrenby house was next to ours. It had an iron fence and an iron deer, and ours had a stone fence and a lily pond. But nobody had lived in the Warrenby house for as long as I could remember. My father didn't allow me to go in there because it was Private Property. Anyway, it was a dark spooky place with shutters on the windows.

The day they moved in I went over to see what size they were, but I didn't tell my mother anything about going. I knew she wouldn't let me go so soon. When you're thirteen years old you have a pretty good idea of everything your mother is going to say—so you're careful.

The house was big and brown with a lot of porches, set in several acres of old trees and high weeds, with a big barn to match the house at the back. We had always lived in our house and never moved, but I knew right away that this was a funny way to move. The doors were open and there were packing cases piled inside, and barrels and all kinds of stuff, but nobody was around. Pretty soon I heard voices out by the barn and I went out and there they were, the whole family—a boy and a girl about my size, and three smaller ones with a lady, and up in a tree was a big man with black hair and a black mustache and a derby hat. He had been putting up a swing.

It was an Indian swing—just one long rope with a loop in the end to put your foot in. They had nailed some boards on the tree for a ladder. I watched the man stand on a high limb, put his foot in the loop and swing off, holding to the rope with his hands. He gave a big whoop and went higher than the eaves of the barn.

It made my stomach squeeze, just watching. The next time he went even higher, and they all whooped. After he had swung a few times, he reached up and grabbed a branch above him and stood on the limb he had started from. He fastened the rope and climbed down the ladder. Then the girl went up and swung. She went high too.

It's the getting off that's hard about an Indian swing. You have to be ready to stop swinging and step back on the limb while you're still going high. You don't let the old cat die, or you can't reach the limb, and you're too high off the ground to get down. I found that out later, but that first day they didn't see me, so I didn't have to swing. I watched awhile, and went home.

About a week later, my mother went to call, and when she came home she told my father she wouldn't be at all surprised if they were the kind of people who kept goats. And do you know, it wasn't very long afterward that they got a goat. It was a little brown goat with long ears, and Mr. Griffith made a wagon for it out of a big box and painted it, and the goat used to pull James and Endicott around in it. The goat's name was Annabelle, and she didn't smell, either, the way my mother said she would. After the first time or two, I wasn't embarrassed when I watched Jasmine milk her. Jasmine wasn't ever embarrassed about anything. She would squirt some milk at me and laugh when I jumped back.

All of them but James could play baseball—even the mother and the father. James was only two. . . .

I helped them cut the tall grass for the ball diamond. The whole batch of them got out there, and in no time at all we had it fixed. The father, Mr. Griffith, was a wonderful hitter, but he always let Endicott be his runner. The mother wasn't bad, considering, and Jasmine was good for a girl. Not as good as Thurman or Humphry, of course. They made lots of noise, hollering and laughing and groaning when they played. It was fun, but it worried me, too, because I knew my mother wouldn't like the noise.

She didn't either.

One day we had to play eleven innings to work off a tie. I did pretty good—the best I ever had—and in the last inning I got caught between third and home and Mr. Griffith tried to tag me out. It was pretty close, but I got home safe, only I tore the knee out of my knickers. Mr. Griffith stood panting a minute, and then he said, as if he could hardly talk, "I'll go—see—if—the bread's—done." He started slowly to the back porch. If he'd been a kid, I'd have thought he was sore, or something.

"I'll go, Jim," Mrs. Griffith said real quick. "Let me go."

He kept on walking, and waved back at her to stay where she was. He didn't look around.

Mrs. Griffith stood there with her hand out and her mouth ready to say something, but she didn't say it. We went ahead with the game after that—there wasn't much more because my run had won for our side.

Then Mrs. Griffith called, "Are you all right, Jim?"

He came to the kitchen door. "Sure, it's all right. It was just done. I took it out. Let's eat the extra loaf."

We all piled into the kitchen. He was sitting in a rocking chair, and on the table was a heap of fresh-baked loaves of bread. The kitchen smelled so wonderful that you never noticed that it was hot in there. I guess there isn't anything that smells so good as baking.

They baked twice a week—Tuesday and Saturday—and each time they made a fat round loaf that they always ate right away while it was hot, along with their tea. I always tried to be there on baking days.

When we had tea at our house, it was for company, and we had pink cakes and fancy sandwiches and nuts and bonbons. But the Griffiths had tea every day, just plain tea and homemade bread and jam. My mother would have had a fit if she'd seen how I stuffed myself with that hot bread.

On this day we argued about the ball game, and Humphry showed with the broom how his mother had swung at a shoe-string pitch, and they all howled and laughed, just as if she weren't their mother at all.

Afterward Jasmine and her mother and Humphry did the dishes and put away, and I helped. Nobody asked me to, but I just wanted to. While we were doing it, Mr. Griffith held James and Endicott on his lap in the rocking chair, and Thurman read aloud from *Treasure Island*. That's when I heard my mother calling me. I didn't know how long she'd been calling— we'd been making so much racket I couldn't have heard her.

I went home and my mother and father were at the table. She saw the hole in my pants, but she didn't say anything—she acted as if I weren't at the table.

"Just what," she said to my father, "does that man *do,* besides play games and shout all day long?"

That's the first time I'd noticed, but Mr. Griffith didn't seem to have any job.

I don't know why I never thought of it before, because all the men I ever heard of worked at something or other, except Jake White, and even he helped out at the freight office when he was sober enough. My father went to the Bank every day— sometimes on Sundays and holidays too.

My father passed my plate to me, full of

food, and I knew I'd better eat some of it, but I wasn't hungry after all that hot bread. I wished I could sit up and say Mr. Griffith was inventing some wonderful machine, or was writing a book, or something like that. And then I began to wonder why he *didn't* do anything, and I began to be ashamed for him, as if he were my own father, not doing anything. But maybe he was going to get a job right away. I'd ask Humphry what his father did.

"—like typical white trash," my mother was saying.

My father leaned back and lit his cigar. "Well, they probably won't be around too long," he said. "I hear the taxes on that place are in arrears. They'll probably lose it and move away."

"That big strapping man!" my mother said. "And she came from such a good family. It's a shame. You'd think she'd have enough pride—but I always say a man is what his wife makes him. All those children too. The old colonel would turn over in his grave if he knew what they're doing to the place."

"I think I'll go down to the Bank for an hour or two," my father said, making a lot of smoke and then getting up. "Arthur," he said from the door with a scowl, "you were late. You go to your room when you finish. And I don't want you hanging around next door. You've got a home, you know."

From upstairs I could see the light on in the kitchen over at the Griffiths'. They were probably all sitting around, still reading *Treasure Island* with their taxes in arrears, while my father was down at the Bank working.

I sat watching their light and wondering if they had enough money to pay the taxes. I hoped they did have, because I didn't want them to move away, but it didn't look to me as if they had much money. They

didn't have any cook or any maid, and they ate in the kitchen at a big table, and even the boys had to set the table and help do the dishes and sweep the floor afterward. They had asked me to stay for supper at their house, but I never did eat there, except the bread and jam. Now I was glad I hadn't, because they were so poor. Anyhow, my mother wouldn't have let me, because she wasn't going to ask them to eat at our house. They weren't our kind of people.

I worried about the taxes and Mr. Griffith's being a loafer. I didn't go over to their house for a couple of weeks. I heard them, though. They made a lot of noise, and when I'd hear Mr. Griffith, I'd wish he had a job.

I sat around on our porch and read and fooled around, and then one day, when I was out at our gate sitting on the fence, I saw Humphry and Jasmine coming home with Annabelle and the wagon full of groceries. They waved and hollered, and I got off the fence and walked to their gate.

"Where you been, Art?" Humphry asked. "You ought to see the tree house we built."

"Did your father help you?"

"Sure. It was his idea. Why?"

"Oh, I just wondered. I thought maybe he was away." That was a lie.

"Away where?" Jasmine said. She didn't sound as friendly as usual.

"Oh, I don't know. Away working maybe."

"He's not going to go away for a long time," she said. "A year or two."

"What does he do when he goes away?" For the first time, hope began to rise in me. Maybe he was an explorer. I don't know what made me think that.

"He's a mining engineer," Humphry said proudly. "He goes to South America and places."

"He does?" I shouted. A mining engineer—that was a good thing to be. A big strong man with black hair and a mustache and muscles in his arms, and he made big mines for taking out gold and silver, so everything was all right. "Can I go up in the tree house?" I asked eagerly.

It was a good tree house, and we had some crackers and apples up there, but I didn't stay very long because I wanted to go home and tell my mother that Mr. Griffith was a mining engineer.

My mother wasn't much impressed. In fact, she gave me the idea that she thought it was worse than ever, to be loafing around home. She would think, she said, that there was a good deal of opportunity for a man who was trained for such specialized and useful work. I explained that he was taking a vacation of a year or two, but I could tell that it sounded peculiar, with the taxes on the house in arrears. That's not the way for a man to do.

I went over sometimes, anyhow, when I didn't have anything to occupy my time. They didn't play baseball so much any more, because now they had a croquet set. It was a good game too. There's a lot of tricks to it. Once in a while I got them to play baseball. Mr. Griffith would umpire. We didn't need it, but he didn't play because he was so much better than the rest of us, I guess. I didn't talk loud over there any more, so my mother wouldn't hear me and know I was there. She and my father never did actually forbid me to go over, but I caught on that they didn't want me to.

I was there one day when my mother came over, all dressed up like she was going someplace. She right away said she just wanted to speak to Mrs. Griffith, and they stood under a tree and talked, but the kids listened, and I heard too. She wanted to know if Jasmine could come over the next day and help serve at a big tea at our house.

"For Armenian Relief, you know," my mother said. "I expect about a hundred people, and I wondered if Jasmine would like to help carry out the teacups and pass plates of sandwiches." She was very nice and polite, as if she was asking a favor. "If she could wear a white apron—"

Mrs. Griffith said, "Well, I think we'd better ask Jasmine. Do you suppose you could use our silver tea service? It's a very large one."

"I remember it," my mother said. "It's such a remarkably handsome set. But I couldn't think of—"

"I'd like very much to have you use it. It's the one that is rather famous in a small way. My great-grandfather brought it from England and it's been used to pour for General Lee. We unpacked and polished it, because we're going to sell it."

My mother was shocked. "You're not going to sell such a valuable set as that!" she exclaimed. "Why, I remember when I was a little girl—"

"Yes, we've decided to," Mrs. Griffith said. She stood straight with her hands at her sides. She was kind of a short little woman, not nearly as nice-looking as my mother, and I think she had on one of Jasmine's dresses, or else maybe it was her dress but Jasmine wore it sometimes. Her hair was faded and plain, but she looked different when she laughed or smiled. "It would be nice if you could use it before it goes out of our hands."

"Well," my mother said, and bit her lips for a minute while she was thinking, "in that case—it's very generous of you. I've always admired it so much. I wonder—" she smiled when there wasn't any reason to—"how much you're asking for it. I hadn't thought of it, but I might be interested myself."

"We're asking a good deal," Mrs. Griffith said. "Three hundred dollars."

My mother looked surprised. "Oh, as much as that?"

"Yes, I'm sure we can get that for it. Would you like to see it?"

They went into the house, and I went along. This was the first time I'd been in the dining room. It had dark red curtains, but no rug on the floor. There were two chairs in front of the fireplace, both of them with their seats worn out, and there were some big dark shiny cupboards with piles of dishes in them. On the table was the biggest teapot and the biggest tray I ever saw. The teapot was on a stand, and you just tipped it without having to lift it when you wanted to pour the tea. There were some other silver dishes too.

My mother admired it, and she ran her hand over the wood of one of the cupboards and admired it, too, and the dishes and she said she'd have to talk to my father about the tea set. She invited Mrs. Griffith to the tea too.

"I just don't see how you can part with it," my mother said, and Mrs. Griffith said, "We never use it." They kept talking, and I went on out.

Next morning the first thing, my mother sent me over to tell Mrs. Griffith we'd take the tea set. I don't know where the kids were, but I went to knock at the back door, and through the screen I could see Mrs. Griffith sitting on Mr. Griffith's lap in the rocking chair. I didn't know whether to knock or not. There was a washtub full of clothes and soapsuds on two chairs, and a boiler on the stove running over once in a while making the smell of steam. Mrs. Griffith had her head against his chin, and they were just sitting there.

I made some noise with my feet and then I knocked. She got up real quick and started shaking the ashes out of the stove while she said, "Come in."

I never saw a grown woman sit on anybody's lap before.

"My mother said to tell you that she'd like to buy the tea set, and she has a check over at the house," I said all in one breath.

"Oh, thank you, Arthur," she said. "We'll send it right over."

"I'll take it," Mr. Griffith said, getting up.

"No. The children can," she said. "They can make two trips. Humphry can carry the pot."

"I'll take it," Mr. Griffith said again.

"You can't carry it, Jim. It's heavy. It's too far."

"I'll take it in the wagon."

"Then I'll go with you," she said. She smoothed her hair up on each side with her hands.

I stood there, but they didn't notice me.

"Celia, girl," Mr. Griffith said. He put his arm around her and tipped her face up with his other hand under her chin. "We made our decision a long time ago. This is the only way we can buy time. Let's not make an occasion of it. I'll just take the thing over."

She looked up at him for quite a while. "You won't mind—too much?" she asked him. "Taking it over?"

"I mind—but not too much," he said. He pinched her cheek. "Do you mind?"

"No. I'm glad we have it to sell."

"I'll help carry it," I said. I didn't see much point in all this talk about who was going to carry it.

We put each piece in a gray bag with a drawstring, and laid them carefully in the wagon. Annabelle pulled it and I walked beside Mr. Griffith over to our house. I knew what my mother was going to say later about bringing it over in the goat wagon. She said it, too. She told several people, and every time she told it I felt old and sad. But, of course, it did look funny for a man to be selling his wife's things and delivering them in a goat wagon. Even if he was a mining engineer. Especially if he was.

Jasmine served at the tea. She hardly looked at me when she passed me. She looked pretty that day—not the way she usually did. She looked like a stranger. Like a girl, instead of one of the kids you played with. That was partly because she was getting older. She'd had her birthday about a month after I had mine, and she was fourteen, too. She was the oldest of them, but Humphry was as tall as she was.

I was in high school and had long trousers myself.

That's the first day I ever noticed she was prettier than Elaine Carpenter. Elaine was sort of my girl. Of course, it wasn't anything serious, but I used to write notes to her in school and stand around and talk to her. She had smooth curly hair and a small face without any bones showing in it. But Jasmine's face had plenty of room for her mouth and her eyes, and her forehead. Her dress fitted her right and she was a regular young lady, all at once.

She could change fast, though. The very next Saturday I was over at their house, and she was tearing around with the boys playing one-legged tag, and she and Humphry got into an argument and nearly had a fight. After that they decided to play follow-the-leader, and she was leader. The first place she took us was on top of the barn, and she slid down to the eaves and jumped off into a pile of hay. Humphry was next, and he did it, and then Thurman. When it was my turn, I had some trouble working my way along the ridgepole. I wasn't allowed on top of roofs—it's bad for the shingles to climb around on them—and I wasn't sure I could slide down and jump off. It took me so long that Endicott was right behind me almost push-

ing me, and the others were down below hollering at me.

I finally slid down and jumped, but I hurt myself some and felt sick for a while. The others were sympathetic, but Jasmine just said:

"What's the matter—was it too high for you?"

What could I say? Besides, I couldn't think very well right then. All these kids had been climbing on and jumping off high things all their lives, I guess, and they weren't afraid of anything. They weren't afraid of going into the attic in the night without a light. They didn't run past billboards after dark.

Anyway, I sat on the porch until I could walk better. Mr. Griffith was reading to Mrs. Griffith while she peeled some apples. Humphry pretended to be my butler—he was always kidding me about being rich—called me "milord," and dusted off a place for me to sit, and brushed imaginary pieces of lint off my clothes. He kept it up for weeks, being my butler, in fun, of course. But Jasmine wasn't in fun.

When we played anything, she always tried her best to beat me. When she did, she'd give me a hard flat look, as if I were some miserable specimen that was barely human. Or else when I'd come over she wouldn't come out and play at all. As I say, though, the rest of them were friendly enough, but I didn't go over much that winter. I was busy at school. I had other friends besides them, anyway.

One Saturday afternoon I ran into Humphry at the library and we walked home together. He asked me in, so I came. It was almost time for the bread to come out of the oven—I could smell it as soon as I got on the back porch. We gathered around and ate the extra loaf, but Mr. Griffith wasn't there.

I thought maybe he had gone off to

South America or somewhere on a job, so I asked and Mrs. Griffith said he was in bed. It wasn't even dark yet.

"What's the matter?" I asked. "Is he sick?"

"He's resting," she said, and right away I thought, just the way my mother would say it, *I don't know what he's been doing to make him tired.*

Humphry and I played checkers on the kitchen table. They had a big black stove that sat in the wall with a big curved tin roof sticking out over the stove, and they had painted flowers on it. Over the stove they had painted, "God Bless Our Cook." It was warm and nice, and quiet, for once, in the kitchen. The rest of the house wasn't warm at all.

Mrs. Griffith looked tired that day, her face kind of drawn and old-looking. It made me feel that I'd like to do something for her, but there wasn't anything I could do, of course. And then Jasmine came into the kitchen. I guess she had just taken a bath and got dressed up, and she looked so pretty, her hair soft and her skin rosy underneath. She sat down and started to read, and I let Humphry get into the king row. I wasn't interested in the checkers any more. She didn't look up or say anything. She just ate hot bread and butter with sugar sprinkled on it and turned the pages in her book, and afterwhile I went home.

The next day I came back, and the next. I hung around a lot, and one night about dark when we were playing out, I hid with her in a game of run-sheep-run. We hid in the barn. I could see the outline of her beside me, and I could hear her breathe. I moved closer and I could smell the warm smell of her hair. I could hear me breathing, too. I reached out and touched her, and she threw my hand off with a jerk.

"Jasmine"—I meant to whisper, but my voice didn't work right and I said it out loud—"don't you like me?"

"Sh-h-h!" she said.

"But don't you like me?"

I heard her breathe some more. "Certainly," she said, without whispering. "Why shouldn't I?"

"Would you go with me to the dinner dance at the club on St. Patrick's Day?" I'd been thinking about asking her, but I knew I ought to ask Elaine Carpenter. The Carpenters and my folks were good friends, and Elaine expected me to ask her. I had a new suit, and this was the first year that I'd been old enough to go. I was in the Younger Set now.

"We don't belong to the club," Jasmine said, moving away from me.

"I know. But we do. I'll take you." I would send her flowers to wear, and I'd take her in a taxi. She'd never been to the club. She would think it was swell, with a big orchestra and colored lights and the dance cards with a little pencil fastened on a string. Maybe she would let me kiss her that night, because she'd had such a good time.

"Why do you bother?" she said, suddenly, angrily. "Do you think I don't know how you feel about us? You're ashamed even to have your folks know you come over here. You think you're too good for us."

"You're talking silly," I said. I put my hand on hers, easy and slow, like I was coming down on a butterfly. She didn't move. My blood was tingling in my arms, and my hand on hers was throbbing as if it were something separate from the rest of me and terribly alive. "I think you're wonderful," I said. "I think your whole family is grand." I didn't know if I meant it or not, but I knew that's what I had to say.

"Do you, Art?" She sounded as if she almost believed me, but not quite.

"Why else do you suppose I hang around your house?" All I could think of now was getting her to say she'd go. Too many times she had taken my measure with that flat look, too many times she'd known that I was afraid to do what she could do without a blink. This time I had to win. "I want you to go, Jasmine." I was laying it on. "I want to take you."

"Well," she said, and I could tell now that she wanted awfully to go, by the way she took a quick breath and squeezed my hand, "I'll ask my folks. I'll see what they say."

"Oh, they'll say yes. They know I'll take good care of you." My heart was pounding and I was so excited that my face and ears were burning. By some kind of figuring, I thought I had won this time— had made her say yes.

But I didn't feel so good about it when I had to tell my folks.

When I'd been sitting there beside her in the dark, I had some wild and crazy thoughts about all the things I'd like to do for her, and when I was old enough and had my own money, I'd buy her everything she'd want. And back of wanting to buy her everything, I couldn't help thinking that I'd have to do that because she might not like me enough just for myself. Maybe none of the whole family liked me enough —just for myself. They thought I was skinny and scared of things, instead of sensible and cautious the way we were at my house. I wanted them to like me. When I was with them, I liked them better than I did my own folks. But when I was away from them, I would think, *What have they got that's so wonderful? Their father is a loafer, and their mother hasn't any pride, and they bring their groceries home in a goat wagon.*

So, after I told my folks that I was going to take Jasmine to the dinner dance, I began to worry. My father gave me a talk about good judgment and choosing friends, and then he said, "But now you've committed yourself, Arthur, and you'll have to go through with it. A man's word must be as good as his bond."

My mother said she probably wouldn't have a party dress, and the other girls would have long dresses, and Jasmine would feel very out of place. And it was true. I would be embarrassed, too, if she came in just an ordinary dress. I wished I hadn't asked her to go.

I hoped her folks would say she couldn't go. Then I could take Elaine Carpenter. She would have the right kind of dress, and the other fellows would want to dance with her, and she'd be friendly with the other girls at the club. It would be fun to go with Elaine.

But her folks said Jasmine could go. They said it was very nice of me to ask her, so there wasn't any way I could get out of it. No way at all.

I was purposely late going after her the night of the dance. I had her flowers in a box, and I hoped they'd got together a decent dress for her. I walked in their drive, all but dragging my feet. I saw there were more lights on than usual. I thought they must be making a fuss over Jasmine tonight. I knocked at the kitchen door and heard somebody coming down the stairs to answer.

It was Mrs. Griffith. She looked at me blank as a post before she said, "Why, hello, Art. You're all dressed up."

"Is Jasmine ready?"

"Jasmine isn't here just now," she said, quickly and nervously brushing her hair up with her hands. "Did you want something special? Won't you come in?"

"Well," I said, beginning to get sore, "this is the night of the dinner dance at the club, and I—"

"Jasmine's gone into town," she said, not paying any attention to what I said. "She went to the drugstore. She'll be back soon. Would you like to wait, or is there something I can do?" She stood there fingering the ruffle on her apron and her eyes kept moving fast from one thing to another without seeing it. "She's gone for some medicine," she said.

"Oh," I said. "Is somebody sick?" Here I was with the flowers, and it was time to go, and Jasmine wasn't even here. When you do go out of your way to be nice to some people, I thought, they don't appreciate it.

Mrs. Griffith rubbed her hand up and down her face and then she laced her fingers in front of her. "Yes," she said firmly, and with an effort at calmness, "Mr. Griffith is—very sick." A tremor passed over her face and right afterward she tried to smile. "He's—very sick. He's"—she put her fist in front of her mouth—"he's been quite sick for several days, but tonight he's worse."

I stared at her. "He is?" I said stupidly. I laid the box of flowers on the kitchen table. I wasn't mad any more. She looked so frail and twitchy, I wondered if it would be all right if I took hold of her hands and held them steady. "I'm awfully sorry," I said. "I didn't know."

Her hands kept moving frantically. I took a step closer to her. I could see down on the top of her head. I wanted to help her, but I didn't know how. I wished she wouldn't smile at me again because I knew it was hard for her. She didn't need to do that with me. I felt that I was tall and strong, and that she needed me. Her face was worn-looking as she brushed her hair up with the back of her hand.

"Is he—I mean, is it dangerous?" I finally asked.

She took a breath. I could see her holding herself together. "Yes, Artie. We've known . . . ever since we've been here, of course. That's why we came. His heart has been getting worse. But I didn't think it would be so soon." Her face crumpled up and tears started. I put my arms awkwardly around her shoulders and she leaned her forehead against me.

"He always seemed so strong," I said. "And he played with the kids all the time."

"He wanted it that way. He didn't want it any other way."

We stood like that for a few minutes. Then she straightened up.

"I'll be all right now. I'm all right when I'm with him and the children."

"You've known it all the time—and you didn't say anything? You've never told anyone?"

I still couldn't picture him being sick, with his black hair and his black mustache and talking and laughing and jumping his checkers over the board with his big hand. I couldn't imagine him dying.

"The children were so little," she was saying. "Jasmine—of course, Jasmine knew. But we didn't tell the others. We decided it would be better—happier, if they didn't know."

Jasmine knew it all the time. And her mother. And *he* knew. And they'd gone right ahead, being happy.

My heart began to swell up until it felt thick all through my chest. I wished I was a man already, and could be the father here and help them and take care of them all when they would need somebody. I wished I belonged here with them.

"If there's anything I can do," I said, "anything—ever—"

She looked me straight in the eyes. "Thank you, Arthur. I know you mean it. I wouldn't have told you, otherwise." She reached up and mussed my hair, hard, and then she went over and shook the stove.

My head was full of thoughts about all of them, and their courage and the way they lived. I thought of the first day I saw Mr. Griffith, swinging high in the Indian swing with all the kids watching and whooping. And then I knew that if it had been my father, he'd have been at the Bank day and night fixing up money so that when he died all that would be left would be piles of stocks and bonds and mortgages and insurance to remember him by.

We heard Jasmine coming on the porch. She was hurrying and she had a little package in her hand.

"Here it is, mother," she said at the door. "How is he?"

"He's resting, dear." Mrs. Griffith took the package and was going out before Jasmine saw me there.

"Artie, I'm sorry," she said. "I was getting ready when father got sick—"

"I know. Would you like to wait awhile and go later?"

"No," she said. "I couldn't go tonight. I . . . couldn't. Why don't you go on? It's not so very late. You could get there in time. I have to set out supper for the kids, and besides—well, my father isn't feeling very well tonight." She took off her coat and turned to hang it on a hook. She knew about him all this time and never told anybody.

"Would I be in the way if I stayed? Maybe there's something I could do—bring in some coal, or run errands or—" I couldn't think of any way they'd really need me. If they thought I was in the way in the house, I would go sit outside and watch the lights of the house and wait. I would stay near them. I'd just sit quietly outside and watch the lights.

"You mean you're not going to the dinner dance?" She turned around, surprised, as if that hadn't occurred to her.

I shook my head. Why should I go there, without Jasmine, when her father was sick and her mother had told me how it was, and had leaned her head against my chest and cried?

Jasmine's eyes were on me, big and clear, and her lips were parted and tremulous. I couldn't look away and I didn't want to. I heard a piece of coal move in the stove, and I heard the teakettle start to sing, but we hadn't moved.

Still looking at her, I took off my coat and hung it beside hers.

"We'd better set the table," she said, going to the cupboard. "You get the plates. And, Artie," she said, turning to me with her hands full of knives and forks, "you'll set a place for yourself, won't you? We'd like you to stay."

It may seem like a little thing, but it made me proud when she said that. And I've been proud of it ever since. Because she didn't mean me just to have a place at the table. She meant a place in their lives. I was just a kid, but I knew that was the real thing.

The woman who wrote this story

ROMA ROSE 1908–

The father of Roma Rose was a country doctor in a small town in Kansas. He was determined that his daughter should be a school teacher, so after attending universities in Kansas, Colorado, and Mexico, she taught for a year. She was unhappy with her job, however, and suffered from "a bad case of the persistent itch for writing." The day school was out, she headed for New York City.

She sold her first story so easily that she immediately bought a ream of erasable paper and began making inquiries about literary agents and copyrights. But it took two years before she was able to sell another story.

After her marriage to another young writer, Mrs. Rose and her husband traveled across the United States, looking for story material and for a place to write. While staying at a house that was much like the Griffith home, Mrs. Rose wrote "The Indian Swing." She prefers to write about the things that she knows well, and says, "All my stories stem from a person, a place, a happening that is personally connected with me."

Let's consider . . .

1. Mr. Griffith chose to enjoy his family during the short time he had to live. What choice did Artie think *his* father would have made? Which choice is better? Why?

2. Mr. and Mrs. Griffith didn't tell the children that their father was ill. Mrs. Griffith said, "We decided it would be better—happier, if they didn't know." How would the family situation have been changed if the children had known? How do you feel about the parents' decision?

3. What did the Griffiths do that made their home life so happy?

4. Why didn't Artie go to the dance? How did his decision change his relationship with Jasmine? What difference did her attitude make in his feeling of belonging?

5. Why did Artie's parents disapprove of the Griffiths? Were they right in discouraging him from visiting next door? Explain your answer.

6. How much should parents have to say about their children's choice of friends?

The writer's craft . . .

You may not have much fun watching a ball game if you don't know anything about the way it is played. In the same way, you may not get the most out of a good story unless you understand something about the way it is written. The more you know about the craft of writing, the more you will enjoy reading. And as you come to understand what makes good writing, your own writing skills will improve.

Throughout *OUR READING HERITAGE* there are sections called *The writer's craft.* . . . These will help you to understand the different literary techniques which writers use in order to make their writing effective. For example, in "The Indian Swing" Roma Rose used the **first-person** technique. She told the story as though she were the boy and the events were actually happening to her. Because she was speaking for this boy, she could tell you exactly how the boy felt.

1. Where in "The Indian Swing" did Artie express his inner feelings?

2. How did knowledge of his feelings help you to understand him better?

3. Write a short paragraph explaining how you feel about stories written in the first person.

Knowing words . . .

Words in themselves are nothing but empty sounds. It is the *meaning* for which a word stands that really counts. *Knowing words* . . . will help you understand the meanings of different words. Some of these words will be new to you. Others will be familiar words used in a new way. All of them will help you increase the size of your vocabulary. And as your vocabulary grows, your reading will become easier, more enjoyable, and far more rewarding.

A good way to discover the meaning of an unfamiliar word is to let the context of the word serve as a guide. The **context** is the sentence or paragraph in which the word occurs. You will find that the context usually provides a clue to the meaning of an unfamiliar word. For example, in "The Indian Swing" Artie's father said, "I hear the taxes on that place are in arrears. They'll probably lose it and move away."

1. From the context, explain the meaning of the word *arrears*.

2. Now check the meaning of the word in the glossary at the back of the book.

3. Was your definition similar to the one given in the glossary?

4. How helpful was the context in understanding the meaning?

It Is Too Late

It is too late to use the map
Our parents used. Lay out your own
Roads westward, curt and confident;
Cross mountains and meridians,
And run to meet your own delight.

It is too late to follow paths
Hard-packed by feet a long time dead.
New areas of pain now lie
Between the traveler and the truth.
Rivers have cut new channels out,
And younger trees are hung with fruit.

Under a strong light spread your map,
And plot the dear essential dream
In the fierce color of your blood.
Then say good-by. Your star is up.
Trust your own heart to set you free
Along the curve of time, and go.

John Holmes

Kid Sister

BOOTH TARKINGTON

To Willie, Miss Pratt was the noblest creature that ever lived; to Jane, she was a silly girl with false side-curls; to Mr. Parcher, she was nothing but a nuisance. Mrs. Baxter realized she was probably all of these, depending on how you looked at her.

"You've got to do something about that child!" he began. "I *cannot* stand it!"

Jane looked at him dumbly, not ceasing, however, to eat; while Mrs. Baxter thoughtfully continued her sprinkling.

"You've been gone all morning, Willie," she said. "I thought your father mentioned at breakfast that he expected you to put in at least four hours a day on your mathematics and—"

"That's neither here nor there," William returned, vehemently. "I just want to say this: if you don't do something about Jane, I will! Just look at her! *Look* at her, I ask you! That's just the way she looked half an hour ago, out on the public sidewalk in front of the house, when I came by here with Miss *Pratt!* That was pleasant, wasn't it? To be walking with a lady on the public street and meet a member of my family looking like that! Oh, *lovely!*"

In the anguish of this recollection his voice cracked, and though his eyes were dry his gestures wept for him. Plainly, he was about to reach the most lamentable portion of his narrative. "And then she *hollered* at me! She hollered, 'Oh, *Will—ee!*'" Here he gave an imitation of Jane's voice, so damnatory that Jane ceased to eat for several moments and drew herself up with a kind of dignity. "She hollered, 'Oh, *Will—ee*' at me!" he stormed. "Anybody would think I was about six years old! She hollered, 'Oh, Will—ee' and she rubbed her stomach and slushed apple sauce all over her face, and she kept hollering, 'Will—ee!' with her mouth full. 'Will—ee, look! Good! Bread-and-butter and apple sauce and sugar! I bet you wish *you* had some, Will—ee!'"

"You did eat some, the other day," said Jane. "You ate a whole lot. You eat it every chance you get!"

"You hush up!" he shouted, and returned to his description of the outrage. "She kept *following* us! She followed us, hollering, 'Will—ee!' till it's a wonder we didn't go deaf! And just look at her! I don't see how you can stand it to have her going around like that and people knowing

16

it's your child! Why, she hasn't got enough *on!*"

Mrs. Baxter laughed. "Oh, for this very hot weather, I really don't think people notice or care much about—"

"'Notice'!" he wailed. "I guess Miss *Pratt* noticed! Hot weather's no excuse for —for outright obesity!" (As Jane was thin, it is probable that William had mistaken the meaning of this word.) "Why, half o' what she *has* got on has come unfastened— especially that frightful thing hanging around her leg—and look at her back, I just beg you! I ask you to look at her back. You can see her spinal cord!"

"Column," Mrs. Baxter corrected. "Spinal column, Willie."

"What do *I* care which it is?" he fumed. "People aren't supposed to go around with it *exposed,* whichever it is! And with apple sauce on their ears!"

"There is not!" Jane protested, and at the moment when she spoke she was right. Naturally, however, she lifted her hands to the accused ears, and the unfortunate result was to justify William's statement.

"*Look!*" he cried, "I just ask you to look! Think of it: that's the sight I have to meet when I'm out walking with Miss *Pratt!* She asked me who it was, and I wish you'd seen her face. She wanted to know who 'that curious child' was, and I'm glad you didn't hear the way she said it. 'Who *is* that curious child?' she said, and I had to tell her it was my sister. I had to tell Miss *Pratt* it was my only *sister!*"

"Willie, who is Miss Pratt?" asked Mrs. Baxter, mildly. "I don't think I've ever heard of—"

Jane had returned to an admirable imperturbability, but she chose this moment to interrupt her mother, and her own eating, with remarks delivered in a tone void of emphasis or expression.

"Willie's mashed on her," she said casually. "And she wears false side-curls. One almost came off."

At this unspeakable desecration William's face was that of a high priest stricken at the altar.

"She's visitin' Miss May Parcher," added the deadly Jane. "But the Parchers are awful tired of her. They wish she'd go home, but they don't like to tell her so."

One after another these insults from the *canaille* fell upon the ears of William. That slanders so atrocious could soil the universal air seemed unthinkable.

He became icily calm.

"*Now* if you don't punish her," he said,

deliberately, "it's because you have lost your sense of duty!"

Having uttered these terrible words, he turned upon his heel and marched toward the house. His mother called after him:

"Wait, Willie. Jane doesn't mean to hurt your feelings—"

"My feelings!" he cried, the iciness of his demeanor giving way under the strain of emotion. "You stand there and allow her to speak as she did of one of the—one of the—" For a moment William appeared to be at a loss, and the fact is that it always has been a difficult matter to describe *the* bright, ineffable divinity of the world to one's mother, especially in the presence of an inimical third party of tender years. "One of the—" he said; "one of the—the noblest—one of the noblest—"

Again he paused.

"Oh, Jane didn't mean anything," said Mrs. Baxter. "And if you think Miss Pratt is so nice, I'll ask May Parcher to bring her to tea with us some day. If it's too hot, we'll have iced tea, and you can ask Johnnie Watson, if you like. Don't get so upset about things, Willie!"

" 'Upset'!" he echoed, appealing to heaven against this word. " 'Upset'!" And he entered the house in a manner most dramatic.

"What made you say that?" Mrs. Baxter asked, turning curiously to Jane when William had disappeared. "Where did you hear any such things?"

"I was there," Jane replied, gently eating on and on. William could come and William could go, but Jane's alimentary canal went on forever.

"You were where, Jane?"

"At the Parchers'."

"Oh, I see."

"Yesterday afternoon," said Jane, "when Miss Parcher had the Sunday-school class for lemonade and cookies."

"Did you hear Miss Parcher say—"

"No'm," said Jane. "I ate too many cookies, I guess, maybe. Anyways, Miss Parcher said I better lay down—"

"*Lie* down, Jane."

"Yes'm. On the sofa in the liberry, an' Mrs. Parcher an' Mr. Parcher came in there an' sat down, after while, an' it was kind of dark, an' they didn't hardly notice me, or I guess they thought I was asleep, maybe. Anyways, they didn't talk loud, but Mr. Parcher would sort of grunt an' ack cross. He said he just wished he knew when he was goin' to have a home again. Then Mrs. Parcher said May *had* to ask her Sunday-school class, but he said he never meant the Sunday-school class. He said since Miss Pratt came to visit, there wasn't anywhere he could go, because Willie Baxter an' Johnnie Watson an' Joe Bullitt an' all the other ones like that were there all the time, an' it made him just sick at the stummick, an' he did wish there was some way to find out when she was goin' home, because he couldn't stand much more talk about love. He said Willie an' Johnnie Watson an' Joe Bullitt an' Miss Pratt were always arguin' somep'm about love, an' he said Willie was the worst. Mamma, he said he didn't like the rest of it, but he said he guessed he could stand it if it wasn't for Willie. An' he said the reason they were all so in love of Miss Pratt was because she talks baby-talk, an' he said he couldn't stand much more baby-talk. Mamma, she has the loveliest little white dog, an' Mr. Parcher doesn't like it. He said he couldn't go anywhere around the place without steppin' on the dog or Willie Baxter. An' he said he couldn't sit on his own porch any more; he said he couldn't sit even in the liberry but he had to hear baby-talk goin' on *somewheres* an' then either Willie Baxter or Joe Bullitt or somebody or another arguin' about love. Mamma, he said"—Jane became impressive—

"he said, mamma, he said he didn't mind the Sunday-school class, but he couldn't stand those dam boys!"

"Jane!" Mrs. Baxter cried, "you *mustn't* say such things!"

"I didn't, mamma. Mr. Parcher said it. He said he couldn't stand those da—"

"*Jane!* No matter what he said, you mustn't repeat—"

"But I'm not. I only said Mr. *Parcher* said he couldn't stand those d—"

Mrs. Baxter cut the argument short by imprisoning Jane's mouth with a firm hand. Jane continued to swallow quietly until released. Then she said:

"But, mamma, how can I tell you what he said unless I say—"

"Hush!" Mrs. Baxter commanded. "You must never, never again use such a terrible and wicked word."

"I won't, mamma," Jane said, meekly. Then she brightened. "Oh, I know! I'll say 'word' instead. Won't that be all right?"

"I—I suppose so."

"Well, Mr. Parcher said he couldn't stand those word boys. That sounds all right, doesn't it, mamma?"

Mrs. Baxter hesitated, but she was inclined to hear as complete as possible a report of Mr. and Mrs. Parcher's conversation, since it seemed to concern William so nearly; and she well knew that Jane had her own way of telling things—or else they remained untold.

"I—I suppose so," Mrs. Baxter said again.

"Well, they kind of talked along," Jane continued, much pleased; "an' Mr. Parcher said when he was young he wasn't any such a—such a word fool as these young word fools were. He said in all his born days Willie Baxter was the wordest fool he ever saw!"

Willie Baxter's mother flushed a little. "That was very unjust and very wrong of Mr. Parcher," she said, primly.

"Oh no, mamma!" Jane protested. "Mrs. Parcher thought so, too."

"Did she, indeed!"

"Only she didn't say word or wordest or anything like that," Jane explained. "She said it was because Miss Pratt had coaxed him to be so in love of her; an' Mr. Parcher said he didn't care whose fault it was, Willie was a—a word calf an' so were all the rest of 'em, Mr. Parcher said. An' he said he couldn't stand it any more. Mr. Parcher said that a whole lot of times, mamma. He said he guess' pretty soon he'd haf to be in the lunatic asylum if Miss Pratt stayed a few more days with her word little dog an' her word Willie Baxter an' all the other word calfs. Mrs. Parcher said he oughtn't to say 'word,' mamma. She said, 'Hush, hush!' to him, mamma. He talked like this, mamma: he said, 'I'll be word if I stand it!' An' he kept gettin' crosser, an' he said, 'Word! Word! *Word!* WOR—'"

"There!" Mrs. Baxter interrupted, sharply. "That will do, Jane! We'll talk about something else now, I think."

The man who wrote this selection

BOOTH TARKINGTON 1869–1946

Throughout his life Booth Tarkington called Indianapolis "home" and drew many of the backgrounds for his stories from this mid-western town. As a thin, frail boy, he tried desperately to be an artist. After several hard years, he admitted, "My hand would never do what my mind wanted to do. . . ."

So he turned to writing.

Once he had started, he covered thousands of pages with his scribbling and often worked twelve hours or more at a time. People came to associate him with the old drawing board he used as a desk and the sheets of bright yellow paper on which he wrote. Here he rapidly created novels and plays, light stories and serious works. Sometimes his writings were severely criticized, but he remained a popular favorite. *Penrod* and *Seventeen,* novels about the life of a boy, are still being read by young people today. Booth Tarkington did not try to be a "great author"; he only tried to write down his understanding of life in the Midwest.

Though his writing brought him success, Tarkington did not have a happy personal life. The death of a favorite daughter brought him great sorrow, and he was constantly troubled by family problems. He even suffered the loss of his eyesight. However, he smiled through all his troubles and cheerfully continued writing until his death.

Let's consider . . .

1. Jane certainly found ways to annoy Willie. Why was he so upset about her behavior and appearance? Why do you think his anger was justified? Or do you think he was being unreasonable?

2. Willie thought that his mother should punish Jane. What is your opinion?

3. How did Jane manage to "overhear" Mr. and Mrs. Parcher's discussion?

4. What do you think of the way Jane avoided profanity when she quoted Mr. Parcher?

5. Is Willie a typical teen-age boy, or has Booth Tarkington exaggerated his behavior? Select passages from "Kid Sister" that illustrate your answer.

6. Mr. Parcher wasn't very happy about his youthful visitors. What were some of his complaints? What complaints do your parents make about you and your friends? How can difficulties of this kind best be solved?

The writer's craft . . .

Although Miss Pratt did not actually appear, you came to know her through the comments of various people in the story. Each of these people saw her in a different light.

1. What was Willie's opinion of Miss Pratt?

2. How did Mr. Parcher react to her?

3. What did Jane think of her?

These differing opinions helped you, the reader, to form an impression of Miss Pratt. Now write your own description of her.

Knowing words . . .

Below are several sentences taken from the selection. Each of the sentences has one word written in italics. If you are not sure of the meaning of a word, consult the glossary at the back of this book. After you are sure of the meaning of the italicized word, use it in a sentence of your own.

1. "That's neither here nor there," William returned, *vehemently.* "I just wanted to say this: if you don't do something about Jane, I will!"

2. In the *anguish* of this recollection his voice cracked.

3. "Hot weather's no excuse for—for outright *obesity!*" (As Jane was thin, it is probable that William had mistaken the meaning of this word.)

4. "My feelings!" he cried, the iciness of his *demeanor* giving way under the strain of emotion.

5. "That was very unjust and very wrong of Mr. Parcher," she said, *primly*.

6. At this unspeakable *desecration* William's face was that of a high priest stricken at the altar.

7. For a moment William appeared to be at a loss, and the fact is that it always has been a difficult matter to describe the bright, *ineffable* divinity of the world to one's mother. . . .

8. That slanders so *atrocious* could soil the universal air seemed unthinkable.

For Anne Gregory

'Never shall a young man,
Thrown into despair
By those great honey-colored
Ramparts at your ear,
Love you for yourself alone
And not your yellow hair.'

'But I can get a hair-dye
And set such color there,
Brown, or black, or carrot
That young men in despair
May love me for myself alone
And not my yellow hair.'

'I heard an old religious man
But yesternight declare
That he had found a text to prove
That only God, my dear,
Could love you for yourself alone
And not your yellow hair.'

William Butler Yeats

That's What Happened to Me

MICHAEL FESSIER

If your schoolmates nicknamed you Bottles and Rubbernose, what would you *do? Poor Bottles Barton had only one escape—his dreams of glory.*

I have done things and had things happen to me and nobody knows about it. So I am writing about it so that people will know. Although there are a lot of things I could tell about, I will just tell about the jumping because that is the most important. It gave me the biggest thrill. I mean high jumping, standing and running. You probably never heard of a standing high jumper but that's what I was. I was the greatest jumper ever was.

I was going to high school and I wasn't on any team. I couldn't be because I had to work for a drugstore and wash bottles and deliver medicine and sweep the floor. So I couldn't go out for any of the teams because the job started soon's school was over. I used to crab to the fellows about how old man Patch made me wash so many bottles and so they got to calling me Bottles Barton and I didn't like it. They'd call me Bottles in front of the girls and the girls'd giggle.

Once I poked one of the fellows for calling me Bottles. He was a big fellow and he played on the football team and I wouldn't have hit him because I was little and couldn't fight very well. But he called me Bottles before Anna Louise Daniels and she laughed and I was so mad I didn't

know whether I wanted to hit her or the football player but finally I hit him. He caught my arm and threw me down and sat on me and pulled my nose.

"Look, Anna Louise," he said. "It stretches."

He pulled my nose again and Anna Louise put her arms around herself and jumped up and down and laughed and then I knew that it was her I should have taken the first poke at. I was more mad at her than the football player although it was him pulling my nose and sitting on me.

The next day I met Anna Louise in the hall going to ancient history class and she was with a couple of other girls and I tried to go past without them noticing me. I don't know why but I had a funny feeling like as if somebody was going to throw a rock at me or something. Anna Louise looked at me and giggled.

"Hello, old rubbernose," she said.

The girls giggled and I hurried down the hall and felt sick and mad and kind of like I was running away from a fight, although nobody'd expect me to fight a girl. And so they called me Bottles sometimes and Rubbernose other times and always whoever was near would laugh. They didn't think it was funny because Jimmy

Wilkins was called Scrubby or Jack Harris was called Doodles. But they thought it was funny I was called Rubbernose and Bottles and they never got tired of laughing. It was a new joke every time.

Scrubby pitched for the baseball team and Doodles was quarterback of the football team.

I could have pitched for the baseball team or played quarterback on the football team. I could have pitched no-hit games and I could have made touchdowns from my own ten-yard line. I know I could. I had it all figured out. I went over how I'd throw the ball and how the batter'd miss and it was easy. I figured out how to run and dodge and straight-arm and that was easy too. But I didn't get the chance because I had to go right to Patch's Drugstore after school was out.

Old man Patch was a pretty good guy but his wife she was nothing but a crab. I'd wash bottles and old man Patch he would look at them and not say anything. But Mrs. Patch, old lady Patch, she would look at the bottles and wrinkle her nose and make me wash half of them over again. When I swept up at night she'd always find some corner I'd missed and she'd bawl me out. She was fat and her hair was all straggly and I wondered why in the deuce old man Patch ever married her, although I guess maybe she didn't look so awful when she was a girl. She couldn't have been very pretty, though.

They lived in back of the drugstore and when people came in at noon or at six o'clock either old man or old lady Patch'd come out still chewing their food and look at the customer and swallow and then ask him what he wanted.

I studied salesmanship at high school and I figured this wasn't very good for business and I wanted to tell them but I never did.

One of the fellows at school was in wait-ing for a prescription and he saw me working at some of the things I did at the drugstore. So when another fellow asked me what I did this fellow laughed and said, "Old Bottles! Why, he rates at that store. Yes he does! He rates like . . ."

That's about the way I did rate but I was planning on how I'd someday own a real, modern drugstore and run the Patches out of business so I didn't mind so much.

What I did mind was Anna Louise at school. She was the daughter of a doctor and she thought she was big people and maybe she was but she wasn't any better'n me. Maybe my clothes weren't so good but that was only temporary. I planned on having twenty suits some day.

I wanted to go up to her and say, "Look here, Anna Louise, you're not so much. Your father isn't a millionaire and someday I'm going to be one. I'm going to have a million dollars and twenty suits of clothes." But I never did.

After she laughed at me and started calling me Rubbernose, I began planning on doing things to make her realize I wasn't what she thought I was. That's how the jumping came about.

It was the day before the track meet and everybody was talking about whether or not our school could win. They figured we'd have to win the high jump and pole vault to do it.

"Lord, if we only had old Heck Hansen back!" said Goobers MacMartin. "He'd outjump those Fairfield birds two inches in the high and a foot in the pole vault."

"Yeah," somebody else said, "but we haven't got Heck Hansen. What we got is pretty good but not good enough. Wish we had a jumper."

"We sure need one," I said.

There was a group of them all talking, boys and girls, and I was sort of on the outside listening.

"Who let you in?" Goobers asked me.

Frank Shay grabbed me by the arm and dragged me into the center of the circle.

"The very man we've been looking for," he said. "Yessir. Old Bottles Rubbernose Barton. He can win the jumping events for us."

"Come on, Bottles," they said. "Save the day for us. Be a good old Rubbernose."

Anna Louise was one who laughed the most and it was the third time I'd wanted to pop her on the nose.

I went away from there and didn't turn back when they laughed and called and whistled at me.

"She'd be surprised if I did," I said.

I kept thinking this over and pretty soon I said, "Well, maybe you could."

Then when I was sweeping the drug-store floor I all of a sudden said, "I can!"

"You can what?" Mrs. Patch asked me.

"Nothing," I said.

"You can hurry about sweeping the floor, that's what you can do," she said.

There was a big crowd out for the track meet and we were tied when I went up to our coach. It was just the time for the jumping to start.

"What the devil are you doing in a track suit?" he asked me.

"I'm going to save the day for Brinkley," I said. "I'm going to jump."

"No, you aren't," he said. "You run along and start a marble game with some other kid."

I looked him in the eye and I spoke in a cold, level tone of voice.

"Mr. Smith," I said, "the track meet depends on the high jump and the pole vault and unless I am entered we will lose those two events and the meet. I can win and I am willing to do it for Brinkley. Do you want to win the meet?"

He looked amazed.

"Where have you been all the time?"

he asked. "You talk like you've got something on the ball."

I didn't say anything, I just smiled.

The crowd all rushed over to the jumping pits and I took my time going over. When everybody had jumped but me the coach turned and said, "Come on now, Barton, let's see what you can do."

"Not yet," I said.

"What do you mean?" he asked.

"I'll wait until the last man has been eliminated," I said. "Then I'll jump."

The crowd laughed but I just stared coldly at them. The coach tried to persuade me to jump but I wouldn't change my mind.

"I stake everything on one jump," I said. "Have faith in me."

He looked at me and shook his head and said, "Have it your own way."

They started the bar a little over four feet and pretty soon it was creeping up toward five feet and a half. That's always been a pretty good distance for high school jumpers. When the bar reached five feet seven inches all our men except one was eliminated. Two from Fairfield were still in the event. They put the bar at five feet nine inches and one man from Fairfield made it. Our man tried hard but he scraped the bar and knocked it off.

The crowd started yelling, thinking Fairfield had won the event.

"Wait a minute," I yelled. "I haven't jumped yet."

The judges looked at their lists and saw it was so. Maybe you think it was against the rules for them to allow me to skip my turn but anyway that's the way it was.

"You can't make that mark," one of the judges said. "Why try? You're not warmed up."

"Never mind," I said.

I walked up close to the jumping standard and stood there.

"Go ahead and jump," one of the judges said.

"I will," I said.

"Well, don't stand there," he said. "Come on back here so's you can get a run at it."

"I don't want any run at the bar," I said. "I'll jump from here."

The judge yelled at the coach and told him to take me out on account of I was crazy.

I swung my arms in back of me and sprung up and down a second and then I jumped over the bar with inches to spare. When I came down it was so silent I could hear my footsteps as I walked across the sawdust pit. The judge that'd crabbed at me just stood and looked. His eyes were bugged out and his mouth hung open.

"Good Lord!" he said. "Almighty most loving Lord!"

Our coach came up and he stood beside the judge and they both looked the same, bug-eyed.

"Did you see that?" the coach asked. "Tell me you didn't. Please do. I'd rather lose this track meet than my mind."

The judge turned slowly and looked at him.

"Good Lord!" he said, "there's two of us."

All of a sudden everybody started yelling and the fellows near me pounded me on the back and tried to shake my hand. I smiled and brushed them aside and walked over to the judge.

"What's the high school record for this state?" I asked.

"Five feet, eleven inches," he said.

"Put her at six," I said.

They put the bar at six and I gathered myself together and gave a heave and went over the bar like I was floating. It was easy. Well, that just knocked the wind out of everybody. They'd thought I couldn't do anything and there I'd broken the state record for the high jump without a running start.

The crowd surrounded me and tried to

shake my hand and the coach and judge got off to one side and reached out and pinched each other's cheek and looked at the bar and shook their heads. Frank Shay grabbed my hand and wrung it and said, "Gosh, Bottles, I was just kidding the other day. I didn't know you were such a ring-tailed wonder. Say, Bottles, we're having a frat dance tonight. Will you come?"

"You know what you can do with your frat," I said. "I don't approve of them. They're undemocratic."

A lot of the fellows that'd made fun of me before crowded around and acted as if I'd been their friend all along.

When Anna Louise crowded through the gang and said, "Oh, you're marvelous!" I just smiled at her and said, "Do you think so?" and walked away. She tagged around after me but I talked mostly with two other girls.

They didn't usually have a public address system at our track meets but they started using one then.

"Ladies and gentlemen," the announcer said, "you have just witnessed a record-breaking performance by Bottles Barton—."

He went on like that telling them what an astonishing thing I'd done and it came to me I didn't mind being called Bottles any more. In fact, I kind of liked it.

Mr. and Mrs. Patch came up and Mrs. Patch tried to kiss me but I wouldn't let her. Old man Patch shook my hand.

"You've made our drugstore famous," he said. "From now on you're a clerk. No more bottle washing."

"We'll make him a partner," old lady Patch said.

"No, you won't," I said. "I think I'll go over to the McManus Pharmacy."

Then they called the pole vault and I did like I'd done before.

I wouldn't jump until our men'd been

eliminated. The bar was at eleven feet.

"It's your turn," our coach told me. "Ever use a pole before?"

"Oh, sure," I told him.

He gave me a pole and the crowd cleared away and grew silent. Everyone was watching me.

I threw the pole down and smiled at the crowd. The coach yelled for me to pick up the pole and jump. I picked it up and threw it ten feet away from me. Everybody gasped. Then I took a short run and went over the bar at eleven feet. It was simple.

This time the coach and the judge took pins and poked them in one another's cheeks. The coach grabbed me and said, "When I wake up I'm going to be so mad at you I'm going to give you the beating of your life."

Anna Louise came up and held my arm and said, "Oh, Bottles, you're so wonderful! I've always thought so. Please forgive me for calling you Rubbernose. I want you to come to our party tonight."

"All right," I said. "I'll forgive you but don't call me Rubbernose again."

They moved the bar up again and the fellow from Fairfield couldn't make it. I took a short run and went over. I did it so easy it came to me I could fly if I wanted to but I decided not to try it on account of people wouldn't think it so wonderful if a fellow that could fly jumped eleven feet without a pole. I'd won the track meet for Brinkley High and the students all came down out of the stand and put me on their shoulders and paraded me around and around the track. A lot of fellows were waving papers at me asking me to sign them and get $1000 a week as a professional jumper. I signed one which threw in an automobile.

That's what I did once and nobody knows about it, so I am writing about it so people will know.

The man who wrote this story

MICHAEL FESSIER 1905–

As his name might indicate, Michael Fessier is the son of French and Irish parents. He was born in a famous little mining town in California called Angel's Camp. When he was a young man, he became a reporter and worked for a number of California newspapers. He had become an editor before he quit journalism to go to Hollywood, where he was a successful writer and producer of motion pictures.

Recently he left the movie business in order to devote himself to original writing. His stories appear frequently in many popular magazines.

Let's consider . . .

1. Bottles was a daydreamer. What were some of his dreams? Why do you suppose he became such a dreamer?

2. Why didn't he get any satisfaction from his work in the drugstore? How might his feelings about his work have been one of the causes of his dreaming?

3. Everyone daydreams at some time or other. At what times do *you* daydream? Why isn't this escape from reality a very successful way to meet problems?

4. Bottles' nicknames embarrassed him and made him angry. Why would he especially dislike these nicknames? Why should you always think twice before giving someone a nickname?

5. Bottles was particularly irritated when Anna Louise laughed at him. Explain why.

6. Bottles daydreamed that the gang asked him to join a fraternity and he refused. He said that fraternities were undemocratic. What other possible reasons might have influenced his decision?

7. If Bottles were a boy in your class, what suggestions could you make that would help him get more enjoyment out of "real" life?

The writer's craft . . .

A. In "That's What Happened to Me," the author, Michael Fessier, told the story as though he were one of the characters. He used the first-person technique. Explain why Bottles was the best person to tell this story.

B. Even though Bottles was an imaginary person, you probably know people just like him. He seemed believable because the author let you know how Bottles looked, felt, and acted. You learned what Bottles thought and said, and what others thought and said about him. This "word picture" of a person is called **characterization.**

One way a writer may characterize someone is to have that person speak in a way that suits his particular age, his general background, what he does, and where he lives. When Bottles spoke of wanting to "pop" Anna Louise on the nose, he was speaking as young boys often do. Find other illustrations of Bottles' use of language that seemed natural for him.

You have now begun to analyze the way writers characterize people in their stories. As you read other selections, listen to the speech of each character and decide if it sounds natural for that particular person.

We Are the Young

JESSE STUART

We are the young today; the power is ours
To clear the hills of brush and plow the ground;
And all the hours we live are silver hours.
Fresh nourishment from earth is in the veins.
We are the young and beauty of the flowers
Makes strong impressive channels in our brains.
Look to the East and West: the purpling sky
Over the earth is lazily floating by—
We are the young and we can reach the sky;
Put out your hands: the sky will come to us
And to our loves; green leaves will sing for us—
The green tobacco leaves and blue corn flowers
That hang out in the wind and love the hours.
We are the young today: the power is ours.

The man who wrote this poem

JESSE STUART 1907–

No one who has seen Jesse Stuart would ever believe that he had been ill twice with typhoid fever and pneumonia. Born in W-Hollow, five miles from Riverton, Kentucky, he was working for wages by the time he was nine. For twenty years, he was constantly torn between his fierce desire for an education and the demands of his empty stomach. Attending schools when he could, he worked as a farm hand and chopped timber. With his grandfather's help, he built the house where he now lives.

At last he enrolled at a small college in Tennessee, earning his way by working in a rock quarry and a kitchen. He was graduated after only three years and two summers and came home to teach school. Later he went to Vanderbilt, existing on one meal a day as he labored for an advanced degree. When a fire destroyed his clothes, poems, and master's thesis, he returned to the farm and decided to give up education.

There he began to write poems on anything that was near at hand: leaves, tobacco sacks, and the smallest slips of paper. For a while, he was editor of a local paper, but when he was offered the position of superintendent of the county schools, he returned to education. Later he retired to live entirely on the results of his writing. Stuart summarizes, "I love life— I love work— I love to write. I envy people that stay out of trouble, but I don't envy any writer."

The poet's art . . .

1. Most poets are people you would like to know. They are active men and women who feel strongly about people and life. Jesse Stuart, for example, is a well-built, sturdy man who has worked not only as a teacher and writer but as a blacksmith as well. Stuart feels strongly about the powers of youth. Look again at the line which opens and closes the poem: "We are the young today; the power is ours." In what ways are *you* powerful? Why does the very fact that you are young make you strong?

2. Speaking for youth, Stuart wrote, "We are the young and we can reach the sky." Think about this line for a moment. In order to communicate the wonderful power of youth, the poet departed from actual fact. He exaggerated the idea.

List all the different ways in which young people can "reach the sky." Then read your list aloud to the class. Now you can see how much meaning can be condensed into a single line of poetry. It is this condensation that requires you to read poetry with care and imagination.

3. Here is another illustration of meaning condensed in a single line: "All the hours we live are silver hours." What does the word *silver* suggest? Now explain why youth can be a time of silver hours.

4. There are several lines in the poem that briefly, yet vividly, express the powers of youth. Choose the one you like the best.

5. Now try your own description of youth. Write three different lines that describe youth's abilities in a striking way.

Huckleberry Finn

MARK TWAIN

Huck Finn grew as wild as the huckleberry he was named after. No wonder that parents punished their children for associating with him. He played hookey, smoked a corn cob pipe, seldom washed, and defied most of the rules of civilized behavior. Yet all the boys idolized him. As Huck tells you about himself in his own lively way, you will soon discover the reason for his popularity.

Chapter 1

You don't know about me without you have read a book by the name of the *Adventures of Tom Sawyer;* but that ain't no matter. That book was made by Mr. Mark Twain, and he told the truth, mainly. There was things which he stretched, but mainly he told the truth. That is nothing. I never seen anybody but lied one time or another, without it was Aunt Polly, or the widow, or maybe Mary. Aunt Polly—Tom's Aunt Polly, she is—and Mary, and the Widow Douglas is all told about in that book, which is mostly a true book, with some stretchers, as I said before.

Now the way that the book winds up is this: Tom and me found the money that the robbers hid in the cave, and it made us rich. We got six thousand dollars apiece —all gold. It was an awful sight of money when it was piled up. Well, Judge Thatcher he took it and put it out at interest, and it fetched us a dollar a day apiece all the year round—more than a body could tell what to do with. The Widow Douglas she took me for her son, and allowed she would sivilize me; but it was rough living in the house all the time, considering how dismal regular and decent the widow was in all her ways; and so when I couldn't stand it no longer I lit out. I got into my old rags and my sugar-hogshead again, and was free and satisfied. But Tom Sawyer hunted me up and said he was going to start a band of robbers, and I might join if I would go back to the widow and be respectable. So I went back.

The widow she cried over me, and called me a poor lost lamb, and she called me a lot of other names, too, but she never meant no harm by it. She put me in them new clothes again, and I couldn't do nothing but sweat and sweat, and feel all cramped up. Well, then, the old thing commenced again. The widow rung a bell for supper, and you had to come to time. When you got to the table you couldn't go right to eating, but you had to wait for the widow to tuck down her head and grumble a little over the victuals, though there warn't really anything the matter with them—that is, nothing only everything was cooked by itself. In a barrel of odds and ends it is different; things get mixed up, and the juice

kind of swaps around, and the things go better.

After supper she got out her book and learned me about Moses and the Bulrushers, and I was in a sweat to find out all about him; but by and by she let it out that Moses had been dead a considerable long time; so then I didn't care no more about him, because I don't take no stock in dead people.

Pretty soon I wanted to smoke, and asked the widow to let me. But she wouldn't. She said it was a mean practice and wasn't clean, and I must try to not do it any more. That is just the way with some people. They get down on a thing when they don't know nothing about it. Here she was a-bothering about Moses, which was no kin to her, and no use to anybody, being gone, you see, yet finding a power of fault with me for doing a thing that had some good in it. And she took snuff, too; of course that was all right, because she done it herself.

Her sister, Miss Watson, a tolerable slim old maid, with goggles on, had just come to live with her, and took a set at me now with a spelling-book. She worked me middling hard for about an hour, and then the widow made her ease up. I couldn't stood it much longer. Then for an hour it was deadly dull, and I was fidgety. Miss Watson would say, "Don't put your feet up there, Huckleberry"; and "Don't scrunch up like that, Huckleberry—set up straight"; and pretty soon she would say, "Don't gap and stretch like that, Huckleberry—why don't you try to behave?" Then she told me all about the bad place, and I said I wished I was there. She got mad then, but I didn't mean no harm. All I wanted was to go somewheres; all I wanted was a change, I warn't particular. She said it was wicked to say what I said; said she wouldn't say it for the whole world; *she* was going to live so as to go to the good place. Well, I couldn't see no advantage in going where she was going, so I made up my mind I wouldn't try for it. But I never said so, because it would only make trouble, and wouldn't do no good.

Now she had got a start, and she went on and told me all about the good place. She said all a body would have to do there was to go around all day long with a harp and sing, forever and ever. So I didn't think much of it. But I never said so. I asked her if she reckoned Tom Sawyer would go there, and she said not by a considerable sight. I was glad about that, because I wanted him and me to be together.

Miss Watson she kept pecking at me, and it got tiresome and lonesome. By and by they had prayers, and then everybody was off to bed. I went up to my room with a piece of candle, and put it on the table. Then I set down in a chair by the window and tried to think of something cheerful, but it warn't no use. I felt so lonesome I most wished I was dead. The stars were shining, and the leaves rustled in the woods ever so mournful; and I heard an owl, away off, who-whooing about somebody that was dead, and a whippowill and a dog crying about somebody that was going to die; and the wind was trying to whisper something to me, and I couldn't make out what it was, and so it made the cold shivers run over me. Then away out in the woods I heard that kind of a sound that a ghost makes when it wants to tell about something that's on its mind and can't make itself understood, and so can't rest easy in its grave, and has to go about that way every night grieving. I got so downhearted and scared I did wish I had some company. Pretty soon a spider went crawling up my shoulder, and I flipped it off and it lit in the candle; and before I could budge it was all shriveled up. I didn't need anybody to tell me that that was an awful bad sign and would fetch me some bad luck, so I was scared and most shook the clothes off

of me. I got up and turned around in my tracks three times and crossed my breast every time; and then I tied up a little lock of my hair with a thread to keep witches away. But I hadn't no confidence. You do that when you've lost a horseshoe that you've found, instead of nailing it up over the door, but I hadn't ever heard anybody say it was any way to keep off bad luck when you'd killed a spider.

I set down again, a-shaking all over, and got out my pipe for a smoke; for the house was all as still as death now, and so the widow wouldn't know. Well, after a long time I heard the clock away off in the town go boom—boom—boom—twelve licks; and all still again—stiller than ever. Pretty soon I heard a twig snap down in the dark amongst the trees—something was a-stirring. I set still and listened. Directly I could just barely hear a *"me-yow! me-yow!"* down there. That was good! Says I, *"me-yow! me-yow!"* as soft as I could, and then I put out the light and scrambled out of the window on to the shed. Then I slipped down to the ground and crawled in among the trees, and, sure enough, there was Tom Sawyer waiting for me.

[*In Chapter 2, Huck tells us that he and Tom meet four or five other boys at a cave two and a half miles down the river. They decide to organize a band of robbers and call it Tom Sawyer's Gang. Huck gets home just before daybreak. His new clothes are dirty and he is very tired.*]

Chapter 3

Well, I got a good going-over in the morning from old Miss Watson on account of my clothes; but the widow she didn't scold, but only cleaned off the grease and clay, and looked so sorry that I thought I would behave awhile if I could. Then Miss Watson she took me in the closet and prayed, but nothing come of it. She told me to pray every day, and whatever I asked for I would get it. But it warn't so. I tried it. Once I got a fish-line, but no hooks. I tried for the hooks three or four times, but somehow I couldn't make it work. By and by, one day, I asked Miss Watson to try for me, but she said I was a fool. She never told me why, and I couldn't make it out no way.

I set down one time back in the woods, and had a long think about it. I says to myself, if a body can get anything they pray for, why don't Deacon Winn get back the money he lost on pork? Why can't the widow get back her silver snuff-box that was stole? Why can't Miss Watson fat up? No, says I to myself, there ain't nothing in it. I went and told the widow about it, and she said the thing a body could get by praying for it was "spiritual gifts." This was too many for me, but she told me what she meant—I must help other people, and do everything I could for other people, and look out for them all the time, and never think about myself. This was including Miss Watson, as I took it. I went out in the woods and turned it over in my mind a long time, but I couldn't see no advantage about it—except for the other people; so at last I reckoned I wouldn't worry about it any more, but just let it go. Sometimes the widow would take me one side and talk about Providence in a way to make a body's mouth water; but maybe next day Miss Watson would take hold and knock it all down again. I judged I could see that there was two Providences, and a poor chap would stand considerable show with the widow's Providence, but if Miss Watson's got him there warn't no help for him any more. I thought it all out, and reckoned I would belong to the widow's if he wanted me, though I couldn't make out how he was a-going to be any better off then than

what he was before, seeing I was so ignorant, and so kind of low-down and ornery. . . .

We played robber now and then about a month, and then I resigned. All the boys did. We hadn't robbed nobody, hadn't killed any people, but only just pretended. We used to hop out of the woods and go charging down on hog-drivers and women in carts taking garden stuff to market, but we never hived any of them. Tom Sawyer called the hogs "ingots," and he called the turnips and stuff "julery," and we would go to the cave and powwow over what we had done, and how many people we had killed and marked. But I couldn't see no profit in it. One time Tom sent a boy to run about town with a blazing stick, which he called a slogan (which was the sign for the Gang to get together), and then he said he had got secret news by his spies that next day a whole parcel of Spanish merchants and rich A-rabs was going to camp in Cave Hollow with two hundred elephants, and six hundred camels, and over a thousand "sumter" mules, all loaded down with di'monds, and they didn't have only a guard of four hundred soldiers, and so we would lay in ambuscade, as he called it, and kill the lot and scoop the things. He said we must slick up our swords and guns, and get ready. He never could go after even a turnip-cart but he must have the swords and guns all scoured up for it, though they was only lath and broomsticks, and you might scour at them till you rotted, and then they warn't worth a mouthful of ashes more than what they was before. I didn't believe we could lick such a crowd of Spaniards and A-rabs, but I wanted to see the camels and elephants, so I was on hand next day, Saturday, in the ambuscade; and when we got the word we rushed out of the woods and down the hill. But there warn't no Spaniards and A-rabs, and there warn't no camels nor no elephants. It warn't anything but a Sunday-school picnic, and only a primer class at that. We busted it up, and chased the children up the hollow; but we never got anything but some doughnuts and jam, though Ben Rogers got a rag doll, and Joe Harper got a hymn-book and a tract; and then the teacher charged in, and made us drop everything and cut. I didn't see no di'monds, and I told Tom Sawyer so. He said there was loads of them there, anyway; and he said there was A-rabs there, too, and elephants and things. I said, why couldn't we see them, then? He said if I warn't so ignorant, but had read a book called *Don Quixote,* I would know without asking. He said it was all done by enchantment. He said there was hundreds of soldiers there, and elephants and treasure, and so on, but we had enemies which he called magicians, and they had turned the whole thing into an infant Sunday-school, just out of spite. I said, all right; then the thing for us to do was to go for the magicians. Tom Sawyer said I was a numskull.

"Why," said he, "a magician could call up a lot of genies, and they would hash you up like nothing before you could say Jack Robinson. They are as tall as a tree and as big around as a church."

"Well," I says, "s'pose we got some genies to help *us*—can't we lick the other crowd then?"

"How you going to get them?"

"I don't know. How do *they* get them?"

"Why, they rub an old tin lamp or an iron ring, and then the genies come tearing in, with the thunder and lightning a-ripping around and the smoke a-rolling, and everything they're told to do they up and do it. They don't think nothing of pulling a shot-tower up by the roots, and belting a Sunday-school superintendent over the head with it—or any other man."

"Who makes them tear around so?"

"Why, whoever rubs the lamp or the ring. They belong to whoever rubs the lamp or the ring, and they've got to do whatever he says. If he tells them to build a palace forty miles long out of di'monds, and fill it full of chewing-gum, or whatever you want, and fetch an emperor's daughter from China for you to marry, they've got to do it—and they've got to do it before sun-up next morning, too. And more: they've got to waltz that palace around the country wherever you want it, you understand."

"Well," says I, "I think they are a pack of flatheads for not keeping the palace themselves 'stead of fooling them away like that. And what's more—if I was one of them I would see a man in Jericho before I would drop my business and come to him for the rubbing of an old tin lamp."

"How you talk, Huck Finn. Why, you'd *have* to come when he rubbed it, whether you wanted to or not."

"What! and I as high as a tree and as big as a church? All right, then; I *would* come; but I lay I'd make that man climb the highest tree there was in the country."

"Shucks, it ain't no use to talk to you, Huck Finn. You don't seem to know anything, somehow—perfect saphead."

I thought all this over for two or three days, and then I reckoned I would see if there was anything in it. I got an old tin lamp and an iron ring, and went out in the woods and rubbed and rubbed till I sweat like an injun, calculating to build a palace and sell it; but it warn't no use, none of the genies come. So then I judged that all that stuff was only just one of Tom Sawyer's lies. I reckoned he believed in the A-rabs and elephants, but as for me I think different. It had all the marks of a Sunday-school.

[Abridged]

The man who wrote this selection

MARK TWAIN   1835–1910

Mark Twain and the Mississippi are almost synonymous. Even the pen name under which he wrote his famous yarns has the spell of the river on it. This champion of American authors was born Samuel Langhorne Clemens, a name too elegant for his tastes. As a boy in Hannibal, Missouri, Sam Clemens and his pals roamed the banks of the vast Mississippi. Without television or movies, these boys invented their own forms of amusement. Most of the time they fished or sought adventure on a raft they had built. Their greatest thrill was to watch a big steamboat round a bend in the river, its whistle blasting, and people shouting. Day and night young Sam dreamed of being a river pilot, or maybe even a captain.

He got his chance some years later. He tired of his first trade as a printer and went to New Orleans in search of the adventure his nature demanded. When he saw a river boat moored to a pier, his boyhood love of the river came back again. He asked a pilot to teach him to navigate the river between St. Louis and New Orleans. The pilot agreed.

A good pilot had to know every channel, sandbar, and sunken wreck in the river. Crewmen would stand on the bow and use long poles to find how deep the water was and then shout their findings to the pilot. If they called "Mark Twain!" they meant that the water was two (twain) fathoms deep. A fathom is six feet. Two fathoms—twelve feet—meant that the boat was in safe water.

Samuel Clemens took "Mark Twain" as his pen name. It was years before many of his readers knew who Mark Twain really was. Even today, the only place you'll find him called by his own name is in the cross reference in the card catalogue of a library. (Twain—see Clemens.)

Twain first gained fame when his story, "The Celebrated Jumping Frog of Calaveras County," was published. Later the people who knew Mark Twain recognized the *Adventures of Tom Sawyer* as the story of his own boyhood. In the *Adventures of Huckleberry Finn,* he wrote what many critics call the greatest novel in American literature and certainly the best story of American boyhood.

Let's consider . . .

1. Although Huck Finn might have been short on formal education, he had a lot of common sense. Find several examples of Huck's practical common sense.

2. Can you get along on just common sense? Or are there other things you need to learn which you can get in school?

3. How successful was Widow Douglas in her attempts to civilize Huck? What other methods would you suggest that might prove more successful? Or would you just let Huck grow up in his own way?

4. Would you like Huckleberry Finn as a friend? Write a short paragraph explaining how you would feel about having him as a friend.

The writer's craft . . .

In this selection from the novel *Adventures of Huckleberry Finn,* you were given a brief character sketch of Huck. Rather than tell you directly the kind of boy Huck was, Mark Twain let Huckleberry speak for himself.

1. One way in which writers make their characters come to life is to have them

speak in a way that seems natural for them. How would you describe the way Huck speaks? Select several examples from the story to illustrate your answer.

2. What did you learn about Huck as you listened to him speak?

3. Huck's language wouldn't rate an "A" in English class. But what would the story lose if he spoke in any other way?

Knowing words . . .

Below are several sentences taken from the selection. Each of the sentences has one word written in italics. After you are sure of the meaning of the italicized word, use it in a sentence of your own. Be sure to use the context as an aid in understanding the meaning of each italicized word.

1. Well, then, the old thing *commenced* again.

2. The stars were shining, and the leaves *rustled* in the woods ever so mournful.

3. But we never got anything but some doughnuts and jam, though Ben Rogers got a rag doll, and Joe Harper got a hymn-book and a *tract*.

4. "Why," said he, "a magician could call up a lot of *genies,* and they would hash you up like nothing before you could say Jack Robinson."

"Snakes"

Along outside of the front fence ran the country road, dusty in the summertime, and a good place for snakes—they liked to lie in it and sun themselves; when they were rattlesnakes or puff adders, we killed them; when they were black snakes, or racers, or belonged to the fabled hoop breed, we fled without shame; when they were house-snakes or garders, we carried them home and put them in Aunt Patsy's workbasket for a surprise, for she was prejudiced against snakes, and always when she took the basket in her lap and they began to climb out of it, it disordered her mind. She never could seem to get used to them; her opportunities went for nothing.

From The Boyhood of Mark Twain *by Mark Twain*

You've Got to Learn

ROBERT MURPHY

Andy forgot that his dog Nicky was foolish and quarrelsome and that the otters had a right to protect their pup. He remembered only that Nicky was a trust his older brother had placed upon him.

It was a little after dawn when the big dog otter's broad, whiskered muzzle broke the calm and flawless mirror of the lake. A widening circle of ripples slid away from him, and he reared half length from the water to look about. The near shore was dim and quiet; on the far shore, the spruce and hemlock made a dark band against the paling sky. The otter whistled, cocked his head to the rolling echoes and dropped back into the water again. He was an animal of great and happy vitality; he began diving and rolling, with movements as effortless and fluid as a dance, hardly disturbing the calmness of the water.

Presently, he vanished as silently as he had appeared. A swift line of bubbles followed him toward the bank; he dived deeper for the submerged entrance of the burrow, followed it above the water line, and in the dark den bounded by roots found his mate with the one pup beside her, and waked them both. There was a short, good-natured scuffle among the three, and then they pushed the pup before them down the tunnel.

When they all appeared on the lake's surface, the pup tried to climb upon his mother's back and ride. She took him off and ducked him when he whimpered, and they began to hunt the bank. They hunted with great thoroughness, from surface to bottom, exploring every hole and cranny, every root hollow and crack among the stones, finding a few crawfish and an occasional frog. These were some easy kills and they let the pup make most of them. His little belly began to bulge, and his mother, growing hungry, left them to catch a pickerel in deeper water and bring it in. They climbed out on the bank and shared it; then, gleaming and sleek from the water, they rolled and galloped about, hissing at one another with mock ferocity.

Day stole in upon them. Out on the lake, the trailing mists of night thinned and vanished; the serrated line of spruces on the distant shore took on depth and shape in the strengthening light. As the long rays of the sun fell on the otters, they gave over their play, cleaned their fur, and went into the water again. They continued up the lake toward one of the streams which fed it. When they reached the stream mouth, the mother and the pup swung away along the shore line. The otter remembered the great brown trout which lived above the bend of the stream, and left them. The trout was old and wise, and the otter had missed it so many times that the contest between them had become a fascinating game.

It was characteristic of the otter that he didn't go directly, his mind fixed on the trout. He zigzagged to and fro across the stream, playing as he went. When he came out of the water to cross the rocks at the first shallows, he heard the distant barking of a dog, up the lake in the direction his mate and the pup had gone. He hesitated for a moment and went on.

He rounded the bend carefully, and began his stalk of the trout. He knew it would be lying like a shadow a little above the sandy bottom in the rushing green gloom of the pocket under a great gray rock. It would be facing upstream, and he would gain an advantage by coming up from the rear. He stretched out full length and, paddling gently and slowly with his forepaws, slid through the water like a stealthy shadow, close to the bank and halfway to the bottom. He came to the corner of the rock and paused, sank until his belly softly scraped the sand, and became one with the bottom's shadows; then, sinuous as a snake, he began to flow around the rock. He saw the trout several yards away, hanging motionless, and tensed for the spring.

The trout caught a slight movement of the otter's shadowy form in the tail of its eye. It drifted a little farther out and swung quartering to him; the otter arched his back swiftly, thrust against the water and darted in. An explosive burst of power sent the trout to the surface; the otter's teeth scored a thin bloody line on its side and the power of its tail stroke rolled him over and over. The trout reached the surface and shattered it by a leap, and the otter righted himself and breached for air. Although a wild chase upstream and

through the rapids was as much a part of the game as the stalk, this time the otter didn't follow. He lay for a moment resting, his sleek head dappled by the sunlight falling through the leaves, and then remembered the barking of the dog.

His game with the trout was over. He started swiftly downstream and came to its mouth. Good fishing water was there, but he didn't hesitate; he turned up the lake. As he rounded the bend, he saw, fifty yards away, the head of his mate break water a good distance from the shore. The pup was just sliding down the bank; and, as the otter watched, the brown-and-white shape of the dog ran out of the hemlocks toward the pup and snapped at it. The pup was startled and confused; it scrambled between the dog's legs, turned again and leaped from the bank. The dog leaped after it with a great splash; and, because the pup had lost time and couldn't get out of the shallows, the dog's long jaw closed on it and it was tossed into the air.

The otter was moving before the dog left the bank, swimming with desperate speed. As the pup curved into the air, a boy ran out on the bank, yelling, and although the otter avoided man above any other creature, he paid no attention to the boy now. He reached the dog a little before his mate, as it leaped for the falling pup, and, rising beneath it, fastened upon its throat. The female swirled away from them, getting behind the pup and driving it before her out into the lake.

The dog reared to free its throat, but the otter overbalanced it, fighting with deadly coolness to get it into deeper water. He was all about it, attacking and slipping away with disconcerting swiftness, always maneuvering it a little farther out. The boy on the bank realized this; he grabbed a branch to use as a club, and, jumping from the bank, began to splash toward them. The otter saw the boy coming and pulled the dog into deeper water. The dog tried wildly to free itself, but the otter fastened implacably on its haunches, pulled it down and entangled it in a pile of brush on the bottom. The dog struggled desperately in a world alien to it, but in which the otter was at home. But it was trapped; the air in its lungs fled in silver bubbles to the surface, and the otter struck again.

Standing up to his chest in the water, Andy Gates stared in helpless anguish at the spot where the dog had gone down. He saw the bubbles burst to the surface, and, a short time later, a swirl far out where the otter breached for air as it followed its mate and the pup. At first he couldn't believe that the dog wouldn't come up again. But time drew out and realization finally came upon him; he dropped the branch he was holding, his fists clenched at his sides and his blue eyes filled with tears. The world about him was suddenly a new and terrible place. He

forgot that the dog had been brash and foolishly quarrelsome, that no one had ever been able to teach it anything, and that it had usually been a nuisance. All that he remembered was his brother, standing by the gate before he left for the South Pacific, saying, "Take care of the pup, Andy. We'll make a bird dog out of him when I get back."

He didn't realize that Joe, who knew the dog would never amount to anything, had said that to make them feel closer to each other for a moment and hold off the threatening tears, to make the parting easier for them both. The dog was a trust Joe had placed upon him, his most immediate link with his brother, and he had let it be killed. He turned and stumbled out of the water, tears blurring his sight. When his feet found the hardpacked surface of the path, he started along it toward home, stumbling a little now and then. There was an aching emptiness within him, an emptiness which seemed to have swallowed up all his strength; halfway up the long

hill, he had to stop, and stood panting, unconscious of the dry fragrance of sun-
warmed hemlock on the morning air.

He stopped crying after a while, and the
world slowly came back to him. He grew
aware of the birds that moved about him,
the leaf shadows on the path and the slow
movement of clouds across the sky. But
he didn't go on. He sat down beside the
path, dry-eyed now, but the emptiness
hadn't gone, and he saw his surroundings
as though from a great distance. Time
stopped as his mind tried to rationalize the
dog's death and soften the shock of it. The
afternoon was growing late when he
crossed the top of the hill and saw the
farm in the little valley below, the big
barn and the sprawling house among the
willows, the file of ducks moving up from
the stream shining white in the lowering
sun, the cows coming in, and his father
walking slowly between the house and the
barn.

His father saw him and waited with his
hands tucked into the top of his levis.
Gates was a kindly and unhurried man; he
looked at the boy's face and didn't mention
the chores that he'd done himself.

"Trouble, Andy?" he asked.

The boy's chin trembled. "Nicky," he
said. "There was an otter—" He couldn't
go on. He began to cry again, and suddenly went to his father as he hadn't done
for years, and leaned against him, crying.
"He went after the little one," he said,
shaking with sobs, "and the big one
drowned him. And Joe—" He couldn't
talk about Joe.

"Joe would understand it, boy," his
father said, sliding an arm around him.
"Joe would know you couldn't help it."

"I was keeping him for Joe," Andy said.
"Joe left him with me. He was Joe's and
mine." He began to cry violently again.
"Joe's and mine," he repeated, remember-

ing Joe at the gate, going away. "I'll kill
him!" he burst out, thumping his father's
broad chest. "I'll find him and kill him!"

The man started to speak and checked
himself, realizing the futility of words. The
boy was extraordinarily moved; it was useless to talk against an emotion so deep that
he could only guess at it. Time would
have to smooth it out—time and what
patient understanding he could give. The
man was silent for a long time, holding the
boy in the crook of his arm.

"Supper, Andy," he said finally. "Get
ready for supper, boy."

"I don't want any supper, dad," Andy
said. "I—I couldn't eat any supper."

"All right," Gates said. "Go along up to
your room, then. Go up the front stairs.
I'll tell mother you won't be down."

The boy went into the house; after waiting for a few minutes, Gates went around
to the back door and into the warm kitchen.
Mrs. Gates was taking a pie from the oven.
She looked around, smiled, and straightened up to put the pie on top of the stove.
She was small and very neat; her movements were deft and quick, and her eyes
were blue like the boy's.

"Andy won't be down, Helen," Gates
said. "We'd better eat without him."

"Why?" she asked. "What's the matter?"

"Well," Gates said. He took off his hat,
hung it behind the door and thought a
moment. "That fool dog," he said finally,
"got himself killed by an otter. There was
a young one, I think, and he went for it.
Andy is— I've never seen him so worked
up. Joe must have said something about
taking care of the dog, and Andy thinks
he's let Joe down. He's going to kill the
otter, he says."

"But it's not like him," she said. "He
doesn't just kill things, Harry."

"No," Gates said. "He's not a cruel
boy."

"You'll have to talk to him," she said. "I don't want him to be that way. Vengeful like, I mean."

"It's not revenge," Gates said. "It's—he's—" He shook his head, irritated by his inarticulateness. "This is a deep thing, Helen. He'll have to work it out himself. Maybe he'll kill that otter, but I hope not. If he kills it, then I'll have to talk to him."

She looked at him, puzzled. "What do you mean, Harry?"

"That's the devil of it," he said, exasperated. "I don't know what I mean. I can't say it, I just feel it. Let's eat, shall we?"

"All right," she said, and began to fill their plates.

Upstairs, the boy lay on his bed. The picture of Joe in his uniform smiled at him from the bureau, but he had stopped looking at it. He felt that he couldn't look at it again until he'd found the otter. As his father had said, he wasn't a cruel boy, but all his emotions confirmed the decision, made so suddenly, that the otter must pay with its life for the life of the dog. The justice of the matter, the fact that the otter had been defending the pup, never occurred to him. Many plans went through his mind, but there was no pleasure, no anticipation of exciting sport connected with any of them.

He went about his hunting with a singleness of purpose unusual in a boy, with a definite and unvarying schedule. First he'd do the chores, carefully and thoroughly, then get his old single-shot .22 rifle and go out. At first, he spent a lot of time at the lake, hiding near the place where the dog had been drowned. He knew, from remembering bits of Gates' talk, that otters didn't stay in one place, but made a wide, periodic circle about the ponds and streams of the countryside. Sooner or later, he thought, they'd come

past him again. He spent days hidden among the hemlocks, and, although he learned a great deal about other animals and birds, he never saw the otters.

The thought came to him finally that they might have passed near dawn, before he got there, or after dusk, when he couldn't see them or had left for home. For several days, disappointment took all the energy out of him; he stayed at home, and his mother thought, with relief, that he'd given up.

"I'm glad it's over, Harry," she said to Gates. "It wasn't like a boy to act like that, going wherever he went, so regular all the time. It was more like a funny little old man."

But Gates had been quietly watching the boy, and he shook his head. "No," he said. "He's not through yet. He's just trying to get away from the place."

Gates was right; the boy was deciding that he would have to move about, to find the otters' route and intercept them somewhere. The place where the dog had died had held him through a wistful, boyish hope that somehow it might come back again. But the bond weakened; reality came closer to him than it had ever come before, and, as hope died, some of his boyishness died with it. He finally broke away from the place and made his first circuit of the lake.

He went too fast at first and found nothing. The otters left very little indication of their passing along the shore line—a few fish scales and bones in widely separated places, a single rare pad mark in damp ground not covered by leaves or vines. On his first trip up the shore he found nothing. Slowing down and going very carefully, he found faint sign at last, and knew how painstakingly he would have to search from then on. He found the place where they left the lake, the stream they used, and how far they followed before leaving it.

In time he knew, between the actual points where they touched and guesses at the routes which connected these points, the otters' entire twenty-five-mile circuit of the country. It was an achievement in woodcraft which few men could have accomplished, because few men would have had the patience or the time. He had covered a tremendous amount of country; he was well scratched by briers, but he was brown and strong, and had filled out surprisingly.

He changed, little by little, during those weeks. The boyish heedlessness with which he had formerly moved through the woods was gone. He grew somewhat like an Indian, a part of the woods rather than an alien presence, drifting quietly about with a mind empty of thought, but blank and clean for the impressions which flowed into it. Time ceased to exist for him. He took no more account of hours than a squirrel, and learned the causes of sounds and the little chains of circumstance which stem from them—the techniques of the hunters and the defenses of the hunted. He saw young grouse freeze and blend with the leaves when the shadow of a hawk swung over them; he watched the steps by which a litter of young foxes learned to catch mice. The play of life about him increased with his skill in seeing it, but his understanding of it and his growing sympathy with it were both completely subconscious until his adventure with the lynx.

He had found its tracks several times. They seemed to be near the places where he had walked or hidden, and he grew curious. He gave over the otters for a time and hunted it, and found that it was stalking him. He spent a good deal of time in the thick hemlocks it liked best; finally, he

went through this woods noisily, backtracked with great care, and hid in a very thick place.

A long time went by before he saw a movement, an indistinct blur as the pale-fawn-colored fur slipped across a patch of sunlight. It came closer, silently, never distinct in the thicket; and then it was standing in a little opening not thirty feet away, the yellow eyes staring at him, the big, soft paws tense and the tufted ears cocked. There was a good deal of wild power in it, but he never thought of being afraid. It stood regarding him, poised, unblinking and feral, framed against the wild tangle of the thicket, but without menace. He smiled, and there suddenly seemed to come upon it a look, an expression, of shame that it had been outmaneuvered and taken in. It made a little sound, turned, and, with great care for its dignity, moved off and vanished.

This dignity was such a human sort of thing that it brought to life in his mind all the animals he had watched as abstractions, rather mechanical figures clothed in fur which had moved about him. For the first time, he realized how much a part of his life they had become and how much he liked them. He realized, too, how clear and simple their reasons for action were, even when they killed.

His thought naturally came to the otters, and swung quickly away, but the fact that he had almost looked upon them sympathetically confused him. He got up, puzzled and a little ashamed, and went home. The disturbing questions which came to him refused to be dismissed. His father was alone in the kitchen; he looked up and saw that the boy was troubled.

"Yes, son?" he asked.

"Dad," he began, knowing that his father would help him, "the otters—"

Just then, his mother came in. "There's

a letter from Joe for you, Andrew," she said. "I put it in your room."

His father watched the swift change of his expression, the closing of his mind against the question, with regret. "I wish you hadn't mentioned that letter, mother," he said after the boy left. "I wish you'd hidden it. I think he's seen something he liked about those otters, and it was about to change his mind."

"Oh, I'm so sorry," she said. "I'm so sorry, Harry. Do you think—"

"I think it's too late," Gates said. "He's right back now where he was before."

The uneasiness which at first had been like a formless shadow in the old dog otter's brain was sharper now, for he encountered the man-smell which evoked it more frequently. To be followed was a new experience to him, and he didn't know what to make of it. It had not been difficult to avoid the infrequent and casual encounters all animals have with man sooner or later; his senses were superior to theirs, and vigilance and care were all that was necessary. He saw or heard or scented them and got out of the way; they passed and were gone, and places which held evidence of their presence were better left alone. But this was different; the smell waited in many places for him, clinging to the underbrush or the banks. His temper grew short with constant watchfulness, and he began to avoid the daylight hours.

The female didn't take well to the curtailed activity either. She was of a more casual temperament than her mate; she had never, as he had long ago, been caught in a trap and nearly drowned. She had not felt the blind terror of it nor lost two toes; her brain wasn't marked by an experience impossible to forget. She chafed at being quiet in the dank blackness of a bankside den when she knew that the world was filled with sunshine and freedom and sport a few feet away. She remembered so many happy places—gloomy thickets they went through between streams where a complexity of fine scents lingered and birds flashed in and out of shadow; deep pools below falls where trout hid among the sunken rocks; long, easy stretches of lazily sparkling water, and precipitous banks where the three of them made slides and plunged down them until they were too weary for anything but lying happily in the sun.

She grew morose, as they all did. Their rollicking vitality, with its urge toward ceaseless activity and play, was frustrated and turned against them. They bickered and snarled at one another.

But this retreat, which would eventually have discouraged the ordinary hunter, was doomed to failure with the boy. All his determination and effort were concentrated solely upon them, and because they could not exist by moving about altogether in the dark, it was inevitable that he find them. The impulse to change his range came to the old otter many times, but he resisted it. The old range was home, familiar and somehow comforting; the memories of his life along its banks and streams were deeply etched into his brain, and they held him there.

Clouds were beginning to cover the late-afternoon sun when the boy found the pad mark on the little sandy margin of the stream. It was very fresh; water was still oozing slowly into it, and he began to tremble. The fact that he had always got home before dark to avoid worrying his mother, and that he wouldn't be able to do it this time if he didn't start at once were forgotten. A strange sort of surety came upon him, and, after a moment, the trembling stopped and he grew calm. He knew that the stream didn't go much farther; that within a quarter of a mile the otters would leave it and go across country, through a hemlock swamp and over a low ridge, to reach the stream on the other side which flowed finally into the lake.

He knew the thicket so well that he could predict where they would pass through it—a marshy little path which had once been a lumber road, cut through a high and tangled bank. He knew he could intercept them there by going through the woods; he knew he had them.

He had so often imagined the feeling of triumph that would be his when he found them that he was confused by the lack of it, by a sort of unwillingness that had suddenly come into his heart. This emotion was inexplicable to him, and seemed like a betrayal of his brother. He thought of his father, who did not approve of the thing he was doing, but who had been patient and kind and had said nothing against it, and suddenly he felt lost and alone. He stood indecisively for a moment in the darkening woods; the thoughts of his father changed to thoughts of Joe, and his back stiffened.

He started to walk. A deeper gloom fell upon him as he went into the hemlock, and a deeper silence; he moved like a ghost, for his feet made no sound in the fallen needles. When he came to the place, the bank above the lumber road, the setting sun came out more brightly and the thicket was filled with a banded, coppery light. The low branches were so thick that he had to crawl to the top on his hands and knees. He reached the top and lay down, stretching out with the rifle cocked in his hands. It was very quiet. The swampy little path lay before him for a few yards, meandering and crooked, masked here and there by low hemlock branches and brown old stumps rotting and green with moss.

The coppery light faded again, and after a long time the brooding silence was suddenly broken by a spitting snarl. The boy raised himself on his elbows quickly; there was a rapid, slurred pattering of feet, and the three otters were bunched below him. The old male's back was claw-raked and bleeding; he snarled at his mate and moved toward her as though to drive her along the path, then turned and galloped the other way. A lynx materialized in front of him, crouched and spitting, its ears laid flat and its teeth gleaming. He went at it hissing, and it gave ground; another bounded off the bank toward the pup, but he whirled and drove it off. Short-legged and awkward on land, he was at a great disadvantage before the pair of lynxes, but somehow he managed to be everywhere at once.

The snarling lynxes, trying to draw both otters away from the pup, were very quick, but the old otter moved like a dark flame. He closed with one of them, took his raking and punished it, and broke away in time to fasten on the throat of the other, which was batting with a hooked claw at his mate. He shook its big body, threw it aside, and whirled again toward the first. Quiet suddenly fell; the lynxes drew off a little, and they all stood panting, glaring at one another.

The path had been so quiet and empty one moment and so full of violent action the next that the boy was held immobile and staring. The sudden quiet freed him. He got up on his knees, his eyes on the otter; he was so filled with a sudden overwhelming admiration for its courage that he nearly shouted encouragement as it stood, black and bloody, and so obviously ready to carry the fight on. One of the lynxes moved; it drew off a little farther, as though deciding to abandon the fight. The boy didn't think; he raised the rifle and fired a quick shot at it. The shot

missed, but the lynx turned tail with a snarl and bounded off through the hemlocks. The other went after it, and the old otter turned its head and looked at him for a moment with curiosity, but no fear. Then it shook itself and drove the female and the pup before it down the path and out of sight.

It was well after dark when the boy heard his father shouting in the distance and answered him; presently, he saw the lantern moving far off among the dark trees, and hurried toward it.

"Are you all right, Andy?" Gates called. "Are you all right, boy?"

"Yes, dad," he said. He came to the circle of yellow light and stopped.

"Your ma was a little worried," Gates said gently.

"I'm sorry," he said; and then, "I found them, dad."

Gates didn't say anything. He just stood there holding the lantern, and the boy could see a star or two among the scattering clouds and branches high above his head. "I found them," he said again. "There were two lynxes after them, and he—the old one, the otter—fought them off. He was wonderful, dad; he licked them both."

"Rabbits must be scarce," Gates said, "to make them tackle him."

"It was the little one," Andy said. "They were after him. But the old one— I—I shot at the lynxes, dad."

There was silence for a long moment, then Gates said, "You're not sorry?"

"No," the boy said. "No. He's not mean, dad. It was the little one all the time. He was watching out for it—even the day he took Nicky; but I didn't know it then. Do you think Joe will understand that, dad?"

"Sure," Gates said. "He'll understand it. He'll be glad you understand it too." His long arm went around the boy's shoulders. "Come on," he said. "Let's get on home."

The man who wrote this story

ROBERT MURPHY   1902–

Mr. Murphy picked out his career while he was still in grammar school. He says of those days, "I wrote by ear; I could never parse a sentence or tell an adjective from an adverb, but I enjoyed English classes and doing themes, and as soon as they'd have me I began to work on the school paper." He continued writing in high school and college.

Most of the material for Mr. Murphy's stories has come from his experiences in the outdoors. He was brought up on the edge of the Dismal Swamp in Virginia and spent his free time tramping in the woods. The otters, turkeys, and many other animals he met became subjects for stories like "You've Got to Learn."

After becoming a professional writer, Mr. Murphy traveled in the West and up near the Arctic, where he gathered material for more stories. Now an associate editor of *The Saturday Evening Post,* he says, "I still like to write outdoor stories."

Let's consider . . .

1. When Andy realized that his dog was drowned, the world about him became a new and terrible place. Explain why the death of Nicky was so important.

2. Andy's father knew that his son planned to kill the otter. Was he right in letting the boy work out the problem for himself? How could he have helped Andy solve this problem?

3. Describe the way Andy tracked the otter. How did his continual presence affect the otters?

4. What do you think Joe would have said if he had known how his young brother was acting? Explain your answer.

5. When Andy finally had the opportunity to kill the otter, he changed his mind. What made him decide to let the animal live? How did you feel about his decision?

6. By the end of the story, Andy had grown up a great deal. He was a much wiser person. What had he learned from his experiences with the otter family?

The writer's craft . . .

If someone were to ask you to name the most important character in "You've Got to Learn," you would probably reply, "Andy." You sympathized with him when his dog drowned. You watched him as he planned his revenge against the otters. And finally you saw how he came to understand why the otter killed his dog. Certainly, Andy's growing up experiences were a very important part of the story. Yet in the beginning of "You've Got to Learn," Andy wasn't even mentioned. Mr. Murphy wanted you first to understand and appreciate the otter family.

1. How did you feel toward the otters as you watched them living together?

2. During the fight between the otter and the dog, whose side were you on? Did the fact that you had already met the otters make any difference in your decision?

3. After Andy came into the story, the otters were no longer the central characters. But you couldn't forget them. Why did they remain so important even though they didn't appear again until much later in the story?

4. How did you feel about Andy's determination to find and kill the otters? How might your feelings have been different if you had not been introduced to the otters earlier?

Knowing words . . .

Often new words are built on root words by adding a prefix. A **root word** is a word which can stand by itself and have meaning. You can change that meaning by adding certain elements to the root word. An element added at the front is a **prefix.** The term *prefix* means, "placed (or fastened) before."

One very common prefix is *in-* which often means "not." When you see a word beginning with the prefix *in-,* imagine that it begins with the word *not* and you will usually be able to tell the meaning. For example, *ineligible* means "not eligible," and *incapable* means "not capable."

Robert Murphy wrote of Mr. Gates, "He shook his head, irritated by his inarticulateness." The word *articulate* means, "able to express oneself through words."

1. What does *inarticulate* mean?

2. Explain the meaning of the italicized words in these sentences taken from the story.

a. A long time went by before he saw a movement, an *indistinct* blur as the pale-fawn-colored fur slipped across a path of sunlight.

b. This emotion was *inexplicable* to him, and seemed like a betrayal of his brother.

Little Things

Little things, that run, and quail,
And die, in silence and despair!

Little things, that fight, and fail,
And fall, on sea, and earth, and air!

All trapped and frightened little things,
The mouse, the coney, hear our prayer!

As we forgive those done to us,
—The lamb, the linnet, and the hare,

Forgive us all our trespasses,
Little creatures, everywhere!

James Stephens

Judge

WALTER D. EDMONDS

The Judge was an impressive man. He had a massive figure, a red face, and strong blue eyes. Young John Haskell was not impressive at all. He was just a lanky, overgrown boy with a pale face and frightened brown eyes. But when he went to collect the dollar that the Judge owed, it was the beginning of a series of events that changed John's whole life.

When Charley Haskell died in the spring, he left a widow with nine children, a four-room house, a rickety barn, and a dollar owing from the Judge for the sale of a calf. The widow was a plain, honest, and fairly easy-going woman. She worked hard enough in the house to keep it and the children's clothes clean, but for outside things she had depended on her husband. For a few weeks after his death she apparently put her trust in God. Then she had a talk with John.

John was the oldest boy. The next oldest was only seven, and in between were girls. She told him, therefore, that it was up to him to take his father's place toward his brothers and sisters. They looked to him for their support, and she depended on him. She kissed him a little tearfully, and took up her existence again exactly where she had left it off when Charley died—as if, by a few words, she had settled it in the accustomed grooves for an indefinite time.

The sight of her unexpected tears, however, had sobered John, so that he hung up his fishing pole and went out to look at the corn patch. He found it full of weeds. It was an unusual thing for him to get the hoe without being told to, but he did, and after he had cleaned the first row, he found that it looked much better when you could see the corn.

When he came in that night to supper, he had a quarter of the field hoed. He called his mother and sisters out to see what he had done and listened with pride as they said that it looked nice. It was while his mother was looking at the corn that she remembered that they had never collected the dollar from the Judge for the calf. She told John that he had better get it that evening.

John was frightened at the idea of going to the Judge's house. In 1830, the settlement at High Falls was a poor place of small houses, which made the Judge's stone house seem like a palace. John, for one, had never seen the inside of it, but he had seen the curtains through the windows, and the oil lamps, when he went by at night, two or even three in the same room. For Judge Doane was the great man of the

48

district. He owned a vast amount of land and held mortgages on most of the rest and had been representative of the county.

John's mother had brushed his coat for him, but even so, it looked very shabby and frayed and outgrown as he knocked on the front door and asked the hired girl if he could see the Judge. He had the feeling that it was an impertinence to ask a person like the Judge to pay a dollar, even when he owed it to you. He thought that probably the Judge would throw him out of the house. But his mother said they needed the dollar for flour, and at least he had to try to get it.

The maid came back for him and led him to the Judge's office, opened the door, and closed it behind him. John stood with his back to the door and his hat in both hands, a lanky, overgrown boy, with a thin, rather pale face, and brown frightened eyes. Compared to the Judge, he looked like someone made of splinters.

"Hello, John," said the Judge. "What do you want with me?"

He sounded not unfriendly, so John managed, after a couple of attempts, to say that he had come for the dollar for the calf.

"Oh, yes," said the Judge. "I'd forgotten about that. I'm sorry."

He got up from his leather armchair and went to his writing desk and took one end of his gold watch chain from the pocket of his well-filled, speckled waistcoat and unlocked a drawer. While his back was turned, John was able to see the room, with the impressive lace on the curtains of the windows, the silver plate hung on the chimney-piece, and the fire on the hearth where the Judge burned wood just for the sake of seeing it burn.

The Judge relocked the drawer, replaced the key in his pocket, and handed John a dollar bill. He resumed his seat and told John to sit down for a minute. John did so, on the edge of the nearest chair.

"How are you making out?" asked the Judge.

"All right, I guess," said John. "I wouldn't have bothered you for this, only we had to have flour."

"That's all right," said the Judge slowly. "I should have remembered it. I didn't think of it because your father owed me money anyway."

"I didn't know that," said John. He couldn't think of anything to say. He only looked at the Judge and wondered how his father had had the nerve to borrow money from a man like him.

The Judge made an impressive figure before his fire. He was a massive man with a red face, strong white hair, and uncompromising light-blue eyes. He was staring at John, too, rather curiously.

He nodded, after a while, and said, "He owed me forty dollars."

That was what John had wanted to know, but he was shocked at the amount of it. All he could think of to say was, "I didn't know that, sir."

"No," said the Judge, "probably not. He was a kind of cousin of my wife's, but we neither of us said much about it. And after Mrs. Doane died he didn't come around much." His brows drew bushily together and he stared into the fire. "How old are you, son?" he asked.

John replied that he was sixteen.

The Judge went on to ask about the family, the age of each child, and what Charley Haskell had got planted that spring. John answered him everything, and as he did he felt a little more confidence. It seemed odd that anyone living in the High Falls settlement could know so little about anyone else. Why, he knew a lot

more about the Judge than the Judge did
about him. He told how high the corn
stood. He said, "It stands as high as any
I've seen around here, excepting yours,
Judge. And now I've started looking out
for it, maybe it will catch up."

The Judge said, "Hoeing is the best
garden fertilizer in the world. And sweat is
the next best thing to money."

"Yes, sir," said John. It made him feel
proud that he had hoed so much of his
corn that day. Tomorrow he'd really get
after the piece.

"You can't live on potatoes and corn
though," said the Judge. "What are you
going to do?"

John was awed to be talking so fa-
miliarly to a man half the town was scared
of; a man, it was said, who had even talked
out in legislature down in Albany. But his
face wrinkled and he managed to grin.

"Work, I guess, sir."

The Judge grunted then.

"You do that and you'll take care of
your family all right. Maybe you'll even
pay back the forty dollars your father owed
me." He held out his hand, which John
hardly dared to take. "When do you suppose that'll be?"

John got white. "I don't know, sir."

The Judge smiled.

"I like that a lot better than easy promises, John."

He walked beside John into the hall,
his meaty hand on John's shoulder.

"Good luck to you," he said from the
front door.

During the summer John managed to get
work from time to time, hiring out for as
much as forty cents a day, sometimes as
often as three days a week. At first he
didn't have much luck getting jobs, for
though he was a good deal stronger than
he appeared to be, and worked hard, people remembered his father and preferred

getting other help when they could. Besides, in the 1830's, there weren't many
people in High Falls who could afford to
hire help, even at forty cents a day; so, by
working in the evenings and on Sundays,
also, John had ample time to take care of
their corn and potatoes and the garden
truck he had planted late himself.

He used to wonder how his father had
ever been able to take life so easily. He
wondered often how it was that he never
had the time to go fishing that summer.
And the one or two times he did have the
time, he thought of the forty dollars he
owed Judge Doane, and he went out and
looked for work. He even found occasional
jobs at Greig, five miles up the river, and
walked back and forth every morning and
evening. Little by little, the forty dollars
became an obsession with him, and though
at first he had given all his earnings to his
mother to spend, he now began to save out
a few pennies here and there. When, at
the end of August, he had saved out his
first complete dollar and held it all at once
in his hand, he realized that some day he
might pay off the debt; and from there his
mind went further, and he began to see
that it was even possible that some day he
would be able to build a decent house for
his mother, perhaps even get married; perhaps, when the settlement became a town,
as they said it would, get elected to the
town board.

By the middle of October, John had
saved up enough money to see the family
through the winter, as he calculated it, for
besides his secret bit, he had persuaded his
mother to lay by some of what he gave her.
Further, she had been moved by the sight
of a decent garden to preserve some beans
and also some berries that the girls had
gathered, especially since it was the first
time in several years that she had felt able
to buy sugar ahead of the immediate de-

mand. The potato piece had yielded forty bushels of potatoes; and the corn, which John had sold, had brought in a few dollars more.

The day before he finished cutting the winter wood supply, John counted up his money and decided he would make the first payment on the forty-dollar debt to the Judge that night. It amounted to five dollars, but to John that seemed a great deal.

He went up to the big house when he felt sure that the Judge would have finished his supper; and he had the same business of knocking and waiting in the hall while the maid took his name in. He found the Judge sitting as he had found him the first time, only the fire was about two logs bigger.

"Sit down, John," said the Judge, "and tell me what I can do for you."

John obviously did not know how to begin his business properly, and after watching him under his brows for a moment, the Judge continued in his gruff voice, "I may as well tell you I've kind of kept my eye on you this summer, John. I like the way you've taken hold. I'm willing to admit, too, that I was kind of surprised. And I'll be glad to help you out."

John flushed right up to his hair.

"I didn't come to ask for anything, Judge." He fished in his pocket and pulled out his coins. His hands were stiffly clumsy. Some of the coins fell to the floor and one rolled musically all the way under the desk. As he went on his knees to retrieve it, John wished he had had the sense to tie them together instead of jingling them loosely in his pocket all the way up. He couldn't bear to look at the Judge when he handed him the coins. He said, "I wanted to pay something back on that forty dollars, sir. It's only five dollars, even." The Judge had to cup his two hands. "Maybe you'd count it, sir." But

it didn't look like so much in the Judge's hands.

The Judge, however, said, "Quite right, John," and counted up the money. Then he went to his desk, put the money in a drawer, and wrote out a receipt which he gave to John.

"Yes, sir," said John, wondering what it was.

The Judge looked grave.

"That's a receipt, John. It says you've paid me back five dollars."

"Why," John said, "it's kind of like money, ain't it?"

"In a way," said the Judge, shaking hands. "What are you going to do this winter, John?"

"I don't know, sir. I tried to get a job from Brown at the hotel, splitting firewood, but he's hired Ance instead. Mr. Freel's got all the help he needs at the tannery."

Those were about the only winter jobs in High Falls a man could hope to find. The Judge nodded, and said, "I'd offer you something if it didn't mean getting rid of someone else, John. I couldn't rightly do that."

"No, sir," John said, and started home.

But somehow, he felt so happy all the way home that when he reached the house and found his mother sitting up in the kitchen, he couldn't help telling her the whole business. He blurted it all out—the way he had saved a little now and then until he had actually got five dollars. And then he showed her the receipt.

His mother didn't say a word as she looked at the receipt, but her head gradually bent farther and farther forward, and all at once she started crying. John could not understand at first. He thought it might be because she was happy. Finally she lifted her face to him.

"Oh, John, why did you do that?"

"I wanted to pay off that debt pa laid up," he said, uneasily. "Ain't that all right?"

"I guess it is, John. But why didn't you tell me first?"

"I kind of wanted to surprise you," he mumbled. "I didn't mean for to make you feel bad, ma. . . ."

She went right on crying.

"But ain't we got enough?" he demanded.

"Oh, yes. You've done fine, John. But the way you've been working had made me kind of different. I got to thinking people talked to us different now. I never thought about that before. Sure," she went on, lifting her face, "I'll be all right. . . ."

As he thought it over during the next two or three days, John felt all torn up in his chest. He began to see that by starting to be respectable, he had done more than just work for himself. He had done something to his mother too. And now, by going through with it, he had put her back where she used to be. It did not seem logical, but that was how it was.

Perhaps he would have fallen back then and there to his old ways of letting the world slide, if he hadn't met Seth one evening at the blacksmith's, where he had gone to get the big cook kettle mended. Seth was there, too, having Jorgen do some work on a few of his beaver traps.

Seth was an Indian. In summer he worked in the sawmills when it occurred to him to do so, but in winter he went into the north woods. People distrusted Seth. They did not like the way he smelled. Even in the forge you could smell him, greasy sweet, through his thick tobacco smoke.

He said he was planning to go north in about two weeks. He was late, but the winter looked slow. He thought the furs would be coming up pretty quick though. Better than last year. Last year he had cleared only two hundred dollars.

"Two hundred dollars," thought John. He wondered how a man like Seth could spend all that. All he knew was that the Indian took it to Utica every spring. He supposed there were places in such a big town that an Indian could go to. Two hundred dollars.

He turned shyly to the Indian.

"How much does a man need to get traps and food for the winter?" he asked.

The Indian turned his brown face. He wasn't amused, or he did not show it if he was.

"Sev'nty-five dollar, maybe. You got a gun?"

John nodded.

"Seventy-five dollars," he thought. He knew only one person who could stake him that much.

The Indian asked, "You going?"

"Maybe," said John.

"You come wit' me. Good range over mine. Plenty room us both. I help you make a cabin."

"I'll see."

It was almost 10:30 at night when he got to the Judge's. He had made up his mind he would ask the Judge, if there was a downstairs light still on when he got there. If not, he wouldn't.

The house was dark on the town side, but when John went round to the office window, his heart contracted to see that the Judge was still up. He tapped on the window. The Judge did not start. He got slowly up and came to the window and opened it to the frosty night. When he saw the boy's white face and large eyes, he said harshly, "What do you want?"

"Please, Judge," said John, "could I talk to you?"

"It's eternal late," said the Judge, staring with his cold blue eyes for a while. Then he shut the window, and presently opened the front door. He was looking a little less threatening by then, but he wasn't looking friendly.

"Be as quick as you can," he said, when they were back in the office.

John was as white as a person could be. His tongue stuttered.

"I wanted to ask you something, Judge. But if you don't like it, say so plain. It's about me and getting to trap this winter, on account of that five dollars I paid you." He couldn't think decently straight.

The Judge barked at him:

"Talk plain, boy! Begin at the beginning. What's the five dollars got to do with it?"

John began to talk. He repeated what had happened with his mother, how she felt, how odd it seemed to him, but there it was. The Judge began to sit less stiffly. He even nodded. "Women are peculiar," he observed. "You want to take back that money?"

"No, no, I don't," John said desperately. "But people don't like giving me work yet, and I want ma to feel respectable. I thought if you could make me a stake to go trapping."

"How much?"

"Seth said seventy-five dollars," he almost whispered. "But I guess I could get along with fifty. I'd get the traps and some powder and ball, and I could go light on the food. I don't eat a great lot and I'm a handy shot, Judge."

"Seventy-five dollars," said the Judge. "You're asking me to lend that much to a sixteen-year-old boy?"

His red face was particularly heavy-looking.

"I'd make it on fifty," said John. "But it was just an idea. If you don't think it's all right, I won't bother you any more."

"Then you want the five back, too, I suppose—makes it eighty. And forty is a hundred and twenty."

"It would be ninety-five, wouldn't it, if you give me fifty?"

"Shut up," barked the Judge. "If I'm going to stake you I'll do it so I'll have a chance of getting my money back. It won't pay me to send you in with so little you'll starve to death before spring, will it?"

John could only gape.

"How about this Seth?" asked the Judge. "He's a brute. Can you trust him?"

"I've met him in the woods," said John. "He's always been nice to me."

The Judge grumbled. He got up and took five dollars from his desk and gave it to John.

"You bring me back that receipt tomorrow night," was all he said.

When John gave the money to his mother, it made her so happy that he felt wicked to feel so miserable himself. It seemed as if all his summer's work had been burned with one spark. And he was frightened to go next night to the Judge's house. But he went.

The Judge only kept him a moment.

He took the receipt and gave John another paper.

"Put a cross in the right-hand bottom corner," he directed; and when John had done so, "That is a receipt for seventy-five dollars. Here's the money. Don't lose it going home."

He walked John to the door and shook hands.

"Good luck. Come here next spring as soon as you get back."

"Thanks," was all John could say.

The Judge made a harsh noise in his throat.

"Good-by," he said.

John got Seth to help select his outfit. The Indian enjoyed doing that. And John felt so proud over his new traps, his powder flask and bullet pouch, and his big basket of provisions, and he felt so grateful to the Indian that he offered to buy him a gift out of the two-shilling bit he had left.

"No gift," said the Indian.

He shared his canoe with John up the Moose River and they spent two weeks getting in to Seth's range. They dumped his stuff in the little log cabin and moved over the range together to the one Seth had selected for John. There they laid up a small cabin just like the Indian's, and built a chimney. They had trouble finding clay to seal the cracks, for by then the frost was hard and snow coming regularly each afternoon.

Then the Indian took John with him while he laid out his own lines, and, after two days, went with John, showing him what to start on. After that the Indian spent all his spare time making John snowshoes. He finished them just in time for the first heavy snow.

John learned a great deal from Seth that fall. First of all he learned that an Indian in the woods is a much different person from the Indian imitating white men. He had always liked Seth, but he had never suspected his generosity and good humor. Even when the snow got heavy, the Indian paid him a weekly visit and asked him back to his cabin in return.

He learned how to make pens for beaver under water and ice, and sink fresh twigs, and when the younger beaver swam in, to drop the closing pole and let them drown. He never got as good as Seth. But Seth said, either you could do that or you could not; there was no shame in not being able.

But John did well. Early in March his bale of furs had mounted up so well that he had Seth come over and appraise them. The Indian said he had more than two hundred dollars' worth. It would depend on the market. By the end of the month

he might have two hundred and fifty dollars' worth.

The snow went down quickly, but the ice held. John began to be eager to leave. He wanted to show his furs. He would be able to pay off the Judge, not only the stake but the share, and also the debt, and he would have a few dollars to start the summer on. Next winter he would make a clear profit. He would put money in the bank.

He went over to Seth's and told him he would start next week. He could not bear to wait, and if he went early he could get across the Moose River on the ice somewhere. The Indian said, "Yes," but he begged John to wait. There was still two weeks for the fur to hold up well, and he had sometimes made some lucky catches in March.

But John's heart was set on going. He couldn't put his mind on trapping any more. He had done so well already. So finally Seth agreed to come over and help him pack his furs and traps. They had a big feed on about the last of John's grub.

In the morning he set out and the Indian walked with him to the end of his own south line.

"You one good boy, John," he said unexpectedly. "You come again next year."

"I will sure," said John. "Thanks for all you've done for me, Seth. Without you I wouldn't have done this." He hitched the heavy pack up on his shoulder. "I guess next the Judge, you're about the best friend I ever had."

The Indian's brown face wrinkled all over beneath his battered hat. He made a big gesture with his hand.

"Oh, sure," he said. "Big country. Nice company. Plenty furs for us both."

He held John's hand.

He said, "Now listen to Seth. If creeks open, you cut two logs crossing. You mind

Seth. You cut two logs. One log roll. Two logs safe crossing water."

"Yes, sure," said John. He wanted to get away. The sun was well up by now. " 'By," said Seth.

John walked hard. He felt strong that morning. He felt like a grown man. The weight of the pack, galling his shoulders, was a pleasure to carry.

Every time he eased it one way or another, he thought about what it was going to mean. He thought about coming home and telling his mother. He would buy her a new dress. He would make a purchase of some calico for his sisters. "Make a purchase," he thought, was quite a mouthful. He'd never even thought of it before.

He would see the Judge. He imagined himself walking into the Judge's office and dropping the pack on the floor, and looking the Judge in the eye. He realized that meant more to him than doing things for his family.

He remembered the way he had started the winter. He had got Seth to estimate the worth of each first pelt. When they had figured up to forty dollars, he had made a bundle of them. They were still packed together in the bottom of the pack. It seemed to him that getting that first forty dollars' worth was twice as much of a job as all the rest for him to have done.

The snow was a little slushy here and there, but it held up well in the big woods and he made pretty good time. Nights, he set himself up a lean-to of cedar and balsam branches, and sitting before his small fire, he would think ahead a few years. He could see himself some day, pretty near like the Judge. He even figured on teaching himself to read and write— write his own name, anyway. No matter how you looked at it, you couldn't make a cross seem like "John Haskell" wrote out

in full, with big and little letters in it.

Mornings, he started with the first gray light, when the mist was like twilight on the water and the deer moused along the runways and eyed him, curious as chipmunks. He walked south down the slopes of the hills across the shadows of the sunrise, when the snow became full of color and the hills ahead wore a bloody purple shadow on their northern faces.

Now and then he heard the first stirring of a small brook under the snow in a sunny place, and he found breath holes under falls wide open.

He had grown taller during the winter, and he seemed even lankier, but his eyes were still the brown, boy's eyes of a year ago.

He crossed the Moose River on the ice about where McKeever now is, just at dusk. He had not made as good time that day. The snow had been a good deal softer and his legs ached and the pack weighed down a bit harder than usual. But though the ice had been treacherous close to shore, he had found a place easily enough.

That night, however, as he lay in his lean-to, he heard the river ice begin to work. It went out in the morning with a grinding roar, and built a jam half a mile below his camp.

He saw it with a gay heart as he set out after breakfast. It seemed to him as if it were the most providential thing he ever had heard of. If he had waited another day before starting, he would have found the river open and he would have had to go back to Seth's cabin and wait till the Indian was ready to come out. But as it was, now, he would have only brooks to cross.

There were a good many of them, and most of them were opening. But he found places to cross them, and he had no trouble till afternoon, when he found some running full. They were high with black snow water, some of them so high that he had to go upstream almost a mile to find a place where he could fell a bridge across.

Each time he dropped two logs and went over easily enough. But each time the delay chafed him a little more. By late afternoon, when he was only five miles from High Falls and began to recognize his landmarks, he came to what he knew was the last creek.

It was a strong stream, with a great force of water, and it was boiling full. Where John happened on it, it began a slide down the steep bank for the river, with one bend and then a straight chute. But it was narrow there, and beside where he stood grew a straight hemlock long enough to reach across.

Hardly stopping to unload his pack, John set to work with his ax. The tree fell nicely, just above the water. There was no other tree close by, but John thought about that only for a moment. It was the last

creek, he was almost home, and his heart was set on getting there that night. Besides, he had had no trouble on the other crossings. He was sure-footed, and in every case he had run across one log.

He gave the tree a kick, but it lay steady, and suddenly he made up his mind to forget what Seth had said. He could get over easy enough and see the Judge that evening.

With his furs on his back, his ax in one hand and his gun in the other, he stepped out on the log. It felt solid as stone under his feet and he went along at a steady pace. The race of water just under the bark meant nothing to John. His head was quite clear and his eyes were on the other side already, and he thought, in his time, he had crossed a lot of logs more rickety than this one.

It was just when he was halfway over that the log rolled without any warning and pitched John into the creek.

The water took hold of him and lugged him straight down and rolled him over and over like a dead pig. He had no chance even to yell. He dropped his gun and ax at the first roll and instinctively tugged at the traps which weighted him so. As he struggled to the top, he felt the fur pack slip off. He made a desperate grab at them, but they went away. When he finally washed up on the bend and crawled out on the snow, he hadn't a thing left but his life.

That seemed worthless to him, lying on the snow. He could not even cry about it.

He lay there for, perhaps, half an hour while the dusk came in on the river. Finally he got to his feet and searched downstream, poking with a stick along the bottom. But he was hopeless. The creek ran like a millrace down the slope for the river and the chances were a hundred to one that the traps as well as the furs had been taken by the strength of water and the slide all the way down to the river.

But he continued his search till nearly dark before he gave up.

By the time he reached High Falls, he had managed to get back just enough of his courage to go straight to the Judge. It was very late, but the office light was still burning, and John knocked and went in. He stood on the hearth, shivering and dripping, but fairly erect, and told the Judge exactly what had happened, even to Seth's parting admonition, in a flat, low voice.

The Judge said never a word till the boy was done. He merely sat studying him from under his bushy white brows.

Finally, John said, "I guess that's all there is to it, Judge."

But the Judge only said in his heavy voice, "You'd better go on home. . . . You'd better start hunting work tomorrow." His voice became gruffer: "Everybody has to learn things. It's been bad luck for us both that you had to learn it like this."

John went home. All he could remember was that the Judge had said it was bad luck for them both. It seemed to him that that was a very kind thing for the Judge to say.

John did not see anything of the Judge that summer. He worked hard, planting corn and potatoes and the garden, and later he managed to find work. He seemed to get work more easily that summer. But his family seemed to need more money. By working hard, though, John found himself in the fall about where he had been on the preceding year.

He had put in a bid with the tannery for winter work and had had the job promised to him. Two days before he would have started, however, the Judge sent word for him to come to the big house.

The Judge made him sit down.

"John," he said, "you've kept your courage up when it must have been hard. I've been thinking about you and me. I think the best thing for us both, the best way I can get my money back, is to give you another stake, if you're willing to go."

John felt that he was much nearer crying than he had been when he lost his furs. He hardly found the voice to say that he would go.

Seth, for no good reason, had decided to move west in the state, so John had to go into the woods alone. But he had good luck that winter, better even than he had had the year before. He stayed right through to the end of the season, and his pack was so heavy he had to leave his traps behind.

The river was open when he reached it, so he had to ferry himself over on a raft. It took a day to build. And from that point on he took plenty of time, when he came to the creeks, and dropped two logs over them, and made a trial trip over and back without his fur pack. It took him three extra days coming out, but he brought his furs with him.

The Judge saw to it that he got good prices; and when the dealer was done with the buying, John was able to pay the Judge for both stakes, and for the forty dollars as well. The year after that he made a clear profit.

John did well in the world. He found time to learn to read and write and handle figures. From time to time he visited the Judge, and he found that the Judge was not a person anyone needed to be afraid of. When the Judge died in John's thirtieth year, John was owner of Freel's tannery and one of the leading men of High Falls.

It is a simple story, this of John Haskell's, but it is not quite done. When the Judge died and the will was read, it was found that he had left to John Haskell the big house and a share of his money. There was also a sealed letter addressed to John.

That night in his house, John opened the letter. It was dated the same day as the one on which John had received the money for his first pack of furs. It was just a few lines long and it contained forty dollars in bills.

Dear John: Here is the forty dollars, and I am making you a confession with it. I liked your looks when you came to me that first time. I thought you had stuff in you. It was a dirty thing to do, in a way, but I wanted to make sure of you. I never liked your father and I would never lend him a cent. I invented that debt. Good luck, John.

The man who wrote this story

WALTER DUMAUX EDMONDS   1903–

Walter Edmonds was born and brought up on a farm in Boonville, New York. During the winters, he went to New York City with his father, who was a patent lawyer. Edmonds remembers these winters as "a mere filling of time." Life on the farm was much more appealing to his imagination.

While at Harvard, Edmonds devoted himself to the *Harvard Advocate*. He worked hard, neglecting his courses, to become president of the magazine. When he failed a chemistry course, he changed his major from chemical engineering to English. Professor Charles T. Copeland's course in writing developed Edmond's talent enough so that he had a story accepted by a national magazine. Since then he has been a professional writer.

He has a great love for New York State, which he uses as the setting for all his writing. His literary specialty is that period in New York State history when the Erie Canal was being built.

Let's consider . . .

1. When the Judge first spoke to John, he was favorably impressed by the boy. What did John say and do that made such a good impression?

2. What were the handicaps John had to overcome? How did he go about overcoming them?

3. John certainly didn't have any extra money. Yet he began to repay the money his family owed the Judge. Why do you think he did this?

4. How did his mother feel about his paying the five dollars to the Judge?

5. John had always liked Seth, but while they trapped together John grew to respect him even more. What did John learn

about Seth that made him value the Indian so highly?

6. How did John react to losing his first pack of furs? What was the Judge's reaction? How do *you* react when you face a bitter disappointment?

7. In the note to John, the Judge confessed that he had invented the debt. He also wrote, "It was a dirty thing to do, in a way, but I wanted to make sure of you." Do you agree that the Judge played a rather low trick on John? In what other way could the Judge have tested John without lying about the debt?

8. The Judge could have let the secret about the false debt die with him, but he chose to tell John in the note. Why do you think the Judge wanted John to know the truth?

Knowing words . . .

You recall that the prefix *in-* means "not." *Un-* is another prefix which also often means "not." Explain the meaning of the italicized words in these sentences from the story. Then use these words in sentences of your own.

1. It was an *unusual* thing for him to get the hoe without being told to, but he did, and after he had cleaned the first row, he found that it looked much better when you could see the corn.

2. He was a massive man with a red face, strong white hair, and *uncompromising* light-blue eyes.

List other words which begin with the prefix *in-* or *un-*, and give the meanings of the words.

Work

Work!
Thank God for the might of it,
The ardor, the urge, the delight of it—
Work that springs from the heart's desire,
Setting the brain and the soul on fire—
Oh, what is so good as the heat of it,
And what is so glad as the beat of it,
And what is so kind as the stern command,
Challenging brain and heart and hand?

Angela Morgan

NOW THINK BACK

THINK FOR YOURSELF

If Willie Baxter were a friend of yours, you two would talk over your experiences. "What would *you* do about Jane?" he'd be likely to ask you. "I give up!" And you'd go on that way. He'd give you his ideas; you'd give him your ideas. You'd agree with one another, argue with one another, and ask questions of one another. Some problems take a while before you can figure them out.

Of course, Willie Baxter was just a character in a book. So were John, Artie, and all the others you met. But their authors did not create these young people out of thin air! They *seemed* real to you because they *were* real—as true to life as you or any of your friends.

It isn't hard, therefore, to imagine yourself talking things over with them. You're at ease with people of your own age. You don't mind their questions.

Think back over the stories you have just read. Among all the characters, which ones interested you most?

Choose one of these young people with whom you would enjoy a friendly talk. Try to visualize what he looks like; try to imagine the sound of his voice. Make your mental picture of him as vivid as possible. Then read through the questions listed below. Assuming that the character of your choice is asking the questions, answer as if you were talking directly to him. Don't hesitate to be frank; this is to be strictly "off the record." After your imaginary conversation, you will probably wish to discuss your answers with other pupils who have read the story. It will be interesting to see if you all reach the same conclusions.

1. You remember my story. But do you see what I was up against? What do you think my problem was?

2. What did I do about it?

3. Would you have done something different? What would you have done if you had been in my place?

4. People tell us that we learn from our experiences. Did I? What did I learn?

5. I guess I can't ask you what you thought of me as a person. I can't stop you from thinking what you please. But what is your opinion of the other people in my story? Was there anyone you liked very much? Why? Was there anyone you disliked? Why?

6. Some adults seem to understand young people, others don't. How would you rate the adults in my story? Give examples to support your answers.

7. Some adults think that we young people like to *exaggerate* our problems—that is, make them seem more serious than they really are. In your opinion, is that true? Why do you think so? Is there anything in my story that proves you are right?

8. What does the author of my story seem to think of young people? How can you tell?

9. Is there any question that you would like to ask of *me*? Naturally, I can't answer your questions. But perhaps someone in your class would take my part and answer for me.

SHARE YOUR IDEAS

1. Most people think their problems are unusual. When you talk things over, you often find that others have problems that are very much like your own. Describe the

problems faced by young people. Which of these problems are the most common?

2. Compare the ways in which these problems were met in PEOPLE LIKE YOU. Which of the characters acted wisely? Which acted foolishly? Give your reasons.

3. Which of the people you met in this part did you like very much? Which did you dislike? Why?

4. Did you learn anything from the experiences of these young people? What did you learn? How may their experiences help you with your personal problems?

5. How do adults differ in their attitudes toward people like you? What examples can you give from reading? What examples from your personal experience?

6. In what ways were the young people you read about different from others you know in real life? In what ways were they similar? Do you prefer friends to be as much like you as possible? Can people who differ in their interests and abilities, and in other ways, still be good friends?

WIDEN YOUR EXPERIENCE

Things to do ...

1. Plan a panel discussion or forum. Some of the suggestions in Activity 5 below may help you to decide on discussion topics. Assign these to individuals or committees in your class. Agree on a title for your discussion. Invite another class to act as audience, and perhaps to contribute *their* viewpoints.

2. Report to your class on radio and television programs for young people. Keep up bulletin board announcements of the programs you consider worth tuning in. If you can arrange it, plan a group or class visit to the studio of a nearby broadcasting station which features such programs.

3. Keep alert for news items, editorials, articles, and letters in your local press that deal with young people. Make an individual or committee scrapbook of such clippings. Write your own letter-to-the-editor when you find a situation on which you want to comment.

4. Choose an incident from one of the selections in this part. Rewrite it as a dramatization. Assign parts and present your dramatization. Here again, you might invite another class to share in the fun. Be sure to allow time to rehearse so that you will give a smooth performance.

5. Write about your own ideas. Here are some possible composition topics to challenge you. If you are a rugged individualist who prefers to dream up his own topic, go right ahead, so long as there is some real connection with the general topic: PEOPLE LIKE YOU.

My Younger Sister (*or* Brother)
I'm an Only Child
Blind Date
"Dutch Treat" on Dates
Cutting Class
T-Shirts Vs. Ties
Why Can't We Be Ourselves?
Friend or Shadow?

More to read ...

The Adventures of Huckleberry Finn by MARK TWAIN. You've already met Huck, so why not join him for the rest of his journey down the Mississippi with his good friend Jim? Harper & Brothers, 1923.

The Human Comedy by WILLIAM SAROYAN. This story is about an American family in wartime and Homer, a fourteen-year-old, who is one of the fastest telegraph messengers around. Harcourt, Brace and Company, Inc., 1943.

Seventeen by BOOTH TARKINGTON. The troubles of Willie Baxter seem to go on and on. Harper & Brothers, 1932.

Junior Miss by SALLY BENSON. Fourteen-year-old Judy Graves leads her mother, father, and sister Lois a merry chase as she tries to shape her family to her ideas of what people should be. Doubleday & Company, Inc., 1941.

National Velvet by ENID BAGNOLD. An English girl wins a horse and enters him in the classic steeplechase, the Grand National. Boys will enjoy this too. William Morrow & Company, Inc., 1935.

Seventeenth Summer by MAUREEN DALY. If you spend the summer in a small town with Angie, in love for the first time, you'll find out why school libraries have trouble keeping this book on the shelves. Dodd, Mead & Company, Inc., 1942.

Spring Comes Riding by BETTY CAVANNA. Horses and fun fill the lives of the Sanderson family. Meg is sixteen and has an attractive older sister. You know what that means. Westminster Press, 1950.

Ride Out the Storm by MARGARET E. BELL. When Lizbeth Craig finds herself far from her Alaska home, at a boarding school in California, she remembers the advice of a sailor: "If a storm comes up and there ain't no harbor, take to the deep water and ride her out." William Morrow & Company, Inc., 1951.

Start of the Trail by LOUISE DICKINSON RICH. Bill, eighteen, is spending his first summer as a Maine hunting and fishing guide. He takes part in an exciting man-hunt which changes his life. J. B. Lippincott Company, 1949.

A Place for Peter by ELIZABETH YATES. As young Peter finds adventure and responsibility on the farm, he and his father come to understand each other. Coward-McCann, Inc., 1952.

Up at City High by JOSEPH GOLLOMB. In this story of life in a city high school, you will see how patriotism triumphed over race prejudice. Harcourt, Brace and Company, Inc., 1945.

City for Lincoln by JOHN R. TUNIS. Imagine the excitement among the students when the athletic coach ran for mayor. Harcourt, Brace and Company, Inc., 1945.

Your Manners Are Showing by BETTY BETZ. Here is an amusing discussion of such topics as "Introducin'," "Bringing Up Parents," and "Advice on Vice." You'll chuckle over the illustrations and the four-line rhymes that accompany the more serious portions. Grosset & Dunlap, Inc., 1946.

How to Be Happy Though Young by GEORGE LAWTON. This book deals with the real problems of real young people. It touches upon family, friends, school, and career, as well as such personal problems as managing moods and overcoming the "blues." J. B. Lippincott Company, 1950.

THIS WIDE WORLD

Do you recall the last time a friend or relative returned from a long trip? All of you gathered in the living room and listened as he told of his adventures in foreign places. As you listened, you may have thought to yourself, "My life is so dull. Nothing exciting ever happens to me." But you can have excitement and adventure by reading about strange places and people you would never meet at home.

No matter where you decide to travel first in THIS WIDE WORLD, you will find a breath-taking experience awaiting you. The authors who will serve as your guides have been carefully chosen. They are not especially interested in the places that attract the average tourist. Instead, they prefer to explore the less popular but more exciting spots. The dangers of a tropical lagoon, the thrills of life at sea, and the mystery of the jungles of India are only a few of the experiences you will share with them.

PART TWO

THIS WIDE WORLD

I Turn Pearl Diver

CHARLES NORDHOFF

The young pearl divers found the bottom of the lagoon a place of beauty and wonder. One day they discovered it was also a place of treachery and death.

My chance came the same afternoon, as we were finishing lunch. At last Uncle Harry lit a cigar and called for coffee. "By Jove!" he remarked as he blew out a cloud of fragrant smoke, "those varos were wonderfully good. I reckon the best restaurant in San Francisco couldn't produce a finer dish!" The moment seemed opportune.

"We can always get plenty when the weather is calm," I said, "in fact it only takes a third of our time to catch more fish than the Tara can use. We were speaking of this to-day and wondering if you wouldn't let us go out with the divers in our spare time; Marama says he has often been down to twelve fathoms, and offers to do the diving if I will open shell. I wish you could let us go—it would be fun and somehow I feel sure that we'd be lucky. Of course, if you'd let me, I'd like to try a little diving myself." My uncle looked at me with a twinkle in his dark eyes.

"I knew you'd ask me that sooner or later," he said. "As a matter of fact I ought not to let you do it—I'm responsible to your father, after all, and old Taura's a

good friend of mine. Diving is always a dangerous business, though I don't believe there are any more bad sharks in the lagoon. Still, the other men do it every day, and you two are old enough to take the same risks. If I had youngsters of my own, they'd have to take their chances with the rest—otherwise they'd miss their share of good times and hard knocks, and become the helpless sort of men and women who are no use in the world. Yes, you may go, and dive too, if you wish. But, for my sake, keep your eyes open and be as careful as you can!"

That evening, when the day's work was over and the people lay on mats before their houses, smoking and gossiping in the brief twilight, we went ashore. My uncle led the way to where old Maruia lived with one of her nephews: Teura, a pleasant and amusing boy, who paddled her canoe to the diving-grounds and opened the shell that she brought up. Her house was surrounded by a fence of stakes, inside which a pair of pigs wandered, rooting up the earth. As we opened the gate, I heard her

voice give the hospitable shout of *"Haere
mai!*—Come in!"

"I have come to talk with you about
Tehare, my nephew," said Uncle Harry,
when a mat had been spread and we had
taken our places on it, native-fashion. "He
and Marama have become so clever at the
sea fishing that we were glutted with fish
and time hangs heavy on their hands. Today they have asked me if they might go
out and dive for shell with you others; they
are strong boys and well grown—it is in
my mind to let them go. What think you
of the plan? Is Iriatai a lagoon overdan-
gerous for boys?"

The old woman shook her head as she
replied.

"There is little danger here," she said.
"Ten fathoms would not hurt a child, and
the great shark you killed was the only
evil shark in the lagoon. And he was not
a shark, as I and all the others know! For
the rest, we have seen neither *tonu* nor
conger eel in all the days we have been
diving, though it is well to watch closely,
for a tonu is an ill thing to meet! But let
them go—they will come to no harm; perhaps they will find a pearl like mine, and
in any case the white boy will have strange
tales to tell when he returns to his own
land. I myself will show them where there
is shell in seven fathoms of water—not so
much as where we dive, but a good place
to begin. Let them beware of the clefts
and crevices where an eel might lurk, and
avoid the dark caverns in the coral, for it
is in such places that the tonu lies in wait.
There seems little to fear in Iriatai, but
one is never sure. As for pearls, watch always for the great lone oysters crusted with
coral and misshapen with old age—*parau
tahito,* we call them, and every diver knows
that they contain the finest pearls."

When the divers went out next morning
Marama and I went with them, our canoe

equipped like the others with basket and
weight and line. Maruia, smoking a cigarette in the bow of her canoe while Teura
paddled, showed us the way to a patch of
shell she had found in shallow water, a
quarter of a mile east of where the others
were diving. "Drop your anchor here,"
she said, bending over the gunwale to examine the bottom. "The depth is seven
fathoms and there is enough shell to keep
you busy, though not so much nor of such
great size as in the deeper water where we
work. Now I must leave—stay here, you
two!"

I weighted the basket with a heavy stone
and lowered it till it rested on the bottom,
while Marama tucked up his pareu,[1] adjusted his goggles, and fastened the glove
on his right hand. Then he went overboard, a grin on his brown good-natured
face. I passed him the weight; at the signal, I let go the line and watched him
shoot down into the blue and green of the
depths. After all, seven fathoms were more
than forty feet. I pulled up the lead,
coiled the line for the next dive, and
waited, watching the figure of my companion, seen dimly in the twilight beneath the canoe, as he moved along the
bottom with deliberate motions of the arms
and legs. Once I thought I saw him place
something in the basket, and finally, when
more than two minutes had elapsed, he
seized the upright line and pulled himself
to the surface. But he gave no shout of
exultation as he raised the goggles from
his eyes.

"Aué!" he exclaimed, shaking his head,
"it is more difficult than I had thought!
The oysters are there, but I have not the
eyes to see them, nor the art to twist them
off the rocks. There is no need to pull up
the basket; I got only two oysters, though

---

[1] *pareu,* skirt made from a rectangular piece of cotton printed with colored designs

in all my life I have never stayed longer beneath the water. But I shall learn!"

All through that morning Marama dove with increasing success. It was well for me that he did not send up as much shell as the older divers, for I was clumsy at opening it and so afraid of missing a pearl that I wasted a great deal of time in useless fumbling under the fringes of the oysters. At midday I had found no pearls, but the shell Marama had brought up was opened and neatly stacked amidships, and the soft bodies of the oysters were thrown into our kerosene-tin for inspection in the evening.

"I am going to dive this afternoon," I announced to Marama, as we lay resting after lunch.

"That is well," he answered. "I am not accustomed to being so long in the water—my bones are chilled! I will open the shell and you can try your hand as I have done. It is strange down there, and very beautiful, with the coral colored like flowers and the great fish passing close at hand. At first I was a little afraid. Do not let yourself grow discouraged; the shell is hard to see and harder still to wrench off until you learn the trick. Remember that the old divers never look upward—to gaze into the blue water overhead gives one a horror of the depth!"

At last, with a beating heart, I made ready for my first dive. I love the sun, which had burned my back and shoulders to the color of mahogany, and I wore nothing but a pareu. This savage garment I hitched about my waist as I had seen the others do, before I polished my glasses and fastened the glove tightly on my wrist. Once in the water, I held the lead-line with my left hand and the toes of my left foot, adjusted the goggles to my eyes and gave the signal to let go. I saw Marama's answering grin—felt the water close over my head. Then, gripping the line tightly, I plunged down into a strange purple twilight.

An instant later there was a gentle shock and the line slackened in my hand. I had reached the bottom. My ears ached and the pressure on my chest and stomach made my body feel as if it were being squeezed flat. I could understand now the curiously deliberate movements of the divers, for my limbs seemed weighted with lead—the same feeling I have had in dreams, when to my horror I have found myself unable to avoid the attack of some nightmare monster. I swallowed as I had been instructed, then held my nose and blew. The pains in my head ceased at once.

Frightened and ill at ease, I let go the line and saw the weight ascending through the deep bluish purple of the sea above me, which seemed, like the earth's atmosphere, to extend upward into infinity. There was no sign of the surface—nothing to catch the eye in the break between sea and air. For a moment I was in a panic; it seemed to me that I should never reach the air again, never feel the friendly warmth of the sun nor see the bright sunlit world above. Then I saw the bottom of the canoe, close over my head. Fifteen or twenty seconds had passed, and though far from feeling at home, I had gained enough assurance to gaze with interest at the strange new world in which I found myself.

Though not so dark as the greater depths I visited later on, there was far less light than I had supposed. The floor of the lagoon, here at seven fathoms, was bathed in a sort of purplish twilight which enabled me to see as clearly, I should say, as on an average moonlight night ashore. But instead of being silvery, like moonlight, the light was purple, and tinged with changing shades of green and blue. The bottom was of dense reef coral, which dies when sheltered from the breaking sea, but a hundred fantastic varieties of still-water coral grew on the dead madrepore, as vegetation grows on the inanimate earth, and its forms were those of vegetation. Close beneath me I saw little coral plants, fragile as violets or anemones; on a level with my head were leafless shrubs, marvelously colored and perfect in trunk and limb and twig; yonder a giant mushroom, ten feet across and growing on a tall thick stalk, towered above the undergrowth. Shoals of small fish, gay as the bird life of the tropics, drifted through the coral foliage or darted into the shelter of the mushrooms when larger fish passed overhead.

The floor of the lagoon was irregular, seamed by gullies and rising in rough hillocks here and there, and my weighted basket lay at the edge of one of these ravines. By swimming slowly in a horizontal position I could move from place to place without great effort, and hoping to find at least one oyster before I was forced to rise for air, I swam along the brink, scanning the coral sharply for the pearl oysters I knew to be plentiful at this place. A great silver cavally, four feet long and with goggle-eyes as large as dollars, darted out of a gloomy cleft, halted to gaze at me for an instant, passed within a foot of my face, and disappeared in the shadows. The fish gave me a start; in the flurry I let go a good half of my breath, which rose in a string of bubbles toward the air. My lungs were cramped. I had reached the limit of endurance.

I made for the line, seized it with both hands, heaved strongly and felt myself bounding upward like a cork. When my head broke water and I raised the goggles from my eyes, I saw that the native boy was bending over me with an air of concern.

"Another moment," he said, "and I would have gone down after you. You were long on the bottom—I feared that you had been seized with cramps."

"It is strange down there," I answered, a little apologetically, "the pressure—the dim light—I was so interested that I nearly forgot to look for shell and when I did look there was none to be seen."

"It was the same with me at first," declared Marama, smiling, "but if you look closely in the rough places, on piles of coral and along the edges of the gullies, you will see the oysters there by hundreds. It is easy to mistake them for lumps of rock —coral and barnacles grow on them as on the rock itself. They lie open like the *pahua* (the tridacna clam), but that helps you little, for their fringes are not blue and yellow like the clam's tongue."

I did not waste my strength by climbing into the canoe, but lay in the water resting as I had seen the natives do. When five minutes had passed I put down my glasses and went to the bottom again, and this time I saw two pearl-oysters. I found them at the edge of the gulley, when I was on the point of giving up in despair of seeing the elusive things. They looked for all the world like irregular lumps of coral, projecting like hundreds of other lumps from the rocky wall, and I would have passed without a second glance if one of them had not moved. Though they have no eyes, in our sense of the word, all bivalves which do not habitually lie buried in sand or mud seem to possess a subtle sense of light. As my body passed over the oyster, shutting off the light, the creature was thus mysteriously warned, and instantly its shells closed with a smooth swiftness. Looking more closely, I recognized the outlines of the *margaritifera,* the pearl oyster, beneath a protective growth of parasites, and grasping it with my gloved hand, I endeavored to wrench it from its fibrous moorings. As I struggled to free it from the coral, the water must have been agitated, for another rough lump closed with the same smooth swift movement revealing a second great oyster. By this time I had been under nearly a minute, and though I tugged with all my might I was unable to wrench the shell free before I rose.

"I have seen the oysters," I told Marama, as I lay resting in the sunlight, "but try as I would, I could not tear one loose!"

He picked up an opened shell from the bottom of the canoe.

"Take hold thus," he instructed me, "and turn the oyster with a sudden wrench. It is useless to pull. Ah—your left hand is bleeding—take care to use the gloved hand only, for the coral cuts like a knife, and oftentimes the wounds are poisoned."

By the third time down I had gained confidence and was beginning to feel at home on the bottom. Now I remembered the trick of which the Paumotan diver had told me, and when I had been half a minute underwater I began to let the air out of my lungs. The native had spoken truly; each little string of bubbles brought its moment of relief and enabled me to go about my work more calmly.

I was beginning to see the oysters now: my eyes were growing accustomed to the dim light. This time I managed to tear off a couple of oysters and put them in the basket before I rose for air. Three dives filled the basket, and when Marama pulled it from the water with its coral-encrusted load, I gave an imitation of the exultant native shout—a cry which brought a grin to my companion's face.

"We are learning," he said mockingly, "but it will be time to shout when we can fill the basket at one dive!"

That afternoon, when we joined the little fleet of canoes to paddle home, Maruia stood up, craning her neck for a look at our catch. "You have done well," she remarked, a smile wrinkling her brown face, "not badly for the first day's diving! I have seen grown men do worse. No pearls? Never mind—you will find them surely. Beginners always have the luck!"

From that day onward the fishing occupied less than a third of our time, and the balance was put in on the lagoon. We learned fast, as boys do, and gradually worked our way into deeper water till we were diving with the rest. Within a few weeks we were bringing in as much shell as the Paumotans, and my uncle was enthusiastic over our success. He could dive with any native, and once or twice, when he had leisure, he sent Marama out alone to fish and accompanied me to the diving-grounds. On those days my uncle's share of the shell went to the native boy's account—growing into a round little sum.

As for me, the diving fascinated me more each day: the beauty and strangeness of the underwater world; the spice of danger —small, but a reality, nevertheless; the thought of the money I was earning; the daily, even hourly, hope of finding a rich pearl, perhaps worth a small fortune. From time to time we found a few small pearls, but when at last good fortune came to us, it came hand in hand with tragedy.

As the nearer shell-patches became worked out, the canoes moved gradually northward, taking the cream of the shell without diving enough to exhaust the beds at any one place. One morning, in the latter part of July, Marama and I anchored close beside Maruia's canoe, on new and very promising grounds. It was my turn to open shell. The Paumotan woman, not ten yards away from me, was loafing that day—letting her nephew dive, for once. Teura was a boy of twenty or twenty-one, a favorite among the natives because of his

skill as a musician and his jokes. I had
grown fond of him since we had been
thrown with the divers, and often went
ashore in the evening to chat with old
Maruia and listen to her nephew's songs,
accompanied by wild native airs on his ac-
cordion.

I remember that morning as if it were
yesterday. The bottom was at about eleven
fathoms, rougher than any part of the lagoon that we had seen. Here and there
pinnacles of coral rose to within a few
yards of the surface; in the shadowy depths
below, the bottom was seamed with crannies and pitted with the mouths of caves.
The look of the place, in fact, was by no
means reassuring, but the men sent out to
survey the bottom reported that the lagoon
there was fairly paved with shell.

It had become my habit to take a water
glass in the canoe, for by now I was expert
at opening the shell, and I found it interesting, in leisure moments, to watch my
companion at his work. The depth was too
great to see clearly, but I watched Marama
plunge feet-first into the shadows, and a
moment later, a second string of bubbles
told me that Maruia's nephew had followed him down. Vaguely in the depths I
could see Marama moving about, a dim

moving shadow when his body passed above a patch of sand. Then, before half a minute had passed, the canoe lurched suddenly and sharply—the native boy was pulling himself up the line in desperate haste.

His head broke water. With a heave and a spring that nearly capsized us, he threw himself into the canoe.

"Ah, the great tonu—he nearly had me!" he panted, trembling with excitement. "Aué! Teura! Where is he?"

I snatched up the water glass, and side by side, with our heads close together, we gazed down into the blue water. Hearing the boy's words, Maruia had seized her own glass. Next moment a sudden sharp wail came from her lips. Then I saw the figure of her nephew, mounting his line with great heaves of both hands—and rising deliberately beneath him a monster hideous as a nightmare memory. It was a huge fish, eight or nine feet long and of enormous bulk. Its great spiny head, four feet across and set with a pair of eyes like saucers, terminated in jaws larger than a shark's; its rough body was spotted and brindled in a way that rendered it almost invisible against the coral; its pectoral fins, frilled and spiny as the fins of a sculpin, spread out like wings on either side. It had the look of an incredibly old and gigantic rock-cod—to which family, indeed, I have been told that the tonu belongs.

We watched in terrible suspense, all three of us. Teura was nearing the surface; in another moment he would be safe. The tonu seemed undecided, as if it were following the man out of curiosity rather than pursuing him. I began to breathe more freely. Then when the diver was within twenty feet of us, the fish reared itself suddenly and came rushing up, huge jaws agape.

In a twinkling it was beneath us, so close

that the water beneath the canoes swirled with its passage. The next instant the monster flashed downward and the man was gone.

The tonu halted, four or five fathoms down, and lay with gently moving fins. It was then I saw, to my unutterable horror, that Teura's feet and the calves of his legs hung from the creature's twitching jaws.

Another spectator was close at hand. "Aué!" cried old Maruia bitterly, in a choking voice. "Teura is gone! But I shall kill that devil as he has killed my boy!"

She had been baptized—she was a churchgoer and a keeper of the Sabbath day; but now I heard her half chanting a strange invocation, in loud and solemn tones. "She prays to the heathen gods," muttered Marama in an awed whisper, "to Taiao, and to Ruahatu, the old shark-god of her people!"

I glanced up. The woman was standing in the stern of her canoe. She wore her usual diving-dress, a loose gown of cotton over a pareu worn as the men wore theirs. The goggles were on her eyes and she had taken up a heavy fish-spear from its place on the outrigger-poles of the canoe. It was a formidable weapon, a haft of tough black wood tipped with a yard of steel: a tapering lance sharpened to a needle-point. I turned my head to look into the water glass. The great fish lay beneath us, a monstrous vision in the blue twilight below; but now the man's legs had disappeared.

Maruia's canoe came alongside. I heard the outrigger knock softly against our own. Then both canoes rocked violently, and we started at the sound of a heavy plunging splash.

Without a word to us or an instant's hesitation, Maruia had leaped overboard. One hand held a leaden diving-weight and the other gripped the spear, point downward. The fish scarcely moved at the turmoil in the water; the hideous lord of the lagoon was making his meal. Our hearts beat fast as we watched what followed, gazing through our little pane of glass. Swift and straight, the woman went down head-first till she was within two yards of the tonu's back. She let go the weight, which plunged down out of sight among the shadows; she drew herself together and struck—struck squarely where the head joined the misshapen body, a foot behind the monstrous goggle eyes. I saw the steel strike deep—saw Maruia raise herself upright in the water to drive the spear home with both hands on the shaft. The fish started; its jaws gaped wide—the sprawled and mangled body of Teura eddied down toward the coral forty feet below. The wounded monster turned on his side, the shaft of the spear protruding from his spiny back, and swam feebly and aimlessly to the surface, where the divers, now gathering from all sides, put a quick end to his struggles.

Then I heard the eerie diver's whistle close beside our canoe and the voice of Maruia calling to us. "I am going home," she said. "Lend me a hand to put Teura in the canoe." She had been nearly four minutes under water and had brought up with her the body of her boy.

The natives did no more diving that day. Anchors came up, gear was stowed away, and one after another the canoes fell in behind old Maruia, while the wailing of the *tangi*, the native mourning for the dead, floated across the lagoon. I reached for our own anchor-line, but Marama stopped me with a gesture.

"Wait," he said seriously, "we will go back soon, but first there is something I must tell you."

"Let us go to the Tara," I answered,

"and tell Seroni what has happened. This place makes me shudder. I have no more heart for diving to-day."

The native boy looked at me solemnly.

"Like you, I am afraid," he confessed, "but I have seen what moves me more strongly than fear. And I know that our fears are baseless, for my grandfather, who was the most skilled fisherman of Raiatea, has told me many times that where one tonu lives, another is never to be found close by.

"Watch well," he went on, "and move the basket if there is danger, for I am going down once more. In the cave where I first saw the tonu, are two *parau tahito*—the old oysters of which divers speak. They are covered with barnacles, very old and huge, and perhaps they hold pearls—great pearls that will make rich men of you and me. But that cave is an evil place! Teura went down with his back to me, and I saw him reach the bottom close to the entrance of the cavern, which he did not see. Then I looked in, and my heart beat fast as I saw that pair of old oysters, just inside. I looked more closely, and there in the shadows were the eyes of the tonu watching me, and his great jaws opening as he made ready to rush out. For a moment my limbs were paralyzed! The rest you saw."

I was becoming infected with my companion's excitement. Ever since we had begun to dive I had heard stories of famous pearls, taken throughout the group in years gone by, and the pearls which fetched the greatest sums and made immortal the names of their finders had always come from these huge, old, and sickly-looking oysters, growing apart from the rest.

Marama had picked up his goggles and was making ready to go over the side, when a saying of my uncle's flashed across my mind. "Never let one of your men do a job you're afraid to do yourself!" Then all at once I knew that I should have no peace unless I acted quickly.

"Stop," I said—a little shakily, at the prospect of the task before me. "You have been down once. Now it is my turn!"

All my life I have found that the more one fears a thing, the quicker it should be done. Without heeding Marama's protests, I snapped on my glasses, tucked up my waistcloth, and went overboard. Next moment I seized the lead-line and signaled Marama to let go.

Never, before or since, have I been more afraid than on that day, as the weight took me plunging down into a bluish gloom. The bottom, as I have said, was at about eleven fathoms—close to seventy feet—and since the coral was of the dark-purple kind, the light was very dim. When my weight struck the coral my heart was beating so that I nearly choked; I lost my bearings and wasted half a minute before I found the entrance of the tonu's cave. Suddenly, five yards ahead of me, I perceived the dark mouth of the cavern, like a low wide doorway, fringed with pink coral and gently waving weeds. As I stared into the darkness which seemed to fill a vast chamber, I felt a prickling at the roots of my hair— what if the tonu had a mate!

Then, dimly in the gloom, I made out the forms of the two great oysters, their barnacled and crusted shells agape. I moved forward to wrench them from the rock. With one in each hand I swam toward the basket, glancing back fearfully as I went. There was no shout of triumph when I reached the surface—I flung myself into the canoe and lay there while Marama pulled up the basket.

"You got them?" he inquired eagerly, without turning his head in my direction.

"They are in the basket," I said, "but if I had not found them, I would not have gone down again!"

"My stomach was cold at the thought of it. Come—let us open the shell and leave this evil place. I can scarce wait to see what is inside!"

"You take one," I suggested, "and I will open the other."

"Yes!" he answered, with a boy's eagerness to prolong the moment of suspense, "I will open mine first, and when we have seen what it contains, you can look into the other one."

He inserted his knife close to the hinge, severed the muscle connecting the shells, and laid the great oyster open on the bottom of the canoe. His fingers, skilled with long practice, went under the fringing mantle where nearly all pearls are found, searching rapidly and in vain. He felt more carefully—uttered an exclamation of disgust.

"There is nothing," he said mournfully, "not so much as a blister pearl!"

I took my knife and opened the oyster he had handed me. It was very old and diseased; the shells seemed half rotten, pierced with holes and borers, and the flesh of the creature inside had a sickly, greenish look. My forefinger went under the mantle —felt something hard and smooth, which moved loosely at the touch. Next moment I laid in Marama's hand a magnificent pearl, the size of a marble, round, flawless, and glimmering with the sheen of perfect orient.

We gazed at it, awed by our good fortune. A man might spend years among the atolls without laying eyes on a pearl one-half so beautiful! My fingers had gone back to the oyster to complete the habitual inspection when Marama found his voice.

"With such a pearl," he said softly, "a man could buy a schooner like the Tara, or an entire island for himself! Not one of the divers has ever seen its match, nor—"

I interrupted him with a frenzied shout,

as I laid in the palm of his hand, beside the first pearl, a second one—its twin in size, in color, in lustre, and perfection of form.

"Marama," I said when we had grown a little calmer, "we must say nothing of this to anyone except Seroni. I know little of pearls, but the value of this matched pair is too great to be made known! The sight of them would tempt a man to things he might regret."

Our mood of exultation was quenched by the wailing of mourners as we passed the islet, and the sight of my uncle's sober face when he met us at the Tara's rail. "I'm glad you came in," he said. "This has been a bad day and I'm feeling anxious and depressed. Teura—poor devil; he was one of the best of the lot; I've known him since he was a lad at school. This business won't stop the diving, of course,—it's all part of the day's work to them,—but it's a pity that such a tragedy has come to spoil our season at Iriatai. I've been jumpy as an old woman since the canoes came in—a silly idea that you might have gone on diving and that there might have been another of those damned tonus about!"

"We want to have a talk with you, Uncle Harry," I said. "Can we go down to your stateroom—all three of us?"

I followed my uncle and Marama into the stateroom and closed the door behind me. Then I unrolled the tuck of my pareu, opened a knotted handkerchief and laid on the table the twin pearls of the tonu's cave. My uncle's dark brilliant eyes opened wide, his eyebrows went up, and he whistled a soft and long-drawn note. Without a word he took up first one pearl and then the other, turning them in his fingers and letting the light play over their gleaming and flawless surfaces.

"By Jove!" he exclaimed at last, "you take my breath away! I reckon this is the most beautiful matched pair that ever came out of the Paumotus—by long, long odds! In Paris, on the Rue de la Paix, the jewelers would fight one another for a chance to bid on them! You can't set a price on a pair of pearls like these. One of them by itself would make you independent in a small way; the fact that they're matched probably doubles the value of each." He turned to the native boy. "Eh Marama," he said to him, in his own tongue; "you are a lucky boy! This morning's work will make you the richest man of Raiatea, with a fine house, a cutter, and plantations enough to keep all your relatives in plenty. But say nothing of this, for not all men are good at heart."

"Of course they are yours," he went on in English, "to do with as you wish; but I advise you two to let me handle this matter for you. They must be sold as a pair, and I know a man on Tahiti who will give us the top of the market. He is buyer for one of the largest firms in Paris, and in a case like this, something more than money is involved. These pearls will make history, you will see; I haven't a doubt they'll end among the jewels of some European court. Sikorsky knows me and knows that I know the game, it will be a matter of naming our own price, within reason, for the acquisition of such a pair of pearls would be a tremendous feather in his cap. Come, we must christen them, for pearls of real importance are always named. What do you say to calling them the *Marama Twins?* Marama means the moon, and their orient has the pure, pale glimmer of moonlight. What beautiful things! If I were a rich man I'd take them off your hands myself!

"See—we'll put them in cotton-wool in this tobacco-tin, and stow it away in the safe. The less said the better, I fancy, even among ourselves. Such a temptation might prove too much for almost any man! But tell me about Teura—his aunt was too much cut up to talk."

Marama left us to go on deck while I told my uncle the story of the morning's happenings. He shook his head when I told of how the canoes had gone home, and of our resolution to go down after the two old oysters Marama had seen. Then I spoke of my feeling that I must be the one to dive, and how I had gone down to bring up the oysters from the tonu's cave.

"I know what you mean," he remarked, as I concluded, "and you did the right thing; but don't take such chances very often! You'll have to keep on diving for a few days, if only for the sake of public morale, but I wish you'd slack off gradually and give it up altogether in a week or two."

The man who wrote this selection

CHARLES NORDHOFF 1887–1947

The American author, Charles Nordhoff, left the United States to fight in the First World War and never again lived here for any length of time. During that war he served with the Lafayette Flying Corps and became a good friend of James Norman Hall, a fellow flyer. Out of this friendship arose the long and successful writing partnership which eventually produced *Mutiny on the Bounty*.

Soon after the war, Nordhoff and Hall realized a life-long dream. They sailed to the South Pacific and made their homes on the island of Tahiti. The pearl fisheries off the coast of Tahiti greatly interested Nordhoff, and he often watched the natives in action. He learned a great deal about the art and business of pearl diving which he used in his adventure story entitled *The Pearl Lagoon*. "I Turn Pearl Diver," a brief excerpt from this book, shows how skillfully he wove facts into his fiction.

On Tahiti Mr. Nordhoff divided his days between two chief interests, fishing and writing. He tried to make his stories as dramatic as possible and to fill them with his own zest for life. These stories expressed his certainty that life was worth living, full of interest and beauty.

Let's consider . . .

1. Uncle Harry knew that diving was always dangerous. Why, then, did he allow Tehare to begin?

2. When Marama emerged from his first dive, he said to Tehare, "It is more difficult than I had thought!" What were some of the difficulties?

3. Tehare was frightened and ill at ease when he reached the bottom of the lagoon. Why did he feel this way? Soon he was fascinated by this strange new world. Describe the bottom of the lagoon as he saw it.

4. Why was it difficult for Tehare to see the oysters? On his second dive he finally noticed some. How did he manage to tear them loose?

5. Describe the great tonu as it rose beneath Maruia's nephew. Why did Maruia dive into the water to kill the monster?

6. After the disaster, Tehare had no more heart for diving, but Marama wished to return to the tonu's cave. What was his reason for returning? Why did Tehare decide to go instead? What was the result of his dive?

7. Why were the pearls named the *Marama Twins*?

8. Do you think the reward Marama gained by returning to the tonu's cave was worth the risk he took? Explain your answer. What would you have done?

The writer's craft . . .

When you tell your friends that you have just read a good story, their first question usually is, "What's it about?" You answer them by telling the plot, or what happened in the story. The **plot** is the series of incidents that make up the total action of a story.

Even though this selection is a chapter from a novel, it has a plot, just as a short story has a plot. To discover how the plot of this story was developed, you would need to see all of the important incidents in the order in which they happened. Here is an example of how you would begin.

1. Tehare's uncle and Maruia decided to let the boys begin diving for pearls.

2. Marama and Tehare had their first experience diving.

On a separate sheet of paper, complete this listing of incidents. When you are through, you should have a series of statements that contain *what happened* in this selection.

Knowing words . . .

Below are several sentences from "I Turn Pearl Diver." Explain the meaning of each of the italicized words. When you are not sure, check each word with the glossary at the back of your book.

1. The moment seemed *opportune*.

2. But he gave no shout of *exultation* as he raised the goggles from his eyes.

3. I found them at the edge of the gulley, when I was on the point of giving up in despair of seeing the *elusive* things.

4. Its rough body was spotted and *brindled* in a way that *rendered* it almost invisible against the coral.

5. Then, dimly in the gloom, I made out the forms of the two great oysters, their *barnacled* and crusted shells *agape*.

6. Then I saw the figure of her nephew, mounting his line with great heaves of both hands—and rising *deliberately* beneath him a monster *hideous* as a nightmare memory.

Write a sentence of your own for each of the italicized words.

"Oh, the Swift Plunge..."

Oh, the swift plunge into the cool, green dark—
The windy waters rushing past me;
Filled with a sense of some heroic lark,
Exulting in a vigor clean and roomy.
Swiftly I rose to meet the feline sea
That sprang upon me with a hundred claws,
And grappled, pulled me down and played with me.
Then, tense and breathless in the tightening pause
When one wave grows into a toppling arc,
I dived headlong into the foremost breaker;
Pitting against a cold and turbulent strife
The feverish intensity of life.

From Swimmers *by Louis Untermeyer*

The Most Beautiful Pagoda

ANNE MORROW LINDBERGH

Beauty is found in unexpected places. The wife of a famous flyer discovered it in a remote region of China.

"By the way," he said, half speaking to himself, half to us, "the most beautiful pagoda in China is down in that region." He spoke lightly and dismissed quickly from our minds the picture he had drawn. It was a lapse into another world, a world we had not time to think about then. We were talking about the floods. The group of men who were investigating the flooded areas, supervising the aid that was to be given, were seated around a table in Nanking, going over maps with my husband. Where was the survey most needed? How far did the waters reach in that direction? How badly flooded was that valley? These were the important questions.

So I never asked about the pagoda, and never really thought about it again, though the phrase remained in the back of my mind like the beginning of a fairy tale: "The most beautiful Princess in the kingdom . . ."

I did not think about it until one day we found it. I do not know—in fact, it was probably not the pagoda our friend was speaking of. But that does not matter. It was "the most beautiful pagoda in China," I am sure of that.

It was at the end of the day. We had flown to the limits of the flood and were now out in wilder land, above a circle of

hills. And there it was. In this circle there was a lake. And on this lake there was an island; and on this island there was a pagoda. There it was, just like the fairy tale.

77

Even the landscape seemed unreal, for in that late afternoon mist the hills and islands looked as they do in some of the old oriental scroll paintings—not placed according to the conventions of perspective, one behind another, but as though each were suspended, one above the other in some atmosphere, some wash all of the same tone.

The pagoda would have been beautiful by virtue of its setting alone, ringed as it was three times by land and water and land—a triple ring that gave it an air of an enchanted pagoda, safely imprisoned there by some wizard's decree. Centered like that, a gem in its frame, it gave one also an indescribable feeling of finality and peace, as though one had reached the end of the journey or come to the heart of some mystery. Its setting also intensified the impression of aloneness. Ringed by silence, the pagoda was. And the things that are alone and ringed by silence must be beautiful. It is James Stephens' poem:

Under a lonely sky a lonely tree
Is beautiful! All that is loneliness
Is beautiful.

And yet it was not only beautiful for its setting. It was beautiful in its very structure; one curved roof on another in a gently tapering tower—sloping roofs with petal-like leaves pointing upward, like the drooping bell of a lily. So that one's eye, although drawn inevitably upward, still retained the impression of those downward-sloping roofs. And the pleasure at the sight was the same as from listening to those climbing songs that rise and fall and rise again to a new height, the same figure repeated over again at a new peak. So the pagoda, although it was the embodiment of all peace and stillness, at the same time suggested growth.

It was—as I have said—the most beautiful pagoda in China.

We flew around it three times and went away.

One night in New York, several years after our return, a traveler from the East was talking about China. I could hardly follow his words, that hot evening, through the complaints of taxi horns pressing in the wide-open windows, when suddenly I was listening as one listens, pricked by a name, across a room full of conversation, to someone talking in the opposite corner.

He was speaking about the pagoda. I recognized it not so much from the description as from the story he told. A story which rang with a truth as compelling as those forgotten tunes which suddenly sing in the mind. One stands still in front of them, waiting with terror and delight, as they dance toward one. For they cannot be forced. And an eager step forward may frighten them away.

"And the pagoda," he continued, "is so beautiful that once a year all the other pagodas in China make a journey there, and bow down before it, on their knees."

The woman who wrote this selection

ANNE MORROW LINDBERGH 1906–

Anne Lindbergh is the daughter of a former United States Ambassador to Mexico. She was born in Englewood, New Jersey, and was educated at Miss Chapin's School and Smith College. Shy and sensitive, she began writing poetry while she was still a young girl.

Soon after her marriage to the famous flyer, Charles Lindbergh, Anne took up flying and became a licensed radio operator.

Two of her books, *North to the Orient* and *Listen, The Wind,* are modest records of flights with her husband. In both of these books she shows that she still finds poetry in life's experiences.

Let's consider . . .

1. You learned from this selection that Mrs. Lindbergh appreciated beautiful things in life. Where did she reveal that she also had a practical side to her personality?

2. How did the setting of the pagoda add to its beauty?

3. "And the things that are alone and ringed by silence must be beautiful," wrote the author. Do you agree? Why is the *aloneness* important? Examine some shop windows on your way home. Which of them display only one or two items? Which are crammed to capacity? Explain the different effect each type of window display has upon you.

4. What feelings did the pagoda arouse in Mrs. Lindbergh?

5. The pagoda suggested both stillness and growth. How did the pagoda's structure make this possible? What buildings do you know that suggest this same quality?

6. Describe a building which you have seen that impressed you as being especially beautiful. What was there about it that you liked particularly?

Knowing words . . .

Each of the sentences below has one word missing. From the list, select the appropriate word. On a separate sheet of paper, copy the completed sentences. Do not write in this book.

> embodiment   inevitably
> tapering   compelling

1. The . . . shape of the cloud formation reminded us of cathedral spires.

2. The painting was an . . . of all that is beautiful in art.

3. At first she wouldn't believe him, but his argument was too . . . to ignore.

4. Returning from the market they would . . . meet some neighbors and stop to chat.

The East Is God's: A Talisman

The East is God's, and so the West:
They both obey his high behest.
To peaceful bond, his hand entices
Both Tropic heats and Arctic ices.
*Edwin Thomason after the German
of Johann Wolfgang von Goethe*

Counters

ELIZABETH COATSWORTH

To think I once saw grocery shops
With but a casual eye
And fingered figs and apricots
As one who came to buy.

To think I never dreamed of how
Bananas sway in rain
And often looked at oranges
Yet never thought of Spain.

And in those wasted days I saw
No sails above the tea,
For grocery shops were grocery shops—
Not hemispheres to me.

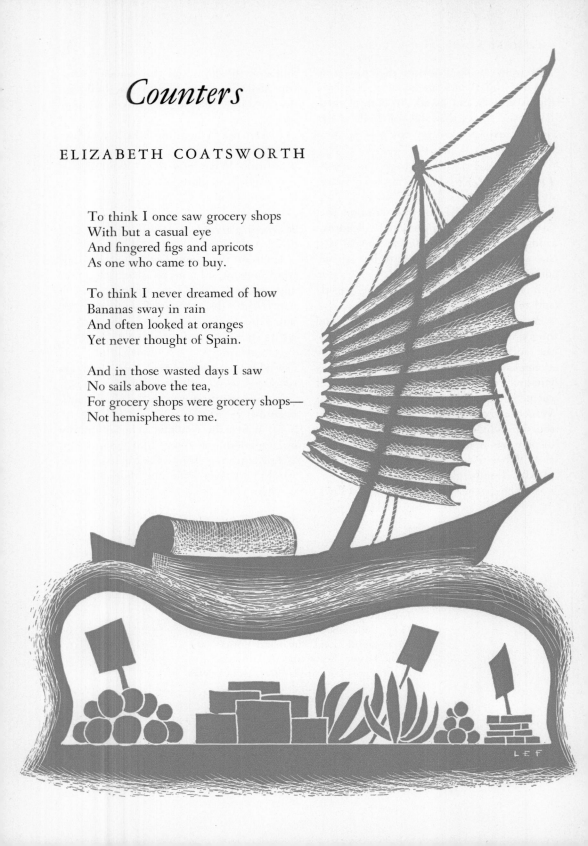

The woman who wrote this poem

ELIZABETH JANE COATSWORTH 1893–

Elizabeth Coatsworth was born into a wealthy family in Buffalo, New York. Her parents took great pains with her education, sending her to a private school that was modeled on the English school system. It allowed little time for play, but it developed Elizabeth's love for poetry and books. Later, after traveling with her family through America, Europe, and Egypt, she completed her education at Vassar and Columbia.

While Miss Coatsworth was still in her twenties, she spent an important year in the Far East, absorbing the Eastern way of life. Soon she was considered an authority on the Orient. This trip also affected her writing. Her verses took on the delicacy and neatness of oriental poetry, and a number of her stories were given far eastern settings.

Elizabeth Coatsworth's literary career has led her into at least three different forms of writing. She has written many poems and a number of children's books. Recently, she has written several adult novels.

The poet's art . . .

1. "Counters" tells how shopping in a grocery store was imaginative travel for Elizabeth Coatsworth. How did the foods stir her imagination?

2. Miss Coatsworth mentioned her former "wasted days." Why did she refer to them in this way?

3. What stores in your community could help *you* take imaginative journeys? What objects or products would start you off on your journeys?

4. List all the foods you can think of which originally came from foreign lands. For example, you might list sauerkraut and spaghetti. After each food write the name of the country from which it came. Then select one food and explain how it could put your imagination to work.

Camel Boy

LOUISE A. STINETORF

To Nasir, the Egyptian camel boy, the Sphinx and Pyramids were just as familiar as the corner drugstore is to you. He could never understand why "foolish" tourists would come from all parts of the world just to look at those huge blocks of stone.

Gizeh is just a poor little town in Egypt with a few houses of sun-dried brick and a half dozen camel-hair tents scattered here and there on its outskirts. All the people who live in Gizeh have one occupation—or just about one occupation. They guide and feed the people from all over the world who come to look at the Pyramids and the Sphinx.

Every day in the year, week days and Sundays, in dry and in rainy season, such visitors come out to Gizeh from Cairo, which is only a few miles away. Nasir had been used to these people, from the four corners of the earth, from the day he was able to toddle outside the family tent and to watch the first automobiles roll up almost before the sky was red in the east. But as well as he knew them, he never quite got over the feeling that they were queer and not at all like ordinary folk—not like himself, or his father and mother and baby sister, for instance. When a car drove up, there was no telling how the people who stepped out of it would be dressed. There were European men who wore trousers and women who wore skirts. There were Chinese men who wore skirts and women who wore trousers. Then the next

car would be full of American women, with nothing between their foolish heads and the blazing African sun. And right after them might be several men from India, with yards and yards of the finest cloth wrapped around their heads.

But regardless of how they dressed, or in what language they spoke, visitors behaved in the same manner. They all chattered and craned their necks and looked at the Pyramids. Then Nasir's father, and also the other men who lived in tents, rented them camels to ride around the Pyramids. Nasir could never understand why anyone wanted to ride around the Pyramids. Each side was exactly the same as the other. Yet everyone who came to look at the great piles of stone hired a camel and rode around the Pyramids—no matter how hard it rained or how hot the sun.

They were such fools, these people! Every one of them! A driver could ask almost any price he wanted for the use of a mangy, sick, flea-bitten old camel; and these people paid it. Sometimes they argued a little bit. But they were little children when it came to bargaining. And if they did not pay the first price asked, they paid only five or ten cents less. More than that, one only had to tell them that one had a sick wife, or a sick child, or that the camels they were riding belong to the sheik, and they poured extra money into one's hands at the end of the ride! Then, if they took one's picture, they gave one still more money.

They were very curious people, Nasir thought. Oh, undoubtedly, they were past all understanding, these people who came from faraway lands to look at Egypt's ancient tombs!

Some of these people climbed the sides of the Pyramids, clambering over the huge blocks of stone to the very top. All they could do, after they had sat in the blazing sun for a while, was to clamber right down again over the same huge steps of stone.

Now and then there would be a man who clambered up on the Pyramids at night, and who would sit on the top in the moonlight. When this happened, someone had to watch him so it could be reported to the police if he fell off. That was how Nasir met Mr. Thompson.

Mr. Thompson was tall and thin, and Nasir knew as soon as he first saw him that he was either American or European because he wore trousers and a coat made of good woolen cloth of a drab color. Mr. Thompson hired a camel just like everyone else who came in his car, and rode around the Pyramids and round the Sphinx. He also climbed to the top of the largest Pyramid.

But as soon as that was over, Mr. Thompson began to behave differently from the average visitor. When Nasir told him that he was riding one of the sheik's camels, he didn't seem at all impressed. Instead, he remarked that the sheik should feed his camels better, and that he ought to treat them for mange. Then Nasir said that his wife and children were all sick— this had never failed to get a generous donation before! Mr. Thompson merely looked at Nasir sharply and suggested that he seemed pretty young to have a wife and children; but that if it were true that a boy of twelve did have a wife and children who were sick, he should call a doctor! Then Nasir suggested that Mr. Thompson take his picture, and Mr. Thompson merely asked, "Why?" When Mr. Thompson settled for his camel, he gave Nasir the amount one Arab would have paid another.

When the visitors piled into the big cars at last and left for Cairo, Mr. Thompson was not with them. He had bought some bread and barbecued meat from a Gizeh street peddler, and he was calmly eating his supper under a palm tree.

That evening, when the moon came up, Nasir saw him start to climb the biggest Pyramid all alone. The police officer had not come to ask Nasir's father to watch the stranger. But Nasir knew that it was dangerous for one unused to clambering over the great blocks of stone to try to do it all by himself, and especially at night. So the boy settled down to watch.

The moon came up and it was almost as clear and bright as daytime. And the stars twinkled. It was as though they were merry and chuckling to themselves at someone. Out on the desert a little fox yelped and the dogs of Gizeh barked. Nasir's head grew heavier and heavier.

"Whoooooooaa!" was the next sound Nasir heard, and there was Mr. Thompson bending over him. Of course, Nasir didn't know what "Whoooooooaa!" meant, for an Arab doesn't say "Whoa" to a camel. Nasir did know, however, that he had fallen asleep and that the stranger had come down off the Pyramid safely and had stumbled over him.

"Did I hurt you?" Mr. Thompson asked. Now, Nasir understood English, for most of the people who came to visit the Pyramids spoke English, and he had heard it ever since he was able to toddle after a camel. But Mr. Thompson was speaking Arabic, Nasir's own language—not pidgin Arabic, at which even the most ignorant peasant would have laughed, but fine, fluent classical Arabic such as the students at the American University at Cairo used.

"I'm sorry," the man said. Then, instead of going away, he sat down beside Nasir and started staring at the Pyramid again.

"It's beautiful, isn't it?" he murmured.

Then Nasir stared at the Pyramid, too, and wondered how anyone could have such a queer notion of beauty. It was big, yes! Bigger than a thousand village houses. Bigger than ten thousand village houses! But even so, it was only blocks of stone with little heaps of desert sand blown into the cracks and crannies.

"What do you see when you look at the Pyramids, my boy?" Mr. Thompson asked suddenly, and then looked at Nasir as carefully as Nasir looked at the Pyramid.

"Well, there's stone, and sand, and dust, and bits of moss on the shady side," Nasir answered in Arabic.

"Don't you see anything else?"

Nasir peered carefully, squinting through his dark lashes.

"No," he finally answered gravely.

"Do you know what I see when I look at the Pyramids?" Mr. Thompson asked.

Of course, there was no telling what a queer foreigner ever saw, or explaining what he did, Nasir thought. But he didn't say so. He didn't say anything at all, and Mr. Thompson went on without waiting for a reply.

"I see men and women who knew much more about many things—building, for instance—than we do today. Men and women who plowed with a crooked stick, yet conquered the desert and made it 'bloom like a rose'; men and women who

had no compasses, yet found their way across the trackless sands; men and women who worked without our tools and created art objects we can't duplicate today; people who had no machinery and yet mined gold and precious gems from the earth; people whose boats were like cockleshells, and yet who set out for strange new territories unafraid; people who had no telescopes and yet who charted the courses of the stars and who used slabs of wet clay for paper and who wrote books on them, who . . ."

Mr. Thompson's voice went on and on, and Nasir stared at him in amazement. Finally he squirmed.

"Don't ask me how they did all these things," Mr. Thompson said to Nasir as though the boy had questioned him. "I don't know—yet! Maybe I'll never know! But this summer I'm going to go into these Pyramids and hunt for the clay tablets which will answer some of the world's questions about the men who built these huge tombs."

The two were quiet for a little while and then the man went on, "I'll need a lot of people to help me. Do you want a job?"

All that summer Nasir worked for Mr. Thompson. Sometimes he carried water. Sometimes he washed dried mud and dust from the stone tablets and pieces of clay jars. Sometimes he sifted the fine dust and sand which was carried out of the Pyramids, for bits of beads and jewels. At other times he just followed Mr. Thompson around and listened to him talk about the people who had lived in Egypt three or four thousand years ago. By the end of the long Egyptian summer, before Mr. Thompson packed up his notebooks and instruments and tents and went away, Nasir, too, was able to look at the Pyramids in the moonlight and see strange things.

"What do you see when you look at this Pyramid?" Nasir asked a visitor one day as

he led the camel on which she was riding.

It was a rainy day, and cold for Egypt; and the visitor was cross.

"Oh, it's just another pile of big stones," she answered shortly.

"It's more than that," Nasir maintained. Then, when the woman looked at him, he went on: "It's the record written in stone of a race of men who have never been equaled. Look at it carefully, lady! Come back tonight and look at it by moonlight. Then, if you will use your imagination, you will see thousands, yes, tens of thousands of slaves—your ancestors, maybe!— working for my forefathers. This pile of rock is the tomb of men who knew much more about some things—building, for instance—than we do today. It is the tomb of men and women who plowed with a crooked stick and yet who conquered the desert and made it 'bloom like a rose'; of men and women who had no compasses and yet who found their way across the trackless sands, and who had no machinery and yet who mined gold and precious gems; of people who set out for strange lands in boats almost as fragile as lotus flowers, and who charted the courses of the planets without telescopes; of people who wrote books on the bark of weeds and on slabs of wet clay. Those folk who see here only a huge pile of rock are ignorant indeed!"

That evening a tourist in a Cairo hotel told a group of fellow travelers about a strange little camel boy out at the Pyramids who recited Egyptian history like a poet.

"I was so amazed and so pleased I gave him ten times too much for a tip," she confessed.

One tourist spoke to another about Nasir. Here was a little guide who did not pretend to have a sick wife and children or the sheik's camels in order to beg money. Neither did he tease to have his picture taken. Instead he talked to them of what was inside the sealed doors of the huge tombs, and told strange things about the lives of the men who had built them.

Nasir became the most popular camel boy at the Pyramids. The tips he received were large, and when Mr. Thompson returned the following summer, Nasir felt almost like a rich man. Again for a whole season he carried water, washed clay tablets and bits of broken pottery, and sifted the dust and sand carried out of the tombs.

But that fall he did not guide camel-mounted tourists around the Pyramids. Instead he sat behind a desk at a mission school in Cairo. There people from Mr. Thompson's country taught him all they knew about his forefathers who had made slaves of their own ancestors.

The woman who wrote this story

LOUISE A. STINETORF

Louise Stinetorf was born and brought up on a Quaker farm in Indiana. Before she started school, her father taught her to read from an old copy of *Plutarch's Lives* that had been published before spelling rules became fixed. "Consequently," she says, "although I work with a dictionary constantly at my elbow, my spelling has little relation to that used by other folk." From a one-room country schoolhouse, Mrs. Stinetorf went on with her education until she had received her master's degree and had spent years in graduate study.

Mrs. Stinetorf has been interested in Africa for many years and has written several books about the natives of Africa.

As a Quaker missionary in Palestine, Mrs. Stinetorf spent her summer vacations in Egypt. It was there that she got the background material for "Camel Boy."

Let's consider . . .

1. Describe the actions of a typical tourist at the Pyramids.

2. In what ways was Mr. Thompson's behavior different from that of the average tourist?

3. What tricks did the natives employ to increase their tips? Why do you think those tricks were usually successful?

4. When Nasir looked at the Pyramids, he saw only stone, sand, and dust. What did Mr. Thompson see when he looked at them? How can you explain the difference in their ways of seeing?

5. After Nasir worked with Mr. Thompson why did he, too, begin to understand the Pyramids?

6. Why do you think Nasir attended the mission school in Cairo?

7. What is *your* local attraction for sightseers? Who are more impressed by it, you and your fellow citizens, or the visitors? Give reasons to explain your answer.

Hold Fast Your Dreams

Hold fast your dreams!
Within your heart
Keep one still, secret spot
Where dreams may go,
And sheltered so,
May thrive and grow—
Where doubt and fear are not.
O, keep a place apart,
Within your heart,
For little dreams to go!
                              Louise Driscoll

The Vagabond

ROBERT LOUIS STEVENSON

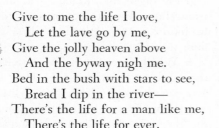

Give to me the life I love,
   Let the lave go by me,
Give the jolly heaven above
   And the byway nigh me.
Bed in the bush with stars to see,
   Bread I dip in the river—
There's the life for a man like me,
   There's the life for ever.

Let the blow fall soon or late,
   Let what will be o'er me;
Give the face of earth around
   And the road before me.
Wealth I seek not, hope nor love,
   Nor a friend to know me;
All I seek, the heaven above
   And the road below me.

Or let autumn fall on me
   Where afield I linger
Silencing the bird on tree,
   Biting the blue finger.
White as meal the frosty field—
   Warm the fireside haven—
Not to autumn will I yield,
   Not to winter even!

Let the blow fall soon or late,
   Let what will be o'er me;
Give the face of earth around,
   And the road before me.
Wealth I ask not, hope nor love,
   Nor a friend to know me;
All I ask, the heaven above
   And the road below me.

The man who wrote this poem

ROBERT LOUIS STEVENSON   1850–1894

From the day of his birth in Edinburgh, Scotland, Robert Louis Stevenson was a weak and ailing child. His parents provided him with constant care, often taking him on visits to more healthful places. There was nothing feeble, however, about his mind or courage. Because he was unable to take part in the usual rough sports all boys enjoy, he read a great deal. He also spent many hours imitating the styles of his favorite authors in his own writing.

Stevenson traveled widely in search of a place where he could live in reasonably good health. He tried Switzerland, France, New York, California, and finally the South Seas. There, on the lovely island of Samoa, he built a house, made close friends with the Samoan chiefs, and worked hard at his writing.

He was a careful writer who made sure that every sentence was just as he wanted it. He believed that fiction should be an escape from life, just as he found escape from the ills of his body in writing.

The poet's art . . .

1. The vagabond said, "Give to me the life I love. . . ." What things in life did he enjoy?

2. Look again at these lines from the poem:

"Wealth I seek not, hope nor love,
   Nor a friend to know me;
All I seek, the heaven above
   And the road below me.

If the vagabond rejected hope, love, and friendship, what satisfactions do you think he found in life? Which of these appeal most to you?

3. Which lines in the poem tell what the vagabond enjoyed in life? How would you describe his feelings toward life?

4. How did you interpret the line, "Let the blow fall soon or late"? How does this line reflect the vagabond's feelings about life?

5. After reading Stevenson's biography, do you think he was speaking of himself, or of the person he would have liked to be? Write several reasons to support your answer.

Song of the Open Road

WALT WHITMAN

Allons! whoever you are come travel with me!
Traveling with me you find what never tires.

The earth never tires,
The earth is rude, silent, incomprehensible at first, nature is rude and incomprehensible
    at first,
Be not discouraged, keep on, there are divine things well envelop'd,
I swear to you there are divine things more beautiful than words can tell.

Allons! we must not stop here,
However sweet these laid-up stores, however convenient this dwelling we cannot remain
    here,
However shelter'd this port and however calm these waters we must not anchor here,
However welcome the hospitality that surrounds us we are permitted to receive it but a
    little while.

The man who wrote this poem

WALT WHITMAN   1819–1892

Walt Whitman's father was a carpenter on Long Island and in Brooklyn, and for a time Walt followed the same trade. But as Walt grew older, he also taught school and worked more and more at typesetting and writing for the newspapers. Through this work, Whitman came to literature.

Walt Whitman loved freedom, democracy, and nature. In his *Specimen Days* he wrote, "I went regularly every week in the mild seasons down to Coney Island, at that time a long, bare, unfrequented shore which I had all to myself, and where I loved, after bathing, to race up and down the hard sand, and declaim Homer or Shakespeare to the surf and sea-gulls by the hour." He rode New York busses and ferries, talking at the top of his voice to drivers and passengers. In the front of an open-top bus, he shouted poetry to the amazed passersby, his long beard fluttering in the wind.

In 1848 Whitman went to New Orleans to work on a newspaper. The new people and strange scenes he noticed on this journey had a great effect upon him, and he later tried to recreate them in his poetry.

Many years of patient writing and rewriting went into his first book of poetry, *Leaves of Grass*. It was not an immediate success, and Whitman revised and added to it until his death. Today *Leaves of Grass* is considered the greatest single work of poetry created by an American.

The poet's art . . .

1. Whitman spoke of the "convenient dwelling" and the "sheltered port." Are you in favor of life in a "sheltered port" or do you prefer the life of a wanderer? What are the advantages of the two ways of life? What are the disadvantages?

2. *Allons* is a French word that means "Let's go." In what way does this brief two-syllable word capture the spirit of the entire poem?

3. What might Whitman have meant when he said, "However welcome the hospitality that surrounds us we are permitted to receive it but a little while"?

4. Whitman wrote, "However shelter'd this port and however calm these waters we must not anchor here." Why must some men always be moving forward? In what sense do *all* men constantly move forward?

5. Perhaps the vigorous "Song of the Open Road" seemed unlike most poems you know. Read it again, then list the ways it differs from other poems you have read.

The Reluctant Tiger

WILLARD PRICE

"I thought I saw something odd out of the corner of my eye. I put on my glasses and looked. On a great rock beside the road lay a magnificent tiger."

Before taking part in a tiger hunt, it is well to have an understanding between you and the tiger as to which one is to do the hunting. This bit of wisdom is the fruit of my recent experience in India.

It was all Nib's fault. Christopher Fortescue Nib was his full name. He was a tall, sun-bitten Britisher. I met him on the train from Bombay to Hyderabad and he was less reticent than most Englishmen— because he had something to sell.

He was a shikari or professional hunter. He told me vivid tales of tiger hunting in the glamorous, little-visited state to which we were bound, Hyderabad, heart of India.

I had not meant to do any hunting. As a correspondent, I was out to learn the extent of India's defenses against a coming foe. Instead I let down my own defenses. Nib said persuasively that I needed a rest. A tiger hunt would freshen me up. He had access to the Nizam's private forests. He could supply a gun. He could go with me—for a reasonable fee.

So I soon found myself in a hunting lodge in the Nizam's preserves, reading dog-eared copies of the *Sphere* and the *Illustrated London News,* and playing "The Campbells are Coming" on a rusty gramophone. This went on for three days.

"Be patient," Nib said. "We don't just go blundering around in the woods looking for a tiger. We wait until the natives report a kill."

We waited. On the fourth day, in desperation, I cranked up an ancient Model T that stood in the yard and went for a ride —alone. I didn't take a gun. If it was so difficult for several score of natives to locate a tiger in the jungle, I was hardly likely to meet one on the road.

At the top of a gentle grade the tired old engine went dead. I got out and cranked. A little of that goes a long way under an Indian sun. When I straightened up to rest and wipe my glasses free of the sweat that streamed down from under the rim of my helmet, I thought I saw something odd out of the corner of my eye. I put on my glasses and looked. What I saw made me perspire afresh.

On a great rock beside the road lay a magnificent tiger. His yellow stripes contrasted brilliantly with his gray, rocky surroundings. Nature didn't bother with protective coloration when she painted the tiger, I reflected. Perhaps she thought he didn't need it. His huge head rested on his paws. But his great green eyes dispelled the hope that he was asleep. They were wide open and they were fixed on me.

My mind spun like a pinwheel. What did one do in a case like this? If I ran, he could overtake me. No use jumping back into a car that wouldn't go. It was an open touring car—he could come in too.

He was only a cat—if I threw the crank at him I might scare him. But I would lose the crank, leave the car stalled, and perhaps draw the tiger. No, better let lying tigers lie.

My only hope was to get the car started. I bent down, watching warily. I put in the crank, turned it. My muscles were jelly. The engine sighed. I cranked again, frantically. The tiger seemed much interested, but didn't move. At last the motor coughed, grabbed, held on. I leaped in and was off down the road like a shot. Glancing back, I saw Stripes lazily turn his head to watch me.

Somehow it was humiliating. A perfectly peaceful cat had scared me out of my wits. At a safe distance I stopped and cooled down. It was necessary to go back by the same road to reach the lodge. I took care not to stall as I thumped back at all the speed the oldtimer could muster past the big rock—but the tiger was gone.

Arriving at the lodge, I told Nib the story of the strangely reluctant tiger.

"He neglected you shamefully," he grinned. "But it wasn't because you weren't a toothsome morsel," he consoled me. "It was just that he'd already had a good dinner. Now, if we can find what he was dining on we'll have him—because it's his practice to eat only part, then come back later for another meal."

Beaters were sent through the woodland and grassland back of the big rock. After two hours one came dripping in with a report of success. He had found the kill—

a young water buffalo, partly eaten. It lay in a small clearing about three miles from camp.

By late afternoon we reached the clearing. The beaters had lashed the kill to a stake so that Stripes would not pull it away into the woods. He might return at sunset—that was a favorite dinner hour—so there was no time to construct platforms. Nib suggested that I perch in a small pipal tree on one side of the clearing while he climbed a young ginkgo on the other. Large trees were too far away from the kill.

With some misgivings, I balanced myself on a branch only as big around as my wrist and but twelve feet from the ground. The elephant gun with which I had been equipped was very heavy. The branch on which I sat soon began to take on the character of a razor blade.

Sunset came, but no tiger. The shadows deepened under the trees and crept out to swallow the clearing. A chill wind came up. No matter how hot the day, a February night in India can be really cold.

Hours passed. Still no sign of our reluctant tiger. I thought lovingly of last year's magazines in the lodge and a log fire blazing on the hearth. And perhaps a glass of something hot and strong, and a game of dominoes. Anything would be less monotonous than this dreary vigil. In spite of the cold, I had trouble keeping awake: my eyelids would droop, my gun slip, and I would come alert with a jerk.

Between 11 and 12 a half-dead moon rose, only to add to the mournful aspect of the scene. I fought sleep.

Then suddenly a chattering of monkeys and scolding of birds roused me, and I looked at the kill. A big black shadow was beside it. The tiger.

Stiffly I brought up my gun and fired. The chief effect of the shot was upon myself. The tremendous backfire nearly shook me from my perch. The tiger whipped about in the grass for a moment as if he had been hit. Then he appeared to sense the cause of his pain and came straight for me.

I hastily drew up a dangling leg as the beast leaped. He fell short, but the bump of his great body against the slender trunk of the tree again nearly jarred me loose.

Then Nib fired. It had been agreed that he would hold his fire to give me first chance. And even now he did not risk a long, dark shot in our direction, but fired into the air to startle Stripes, who lost no time in making off into the jungle.

"You creased him," called the shikari. "Watch out for him. He'll be back."

I watched. I had no sleep in me now. I could hardly believe there could be such a change in my languid tiger. Now, at last, he was interested in me, but I got no pleasure out of the fact. If it had been a bore to be the hunter, it was no bore to be the hunted. Every nerve was on edge.

I noticed that the leaves of my pipal tree were shaking. The pipal is an object of superstition to the natives because its leaves quiver without any apparent reason. They believe the tree to be the home of restless spirits. The real reason is that the stem of the leaf is long and twisted like that of the aspen, allowing the leaf to oscillate even in the slightest breeze. But there was no breath of air now and I suspected that there was another reason for the trembling of this tree.

There was no telling where he would come from. He might try to approach from behind—I kept revolving so that there would be no behind. He might jump higher this time and not miss. But there was no higher branch in the little pipal strong enough to support me. My only hope was to be quick on the trigger. My finger fondled it constantly—and nervously.

There he was—two eyes in the gloom! I fired. An amazing thing happened. The two eyes went off in opposite directions. Was I losing my head?

"What was it?" called the shikari.

I told him.

"A couple of field mice," he conjectured. He seemed a bit disgusted with me and I didn't blame him.

At last the black grayed, and another day, which I had given up hoping for, began to dawn. When I could distinguish stumps from tigers, I slid to the ground. How good the flat earth felt beneath me! It soothed the deep-cut creases left upon me by my night on a limb. I called to Nib.

"Come on. Let's go home."

"Not alone," replied Nib. "Wait till the men come. Nothing so dangerous as a wounded tiger. Better climb back on your branch."

"I prefer the tiger," I said brashly, and struck off toward the lodge. He had to follow. Passing me, he took the lead, being surer of the trail. My spine began to itch and I kept looking back. There was nothing to see but the slender bamboos and tall wild-coconut palms and the banyans in whose branches the monkeys climbed and chattered. But in the dark catacombs among the many dropped roots of the banyans, Stripes might be lurking.

One mile. Two miles. I turned less frequently. If it had been going to happen, it would have happened before now. I began looking for the lodge. When I did casually glance back, I felt myself suddenly freeze from the ears down.

Stripes was emerging from a bamboo thicket. He seemed to be only a part of the bushes, and I realized that however prominent he was against a plain background, in an environment of long grass and brush his protective coloration left nothing to be desired. Only his movement betrayed him. He was not moving rapidly. But he was moving in our direction.

I swung my Big Bertha around and fired. I was too quick about it. The shot missed. Nib came tumbling back. He dropped to one knee, raised his gun—and did nothing.

I waited nervously. "Go ahead," I said. "It's yours. Take it."

"All in good time."

The tiger was close to the ground now, creeping forward. He did not run, leap, roar, or do anything that the novice would expect a tiger to do. He was unpleasantly quiet, as if he meant business. The glossy gold between his stripes reflected the sun. His fixed green eyes had a numbing effect. The hair on his cheeks spread out like side whiskers. His big pads made no noise on the ground.

Nib said, "Why don't you get on down the trail? You don't need to wait."

"I wouldn't miss it," I said through blue lips. Probably I could not have run if I had wanted to.

The tiger began to slide forward more rapidly, like a ship gaining speed on the launching ways. Fifty yards away now. Then forty. Then thirty. Was Nib paralyzed? Just suppose there was a dud in that gun. A lot depended on this one shot. Suppose the sights were out. . . .

Crash!

Birds and monkeys screamed and the woods came to life. But the king of the woods slumped dead. He lay as if asleep, his head on his paws, much as he had looked when I first saw him. Was he pretending? Nib was evidently sure of his shot, for he jumped up and ran to the carcass. I followed, more diffidently. Through the head was a neat hole as definite as a caste mark on a Hindu forehead. Nib's bullet had done that.

The man who wrote this story

WILLARD PRICE 1887–

Although Mr. Price was born in Canada, he began his travels early by coming to the United States to attend school. After he received his master's degree from Columbia, he became the editor of several publications about foreign affairs.

Mr. Price then served as a foreign correspondent, until he began to make expeditions for the American Museum of Natural History and the National Geographic Society. Since then he has been constantly on the move and has now traveled in more than seventy-seven countries. He has been in the Sahara Desert, China, the Upper Amazon, and the Valley of the Nile. From his amazing experiences as an explorer, he has written many books and tales of adventure.

Let's consider . . .

1. When Willard Price first saw the tiger, the animal's yellow stripes contrasted brilliantly with the gray, rocky surroundings. How did Price explain this lack of protective coloring?

2. How did he discover that in other surroundings the stripes helped to protect the tiger? Describe the protective markings of different kinds of wild life. In each case, tell how these markings are useful.

3. Price became nervous after he had wounded the tiger. Was he justified in feeling that way, or was he being cowardly? Give several reasons to support your answer.

4. Several times Price revealed his inexperience as a jungle hunter. Describe *one* occasion in which he showed this lack of experience. In what ways did Nib reveal that *he* was an experienced hunter?

5. Some people believe that men should never kill wild animals. Other people enjoy the sport. Under what conditions do *you* think that men are justified in killing wild animals?

The writer's craft . . .

As you read this story, you probably kept wondering, "What's going to happen next?" The author used a variety of means to build **suspense.** He tried to keep you guessing and to hold your interest until the very last line.

1. When did you think the tiger was going to be the victor?

2. When did you think that Willard Price would win the battle with the tiger?

3. At what point was the suspense the greatest?

4. What other stories have you read in which suspense played an important part?

5. Select a movie, a radio program, or television program that relies on suspense to hold your interest. Analyze it to see what part the following items play in building the suspense.

a. The background music

b. A setting which creates a mood

c. The role which a given actor always plays

d. A particular type of "tip-off" situation, such as a telephone call in the night

Knowing words . . .

After Willard Price had wounded the tiger, he wrote, "I could hardly believe there could be such a change in my languid tiger." Try to form a definition of *languid* from the story context. Then check your definition with the glossary.

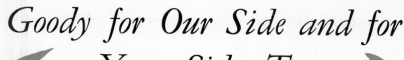

Goody for Our Side and for Your Side, Too

OGDEN NASH

Foreigners are people somewhere else,
Natives are people at home;
If the place you're at is your habitat,
You're a foreigner, say in Rome.
But the scales of Justice balance true,
And tit only leads to tat,
So the man who's at home when he stays in Rome
Is abroad when he's where you're at.

When we leave the limits of the land in which
Our birth certificates sat us,
It does not mean just a change of scene,
But also a change of status.
The Frenchman with his fetching beard,
The Scot with his kilt and sporran,
One moment he may a native be,
And the next may find him foreign.

There's many a difference quickly found
Between the different races,
But the only essential differential
Is living in different places.
Yet such is the pride of prideful man,
From Austrians to Australians,
That wherever he is, he regards as his,
And the natives there, as aliens.

Oh, I'll be friends if you'll be friends,
The foreigner tells the native,
And we'll work together for our common ends
Like a preposition and a dative.
If our common ends seem mostly mine,
Why not, you ignorant foreigner?
And the native replies contrariwise;
And hence, my dears, the coroner.

So mind your manners when a native, please,
And doubly when you're not,
And Vickers and Krupp will soon fold up,
And Sopwith pawn his yacht.
One simple thought, if you have it pat,
Will eliminate the coroner:
You may be a native in your habitat,
But to foreigners you're just a foreigner.

The man who wrote this poem

OGDEN NASH 1902–

Frederick Ogden Nash was born in Rye, New York. When his family sent him to a private school in Rhode Island, they unknowingly were starting him off on a writing career. For it was at this school that he learned the fundamentals of writing. After a year at Harvard, Nash moved to New York and went to work for a publishing firm.

Then he began to write light verse. In a short time his humorous poems were quoted across the nation and printed in magazines and books. He had a knack for rhyming seemingly impossible combinations of words. And he took special joy in giving an unusual and unconventional turn to almost every idea. Like Robert Benchley, he loved to make fun of our so-called civilized way of life.

Because of his success as a poet, he decided to retire from publishing and devote his full time to writing. He now writes quantities of humorous verse which can be read in most national magazines. On the side, Nash frequently tours the country reciting his favorite poems with great skill and pleasure.

The poet's art . . .

1. Most readers like humorous poetry. Choose your favorite stanza of "Goody for Our Side and for Your Side, Too" and read it aloud to the class.

2. You can often find wisdom in light, humorous verse. What "truth" is there in Ogden Nash's poem?

3. When are *you* a foreigner? How did the poet advise you to act on such occasions?

4. Ogden Nash found humor in the idea that everyone is a foreigner when he's not at home. If everyone understood this idea, why would the world be a friendlier place in which to live?

Doubling Cape Horn

RICHARD HENRY DANA, JR.

Cape Horn is at the extreme southern tip of South America. Sailing around the Cape from west to east was an invitation to disaster. Dana soon found out why.

In our first attempt to double [1] the Cape, when we came up to the latitude of it, we were nearly seventeen hundred miles to the westward, but in running for the Straits of Magellan we stood so far to the eastward that we made our second attempt at a distance of not more than four or five hundred miles; and we had great hopes, by this means, to run clear of the ice. We made great way toward the southward, and almost every watch, when we came on deck, the air seemed to grow colder, and the sea to run higher. Still we saw no ice, and had great hopes of going clear of it altogether, when, one afternoon, about three o'clock, while we were taking a *siesta* [2] during our watch below, "All hands!" was called in a loud and fearful voice. "Tumble up here, men! tumble up; don't stop for your clothes—before we're upon it!" We sprang out of our berths and hurried up on deck. The loud sharp voice of the captain was heard giving orders, as though for life or death, and we ran aft to the braces, not waiting to look ahead, for not a moment was to be lost. Slowly, we swung round, leaving behind us, directly under our larboard quarter,[3] a large ice island, peering out of the mist, and reaching high above our tops; while astern, and on either side of the island, large tracts of field-ice were dimly seen, heaving and rolling in the sea. We were now safe, and standing to the northward; but, in a few minutes more, had it not been for the sharp lookout of the watch, we should have been fairly upon the ice, and left our ship's old bones adrift in the Southern Ocean. All night long a bright lookout was kept from every part of the deck; and whenever ice was seen on the one bow or the other the helm was shifted and the yards braced,[4] and, by quick working of the ship,

[1] *double,* sail around
[2] *siesta,* nap after the midday meal

[3] *larboard quarter,* the part of a ship halfway between the stern and the center of the ship, on the left-hand side as one faces the bow
[4] *yards braced,* the ropes used for lowering or raising the yards (timbers to which sails are attached) were tightened

she was kept clear. The accustomed cry of "Ice ahead!" "Ice on the lee bow!" "Another island!" in the same tones, and with the same orders following them, seemed to bring us directly back to our old position of the week before.

During our watch on deck, which was from twelve to four, the wind came out ahead, with a pelting storm of hail and sleet. During the next watch it fell calm with a drenching rain until daybreak, when the wind came out to the westward, and the weather cleared up, and showed us the whole ocean, in the course which we should have steered, had it not been for the head wind and calm, completely blocked up with ice. Here, then, our progress was stopped, and we wore ship,[5] and once more stood to the northward and eastward; not for the Straits of Magellan, but to make another attempt to double the Cape, still farther to the eastward; for the captain was determined to get round if perseverance could do it, and the third time, he said, never failed.

With a fair wind we soon ran clear of the field-ice, and by noon had only the stray islands floating far and near upon the ocean. The sun was out bright, the sea of a deep blue, fringed with the white foam of the waves, which ran high before a strong south-wester; our solitary ship tore on through the open water as though glad to be out of her confinement; and the ice islands lay scattered here and there, of various sizes and shapes, reflecting the bright rays of the sun, and drifting slowly northward before the gale. It was a contrast to much that we had lately seen, and a spectacle not only of beauty, but of life; for it required but little fancy to imagine these islands to be animate masses which

had broken loose from the "thrilling regions of thick-ribbed ice," and were working their way, by wind and current, some alone, and some in fleets, to milder climes.

No pencil has ever yet given anything like the true effect of an iceberg. In a picture, they are huge, uncouth masses, stuck in the sea, while their chief beauty and grandeur—their slow, stately motion, the whirling of the snow about their summits, and the fearful groaning and cracking of their parts—the picture cannot give. This is the large iceberg, while the small and distant islands, floating on the smooth sea, in the light of a clear day, look like floating fairy isles of sapphire.

From a north-east course we gradually hauled to the eastward, and after sailing about two hundred miles, which brought us as near to the western coast of Terra del Fuego as was safe, and having lost sight of the ice altogether, for the third time we put the ship's head to the southward, to try the passage of the Cape. The weather continued clear and cold, with a strong gale from the westward, and we were fast getting up with the latitude of the Cape, with a prospect of soon being round. One fine afternoon, a man, who had gone into the foretop to shift the rolling tackles,[6] sung out at the top of his voice, and with evident glee, "Sail ho!" Neither land nor sail had we seen since leaving San Diego; and only those who have traversed the length of a whole ocean alone can imagine what an excitement such an announcement produced on board. "Sail ho!" shouted the cook, jumping out of his galley; "Sail ho!" shouted a man, throwing back the slide of the scuttle, to the watch below, who were soon out of their berths and on deck; and "Sail ho!" shouted the captain down the companion-way to the passenger in the cabin.

---

[5] *wore ship,* turned the ship away from the wind until the wind was on the opposite side of the ship

[6] *tackles,* ropes and pulleys used for handling sails

Besides the pleasure of seeing a ship and human beings in so desolate a place, it was important for us to speak a vessel, to learn whether there was ice to the eastward, and to ascertain the longitude; for we had no chronometer, and had been drifting about so long that we had nearly lost our reckoning. The excitement in our little community was running high, and conjectures were made, and everything thought of for which the captain would hail, when the man aloft sung out—"Another sail, large on the weather bow!" This was a little odd, but so much the better, and did not shake our faith in their being sails. At length the man in the top hailed, and said he believed it was land, after all. "Land in your eye!" said the mate, who was looking through the telescope; "they are ice islands, if I can see a hole through a ladder"; and a few moments showed the mate to be right; and all our expectations fled; and instead of what we most wished to see we had what we most dreaded, and what we hoped we had seen the last of. We soon, however, left these astern, having passed within two miles of them, and at sundown the horizon was clear in all directions.

Having a fine wind, we were soon up with and passed the latitude of the Cape. But ill luck seemed to have lighted upon us. Not four hours had we been standing on in this course before it fell dead calm, and in half an hour it clouded up; a few straggling blasts, with spits of snow and sleet, came from the eastward. In an hour more we lay hove-to [7] under a close-reefed maintopsail,[8] drifting bodily off to leeward before the fiercest storm that we had yet felt, blowing dead ahead, from the east-

ward. It seemed as though the genius of the place had been roused at finding that we had nearly skipped through his fingers, and had come down upon us with tenfold fury. The sailors said that every blast, as it shook the shrouds, and whistled through the rigging, said to the old ship, "No, you don't!" "No, you don't!"

For eight days we lay drifting about in this manner. Sometimes—generally toward noon—it fell calm; once or twice a round copper ball showed itself for a few moments in the place where the sun ought to have been, and a puff or two came from the westward, giving some hope that a fair wind had come at last. We had less snow and hail than when we were farther to the westward, but we had an abundance of what is worse to a sailor in cold weather—drenching rain. Snow is blinding, and very bad when coming upon a coast, but, for genuine discomfort, give me rain with freezing weather. A snow storm is exciting, and it does not wet through the clothes (a fact important to a sailor); but a constant rain there is no escaping from. It wets to the skin, and makes all protection vain. We had long ago run through all our dry clothes, and as sailors have no other way of drying them than by the sun, we had nothing to do but to put on those which were the least wet. At the end of each watch, when we came below, we took off our clothes and wrung them out; two taking hold of a pair of trousers, one at each end—and jackets in the same way. Stockings, mittens, and all, were wrung out also, and then hung up to drain and chafe dry against the bulkheads.[9] Then, feeling all our clothes, we picked out those which were the least wet, and put them on, so as to be ready for a call, and turned-in, covered ourselves up with blankets, and slept until

---

[7] *hove-to,* without forward motion

[8] *close-reefed maintopsail,* sail on the main mast, tied and fastened to yards so that the smallest amount of sail is exposed to the wind

[9] *bulkheads,* vertical partitions inside a ship

three knocks on the scuttle, and the dismal sound of "All Starbowlines ahoy! Eight bells, there below! Do you hear the news?" drawled out from on deck, and the sulky answer of "Aye, aye!" from below, sent us up again.

On deck all was dark, and either a dead calm, with the rain pouring steadily down, or, more generally, a violent gale dead ahead, with rain pelting horizontally, and occasional variations of hail and sleet; decks afloat with water swashing from side to side, and constantly wet feet, for boots could not be rung out like drawers, and no compositions could stand the constant soaking. In fact, wet and cold feet are inevitable in such weather, and are not the last of those items which go to make up the grand total of the discomforts of a winter passage round Cape Horn.

Few words were spoken between the watches as they shifted. The bells seemed to be an hour or two apart, instead of half an hour, and an age to elapse before the welcome sound of eight bells. The sole object was to make the time pass on. Any change was sought for which would break the monotony of the time; and even the two hours' trick at the wheel, which came round to us in turn, once in every other watch, was looked upon as a relief. The never-failing resource of long yarns, which eke out many a watch, seemed to have failed us now; for we had been so long together that we had heard each other's stories told over and over again till we had them by heart; each one knew the whole history of each of the others, and we were fairly and literally talked out. Singing and joking we were in no humour for; and, in fact, any sound of mirth or laughter would have struck strangely upon our ears, and would not have been tolerated any more than whistling or a wind instrument. The last resort, that of speculating upon the future, seemed now to fail us, for our discouraging situation, and the danger we were really in (as we expected every day to find ourselves drifted back among the ice), "clapped a stopper" upon all that. From saying *"when* we get home," we began insensibly to alter it to *"if* we get home," and at last the subject was dropped by a tacit consent.

As soon as I came on deck, and took my place and regular walk, I began with repeating over to myself in regular order a string of matters which I had in my memory—the multiplication table and the tables of weights and measures; then the States of the Union, with their capitals; the counties of England, with their shire towns; and the kings of England in their order, and other things. This carried me through my facts, and, being repeated deliberately, with long intervals, often eked out the first two bells. Then came the Ten Commandments, the thirty-ninth chapter of Job, and a few other passages from Scripture. After I had got through these, I allowed myself a more general range among everything that I could remember, both in prose and verse. In this way, with an occasional break by relieving the wheel, heaving the log, and going to the scuttlebutt for a drink of water, the longest watch was passed away; and I was so regular in my silent recitations that, if there was no interruption by ship's duty, I could tell very nearly the number of bells by my progress.

Our watches below were no more varied than the watch on deck. All washing, sewing, and reading were given up, and we did nothing but eat, sleep, and stand our watch, leading what might be called a Cape Horn life. The forecastle was too uncomfortable to sit up in; and whenever we were below we were in our berths. To prevent the rain and the sea-water which

broke over the bows from washing down, we were obliged to keep the scuttle closed, so that the forecastle was nearly air-tight. In this little, wet, leaky hole we were all quartered, in an atmosphere so bad that our lamp, which swung in the middle from the beams, sometimes actually burned blue, with a large circle of foul air about it. Still, I was never in better health than after three weeks of this life. I gained a great deal of flesh, and we all ate like horses. At every watch when we came below, before turning in, the bread barge and beef kid were overhauled. Each man drank his quart of hot tea night and morning, and glad enough we were to get it; for no nectar and ambrosia were sweeter to the lazy immortals than was a pot of hot tea, a hard biscuit, and a slice of cold salt beef to us after a watch on deck. To be sure, we were mere animals, and had this life lasted a year instead of a month, we should have been little better than the ropes in the ship. Not a razor, nor a brush, nor a drop of water, except the rain and the spray, had come near us all the

time; for we were on an allowance of fresh water; and who would strip and wash himself in salt water on deck, in the snow and ice, with the thermometer at zero?

One night, when all hands had been up a great part of the time, our watch was left on deck. It came on to blow worse and worse, with hail and snow beating like so many furies upon the ship, it being as dark and thick as night could make it. The mainsail was blowing with a noise like thunder, when the captain came on deck and ordered it to be furled. The mate was about to call all hands, when the captain stopped him, and said that the men would be beaten out if they were called up so often; that, as our watch must stay on deck, it might as well be doing that as anything else. We went upon the yard; and never shall I forget that piece of work. Our watch had been so reduced by sickness, and by some having been left in California, that, with one man at the wheel, we had only the third mate and three besides myself to go aloft. It blew a perfect hurricane, with alternate blasts of snow, hail and rain. We had to *fist* the sail with bare hands. No one could trust himself to mittens, for if he slipped he was a gone man. All the boats were hoisted in on deck, and there was nothing to be lowered for him. We had need of every finger God had given us. Several times we got the sail upon the yard, but it blew away again before we could secure it. It required men to lie over the yard to pass each turn of the gaskets, and when they were passed it was almost impossible to knot them so that they would hold. Frequently we were obliged to leave off altogether and take to beating our hands upon the sail to keep them from freezing. We got all secure at last, but we had been nearly an hour and a half upon the yard, and it seemed an age. We were glad enough to get on deck, and still more to go below. The oldest sailor in the watch said, as he went down, "I shall never forget that mainyard; it beats all my going a-fishing. Fun is fun, but furling one yard-arm of a course at a time, off Cape Horn, is no better than man-killing."

Friday, July 22nd. This day we had a steady gale from the southward, and stood on under close sail, with the yards eased a little by the weather braces, the clouds lifting a little, and showing signs of breaking away. In the afternoon, I was below with Mr. Hatch, the third mate, and two others, filling the bread locker in the steerage from the casks, when a bright gleam of sunshine broke out and shone down the companionway and through the skylight, lighting up everything below, and sending a warm glow through the hearts of all. It was a sight we had not seen for weeks—an omen, a godsend. Even the roughest and hardest face acknowledged its influence. Just at that moment we heard a loud shout from all parts of the deck, and the mate called out down the companionway to the captain, who was sitting in the cabin. What he said we could not distinguish, but the captain kicked over his chair, and was on deck at one jump. We could not tell what it was; and, anxious as we were to know, the discipline of the ship would not allow of our leaving our places. Yet, as we were not called, we knew there was no danger. We hurried to get through with our job, when seeing the steward's face peering out of the pantry, Mr. Hatch hailed him to know what was the matter. "Lan'o, to be sure, sir! No you hear 'em sing out, 'Lan'o?' "

This gave us a new start, and we were soon through our work and on deck; and there lay the land, fair upon the larboard beam, and slowly edging away from the quarter. All hands were busy looking at it—the captain and mates from the quarter-deck, the cook from his galley, and the sailors from the forecastle; and even Mr. Nuttall, the passenger, who had kept in his shell for nearly a month, and hardly been seen by anybody, and whom we had almost forgotten was on board, came out like a butterfly, and was hopping round just as bright as a bird.

The land was the island of Staten Land, just to the eastward of Cape Horn; and a more desolate-looking spot I never wish to set eyes upon—bare, broken, and girt with rocks and ice, with here and there, between the rocks and broken hillocks, a little stunted vegetation of shrubs. It was a place well suited to stand at the junction [10] of the two oceans, beyond the reach of human cultivation, and encounter the blasts and snows of a perpetual winter. Yet, dismal as it was, it was a pleasant sight to us; not only as being the first land we had seen, but because it told us that we had passed the Cape—were in the At-

---

[10] *junction,* joining-place

lantic—and that, with twenty-four hours of this breeze, we might bid defiance to the Southern Ocean. It told us, too, our latitude and longitude better than any observation; and the captain now knew where we were, as well as if we were off the end of Long Wharf.

In the general joy, Mr. Nuttall said he should like to go ashore upon the island and examine a spot which probably no human being had ever set foot upon; but the captain intimated that he would see the island, specimens and all, in—another place, before he would get out a boat or delay the ship one moment for him.

We left the land gradually astern; and at sundown had the Atlantic Ocean clear before us.

The man who wrote this selection

RICHARD HENRY DANA, JR.
1815–1882

The son of a poet and journalist, Richard Henry Dana had a boyhood ambition which his family did not support. He wanted to join the navy, but his family was determined that he study law at Harvard. However, in his junior year, his eyesight began to trouble him, and he decided he needed a rest from books. Dana remembered his old wish and shipped out on the brig, *Pilgrim*. He served as an ordinary seaman on the voyage from Boston, around Cape Horn, to California, and back again. Down in the forecastle, that part of the ship "before the mast," he wrote a diary of his life at sea.

When Dana landed in Boston again, he returned to Harvard to complete his degree in law. Then he wrote *Two Years Before the Mast*, a vivid account of life at sea from the common sailor's viewpoint. He exposed the brutality of the officers, the wretched living conditions, and the rugged seaman's life. The book quickly became famous and, with Melville's *White Jacket*, brought about reforms in the treatment of common sailors. His book stands today as a valuable historical record and one of the best true stories of the sea.

Let's consider . . .

1. "Doubling Cape Horn" is a chapter from the book *Two Years Before the Mast* which Richard Henry Dana wrote when he returned from his first sea voyage as a sailor. He was furious over the treatment he and the other sailors had received aboard ship. Select an incident from this chapter which Dana might have felt was unjust.

2. Because Dana was in poor health, his doctor prescribed a sea voyage as a possible cure. When Dana returned from the trip, he was in excellent health. What clues did you find that indicated he was far from being a sick man? Why do you think the life at sea improved his health?

3. In his preface to *Two Years Before the Mast*, Dana wrote that his book was one of the first to give a picture of life at sea from the viewpoint of the ordinary seaman. Other books, he said, were written from the viewpoint of naval officers or passengers. There were several dramatic incidents in this chapter which you saw through the sailors' eyes. Which ones wouldn't you have known about at all if the story had been told by an officer? Which probably would have been told differently by an officer? What changes would he probably have made?

4. How did Dana pass the lonely time

during his watch on deck? What did this tell you about his interests? What tricks do *you* use when you have to kill time?

The writer's craft . . .

The salty language that Dana used in "Doubling Cape Horn" gave his writing a true nautical flavor. Find as many seafaring expressions as you can. After each term, write the same idea as it would be expressed by someone who was unfamiliar with sailors' language. For example, Dana wrote, "We sprang out of our berths." A landlubber would say, "We jumped out of our beds."

When you have completed this exercise, you will see how important appropriate language is to good writing. Without these authentic nautical terms, "Doubling Cape Horn" would have lost its flavor of the sea.

Knowing words . . .

The following italicized words are related in some way to ships and the sea. Explain the meaning of each italicized word. Then use it in a sentence of your own.

1. We had no *chronometer* and had been drifting about so long that we had nearly lost our *reckoning*.

2. We soon, however, left these *astern*.

3. Stockings, mittens, and all, were wrung out also, and then hung up to drain and *chafe* dry against the *bulkheads*.

4. We had only the third mate and three besides myself to go *aloft*.

5. All hands were busy looking at it— the captain and mates from the *quarterdeck*, the cook from his *galley*, and the sailors from the *forecastle*.

6. All the boats were *hoisted* in on deck, and there was nothing to be *lowered*.

"Blow, Boys, Blow!"

Solo: How do you know she's a Yankee clipper?
Chorus: Blow, boys, *blow!*
Solo: The Stars and Stripes they fly above her,
Chorus: Blow, my bully boys, *blow!*

Solo: What do you think they have for dinner?
Chorus: Blow, boys, *blow!*
Solo: Hot water soup, but slightly thinner,
Chorus: Blow, my bully boys, *blow!*

From a sea chanty

NOW THINK BACK

your travels, your memories would be much sharper.

On your trip into THIS WIDE WORLD you visited people and places you would like to remember. If you used your mind as a camera, you could now fill a memory album with the word pictures which the authors created for you.

Pick out one or two word pictures in each story that you would like to have in your memory album. Then on a separate sheet of paper, make a chart like the one suggested here. Compare your word pictures with those of your classmates. Using the word pictures you have collected, compare the writing abilities of these authors as they helped you share their experiences.

THINK FOR YOURSELF

Whenever you go on a trip, you return with many memories of what you have seen. Even though you may recall experiences of your trip, it is often difficult to describe them. But suppose you had a camera. If you could take snapshots of the unusual places and people you meet in

Snapshot	Travel Experience	Item	Author's Word Pictures
1.	"I Turn Pearl Diver"	The floor of the lagoon	". . . little coral plants, fragile as violets or anemones;" "shoals of small fish, gay as the bird life of the tropics . . ."
2.	"The Most Beautiful Pagoda"	The pagoda	". . . a gem in its frame . . ." "Ringed by silence . . ."

SHARE YOUR IDEAS

1. Many of the selections in THIS WIDE WORLD were filled with suspense. List each selection in which you found suspense. Then choose the one story in which you felt the suspense was greatest. Which incidents in that selection created the suspense?

2. Your author-guides took you to many different parts of the world. Which guide gave you the most information about a foreign land? Briefly describe what you learned about that country or the habits of the people living there.

3. The travelers in THIS WIDE WORLD went by land, sea, and air. Which method of transportation do you prefer? What are the advantages and disadvantages of each? When you discuss this question, refer to the experiences you have had in your reading or in your actual travel.

4. Do tourists find your community just as interesting and exciting as you find other places in the world? If you were their guide, what places would you show them? What information would you give them? What legends or local color stories could you narrate? What personal experiences could you add?

WIDEN YOUR EXPERIENCE

Things to do . . .

1. You may find it interesting to keep a master chart or map of your class's reading adventures. Stake out a part of your bulletin board space. Put up a large map of the world. Make an original one if a real map is not available for your use.

Use small tacks to mark the places in the world where you are traveling. Draw lines (or strings) from these spots to spaces off the edges of the map. Use each space to give such information as (a) the title of the selection you are using for each travel experience; (b) the geographical name of the place of your visit; and (c) the names of the members, leader, and guide in each travel party, if you are working in groups.

2. Use whatever display space is available for any of the following projects:

a. Make original drawings to illustrate any of the travel experiences. Use the details (word pictures) given you by the author.

b. Post letters to the folks back home, telling them about your experiences. Help them to see what you have seen by including sufficient detail and by creating word pictures of your own.

c. Ask your librarian to help you find photographs of some of the author-guides in this part. Put these on display. If photographs or other pictures are not available, or are too large for your limited display space, have someone sketch or paint a copy of the author's portrait.

3. Make or sketch some of the interesting objects you discovered as you read this unit. Arrange them in an exhibit as if they were souvenirs of your own travels. Also include "souvenirs" from travel books you have read.

What souvenirs can you display? That depends, of course, on the selections or books you have read. Just read carefully for the details about Africa, Egypt, and the other places that the authors visit and describe. Or—read about new and interesting places in other books you will find in your class or school library.

4. Now it is time to match your skill with that of more seasoned writers. If you have ever taken a trip anywhere, you'll have something to talk about. If not, you can plan a trip you want to take. Illustrate your composition with snapshots, postcards, or original sketches, if you wish. Remember to keep your writing personal. Your readers are not interested in a miniature geography lesson. They want to know about you and your reactions. Perhaps you will want to use one of these titles:

Flying Is Fun
Hitchhiking to . . . .
A Disappointing Journey
Camera Fiend on Wheels
I Want to Go Back to . . . .
Tourists Are Crazy
Why Not Go by Water?
The Trip I Dream about

More to read . . .

North to the Orient by ANNE MORROW LINDBERGH. The author's warmth and humor add to your enjoyment of this description of a flight with her husband to the Orient by the Arctic route. Harcourt, Brace and Company, Inc., 1935.

Wind, Sand, and Stars by ANTOINE DE ST. EXUPÉRY. The author recalls his adventures as a flyer during the dangerous early days of aviation. There are crash landings in the Sahara Desert and on the snow-covered peaks of the Andes. Harcourt, Brace and Company, Inc., 1939.

Rockets, Missiles, and Space Travel by WILLY LEY. After you have read this, you may want to start packing up for one of the expeditions described here. The Viking Press, Inc., 1951.

Captains Courageous by RUDYARD KIPLING. Deep-sea fishermen are the main characters in this dramatic story. The spoiled boy they rescue from the ocean learns to appreciate their courage and worth. Doubleday & Company, Inc., 1897.

Two Years Before the Mast by RICHARD HENRY DANA, JR. This famous account of life on an American ship in 1830 includes a voyage around Cape Horn to the western coast of America. Houghton Mifflin Company, 1929. (First published about 1840.)

Saltwater Poems and Ballads by JOHN MASEFIELD. Only this famous poet of the sea could create such fine lyrics and stirring narratives. The Macmillan Company, 1942.

Pearl Lagoon by CHARLES B. NORDHOFF. A California ranch boy combats sharks, pirates, and the sea itself, while pearl-hunting in the South Seas. Little, Brown and Company, 1924.

South Sea Shilling by ERIC SWENSON. The voyages of that bold eighteenth-century explorer, Captain Cook, are described in this swift and exciting story. The Viking Press, Inc., 1952.

Strange Lands and Friendly People by WILLIAM O. DOUGLAS. In this vivid account of his travels through Persia, Greece, India, and other countries, Justice Douglas describes the people and how they live. Harper & Brothers, 1951.

I Married Adventure by OSA JOHNSON. If you like travel and adventure, you will enjoy Martin and Osa Johnson's story of their experiences through twenty years in Africa, Borneo, and the South Seas. J. B. Lippincott Company, 1940.

Exploring with Byrd by RICHARD E. BYRD. This account of the great explorer's career is as exciting as the episode you find in this book. G. P. Putnam's Sons, 1937.

Adrift on an Ice Pan by SIR WILFRED GRENFELL. Dr. Grenfell and his dog team are marooned on floating ice off the coast of Labrador. Houghton Mifflin Company, 1909.

Green Mansions by W. H. HUDSON. A young man discovers a beautiful and mysterious girl in the South American forest where he has been living with savage Indians. Alfred A. Knopf, Inc., 1943. (First published 1904.)

The Martian Chronicle by RAY BRADBURY. Here you will find a vivid picture of people pioneering on Mars. Doubleday & Company, Inc., 1952.

The Jules Verne Omnibus by JULES VERNE. The author of this collection of extraordinary experiences imagined many things which later became realities. See what you think of his submarine, in *Twenty Thousand Leagues Under the Sea,* and of the man who went *Around the World in Eighty Days* without any help from airplanes. J. B. Lippincott Company, 1951.

FAIR PLAY AND FOUL

The umpire calls, "You're out!" and the bleachers echo with boos. Your parents say, "No movies during the week," and you feel they just don't understand. All of you have definite ideas about what you think is fair play, especially when it affects you. But what about fair play when you are dealing with ghosts, dragons, or a strong-minded dog? Let the people in FAIR PLAY AND FOUL show you what they did.

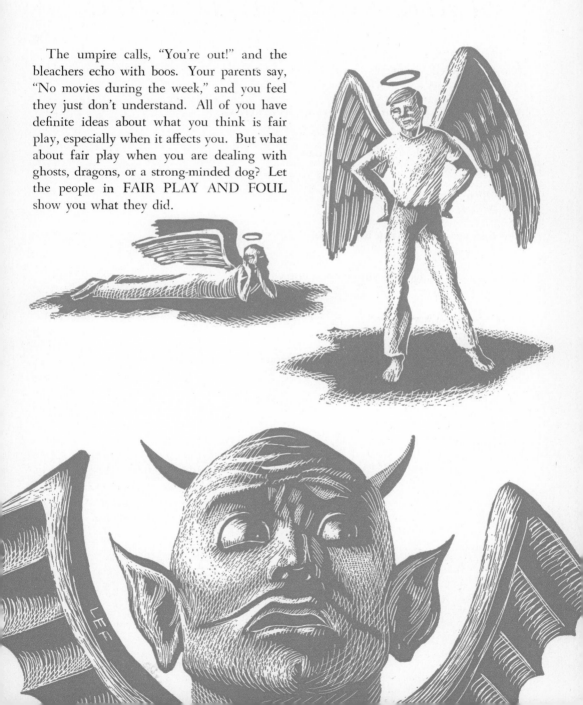

PART THREE

FAIR PLAY AND FOUL

The Red-headed League

SIR ARTHUR CONAN DOYLE

Match your wits with the master detective, Sherlock Holmes. The clues are all here. Try to solve the mystery before he does.

I had called upon my friend, Mr. Sherlock Holmes, one day last year, and found him with a stout, florid-faced, elderly gentleman, with fiery red hair.

"You could not possibly have come at a better time, my dear Watson," he said cordially. "Mr. Jabez Wilson here has a story that promises to be one of the most singular[1] which I have listened to for some time. The facts are, to the best of my belief, unique."

The portly client puffed out his chest with pride, and pulled a dirty and wrinkled newspaper from the inside pocket of his overcoat. He glanced down the advertisement column, and said: "Here it is. This is what began it all. You just read it for yourself, sir."

I took the paper from him and read as follows:

To the Red-headed League:

On account of the bequest of the late Ezekiah Hopkins, of Lebanon, Pa., U. S. A., there is now another vacancy open which entitles a member of the League to a salary of £4[2] a week for purely nominal services. All

---

[1] *singular,* extraordinary
[2] *£4,* four pounds; English money worth about $11.50

red-headed men who are sound in body and mind, and above the age of twenty-one years, are eligible. Apply in person on Monday, at eleven o'clock, to Duncan Ross, at the offices of the League, 7 Pope's Court, Fleet Street.

"What on earth does this mean?" I cried out, after I had twice read over the extraordinary announcement.

Holmes chuckled and wriggled in his chair, as was his habit when in high spirits. "It is a little off the beaten track, isn't it?" said he. "And now, Mr. Wilson, tell us all about yourself, your household, and the effect which this advertisement had upon your fortunes. You will first make a note, Doctor, of the paper and the date."

"It is *The Morning Chronicle* of April 27. Just two months ago."

"Very good. Now, Mr. Wilson?"

"Well, it is just as I have been telling you, Mr. Sherlock Holmes," said Jabez Wilson, mopping his forehead; "I have a small pawnbroker's business at Coburg Square, near the City. It's not a very large affair, and of late years it has not done more than just give me a living. I used to be able to keep two assistants, but now I only keep one; and I would have a job to pay him but that he is willing to come for half wages, so as to learn the business."

"What is his name?" asked Sherlock Holmes.

"His name is Vincent Spaulding. I should not wish a smarter assistant, Mr. Holmes; and I know very well that he could better himself and earn twice what I am able to give him. But, after all, if he is satisfied, why should I put ideas into his head?"

"Why, indeed? You seem most fortunate in having an employee who comes under the full market price. It is not a common experience among employers in this age. I don't know that your assistant is not as remarkable as your advertisement."

"Oh, he has his faults, too," said Mr. Wilson. "Never was such a fellow for photography. Snapping away with a camera when he ought to be improving his mind, and then diving down into the cellar like a rabbit into its hole to develop his pictures. That is his main fault, but on the whole he's a good worker. There's no vice in him."

"He is still with you, I presume?"

"Yes, sir. He and a girl of fourteen, who does a bit of simple cooking and keeps the place clean—that's all I have in the house, for I am a widower and never had any family. We live very quietly, sir, the three of us; and we keep a roof over our heads and pay our debts, if we do nothing more.

"The first thing that put us out was that advertisement. Spaulding, he came down into the office just this day eight weeks, with this very paper in his hand, and he says:

" 'I wish to the Lord, Mr. Wilson, that I was a red-headed man.'

" 'Why that?' I asks.

" 'Why,' says he, 'here's another vacancy in the League of Red-headed Men. It's worth quite a little fortune to any man who gets it, and I understand that there are more vacancies than there are men, so that the trustees are at their wits' end what to do with the money. If my hair would only change color, here's a nice little crib all ready for me to step into.'

" 'Why, what is it, then?' I asked. You see, Mr. Holmes, I am a very stay-at-home man, and as my business came to me instead of my having to go to it, I was often weeks on end without putting my foot over the doormat. In that way I didn't know much of what was going on outside, and I was always glad of a bit of news.

" 'Have you never heard of the League of the Red-headed Men?' he asked, with his eyes open.

" 'Never.'

" 'Why, I wonder at that, for you are eligible yourself for one of the vacancies.'

" 'And what are they worth?' I asked.

" 'Oh, merely a couple of hundred a year, but the work is slight, and it need not interfere very much with one's other occupations.'

"Well, you can easily see how that made me prick up my ears, for the business has not been over-good for some years, and an extra couple of hundred would have been very handy.

" 'Tell me all about it,' said I.

" 'Well,' said he, showing me the advertisement, 'you can see for yourself that the League has a vacancy, and there is the address where you should apply for particulars. As far as I can make out, the League was founded by an American millionaire, Ezekiah Hopkins, who was very peculiar in his ways. He was himself red-headed, and he had a great sympathy for all red-headed men; so, when he died, they found that he had left his enormous fortune in the hands of trustees, with instructions to apply the interest to the providing of easy berths to men whose hair is of that color. From all I hear it is splendid pay, and very little to do.'

"'But,' said I, 'there would be millions of red-headed men who would apply.'

"'Not so many as you might think,' he answered. 'You see it is really confined to Londoners, and to grown men. This American had started from London when he was young, and he wanted to do the old town a good turn. Then, again, I have heard it is no use your applying if your hair is light red, or dark red, or anything but real bright, blazing, fiery red. Now, if you cared to apply, Mr. Wilson, you would just walk in; but perhaps it would be hardly worth your while to put yourself out of the way for the sake of a few hundred pounds.'

"Now, it is a fact, gentlemen, as you may see for yourselves, that my hair is of a very full and rich tint, so that it seemed to me that, if there was to be any competition in the matter, I stood as good a chance as any man that I had ever met. Vincent Spaulding seemed to know so much about it that I thought he might prove useful, so I just ordered him to put up the shutters for the day and to come right away with me. He was very willing to have a holiday, so we shut the business up and started off for the address that was given us in the advertisement.

"I never hope to see such a sight as that again, Mr. Holmes. From north, south, east and west every man who had a shade of red in his hair had tramped into the city to answer the advertisement. Fleet Street was choked with red-headed folk. I should not have thought there were so many in the whole country as were brought together by that single advertisement. Every shade of color they were—straw, lemon, orange, brick, Irish-setter, liver, clay; but as Spaulding said, there were not many who had the real vivid flame-colored tint. When I saw how many were waiting, I would have given it up in despair; but

Spaulding would not hear of it. How he did it I could not imagine, but he pushed and pulled and butted until he got me through the crowd, and right up to the steps which led to the office. There was a double stream upon the stair, some going up in hope, and some coming back dejected; but we wedged in as well as we could, and soon found ourselves in the office."

"Most entertaining," remarked Holmes.

"There was nothing in the office but a couple of wooden chairs and a deal table, behind which sat a small man with a head that was even redder than mine. He said a few words to each candidate as he came up, and then he always managed to find some fault in them which would disqualify them. Getting a vacancy did not seem to be such a very easy matter, after all. However, when our turn came, the little man was much•more favorable to me than to any of the others, and he closed the door as we entered, so that he might have a private word with us.

"'This is Mr. Jabez Wilson,' said my assistant, 'and he is willing to fill a vacancy in the League.'

"'And he is admirably suited for it,' the other answered. 'He has every requirement. I cannot recall when I have seen anything so fine.' He took a step backward, cocked his head on one side, and gazed at my hair until I felt quite bashful. Then suddenly he plunged forward, wrung my hand, and congratulated me warmly on my success.

"'It would be injustice to hesitate,' said he. 'You will, however, I am sure, excuse me for taking an obvious precaution.' With that he seized my hair in both his hands, and tugged until I yelled with the pain. 'There is water in your eyes,' said he as he released me. 'All is as it should be. But we have to be careful, for we have twice been deceived by wigs and once by paint. I could tell you tales of cobbler's wax which would disgust you with human nature.' He stepped over to the window and shouted through it at the top of his voice that the vacancy was filled. A groan of disappointment came up from below, and the folk all trooped away in different directions until there was not a red head to be seen except my own and that of the manager.

" 'My name,' said he, 'is Mr. Duncan Ross. When shall you be able to enter upon your new duties?'

" 'Well, it is a little awkward, for I have a business already,' said I.

" 'Oh, never mind about that, Mr. Wilson!' said Vincent Spaulding. 'I should be able to look after that for you.'

" 'What would be the hours?' I asked.

" 'Ten to two.'

"Now a pawnbroker's business is mostly done of an evening, Mr. Holmes, especially Thursday and Friday evening, which is just before payday; so it would suit me very well to earn a little in the mornings. Besides, I knew that my assistant was a good man, and that he would see to anything that turned up.

" 'That would suit me very well,' said I. 'And the pay?'

" 'Is £4 a week.'

" 'And the work?'

" 'Is purely nominal.'

" 'What do you call purely nominal?'

" 'Well, you have to be in the office, or at least in the building, the whole time. If you leave, you forfeit your whole position forever. The will is very clear upon that point. You don't comply with the conditions if you budge from the office during that time.'

" 'It's only four hours a day, and I should not think of leaving' said I.

" 'No excuse will avail,' said Mr. Dun-

can Ross; 'neither sickness nor business nor anything else. There you must stay, or you lose your job.'

" 'And the work?'

" 'Is to copy out the *Encyclopædia Britannica*. There is the first volume of it in that press. You must find your own ink, pens, and blotting paper, but we provide this table and chair. Will you be ready tomorrow?'

" 'Certainly,' I answered.

" 'Then, good-by, Mr. Jabez Wilson, and let me congratulate you once more on the important position which you have been fortunate enough to gain.' He bowed me out of the room, and I went home with my assistant, hardly knowing what to say or do, I was so pleased at my own good fortune.

"Well, I thought over the matter all day, and by evening I was in low spirits again; for I had quite persuaded myself that the whole affair must be some great hoax or fraud, though what its object might be I could not imagine. It seemed altogether past belief that anyone could make such a will, or that they would pay such a sum for doing anything so simple as copying out the *Encyclopædia Britannica*. Vincent Spaulding did what he could to cheer me up, but by bedtime I had reasoned myself out of the whole thing. However, in the morning I determined to have a look at it anyhow, so I bought a penny bottle of ink, and with a quill pen, and seven sheets of foolscap paper, I started off for Pope's Court.

"Well, to my surprise and delight, everything was as right as possible. The table was set out ready for me, and Mr. Duncan Ross was there to see that I got fairly to work. He started me off upon the letter *A,* and then he left me; but he would drop in from time to time to see that all was right with me. At two o'clock he bade me good day, complimented me upon the amount that I had written, and locked the door of the office after me.

"This went on day after day, Mr. Holmes, and on Saturday the manager came in and planked down four golden sovereigns for my week's work. It was the same next week, and the same the week after. Every morning I was there at ten, and every afternoon I left at two. By degrees Mr. Duncan Ross took to coming in only once of a morning, and then, after a time, he did not come in at all. Still, of course, I never dared to leave the room for an instant, for I was not sure when he might come, and the job was such a good one, and suited me so well, that I would not risk the loss of it.

"Eight weeks passed away like this, and I had written about Abbots and Archery and Armor and Architecture and Attica, and hoped with diligence that I might get on to the B's before very long. It cost me something in foolscap, and I had pretty nearly filled a shelf with my writings. And then suddenly the whole business came to an end."

"To an end?"

"Yes, sir. And no later than this morning. I went to my work as usual at ten o'clock, but the door was shut and locked, with a little square of cardboard hammered onto the middle of the panel with a tack. Here it is, and you can read for yourself."

He held up a piece of white cardboard about the size of a sheet of note paper. It read in this fashion:

THE RED-HEADED LEAGUE

IS

DISSOLVED.

July 9, 1890.

Sherlock Holmes and I surveyed this curt announcement and the rueful face behind it, until the comical side of the affair so completely overtopped every other consideration that we both burst out into a roar of laughter.

"I cannot see that there is anything very funny," cried our client, flushing up to the roots of his flaming head. "If you can do nothing better than laugh at me, I can go elsewhere."

"No, no," cried Holmes, shoving him back into the chair from which he had half risen. "I really wouldn't miss your case for the world. It is most refreshingly unusual. But there is, if you will excuse my saying so, something just a little funny about it. Pray what steps did you take when you found the card upon the door?"

"I was staggered, sir. I did not know what to do. Then I called at the offices round, but none of them seemed to know anything about it. Finally, I went to the landlord, who is an accountant living on the ground-floor, and I asked him if he could tell me what had become of the Red-headed League. He said that he had never heard of any such body. Then I asked him who Mr. Duncan Ross was. He answered that the name was new to him.

"'Well,' said I, 'the gentleman at No. 4.'

"'What, the red-headed man?'

"'Yes.'

"'Oh,' said he, 'his name was William Morris. He was a solicitor and was using my room as a temporary convenience until his new premises were ready. He moved out yesterday.'

"'Where could I find him?'

"'Oh, at his new offices. He did tell me the address. Yes, 17 King Edward Street, near St. Paul's.'

"I started off, Mr. Holmes, but when I got to that address it was a manufactory [3] of artificial kneecaps and no one in it had ever heard of either Mr. William Morris or Mr. Duncan Ross."

---

[3] *manufactory,* place where something is made

"And what did you do then?" asked Holmes.

"I went home to Saxe-Coburg Square, and I took the advice of my assistant. But he could not help me in any way. He could only say that if I waited I should hear by post. But that was not quite good enough, Mr. Holmes. I did not wish to lose such a place without a struggle, so, as I had heard that you were good enough to give advice to poor folk who were in need of it, I came right away to you."

"And you did very wisely," said Holmes. "Your case is an exceedingly remarkable one, and I shall be happy to look into it. From what you have told me I think that it is possible that graver issues hang from it than might at first sight appear."

"Grave enough!" said Mr. Jabez Wilson. "Why, I have lost four pounds a week."

"As far as you are personally concerned," remarked Holmes, "I do not see that you have any grievance against this extraordinary league. On the contrary, you are, as I understand, richer by some £30, to say nothing of the minute knowledge which you have gained on every subject which comes under the letter A. You have lost nothing by them."

"No, sir. But I want to find out about them, and who they are, and what their object was in playing this prank—if it was a prank—upon me. It was a pretty expensive joke for them, for it cost them two and thirty pounds."

"We shall endeavor to clear up these points for you. And, first, one or two questions, Mr. Wilson. This assistant of yours who first called your attention to the advertisement—how long had he been with you?"

"About a month then."

"How did he come?"

"In answer to an advertisement."

"Was he the only applicant?"

"No, I had a dozen."

"Why did you pick him?"

"Because he was handy and would come cheap."

"At half wages, in fact."

"Yes."

"What is he like, this Vincent Spaulding?"

"Small, stout-built, very quick in his ways, no hair on his face, though he's close to thirty. Has a white splash of acid upon his forehead."

Holmes sat up in his chair in great excitement. "I thought as much," said he. "Have you ever observed that his ears are pierced for earrings?"

"Yes, sir. He told me that a gypsy had done it for him when he was a lad."

"Hum!" said Holmes, sinking back in deep thought. "He is still with you?"

"Oh, yes, sir; I have only just left him."

"And has your business been attended to in your absence?"

"Nothing to complain of, sir. There's never very much to do of a morning."

"That will do, Mr. Wilson. I shall be happy to give you an opinion in a day or two. Today is Saturday, and I hope that by Monday we may come to a conclusion."

"Well, Watson," said Holmes when our visitor had left us, "what do you make of it all?"

"I make nothing of it," I answered frankly. "It is a most mysterious business."

"As a rule," said Holmes, "the more bizarre a thing is the less mysterious it proves to be. What do you think, Watson? Could your patients spare you for a few hours?"

"I have nothing to do today. My practice is never very absorbing."

"Then put on your hat and come along!"

We went to Saxe-Coburg Square, the scene of the story which we had listened to. It was a poky, little shabby-genteel place, where four lines of dingy two-storied brick houses looked out into a small railed-in enclosure, where a lawn of weedy grass and a few clumps of faded laurel bushes made a hard fight against a smoke-laden and uncongenial atmosphere. Three gilt balls and a brown board with "Jabez Wilson" in white letters, upon a corner house, announced the place where our red-headed client carried on his business. Sherlock Holmes stopped in front of it with his head on one side, and looked it all over, with his eyes shining brightly between puckered lids. Then he walked slowly up the street, and then down again to the corner, still looking keenly at the houses. Finally he returned to the pawnbroker's, and, having thumped vigorously upon the pavement with his stick two or three times, he went up to the door and knocked. It was instantly opened by a bright-looking, clean-shaven young fellow, who asked him to step in.

"Thank you," said Holmes, "I only wished to ask you how you would go from here to the Strand."

"Third right, fourth left," answered the assistant promptly, closing the door.

"Smart fellow, that," observed Holmes as we walked away. "He is, in my judgment, the fourth smartest man in London, and for daring I am not sure that he has not a claim to be third. I have known something of him before."

"Evidently," said I, "Mr. Wilson's assistant counts for a good deal in this mystery of the Red-headed League. I am sure that you inquired your way merely in order that you might see him."

"Not him."

"What then?"

"The knees of his trousers."

"And what did you see?"

"What I expected to see."

"Why did you beat the pavement?"

"My dear Doctor, this is a time for observation, not for talk. We are spies in an enemy's country. We know something of Saxe-Coburg Square. Let us now explore the parts which lie behind it."

The road in which we found ourselves as we turned round the corner presented as great a contrast to it as the front of a picture does to the back. It was one of the main arteries which convey the traffic of the City to the north and west. The roadway was blocked with the immense stream of traffic flowing in a double tide inward and outward, while the footpaths were black with the hurrying swarm of pedestrians. It was difficult to realize as we looked at the line of fine shops and stately business premises that they really abutted on the other side upon the faded and stagnant square which we had just quitted.

"Let me see," said Holmes, standing at the corner and glancing along the line, "I should like just to remember the order of the houses here. It is a hobby of mine to have an exact knowledge of London. There is Mortimer's, the tobacconist, the little newspaper shop, the Coburg branch of the City and Suburban Bank, the Vegetarian Restaurant, and McFarlane's carriage-building depot. That carries us right on to the other block. And now, Doctor, we've done our work. This business at Coburg Square is serious."

"Why serious?"

"A considerable crime is in contemplation. I have every reason to believe that we shall be in time to stop it. But today being Saturday rather complicates matters. I shall want your help tonight."

"At what time?"

"Ten will be early enough."

"I shall be at Baker Street at ten."

"Very well. And, I say, Doctor, there may be some little danger, so kindly put your army revolver in your pocket." He waved his hand, turned on his heel, and disappeared in an instant among the crowd.

It was a quarter past nine when I started from home and made my way across the Park, and so through Oxford Street to Baker Street. Two hansoms were standing at the door, and as I entered the passage I heard the sound of voices from above. On entering his room I found Holmes in animated conversation with two men, one of whom I recognized as Peter Jones, the official police agent, while the other was a long, thin, sad-faced man, with a very shiny hat and oppressively respectable frock coat.

"Ha! our party is complete," said Holmes, buttoning up his pea jacket and taking his heavy hunting crop from the rack. "Watson, I think you know Mr. Jones, of Scotland Yard? Let me introduce you to Mr. Merryweather, who is to be our companion in tonight's adventure."

"We're hunting in couples again, Doctor, you see," said Jones. "Our friend here is a wonderful man for starting a chase. All he wants is an old dog to help him to do the running down."

"I hope a wild goose may not prove to be the end of our chase," observed Mr. Merryweather gloomily.

"I think you will find," said Sherlock Holmes, "that the game will be more exciting. For you, Mr. Merryweather, the stake will be some £30,000; and for you, Jones, it will be the man upon whom you wish to lay your hands."

"John Clay, the murderer, thief, smasher, and forger. He's a young man, Mr. Merryweather, but he is at the head of his profession, and I would rather have my bracelets on him than on any criminal in London."

"It is past ten," Holmes said, "and quite time that we started. If you two will take the first hansom, Watson and I will follow in the second."

We rattled through an endless labyrinth of gas-lit streets until we emerged into Farringdon Street.

"We are close there now," my friend remarked. "This fellow Merryweather is a bank director, and personally interested in the matter. I thought it as well to have Jones with us also. He is not a bad fellow, though an absolute imbecile in his profession. He has one positive virtue. He is as brave as a bulldog and as tenacious as a lobster if he gets his claws upon anyone. Here we are, and they are waiting for us."

We had reached the same crowded thoroughfare in which we had found ourselves in the morning. Following Mr. Merryweather, we passed down a narrow passage and through a side door, which he opened for us. Within there was a small corridor, which ended in a very massive iron gate. This also was opened, and led down a flight of winding stone steps, which ended at another formidable gate. Mr. Merryweather stopped to light a lantern, and then conducted us down a dark, earth-smelling passage, and so, after opening a third door, into a huge vault or cellar, which was piled all round with crates and massive boxes.

"You are not very vulnerable from above," Holmes remarked as he held up the lantern and gazed about him.

"Nor from below," said Mr. Merryweather, striking his stick upon the flags which lined the floor. "Why, dear me, it sounds quite hollow!" he remarked, looking up in surprise.

"I must really ask you to be a little more quiet!" said Holmes severely. "You have already imperilled the whole success of our expedition."

He fell upon his knees upon the floor and, with the lantern and a magnifying lens, began to examine minutely the cracks between the stones. A few seconds sufficed

to satisfy him, for he sprang to his feet again and put his glass in his pocket.

"We have at least an hour before us," he remarked, "for they can hardly take any steps until the good pawnbroker is safely in bed. Then they will not lose a minute, for the sooner they do their work the longer time they will have for their escape. We are at present, Doctor—as no doubt you have divined—in the cellar of the City branch of one of the principal London banks. Mr. Merryweather is the chairman of directors, and he will explain to you that there are reasons why the more daring criminals of London should take a considerable interest in this cellar at present."

"It is our French gold," whispered the director. "We have had several warnings that an attempt might be made upon it."

"Your French gold?"

"Yes. Some months ago we borrowed 30,000 napoleons [4] from the Bank of France. It has become known that we have never had occasion to unpack the money, and that it is still lying in our cellar. The crate upon which I sit contains 2,000 napoleons packed between layers of lead foil."

"And now," observed Holmes, "it is time that we arranged our little plans. I expect that within an hour matters will come to a head. In the meantime, Mr. Merryweather, we must put the screen over that dark lantern."

"And sit in the dark?"

"I am afraid so. The enemy's preparations have gone so far that we cannot risk the presence of a light. And, first of all, we must choose our positions. These are daring men, and though we shall take them at a disadvantage, they may do us some harm unless we are careful. I shall stand behind this crate, and you conceal yourselves behind those. Then, when I flash a light upon them, close in swiftly. If they

_____
[4] *napoleons,* French gold coins

fire, Watson, have no compunction about shooting them down."

I placed my revolver, cocked, upon the top of the wooden case behind which I crouched. Holmes shot the slide across the front of his lantern, and left us in pitch darkness.

What a time it seemed! From comparing notes afterwards it was but an hour and a quarter, yet it appeared to me that the night must have almost gone, and the dawn be breaking above us. Suddenly my eyes caught the glint of a light.

At first it was but a lurid spark upon the stone pavement. Then it lengthened out until it became a yellow line, and then, without any warning or sound, a gash seemed to open and a hand appeared; a white, almost womanly hand, which felt about in the center of the little area of light. For a minute or more the hand, with its writhing fingers, protruded out of the floor. Then it was withdrawn as suddenly as it appeared, and all was dark again save the single lurid spark which marked a chink between the stones.

Its disappearance, however, was but momentary. With a rending, tearing sound, one of the broad, white stones turned over upon its side and left a square, gaping hole, through which streamed the light of a lantern. Over the edge there peeped a clean-cut boyish face, which looked keenly about it, and then, with a hand on either side of the opening, drew itself shoulder-high and waist-high, until one knee rested upon the edge. In another instant he stood at the side of the hole, and was hauling after him a companion, lithe and small like himself, with a pale face and a shock of very red hair.

"It's all clear," he whispered. "Have you the chisel and the bags? Great Scott! Jump, Archie, jump, and I'll swing for it!"

Sherlock Holmes had sprung out and seized the intruder by the collar. The other dived down the hole. The light flashed upon the barrel of a revolver, but Holmes's hunting crop came down on the man's wrist, and the pistol clinked upon the stone floor.

"It's no use, John Clay," said Holmes blandly. "You have no chance at all."

"So I see," the other answered, with the utmost coolness. "I fancy that my pal is all right."

"There are three men waiting for him at the door," said Holmes.

"Oh, indeed! You seem to have done the thing very completely. I must compliment you."

"And I you," Holmes answered. "Your red-headed idea was very new and effective."

"You see, Watson," he explained in the early hours of the morning as we sat over our coffee in Baker Street, "it was perfectly obvious from the first that the only possible object of this rather fantastic business of the advertisement of the League, and the copying of the Encyclopædia, must be to get this not overbright pawnbroker out of the way for a number of hours every day. It was a curious way of managing it, but, really, it would be difficult to suggest a better. The method was no doubt suggested to Clay's ingenious mind by the color of his accomplice's hair. The £4 a week was a lure which must draw him, and what was it to them, who were playing for thousands? They put in the advertisement. One rogue has the temporary office, the other rogue incites the man to apply for it. Together they manage to secure his absence every morning in the week. From the time that I heard of the assistant having come for half wages, it was obvious to me that he had some strong motive for getting the job."

"But how could you guess what the motive was?"

"The man's business was a small one, and there was nothing in his house which could account for such elaborate preparations, and such an expenditure as they were at. It must, then, be something out of the house. What could it be? I thought of the assistant's fondness for photography, and his trick of vanishing into the cellar. The cellar! Then I made inquiries as to this mysterious assistant, and found that I had to deal with one of the coolest and most daring criminals in London. He was doing something in the cellar—something which took many hours a day for months on end. What could it be, once more? I could think of nothing save that he was running a tunnel to some other building.

"I had got so far when we went to visit the scene of action. I surprised you by beating upon the pavement with my stick. I was learning whether the cellar stretched out in front or behind. It was not in front. Then I rang the bell, and, as I hoped, the assistant answered it. We have had some skirmishes, but we had never set eyes upon each other before. I hardly looked at his face. His knees were what I wished to see.

You must yourself have remarked how worn, wrinkled, and stained they were. They spoke of those hours of burrowing. The only remaining point was what they were burrowing for. I walked round the corner, saw the City and Suburban Bank abutted on our friend's premises, and felt that I had solved my problem. I called upon Scotland Yard, and upon the chairman of the bank directors, with the result that you have seen."

"And how could you tell that they would make their attempt tonight?" I asked.

"Well, when they closed their League offices that was a sign that they cared no longer about Mr. Jabez Wilson's presence—in other words, that they had completed their tunnel. But it was essential that they should use it soon, as it might be discovered, or the bullion might be removed. Saturday would suit them better than any other day, as it would give them two days for their escape. For all these reasons I expected them to come tonight."

"You reasoned it out beautifully," I exclaimed, in admiration. "It is so long a chain, and yet every link rings true."

"It saved me from boredom," he answered, yawning.

[Adapted]

The man who wrote this story

SIR ARTHUR CONAN DOYLE
1859–1930

Before he was ten, Conan Doyle wrote and illustrated his first book. Even as a child, he was a rapid and wide reader. Though his father was a poor, unrecognized artist, Doyle received the usual education given to sons of the nobility. It was while he was in medical school at Edinburgh that he met Joseph Bell, an exceptional teacher whose influence changed Doyle's career.

As soon as he was graduated from medical school, Doyle signed on a whaler bound for the arctic. He made several other voyages as ship's surgeon, before he set up his own practice. From the first, this practice was unsuccessful. All his rooms became waiting rooms; there were no patients. In a short while he was so poor that the authorities returned his income tax form with the comment, "Most unsatisfactory." Doyle returned it after scribbling across the bottom, "I agree."

While Doyle sat and waited for patients, he had plenty of time to think. He recalled his old instructor, Joseph Bell, and his amazing gift for observing the tiniest detail. In desperation, Doyle seized his pen—intended for writing prescriptions—and dashed off "The Study in Scarlet," the first of his famous Sherlock Holmes stories.

In later life, Doyle wrote travel books, treatises on spiritualism, and historical novels, but he is best remembered as the creator of Sherlock Holmes.

Let's consider . . .

1. The Red-headed League was a most unusual organization. Why did Jabez Wilson think the League was organized? What was the real reason for its existence?

2. Jabez Wilson wasn't suspicious of the League's activities. Why then did he come to Holmes for help?

3. Would you have been suspicious of the League? What incidents would have aroused your suspicions?

4. Who is your favorite detective in fiction? How does he differ from Sherlock Holmes in his method of solving crimes?

5. Many of the Sherlock Holmes stories have been effectively adapted for radio and television. How would you present "The Red-headed League," being sure to keep the suspense and the exciting ending?

a. Begin with sound effects. When Holmes and Watson were following Mr. Merryweather to the vault, they passed through several doors and gates. What sounds should the audience hear?

b. Find other places in which sound effects would add to the suspense. Describe how you would produce these sounds and

what effect you would want them to have on the listening audience.

c. What kind of background music would you play? Which scenes definitely need music? Explain why music would make these scenes more dramatic.

d. What popular actors do you think could best play each of the characters in the story?

The writer's craft . . .

Half the fun of reading mystery stories is seeing if you can solve the crime before the author tells you the solution. He gives you all the clues, but he also tries to keep you from guessing which clues to use and how to put them together to solve the mystery. He may also include hints that will mislead you.

1. Did Conan Doyle present any misleading clues in "The Red-headed League"?

2. Among the clues which led to the right solution, which ones do you think Sherlock Holmes used in solving the mystery?

3. The placement of clues is always important. Some writers withhold part of the evidence until the end of the story. For example, in this story you didn't learn about the gold hidden in the basement of the bank until the mystery was about to be solved. Do you think the author should have given you this information earlier in the story? Why, or why not?

Knowing words . . .

Each of the following sentences has one word missing. From the list, select the appropriate word. On a separate sheet of paper, copy the completed sentences. Do not write in this book.

bequest premises
particulars vulnerable
hoax avail

1. After the fire in the old office building, the firm had to move to new . . . on the other side of town.

2. He pleaded, but with no . . . , for a second chance.

3. The town council knew that the village would be extremely . . . to an enemy attack.

4. Anyone who is interested should apply for further . . . at his local post office.

5. The old woman made a . . . of several thousand dollars for the upkeep of the Community Center.

6. It was only a . . . , but many people believed him.

A Tragic Story

There lived a sage in days of yore,
And he a handsome pigtail wore;
But wondered much, and sorrowed more,
    Because it hung behind him.

He mused upon this curious case,
And swore he'd change the pigtail's place,
And have it hanging at his face,
    Not dangling there behind him.

Says he, "The mystery I've found,—
I'll turn me round,"—he turned him round;
    But still it hung behind him.

Then round and round, and out and in,
All day the puzzled sage did spin;
In vain—it mattered not a pin,—
    The pigtail hung behind him.

And right, and left, and round about,
And up, and down, and in, and out
He turned; but still the pigtail stout
    Hung steadily behind him.

And though his efforts never slack,
And though he twist, and twirl, and tack,
Alas! still faithful to his back,
    The pigtail hangs behind him.
            William Makepeace Thackeray

The Canterville Ghost

OSCAR WILDE

The ghost of Canterville Chase had enjoyed terrifying success for over three hundred years. Then an American family moved in. What could a dignified English ghost do when his victims refused to believe in him?

When Mr. Hiram B. Otis, the American Minister, bought Canterville Chase, every one told him he was doing a very foolish thing. There was no doubt at all that the place was haunted. Indeed, Lord Canterville himself had felt it his duty to mention the fact to Mr. Otis when they came to discuss terms.

"We have not cared to live in the place ourselves," said Lord Canterville, "since my grandaunt, the Dowager Duchess of Bolton, was frightened into a fit by two skeleton hands being placed on her shoulders as she was dressing for dinner. I feel bound to tell you, Mr. Otis, that the ghost has been seen by several living members of my family—as well as by the rector of the parish. After the unfortunate accident to the Duchess, none of our younger servants would stay with us. Lady Canterville often got very little sleep at night, because of the mysterious noises that came from the corridor and the library."

"My lord," answered Mr. Otis. "I will take the furniture and the ghost. I come from a modern country, where we have everything that money can buy. I reckon if there were such a thing as a ghost in Europe, we'd have it at home in a very short time in one of our public museums, or on the road in a show."

"I fear that the ghost exists," said Lord Canterville, smiling, "though it may have resisted the overtures of your enterprising impresarios. It has been well known for three centuries—since 1584, in fact—and always makes its appearance before the death of any member of our family."

"Well, so does the family doctor for that matter, Lord Canterville. But there is no such thing, sir, as a ghost, and I guess the laws of Nature aren't going to be suspended for the British aristocracy."

"You are certainly very natural in America," answered Lord Canterville, "and if you don't mind a ghost in the house, it is all right. Only you must remember I warned you."

A few weeks after this, the purchase was completed, and at the close of the season, Mr. Otis and his family went down to Canterville Chase. Mrs. Otis, who had been a celebrated New York belle, was now a very handsome, middle-aged woman, with fine eyes, and a superb profile. Her eldest son, christened Washington by his parents in a moment of patriotism (which he never ceased to regret), was a fair-haired, rather good-looking young man. Miss Virginia E. Otis was a little girl of fifteen, lithe and lovely as a faun, and with a fine freedom in her large blue eyes. After Virginia came the twins, who were usually called "The Stars and Stripes," as they were always getting swished. They were delightful boys.

Standing on the steps of Canterville Chase to receive them was an old woman, neatly dressed in black silk, with a white cap and apron. This was Mrs. Umney, the housekeeper, whom Mrs. Otis, at Lady Canterville's earnest request, had consented to keep on in her former position. She made them each a low curtsey as they alighted, and said in a quaint, old-fashioned manner: "I bid you welcome to Canterville Chase." Following her, they passed through the fine Tudor hall into the library, a long, low room, panelled in black oak, at the end of which was a large stained glass window. Here they found tea laid out for them. After taking off their wraps, they sat down and began to look around, while Mrs. Umney waited on them.

Suddenly, Mrs. Otis caught sight of a dull red stain on the floor just by the fireplace. She said to Mrs. Umney, "I am afraid something has been spilt there."

"Yes, madam," replied the old housekeeper in a low voice, "blood has been spilt on that spot."

"How horrid," cried Mrs. Otis. "I don't at all care for blood-stains in a sitting-room. It must be removed at once."

The old woman smiled, and answered in the same low, mysterious voice, "It is the blood of Lady Eleanore de Canterville, who was murdered on that very spot by her own husband, Sir Simon de Canterville, in 1575. Sir Simon survived her nine years, and disappeared under very mysterious circumstances. His body has never been discovered, but his guilty spirit still haunts the Chase. The blood-stain has been much ad-

mired by tourists and others, and cannot be removed."

"That is all nonsense," cried Washington Otis. "Pinkerton's Champion Stain Remover and Paragon Detergent will clean it up in no time," and before the terrified housekeeper could interfere he had fallen upon his knees, and was rapidly scouring the floor with a small stick of what looked like a black cosmetic. In a few moments no trace of the blood-stain could be seen.

"I knew Pinkerton would do it," he exclaimed, triumphantly, as he looked at his admiring family; but no sooner had he said these words than a terrible flash of lightning lit up the sombre room, a fearful peal of thunder made them all start to their feet, and Mrs. Umney fainted.

"What a monstrous climate!" said Mr. Otis, calmly, as he lit a long cigar. "I guess the old country is so overpopulated that they have not decent weather for everybody."

In a few moments, Mrs. Umney came to. There was no doubt, however, that she was extremely upset, and she sternly warned Mr. Otis to beware of some trouble coming to the house.

"I have seen things with my own eyes, sir," she said, "that would make any Christian's hair stand on end, and many and many a night I have not closed my eyes in sleep for the awful things that are done here." Mr. Otis, however, and his wife warmly assured the honest soul that they were not afraid of ghosts.

2.

The storm raged fiercely all that night, but nothing of particular note occurred. The next morning, however, when they came down to breakfast, they found the terrible stain of blood once again on the floor.

"I don't think it can be the fault of the Paragon Detergent," said Washington, "for

LEONARD EVERETT FISHER

I have tried it with everything. It must be the ghost." Then he rubbed out the stain a second time; but the second morning it appeared again. The third morning also it was there, though the library had been locked up at night by Mr. Otis himself, and the key carried upstairs.

The day had been warm and sunny; and, in the cool of the evening, the whole family went out for a drive. They did not return until nine o'clock, when they had a light supper.

At eleven o'clock the family retired, and by half-past all the lights went out. Some time after, Mr. Otis was awakened by a curious noise in the corridor outside his room. It sounded like the clank of metal, and seemed to be coming nearer every moment. He got up at once, struck a match, and looked at the time. It was exactly one o'clock. He was quite calm, and felt his pulse, which was not at all feverish. The strange noise still continued, and with it he heard distinctly the sound of footsteps. He put on his slippers, took a small oblong phial [1] out of his dressing-case, and opened the door. Right in front of him he saw, in the wan moonlight, an old man of terrible aspect. His eyes were as red burning coals; long gray hair fell over his shoulders in matted coils; his garments, which were of antique cut, were soiled and ragged, and from his wrists and ankles hung heavy manacles and rusty gyves. [2]

"My dear sir," said Mr. Otis, "I really must insist on your oiling those chains, and have brought you for that purpose a small bottle of Rising Sun Lubricator. I shall leave it here for you by the bedroom candles, and will be happy to supply you with more should you require it." With these words, Mr. Otis laid the bottle down on a

[1] *phial,* small glass bottle
[2] *manacles and rusty gyves,* handcuffs and rusty chains

marble table, and, closing his door, retired to rest.

For a moment, the Canterville Ghost stood quite motionless in natural indignation; then, dashing the bottle violently upon the polished floor, he fled down the corridor, uttering hollow groans, and emitting a ghastly green light. Just, however, as he reached the top of the great oak staircase, a door was flung open, two little white-robed figures appeared, and a large pillow whizzed past his head! There was evidently no time to be lost, so hastily adopting the Fourth Dimension of Space as a means of escape, he vanished through the wainscoting,[3] and the house became quite quiet.

On reaching a small secret chamber in the left wing, he leaned up against a moonbeam to recover his breath, and began to try and realize his position. Never, in a brilliant and uninterrupted career of three hundred years, had he been so grossly insulted. It was quite unbearable. Besides, no ghost in history had ever been treated in this manner. Accordingly, he determined to have vengeance, and remained till daylight in an attitude of deep thought.

3.

The next morning when the Otis family met at breakfast, they discussed the ghost at some length. Mr. Otis was naturally a little annoyed to find that his present had not been accepted. "I have no wish," he said, "to do the ghost any personal injury, and I must say that, considering the length of time he has been in the house, I don't think it is at all polite to throw pillows at him"—a very just remark, at which, I am sorry to say, the twins burst into shouts of laughter.

"On the other hand," he continued, "if

_____
[3] *wainscoting,* wooden paneling extending partway up a wall

he really declines to use the Rising Sun Lubricator, we shall have to take his chains from him. It would be impossible to sleep, with such a noise going on outside the bedrooms."

For the rest of the week, however, they were undisturbed. The only thing that excited any attention was the continual renewal of the blood-stain on the library floor. This certainly was very strange, as the door was always locked at night by Mr. Otis, and the windows kept closely barred. The chameleon-like color, also, of the stain excited a good deal of comment. Some mornings it was dull (almost Indian) red; then it would be vermilion, then a rich purple, and once when they came down, they found it a bright emerald-green. These rapid changes naturally amused the party very much, and bets on the subject were freely made every evening. The only person who did not enter the joke was Virginia, who, for some unexplained reason, was always a good deal distressed at the sight of the blood-stain, and very nearly cried the morning it was emerald-green.

The second appearance of the ghost was on Sunday night. Shortly after they had gone to bed they were suddenly alarmed by a fearful crash in the hall. Rushing downstairs, they found that a large suit of armor had become detached from its stand, and had fallen on the floor. Seated in a high-backed chair, was the Canterville Ghost, rubbing his knees with an expression of acute agony on his face. The twins, having brought their pea-shooters with them, at once discharged two pellets on him, while Mr. Otis covered him with his revolver, and called upon him to hold up his hands! The ghost started up with a wild shriek of rage, and swept through them like a mist, extinguishing Washington Otis's candle as he passed, and so leaving them all in total darkness. On reaching the top of the staircase he recovered himself, and determined to give his celebrated peal of demoniac laughter. He laughed his most horrible laugh, till the old vaulted roof rang and rang again. Hardly had the fearful echo died away when a door opened, and Mrs. Otis came out in a light blue dressing-gown.

"I am afraid you are far from well," she said, "and have brought you a bottle of Dr. Dobell's tincture. If it is indigestion, you will find it a most excellent remedy." The ghost glared at her in fury, and vanished with a deep churchyard groan.

On reaching his room he entirely broke down. What really distressed him most was that he had been unable to wear the suit of mail. He had hoped that even modern Americans would be thrilled by the sight of a Spectre in armor. Besides, it was his own suit. He had worn it with great success at the Kenilworth tournament. Yet when he had put it on, he had been completely overpowered by the weight of the huge breastplate and steel casque, and had fallen heavily on the stone pavement, barking both his knees severely, and bruising the knuckles of his right hand.

For some days after this he was extremely ill, and hardly stirred out of his room at all, except to keep the blood-stain in proper repair. However, by taking great care of himself, he recovered, and resolved to make a third attempt to frighten Mr. Otis and his family.

He selected Friday, the 17th of August, for his appearance, and spent most of the day in looking over his wardrobe. Finally he decided in favor of a large slouched hat with a red feather, a winding-sheet frilled at the wrists and neck, and a rusty dagger. Towards evening a violent storm of rain came on, and the wind was so high that all the windows and doors in the old house shook and rattled. In fact, it was just such weather as he loved.

His plan of action was this: he was to make his way quietly to Washington Otis's room, gibber at him from the foot of the bed, and stab himself three times in the throat to the sound of slow music. He bore Washington a special grudge. It was he who was in the habit of removing the famous Canterville blood-stain, by means of Pinkerton's Paragon Detergent. Having reduced the reckless and foolhardy youth to a condition of abject terror, he was then to proceed to the room occupied by Mr. Otis and his wife. There he would place a clammy hand on Mrs. Otis's forehead, while he hissed into her trembling husband's ear the awful secrets of the charnel-house.[4] With regard to Virginia, he had not quite made up his mind. She had never insulted him in any way, and was pretty and gentle. A few hollow groans from the wardrobe, he thought, would be more than sufficient; or, if that failed to wake her, he might grabble at the counterpane with palsy-twitching fingers. As for the twins, he was quite determined to teach them a lesson. The first thing to be done was, of course, to sit upon their chests so as to produce the stifling sensation of nightmare. Then, as their beds were quite close to each other, to stand between them in the form of a green, icy-cold corpse, till they became paralyzed with fear; and finally, to throw off the winding-sheet, and crawl around the room, with white bleached bones and one rolling eyeball.

At half-past ten he heard the family going to bed. For some time he was disturbed by wild shrieks of laughter from the twins; but at a quarter past eleven all was still, and, as midnight sounded, he sallied forth. The owl beat against the window-panes, the raven croaked from the old yew-

---

[4] *charnel-house,* place where dead bodies are piled

tree, and the wind wandered moaning round the house like a lost soul; but the Otis family slept unconscious of their doom, and high above the rain and storm he could hear the steady snoring of Mr. Otis.

He stepped stealthily out of the wainscoting, with an evil smile on his cruel, wrinkled mouth. The moon hid her face in a cloud as he stole past the great oriel window. On and on he glided, like an evil shadow, the very darkness seeming to loathe him as he passed. Once he thought he heard something call, and stopped; but it was only the baying of a dog from the Red Farm, and he went on, muttering strange sixteenth-century curses, and ever and anon brandishing the rusty dagger in the midnight air. Finally he reached the corner of the passage that led to the luckless Washington's room. For a moment he paused there, the wind blowing his long gray locks about his head, and twisting into grotesque and fantastic folds the nameless horror of the dead man's shroud. Then the clock struck the quarter, and he felt the time was come.

He chuckled to himself, and turned the corner; but no sooner had he done so than, with a piteous wail of terror, he fell back, and hid his blanched face in his long, bony hands. Right in front of him was standing a horrible spectre, motionless as a carven image, and monstrous as a madman's dream! Its head was bald and burnished; its face round, and fat, and white; and hideous laughter seemed to have writhed its features into an eternal grin. From the eyes streamed rays of scarlet light, the mouth was a wide well of fire, and a hideous garment, like his own, swathed with its silent snows the Titan form. On its breast was a placard with strange writing in antique characters.

Never having seen a ghost before, he naturally was terribly frightened. He fled back to his room, tripping up in his long winding-sheet as he sped down the corridor, and finally dropping the rusty dagger into Mr. Otis's jack-boots, where it was found in the morning by the butler. He flung himself down on a bed, and hid his face under the clothes. After a time, however, the brave old Canterville spirit asserted itself, and he determined to go and speak to the other ghost as soon as it was daylight.

Accordingly, just as the dawn was touching the hills with silver, he returned towards the spot where he had first laid eyes on the grisly phantom. On reaching the spot, however, a terrible sight met his gaze. Something had evidently happened to the spectre, for the light had entirely faded from its hollow eyes, and it was leaning up against the wall in a straight and uncomfortable attitude. He rushed forward and seized it in his arms, when, to his horror, the head slipped off and rolled on the floor, the body assumed a recumbent posture, and he found himself clasping a white dimity bedcurtain, with a sweeping-brush, a kitchen cleaver, and a hollow turnip lying at his feet! Unable to understand this curious transformation, he clutched the placard with feverish haste, and there, in the grey morning light, he read these fearful words:—

Ꝑe Otis Ghoste.
Ꝑe Onlie True and Original Spook.
Beware of Ꝑe Imitationes.
All others are Counterfeite.

4.

The next day the ghost was very weak and tired. The terrible excitement of the last four weeks was beginning to have its effect. His nerves were completely shattered, and he started at the slightest noise. He now gave up all hope of ever frightening this rude American family, and as a rule contented himself with creeping about the passages in list slippers, with a thick red muffler round his throat for fear of draughts, and a small gun, in case he should be attacked by the twins.

The final blow he received occurred on the 19th of September. He had gone downstairs to the great entrance-hall. He was simply but neatly clad in a long shroud, spotted with churchyard mould, had tied up his jaw with a strip of yellow linen, and carried a small lantern and a sexton's spade. It was about a quarter-past two o'clock in the morning, and no one was stirring. As he was strolling towards the library, however, to see if there were any traces left of the blood-stain, suddenly there leaped out on him from a dark corner two figures, who waved their arms wildly above their heads, and shrieked out "BOO!" in his ear.

Seized with a panic, he rushed for the staircase, but found Washington Otis waiting for him there with the big garden-syringe; and being thus hemmed in by his enemies on every side, and driven almost to bay, he vanished into the great iron stove, which, fortunately for him, was not lit. He had to make his way home through the flues and chimneys, arriving at his own room in a terrible state of dirt, disorder, and despair.

5.

A few days after this, Virginia went out riding and tore her habit in getting through a hedge. On her return home, she made up her mind to go up by the back staircase so as not to be seen. As she was running past the Tapestry Chamber, the door of which happened to be open, she thought she saw some one inside. Thinking it was her mother's maid, who sometimes used to bring her work there, Virginia looked in to ask her to mend her riding habit. To her immense surprise, however, it was the Canterville Ghost himself. He was sitting by the window. His head was leaning on his hands. He looked so forlorn that Virginia was filled with pity, and determined to try and comfort him.

"I am so sorry for you," she said, "but my brothers are going back to Eton [5] tomorrow, and then, if you behave yourself, no one will annoy you."

"It is absurd asking me to behave myself," he answered. "Quite absurd. I must rattle my chains, and groan through keyholes, and walk about at night, if that is what you mean. It is my only reason for existing."

"It is no reason at all for existing, and you know you have been very wicked. Mrs. Umney told us, the first day we arrived here, that you had killed your wife."

"Well, I quite admit it," said the ghost petulantly, "but it was purely a family matter, and concerned no one else."

"It is very wrong to kill any one," said Virginia.

"My wife was very plain, never had my ruffs properly starched, and knew nothing about cookery. Why, there was a buck I had shot, and do you know how she had it sent up to table? However, it is no matter now, for it is all over, and I don't think it was very nice of her brothers to starve me to death, though I did kill her."

"Starve you to death? Oh, Mr. Ghost, I mean Sir Simon, are you hungry? I have a sandwich in my case. Would you like it?"

"No, thank you, I never eat anything now; but it is very kind of you, all the

---

[5] *Eton,* one of the best-known English schools for boys

same, and you are much nicer than the rest of your horrid, rude, vulgar, and dishonest family."

"Stop!" cried Virginia. "It is you who are rude, and horrid, and vulgar, and as for dishonesty, you know you stole the paints out of my box to try and furbish up that ridiculous blood-stain in the library. First you took all my reds, including the vermilion, and I couldn't do any more sunsets; then you took the emerald-green and the chrome-yellow; and finally I had nothing left but indigo and Chinese white, and could only do moonlight scenes, which are always depressing to look at, and not at all easy to paint. I never told on you, though I was very much annoyed, and it was most ridiculous, the whole thing; for who ever heard of emerald-green blood?"

"Well, really," said the ghost, rather meekly, "what was I to do? It is a very difficult thing to get real blood nowadays, and as your brother began it all with his Paragon Detergent, I certainly saw no reason why I should not have your paints. As for color, that is always a matter of taste: the Cantervilles have blue blood, for instance, the very bluest in England; but I know you Americans don't care for things of this kind."

"You know nothing about it," said Virginia. "Good evening."

"Please don't go, Miss Virginia," he cried; "I am so lonely and so unhappy, and I really don't know what to do. I want to go to sleep and I cannot."

"That's quite absurd! You have merely to go to bed and blow out the candle. It is very difficult sometimes to keep awake, especially at church, but there is no difficulty at all about sleeping. Why, even babies know how to do that, and they are not very clever."

"I have not slept for three hundred years," he said sadly, and Virginia's blue eyes opened in wonder. "For three hundred years I have not slept, and I am so tired."

"Poor, poor Ghost," she murmured; "have you no place where you can sleep?"

"Far away beyond the pine-woods," he answered, in a low, dreamy voice, "there is a little garden. There the grass grows long and deep; there are the great white stars of the hemlock flower; there the nightingale sings all night long. All night long he sings, and the cold, crystal moon looks down, and the yew-tree spreads out its giant arms over the sleepers."

Virginia's eyes grew dim with tears, and she hid her face in her hands.

"You mean the Garden of Death," she whispered.

"Yes, Death. Death must be so beautiful. To lie in the soft brown earth, with the grasses waving above one's head, and listen to silence. To have no yesterday, and no tomorrow. To forget time, to forget life, to be at peace. You can help me. You can open for me the portals of Death's house, for Love is always with you, and Love is stronger than Death is."

Virginia trembled, a cold shudder ran through her, and for a few moments there was silence. She felt as if she was in a terrible dream.

Then the ghost spoke again, and his voice sounded like the sighing of the wind.

"Have you ever read the old prophecy on the library window?"

"Oh, often," cried the girl, looking up. "I know it quite well. It is painted in curious black letters, and it is difficult to read. There are only six lines:

" 'When a golden girl can win
    Prayer from out the lips of sin,
    When the barren almond bears,
    And a little child gives away its tears,
    Then shall all the house be still
    And peace come to Canterville.'

But I don't know what they mean."

"They mean," he said sadly, "that you must weep with me for my sins, because I have no tears, and pray with me for my soul, because I have no faith; and then, if you have always been sweet, and good, and gentle, the Angel of Death will have mercy on me. You will see fearful shapes in darkness, and wicked voices will whisper in your ear, but they will not harm you, for against the purity of a child the powers of Hell cannot prevail."

Virginia made no answer, and the ghost wrung his hands in wild despair as he looked down at her bowed golden head. Suddenly she stood up, very pale, and with a strange light in her eyes. "I am not afraid," she said firmly, "and I will ask the Angel to have mercy on you."

He rose from his seat with a faint cry of joy, and taking her hand bent over it with old-fashioned grace and kissed it. His fingers were as cold as ice, and his lips burned like fire; but Virginia did not falter, as he led her across the dusky room. On the faded green tapestry were broidered little huntsmen. They blew their tasselled horns and with their tiny hands waved her to go back.

"Go back! little Virginia," they cried, "go back!" but the ghost clutched her hand more tightly, and she shut her eyes against them. Horrible animals with lizard tails, and goggle eyes, blinked at her and murmured, "Beware! little Virginia, beware! we may never see you again," but the ghost glided on more swiftly, and Virginia did not listen. When they reached the end of the room he stopped, and muttered some words she could not understand. She opened her eyes, and saw the wall slowly fading away like a mist, and a great black cavern in front of her. A bitter cold wind swept round them, and she felt something pulling at her dress. "Quick, quick," cried the ghost, "or it will be too late," and in a moment, the wainscoting had closed behind them, and the Tapestry Chamber was empty.

6.

About ten minutes later, the bell rang for tea. As Virginia had not come down, Mrs. Otis sent up one of the footmen to tell her. After a little time he returned and said that he could not find Miss Virginia anywhere. As she was in the habit of going out to the garden every evening to get flowers for the dinner-table, Mrs. Otis was not at all alarmed at first; but when six o'clock struck, and Virginia did not appear, she became really agitated, and sent the boys out to look for her, while she herself and Mr. Otis searched every room in the house. At half past six the boys came back and said that they could find no trace of their sister anywhere.

They were all now in the greatest state of excitement, and didn't know what to do. Suddenly Mr. Otis remembered that, some few days before, he had given a band of gypsies permission to camp in the park. He set off at once for Blackfell Hollow, where he knew they were.

On arriving at the spot, however, he found that the gypsies had gone. He ran home, and sent telegrams to all the police inspectors in the county, telling them to look out for a little girl who had been kidnaped by tramps or gypsies. He then ordered his horse to be brought round, and, after insisting on his wife and three boys sitting down to dinner, rode off.

After riding all over the common, he turned homewards, and reached the Chase about eleven o'clock, dead-tired and almost heart-broken. He found Washington and the twins waiting. Not the slightest trace of Virginia had been discovered. It was in the deepest depression that Mr. Otis and the boys walked up to the house. In the hall they found a group of frightened servants, and lying on a sofa in the library was poor Mrs. Otis, almost out of her mind with terror and anxiety. Mr. Otis insisted at once on her having something to eat, and ordered supper.

It was a melancholy meal. Hardly anyone spoke, and even the twins were awestruck and subdued. When they had finished, Mr. Otis ordered them all to bed, saying that nothing more could be done that night, and that he would telegraph in the morning to Scotland Yard for some detectives to be sent down immediately. Just as they were passing out of the dining-room, midnight began to boom from the clock tower; when the last stroke sounded they heard a crash and a sudden shrill cry. A dreadful peal of thunder shook the house; a strain of unearthly music floated through the air; a panel at the top of the staircase flew back with a loud noise; and out on the landing, looking very pale and white, with a little casket in her hand, stepped Virginia!

"Good heavens! child, where have you been?" said Mr. Otis.

"Papa," said Virginia quietly, "I have been with the ghost. He is dead, and you must come and see him. He had been very wicked, but he was really sorry for all that he had done, and he gave me this box of beautiful jewels before he died."

The whole family gazed at her in mute amazement, but she was quite grave and serious. Turning round, she led them through the opening in the wainscoting down a narrow secret corridor. Finally, they came to a great oak door, studded with rusty nails. When Virginia touched it, it swung back on its heavy hinges, and they found themselves in a little low room, with a vaulted ceiling, and one tiny grated window. Imbedded in the wall was a huge iron ring, and chained to it was a gaunt skeleton, that was stretched out at full length on the stone floor. It seemed to be trying to grasp with its long fleshless fingers an old-fashioned trencher and ewer,[6] that were placed just out of its reach. The jug had evidently been once filled with water, as it was covered inside with a green mould. There was nothing on the trencher but a pile of dust. Virginia knelt down beside the skeleton, and, folding her hands together, began to pray silently. The rest of the party looked on in wonder at the terrible tragedy whose secret was now disclosed to them.

"Hello," suddenly exclaimed one of the twins, who had been looking out of the window to try and discover in what wing of the house the room was situated. "The old withered almond tree has blossomed. I can see the flowers plainly in the moonlight."

"God has forgiven him," said Virginia gravely, as she rose to her feet, and a beautiful light seemed to illumine her face.

[Abridged]

---

[6] *trencher and ewer,* wooden plate and jug

The man who wrote this story

OSCAR WILDE 1856–1900

Oscar Wilde was the talented son of a talented family. His father was Sir William Wilde, a famous Irish surgeon, and his mother was noted for her elegant prose and poetry. Wilde distinguished himself both at Trinity College in Dublin and at Oxford, winning many scholastic and literary prizes. At Oxford, Wilde began to gain a reputation as a wit, and his remarks were quoted all over England.

Wilde wrote charming fairy tales and serious poetry, but he is remembered chiefly for his plays, *The Importance of Being Earnest* and *Lady Windermere's Fan,* which poked fun at some of the artificial manners of his time. He scorned stupidity and staleness. In a single phrase he could neatly ridicule stuffy fathers, eager social-climbers, neat little prigs, and affected young ladies. These plays are still so popular that they continue to appear on Broadway and as motion pictures.

Let's consider ...

1. The Otis family just would not be frightened by the Canterville Ghost. Describe two incidents that show the family's attitude toward their ghost.

2. What traits does the Canterville Ghost have in common with other spirits you have heard or read about? In what ways is he different from most ghosts?

3. This tale began like any other ghost story. At what point did you begin to suspect that it was not like the usual ghost story?

4. At the end, the story became serious. What had to happen before the ghost could find peace? How did Virginia help him find it?

5. What do you think of the Otis family's treatment of the ghost? If you had moved into Canterville Chase, how would you have treated him?

6. There are several attitudes toward ghosts in this story. Describe how each of the following people felt and behaved toward the Canterville Ghost: Mr. Otis, the twins, Virginia, Lord Canterville, Mrs. Umney. With which of these attitudes does Oscar Wilde seem to sympathize most?

The writer's craft ...

Satire is a kind of writing which criticizes customs and manners in a humorous and witty way. In "The Canterville Ghost" Oscar Wilde satirized certain American manners. For example, Wilde invented "Pinkerton's Champion Stain Remover and Paragon Detergent" to poke fun at American "know-how." What other humorous products did Wilde invent for this story?

1. Mr. Otis said, "I come from a modern country, where we have everything that money can buy." What characteristic of many Americans was Wilde satirizing at this point? Do you think he was justified in this criticism of Americans?

2. At any point in the story did Wilde satirize British customs too?

3. Although, at the beginning, the story was written in a humorous, satirical style, it became serious and gentle at the end. Wilde chose not to satirize Virginia's understanding attitude toward the ghost. How did your feelings toward the ghost change when she began to help him? Why do you think Wilde dropped his satirical style at this point?

The Open Window

SAKI

Framton was in a nervous state when he called on the Sappletons. When he left, he was a complete wreck.

"My aunt will be down presently, Mr. Nuttel," said a very self-possessed young lady of fifteen; "in the meantime you must try and put up with me."

Framton Nuttel endeavoured to say the correct something which should duly flatter the niece of the moment without unduly discounting the aunt that was to come. Privately he doubted more than ever whether these formal visits on a succession of total strangers would do much towards helping the nerve cure which he was supposed to be undergoing.

"I know how it will be," his sister had said when he was preparing to migrate to this rural retreat; "you will bury yourself down there and not speak to a living soul, and your nerves will be worse than ever from moping. I shall just give you letters of introduction to all the people I know there. Some of them, as far as I can remember, were quite nice."

Framton wondered whether Mrs. Sappleton, the lady to whom he was presenting one of the letters of introduction, came into the nice division.

"Do you know many of the people round here?" asked the niece, when she judged they had had sufficient silent communion.

"Hardly a soul," said Framton. "My sister was staying here, at the rectory, you know, some four years ago, and she gave me letters of introduction to some of the people here."

He made the last statement in a tone of distinct regret.

"Then you know practically nothing about my aunt?" pursued the self-possessed young lady.

"Only her name and address," admitted the caller. He was wondering whether Mrs. Sappleton was in the married or widowed state. An undefinable something about the room seemed to suggest masculine habitation.

"Her great tragedy happened just three years ago," said the child; "that would be since your sister's time."

"Her tragedy?" asked Framton; somehow in this restful country spot tragedies seemed out of place.

"You may wonder why we keep that window wide open on an October afternoon," said the niece, indicating a large French window that opened on to a lawn.

"It is quite warm for the time of the year," said Framton; "but has that window got anything to do with the tragedy?"

"Out through the window, three years ago to a day, her husband and her two young brothers went off for their day's shooting. They never came back. In crossing the moor to their favourite snipe-shooting ground they were all three engulfed in a treacherous piece of bog. It had been that dreadful wet summer, you know, and places that were safe in other years gave way suddenly without warning. Their bodies were never recovered. That was the dreadful part of it." Here the child's voice lost its self-possessed note and became falteringly human. "Poor aunt always thinks that they will come back some day, they and the little brown spaniel that was lost with them, and walk in at that window, just as they used to do. That is why the window is kept open every evening till it is quite dusk. Poor dear aunt, she has often told me how they went out, her husband with his white waterproof coat over his arm, and Ronnie, her youngest brother, singing 'Bertie, why do you bound?' as he always did to tease her, because she said it got on her nerves. Do you know, sometimes on still, quiet evenings like this, I almost get a creepy feeling that they will all walk in through that window—"

She broke off with a little shudder. It was a relief to Framton when the aunt bustled into the room with a whirl of apologies for being late in making her appearance.

"I hope Vera has been amusing you?" she said.

"She has been very interesting," said Framton.

"I hope you don't mind the open window," said Mrs. Sappleton briskly; "my husband and brothers will be home directly from shooting, and they always come in this way. They've been out for snipe in the marshes to-day, so they'll make a fine mess over my poor carpets. So like you men-folk, isn't it?"

She rattled on cheerfully about the shooting and the scarcity of birds, and the prospects for duck in the winter. To Framton it was all purely horrible. He made a desperate but only partially successful effort to turn the talk on to a less ghastly topic; he was conscious that his hostess was giving him only a fragment of her attention, and her eyes were constantly straying past him to the open window and the lawn beyond. It was certainly an unfortunate coincidence that he should have paid his visit on this tragic anniversary.

"The doctors agree in ordering me complete rest, an absence of mental excitement, and avoidance of anything in the nature of violent physical exercise," announced Framton, who laboured under the tolerably wide-spread delusion that total strangers and chance acquaintances are hungry for the least detail of one's ailments and infirmities, their cause and cure. "On the matter of diet they are not so much in agreement," he continued.

"No?" said Mrs. Sappleton, in a voice which only replaced a yawn at the last moment. Then she suddenly brightened into alert attention—but not to what Framton was saying.

"Here they are at last!" she cried. "Just in time for tea, and don't they look as if they were muddy up to the eyes!"

Framton shivered slightly and turned towards the niece with a look intended to convey sympathetic comprehension. The child was staring out through the open window with dazed horror in her eyes. In a chill shock of nameless fear Framton swung round in his seat and looked in the same direction.

In the deepening twilight three figures were walking across the lawn towards the window; they all carried guns under their arms, and one of them was additionally burdened with a white coat hung over his shoulders. A tired brown spaniel kept close at their heels. Noiselessly they neared the house, and then a hoarse young voice chanted out of the dusk: "I said Bertie, why do you bound?"

Framton grabbed wildly at his stick and hat; the hall-door, the gravel-drive, and the front gate were dimly noted stages in his headlong retreat. A cyclist coming along the road had to run into the hedge to avoid imminent collision.

"Here we are, my dear," said the bearer of the white mackintosh, coming in through the window; "fairly muddy, but most of it's dry. Who was that who bolted out as we came up?"

"A most extraordinary man, a Mr. Nuttel," said Mrs. Sappleton; "could only talk about his illnesses, and dashed off without a word of good-bye or apology when you arrived. One would think he had seen a ghost."

"I expect it was the spaniel," said the niece calmly; "he told me he had a horror of dogs. He was once hunted into a cemetery somewhere on the banks of the Ganges by a pack of pariah dogs, and had to spend the night in a newly dug grave with the creatures snarling and grinning and foaming just above him. Enough to make anyone lose their nerve."

Romance at short notice was her speciality.

The man who wrote this story

SAKI (H. H. MUNRO)   1870–1916

Munro was born in Burma but lived there only two years. When his mother died, he was sent to England to be raised by a pair of strict aunts. He seldom saw any children except his brother and sister, and was so sickly that he did not start school until he was twelve. When he was seventeen, his father retired from military service and took over the young Munros' education. After six years of study in Europe, Munro was sent to Burma to serve in the police force. Within a short time he was forced to return to England, his health badly shaken by malaria.

At twenty-five Munro began to earn his living as a writer. He chose Saki for his pen name, after the cup-bearer in the *Rubáiyát* of Omar Khayyam. His short stories soon began to attract attention for their wit, humor, and underlying sense of tragedy.

When the First World War broke out, Saki quit writing to be the first to enlist. He served as a corporal in the Royal Fusiliers, refusing to accept the commission which was offered him. Saki stayed at the front over a year. He was killed one day while lying in a shell hole.

Let's consider . . .

1. Vera made sure that her plot would be successful. Each of her questions and remarks was planned with care.

a. Why did she ask Framton, "Then you know practically nothing about my aunt?"

b. How did she explain why the window was open?

c. What other steps did she take to insure the success of her plot?

2. How did she explain Framton's sudden departure? Do you know anyone with a gift for dreaming up tall tales on the spur of the moment? Are you entertained or annoyed by such people? Why?

3. Why did Saki portray Framton as a nervous man rather than as the hearty type?

4. What is your method of handling strange visitors whom you are left to entertain? In what ways do some adults make it difficult for you to talk with them?

5. Though few families go through an experience like the one Saki described in his story, recall an occasion when either you or your brothers and sisters caused embarrassment to a guest. What makes young people act this way?

Knowing words . . .

From the context, determine the meaning of the italicized words. "Framton Nuttel endeavored to say the correct something which should *duly* flatter the niece of the moment without *unduly* discounting the aunt that was to come." What does the prefix *un-* signify?

List several other words which begin with the prefix *un-*. Explain their meanings.

The Listeners

WALTER DE LA MARE

"Is there anybody there?" said the Traveller,
    Knocking on the moonlit door;
And his horse in the silence champed the grasses
    Of the forest's ferny floor:
And a bird flew up out of the turret,
    Above the Traveller's head:
And he smote upon the door again a second time;
    "Is there anybody there?" he said.
But no one descended to the Traveller;
    No head from the leaf-fringed sill
Leaned over and looked into his grey eyes,
    Where he stood perplexed and still.
But only a host of phantom listeners
    That dwelt in the lone house then
Stood listening in the quiet of the moonlight
    To that voice from the world of men:
Stood thronging the faint moonbeams on the dark stair,
    That goes down to the empty hall,
Hearkening in an air stirred and shaken
    By the lonely Traveller's call.
And he felt in his heart their strangeness,
    Their stillness answering his cry,

While his horse moved, cropping the dark turf,
   'Neath the starred and leafy sky;
For he suddenly smote on the door, even
   Louder, and lifted his head:—
"Tell them I came, and no one answered,
   That I kept my word," he said.
Never the least stir made the listeners,
   Though every word he spake
Fell echoing through the shadowiness of the still house
   From the one man left awake:
Ay, they heard his foot upon the stirrup,
   And the sound of iron on stone,
And how the silence surged softly backward,
   When the plunging hoofs were gone.

The man who wrote this poem

WALTER DE LA MARE   1873–

The fact that Walter de la Mare is related to Robert Browning may explain why he showed such an early interest in writing. He was a dreamy, thoughtful boy who liked to read and write. While attending Saint Paul's School, he founded the students' magazine. Then he went to work for a large oil company as a bookkeeper.

For eighteen years, De la Mare wrote as an escape from the dull world of figures and statistics. At last his talent was recognized, and he was granted a small pension from the government. With this money and what he could earn from book reviewing, he was able to quit his job and devote all his time to writing.

Walter de la Mare is at home in the shadowy world between the real and the unreal. He states that "an imaginative experience is not only as real as, but far realer than, an unimaginative one." This idea characterizes the works of Walter de la Mare.

The poet's art . . .

"The Listeners" is a poem that *suggests* rather than *tells*. The poet tries to stimulate your imagination so that you will bring your own meaning to the poem. As you think about the following questions, be sure to give your imagination free rein.

1. Who might the Traveller be? Why do you suppose he came knocking on the moonlit door?

2. He called out, "Tell them I came and no one answered, That I kept my word." What do you think he had promised? Why had he made such a promise?

3. The poet spoke of the "phantom listeners" who dwelt in the house. Were they real people or ghosts? Why didn't they answer the Traveller? What were they doing there?

4. What feelings did the poem arouse in you? Read aloud the lines that helped to create these feelings?

5. Discuss your answers to the above questions with your classmates. You may discover that they interpreted the poem quite differently.

The Fifty-first Dragon

HEYWOOD BROUN

Gawaine was studying to become a knight, but he seemed to lack the proper spirit. To help mould the boy's character, the Headmaster decided to train him in dragon-slaying. This idea may seem a bit fantastic, but you will find there is more to it—if you just read between the lines.

Of all the pupils at the knight school Gawaine le Coeur-Hardy was among the least promising. He was tall and sturdy, but his instructors soon discovered that he lacked spirit. He would hide in the woods when the jousting class [1] was called, although his companions and members of the faculty sought to appeal to his better nature by shouting to him to come out and break his neck like a man. Even when they told him that the lances were padded, the horses no more than ponies, and the field unusually soft for late autumn, Gawaine refused to grow enthusiastic. The Headmaster and the Assistant Professor of Pleasaunce were discussing the case one spring afternoon and the Assistant Professor could see no remedy but expulsion.

"No," said the Headmaster, as he looked out at the purple hills which ringed the school, "I think I'll train him to slay dragons."

"He might be killed," objected the Assistant Professor.

"So he might," replied the Headmaster

brightly, "but," he added, more soberly, "we must consider the greater good. We are responsible for the formation of this lad's character."

"Are the dragons particularly bad this year?" interrupted the Assistant Professor. This was characteristic. He always seemed restive when the head of the school began to talk ethics and the ideals of the institution.

"I've never known them worse," replied the Headmaster. "Up in the hills to the south last week they killed a number of peasants, two cows, and a prize pig. And if this dry spell holds there's no telling when they may start a forest fire simply by breathing around indiscriminately."

"Would any refund on the tuition fee be necessary in case of an accident to young Coeur-Hardy?"

"No," the principal answered, judicially, "that's all covered in the contract. But as a matter of fact he won't be killed. Before I send him up in the hills I'm going to give him a magic word."

"That's a good idea," said the Assistant Professor. "Sometimes they work wonders."

---

[1] *jousting class,* class in fighting with lances while on horseback

From that day on Gawaine specialized in dragons. His course included both theory and practice. In the morning there were long lectures on the history, anatomy, manners, and customs of dragons. Gawaine did not distinguish himself in these studies. He had a marvelously versatile gift for forgetting things. In the afternoon he showed to better advantage, for then he would go down to the South Meadow and practice with a battle-ax. In this exercise he was truly impressive, for he had enormous strength as well as speed and grace. He even developed a deceptive display of ferocity. Old alumni say that it was a thrilling sight to see Gawaine charging across the field toward the dummy paper dragon which had been set up for his practice. As he ran he would brandish his ax and shout, "A murrain [2] on thee!" or some other vivid bit of campus slang. It never took him more than one stroke to behead the dummy dragon.

Gradually his task was made more difficult. Paper gave way to papier-mâché and finally to wood, but even the toughest of these dummy dragons had no terrors for Gawaine. One sweep of the ax always did the business. There were those who said that when the practice was protracted until dusk and the dragons threw long, fantastic shadows across the meadow, Gawaine did not charge so impetuously nor shout so loudly. It is possible there was malice in this charge. At any rate, the Headmaster decided by the end of June that it was time for the test. Only the night before a dragon had come close to the school grounds and had eaten some of the lettuce from the garden. The faculty decided that Gawaine was ready. They gave him a diploma and a new battle-ax and the Headmaster summoned him to a private conference.

[2] *murrain,* plague

"Sit down," said the Headmaster. "Have a cigarette."

Gawaine hesitated.

"Oh, I know it's against the rules," said the Headmaster. "But after all, you have received your preliminary degree. You are no longer a boy. You are a man. Tomorrow you will go out into the world, the great world of achievement."

Gawaine took a cigarette. The Headmaster offered him a match, but he produced one of his own and began to puff away with a dexterity which quite amazed the principal.

"Here you have learned the theories of life," continued the Headmaster, resuming the thread of his discourse, "but after all, life is not a matter of theories. Life is a matter of facts. It calls on the young and the old alike to face these facts, even though they are hard and sometimes unpleasant. Your problem, for example, is to slay dragons."

"They say that those dragons down in the south wood are five hundred feet long," ventured Gawaine, timorously.

"Stuff and nonsense!" said the Headmaster. "The curate saw one last week from the top of Arthur's Hill. The dragon was sunning himself down in the valley. The curate didn't have an opportunity to look at him very long because he felt it was his duty to hurry back to make a report to me. He said the monster—or shall I say, the big lizard?—wasn't an inch over two hundred feet. But the size has nothing at all to do with it. You'll find the big ones even easier than the little ones. They're far slower on their feet and less aggressive, I'm told. Besides, before you go I'm going to equip you in such fashion that you need have no fear of all the dragons in the world."

"I'd like an enchanted cap," said Gawaine.

"What's that?" asked the Headmaster testily.

"A cap to make me disappear," explained Gawaine.

The Headmaster laughed indulgently. "You mustn't believe all those old wives' stories,"[3] he said. "There isn't any such thing. A cap to make you disappear, indeed! What would you do with it? You haven't even appeared yet. Why, my boy, you could walk from here to London, and nobody would so much as look at you. You're nobody. You couldn't be more invisible than that."

Gawaine seemed dangerously close to a relapse into his old habit of whimpering. The Headmaster reassured him: "Don't worry; I'll give you something much better than an enchanted cap. I'm going to give you a magic word. All you have to

---

[3] *old wives' stories,* stories without factual basis which are passed from generation to generation by word of mouth

do is to repeat this magic charm once and no dragon can possibly harm a hair of your head. You can cut off his head at your leisure."

He took a heavy book from the shelf behind his desk and began to run through it. "Sometimes," he said, "the charm is a whole phrase or even a sentence. I might, for instance, give you 'To make the—' no, that might not do. I think a single word would be best for dragons."

"A short word," suggested Gawaine.

"It can't be too short or it wouldn't be potent. There isn't so much hurry as all that. Here's a splendid magic word: 'Rumplesnitz.' Do you think you can learn that?"

Gawaine tried and in an hour or so he seemed to have the word well in hand. Again and again he interrupted the lesson to inquire, "And if I say 'Rumplesnitz' the dragon can't possibly hurt me?" And always the Headmaster replied, "If you only

say 'Rumplesnitz,' you are perfectly safe."

Toward morning Gawaine seemed resigned to his career. At daybreak the Headmaster saw him to the edge of the forest and pointed him to the direction in which he should proceed. About a mile away to the southwest a cloud of steam hovered over an open meadow in the woods and the Headmaster assured Gawaine that under the steam he would find a dragon. Gawaine went forward slowly. He wondered whether it would be best to approach the dragon on the run as he did in his practice in the South Meadow or to walk slowly toward him, shouting "Rumplesnitz" all the way.

The problem was decided for him. No sooner had he come to the fringe of the meadow than the dragon spied him and began to charge. It was a large dragon and yet it seemed decidedly aggressive in spite of the Headmaster's statement to the contrary. As the dragon charged it released huge clouds of hissing steam through its nostrils. It was almost as if a gigantic teapot had gone mad. The dragon came forward so fast and Gawaine was so frightened that he had time to say "Rumplesnitz" only once. As he said it, he swung his battle-ax and off popped the head of the dragon. Gawaine had to admit that it was even easier to kill a real dragon than a wooden one if only you said "Rumplesnitz."

Gawaine brought the ears home and a small section of the tail. His schoolmates and the faculty made much of him, but the Headmaster wisely kept him from being spoiled by insisting that he go on with his work. Every clear day Gawaine rose at dawn and went out to kill dragons. The Headmaster kept him at home when it rained, because he said the woods were damp and unhealthy at such times and that he didn't want the boy to run needless risks. Few good days passed in which Gawaine failed to get a dragon. On one particularly fortunate day he killed three, a husband and wife and a visiting relative. Gradually he developed a technique. Pupils who sometimes watched him from the hilltops a long way off said that he often allowed the dragon to come within a few feet before he said "Rumplesnitz." He came to say it with a mocking sneer. Occasionally he did stunts. Once when an excursion party from London was watching him, he went into action with his right hand tied behind his back. The dragon's head came off just as easily.

As Gawaine's record of killings mounted higher the Headmaster found it impossible to keep him completely in hand. He fell into the habit of stealing out at night and engaging in long drinking bouts at the village tavern. It was after such a debauch that he rose a little before dawn one fine August morning and started out after his fiftieth dragon. His head was heavy and his mind sluggish. He was heavy in other respects as well, for he had adopted the somewhat vulgar practice of wearing his medals, ribbons and all, when he went out dragon hunting. The decorations began on his chest and ran all the way down to his abdomen. They must have weighed at least eight pounds.

Gawaine found a dragon in the same meadow where he had killed the first one. It was a fair-sized dragon, but evidently an old one. Its face was wrinkled and Gawaine thought he had never seen so hideous a countenance. Much to the lad's disgust, the monster refused to charge and Gawaine was obliged to walk toward him. He whistled as he went. The dragon regarded him hopelessly, but craftily. Of course it had heard of Gawaine. Even when the lad raised his battle-ax the dragon made no move. It knew that there was

no salvation in the quickest thrust of the head, for it had been informed that this hunter was protected by an enchantment. It merely waited, hoping something would turn up. Gawaine raised the battle-ax and suddenly lowered it again. He had grown very pale and he trembled violently. The dragon suspected a trick. "What's the matter?" it asked, with false solicitude.

"I've forgotten the magic word," stammered Gawaine.

"What a pity," said the dragon. "So that was the secret. It doesn't seem quite sporting to me, all this magic stuff, you know. Not cricket, as we used to say when I was a little dragon; but, after all, that's a matter of opinion."

Gawaine was so helpless with terror that the dragon's confidence rose immeasurably and it could not resist the temptation to show off a bit.

"Could I possibly be of any assistance?" it asked. "What's the first letter of the magic word?"

"It begins with an *r*," said Gawaine weakly.

"Let's see," mused the dragon, "that doesn't tell us much, does it? What sort of a word is this? Is it an epithet, do you think?"

Gawaine could do no more than nod.

"Why, of course," exclaimed the dragon, *"reactionary."*

Gawaine shook his head.

"Well, then," said the dragon, "we'd better get down to business. Will you surrender?"

With the suggestion of a compromise Gawaine mustered up enough courage to speak.

"What will you do if I surrender?" he asked.

"Why, I'll eat you," said the dragon.

"And if I don't surrender?"

"I'll eat you just the same."

"Then it doesn't mean any difference, does it?" moaned Gawaine.

"It does to me," said the dragon with a smile. "I'd rather you didn't surrender. You'd taste much better if you didn't."

The dragon waited for a long time for Gawaine to ask "Why?" but the boy was too frightened to speak. At last the dragon had to give the explanation without his cue line. "You see," he said, "if you don't surrender you'll taste better because you'll die game."

This was an old and ancient trick of the dragon's. By means of some such quip he was accustomed to paralyze his victims with laughter and then to destroy them. Gawaine was sufficiently paralyzed as it was, but laughter had no part in his helplessness. With the last word of the joke the dragon drew back his head and struck. In that second there flashed into the mind of Gawaine the magic word "Rumplesnitz," but there was no time to say it. There was time only to strike and, without a word, Gawaine met the onrush of the dragon with a full swing. He put all his back and shoulders into it. The impact was terrific and the head of the dragon flew almost a hundred yards and landed in a thicket.

Gawaine did not remain frightened very long after the death of the dragon. His mood was one of wonder. He was enormously puzzled. He cut off the ears of the monster almost in a trance. Again and again he thought to himself, "I didn't say 'Rumplesnitz'!" He was sure of that and yet there was no question that he had killed the dragon. In fact, he had never killed one so utterly. Never before had he driven a head for anything like the same distance. Twenty-five yards was perhaps his best previous record. All the way back to the knight school he kept rumbling about in his mind, seeking an explanation for what had occurred. He went to the Headmaster immediately and after closing the door told him what had happened. "I didn't say 'Rumplesnitz,'" he explained with great earnestness.

The Headmaster laughed. "I'm glad you've found out," he said. "It makes you

ever so much more of a hero. Don't you see that? Now you know that it was you who killed all these dragons and not that foolish little word 'Rumplesnitz.'"

Gawaine frowned. "Then it wasn't a magic word after all?" he asked.

"Of course not," said the Headmaster, "you ought to be too old for such foolishness. There isn't any such thing as a magic word."

"But you told me it was magic," protested Gawaine. "You said it was magic and now you say it isn't."

"It wasn't magic in a literal sense," answered the Headmaster, "but it was much more wonderful than that. The word gave you confidence. It took away your fears. If I hadn't told you that, you might have been killed the very first time. It was your battle-ax that did the trick."

Gawaine surprised the Headmaster by his attitude. He was obviously distressed by the explanation. He interrupted a long philosophic and ethical discourse by the Headmaster with "If I hadn't of hit 'em all mighty hard and fast any one of 'em might have crushed me like a, like a—" He fumbled for a word.

"Egg shell," suggested the Headmaster.

"Like an egg shell," assented Gawaine, and he said it many times. All through the evening meal people who sat near him heard him muttering, "Like an egg shell, like an egg shell."

The next day was clear, but Gawaine did not get up at dawn. Indeed, it was almost noon when the Headmaster found him cowering in bed, with the clothes pulled over his head. The principal called the Assistant Professor of Pleasaunce, and together they dragged the boy toward the forest.

"He'll be all right as soon as he gets a couple more dragons under his belt," explained the Headmaster.

The Assistant Professor of Pleasaunce agreed. "It would be a shame to stop such a fine run," he said. "Why, counting that one yesterday, he's killed fifty dragons."

They pushed the boy into a thicket above which hung a meager cloud of steam. It was obviously quite a small dragon. But Gawaine did not come back that night or the next. In fact, he never came back. Some weeks afterward brave spirits from the school explored the thicket, but they could find nothing to remind them of Gawaine except the metal parts of his medals. Even the ribbons had been devoured.

The Headmaster and the Assistant Professor of Pleasaunce agreed that it would be just as well not to tell the school how Gawaine had achieved his record and still less how he came to die. They held that it might have a bad effect on school spirit. Accordingly, Gawaine has lived in the memory of the school as its greatest hero. No visitor succeeds in leaving the building today without seeing a great shield which hangs on the wall of the dining hall. Fifty pairs of dragons' ears are mounted upon the shield and underneath in gilt letters is "Gawaine la Coeur-Hardy," followed by the simple inscription, "He killed fifty dragons." The record has never been equaled.

The man who wrote this story

HEYWOOD BROUN   1888–1939

While Broun served as editor of the student paper at Horace Mann School, he learned the first essentials of the job that became his career. His wealthy father supported him through Harvard, but Broun never received his degree. Rather than complete the requirements for graduation, he went to work as a reporter on the sports section of the old New York *Telegraph*.

In the First World War, Broun plodded through France as a correspondent for the American Army. When he was again a civilian, he wrote several baseball stories that brought him recognition. However, it was his column in the *Tribune* that established him as a well-known figure in the 1920's and 1930's. His talents were numerous (he wrote a musical comedy and painted), but he is remembered most for his stories which expressed the humor, depth, and warmth of his character.

Let's consider . . .

1. Because Gawaine was a boy who lacked spirit and self-confidence, the Headmaster felt he should help him develop these qualities. How was Gawaine's training different from the other students' training?

2. Explain why the Headmaster's plan was really unfair to Gawaine.

3. If you had been the Headmaster, what better plan would you have worked out to help Gawaine develop self-confidence?

4. Gawaine thought that the magic word *Rumplesnitz* killed the dragons. What actually killed them?

5. Explain why Gawaine lost his battle with the fifty-first dragon.

6. In what ways are superstitions, such as carrying a rabbit's foot for good luck, similar to Gawaine's magic word?

7. What superstitions do you believe in? Why do you believe in them?

8. Some baseball players, jockeys, and actors are so superstitious about a piece of

clothing, coin, or souvenir that they won't perform without it. Tell the class of any such personal superstitions you have heard or read about.

9. Did you enjoy the humor in "The Fifty-first Dragon"? Select a passage that you particularly enjoyed and read it aloud to the class.

The writer's craft . . .

"The Fifty-first Dragon" is a kind of story-fable. **Fables** are brief stories that set forth a moral. The characters in fables are often animals which think, talk, and act like human beings. Sometimes fables seem humorous, but they are nearly always intended to be taken seriously. In fact, the main purpose of a fable is to illustrate a particular idea.

1. What is the moral, or idea, which Heywood Broun developed in "The Fifty-first Dragon"?

2. List the characteristics of the "Fifty-first Dragon" which justify its being called a fable.

3. Try writing your own fable. Using the moral of "The Fifty-first Dragon," as your idea, make up a fable that will illustrate that idea.

Knowing words . . .

Below are several sentences taken from the selection. Each of the sentences has one word written in italics. Explain the meaning of each italicized word. Then use the word in a sentence of your own.

1. "It wasn't magic in a *literal* sense," answered the Headmaster, "but it was much more wonderful than that."

2. "And if this dry spell holds, there's no telling when they may start a forest fire simply by breathing around *indiscriminately*."

3. He had a marvelously *versatile* gift for forgetting things.

4. The Headmaster laughed *indulgently*. "You mustn't believe all those old wives' stories," he said.

5. The dragon suspected a trick. "What's the matter?" it asked, with false *solicitude*.

That Spot

JACK LONDON

Spot was a Klondike dog with a mind of his own. He was exposed to death—lured to it, you might say—so often it became almost monotonous. But there was something about that dog. Well, *you* try to figure it out.

I don't think much of Stephen Mackaye any more, though I used to swear by him. I know that in those days I loved him more than my own brother. If ever I meet Stephen Mackaye again, I shall not be responsible for my actions. It passes beyond me that a man with whom I shared food and blanket, and with whom I mushed over the Chilcoot Trail,[1] should turn out the way he did. I always sized Steve up as a square man, a kindly comrade, without an iota of anything vindictive or malicious in his nature. I shall never trust my judgment in men again. Why, I nursed that man through typhoid fever; we starved together on the headwaters of the Stewart; and he saved my life on the Little Salmon. And now, after the years we were together, all I can say of Stephen Mackaye is that he is the meanest man I ever knew.

We started for the Klondike in the fall rush of 1897, and we started too late to get over Chilcoot Pass before the freeze-up. We packed our outfit on our backs part way over, when the snow began to fly, and then we had to buy dogs in order to sled it the rest of the way. That was how we came to get that Spot. Dogs were

---
[1] *Chilcoot Trail,* trail in Alaska

high, and we paid one hundred and ten dollars for him. He looked worth it. I say *looked,* because he was one of the finest-appearing dogs I ever saw. He weighed sixty pounds, and he had all the lines of a good sled animal. We never could make out his breed. He wasn't husky, nor Malemute, nor Hudson Bay; he looked like all of them and he didn't look like any of them. . . . On one side, in the thick of the mixed yellow-brown-red-and-dirty-white that was his prevailing color, there was a spot of coal-black as big as a water-bucket. That was why we called him Spot.

He was a good looker all right. When he was in condition his muscles stood out in bunches all over him. And he was the strongest-looking brute I ever saw in Alaska, also the most intelligent-looking. To run your eyes over him, you'd think he could outpull three dogs of his own weight. Maybe he could, but I never saw it. His intelligence didn't run that way. He could steal and forage to perfection; he had an instinct that was positively grewsome for divining when work was to be done and and for making a sneak accordingly; and for getting lost and not staying lost he was nothing short of inspired. But when it

149

came to work, the way that intelligence dribbled out of him and left him a mere clot of wobbling, stupid jelly would make your heart bleed.

There are times when I think it wasn't stupidity. Maybe, like some men I know, he was too wise to work. I shouldn't wonder if he put it all over us with that intelligence of his. Maybe he figured it all out and decided that a licking now and again and no work was a whole lot better than work all the time and no licking. He was intelligent enough for such a computation. I tell you, I've sat and looked into that dog's eyes till the shivers ran up and down my spine and the marrow crawled like yeast, such was the intelligence I saw shining out. I can't express myself about that intelligence. It is beyond mere words. I saw it, that's all. At times it was like gazing into a human soul, to look into his eyes; and what I saw there frightened me and started all sorts of ideas in my own mind of reincarnation and all the rest. I tell you I sensed something big in that brute's eyes; there was a message there, but I wasn't big enough myself to catch it. Whatever it was (I know I'm making a fool of myself)—whatever it was, it baffled me. I can't give an inkling of what I saw in that brute's eyes; it wasn't light, it wasn't color; it was something that moved, away back; when the eyes themselves weren't moving. And I guess I didn't see it move, either; I only sensed that it moved. It was an expression,—that's what it was—and I got an impression of it. No; it was different from a mere expression; it was more than that. I don't know what it was, but it gave me a feeling of kinship just the same. Oh, no, not sentimental kinship. It was, rather, a kinship of equality. Those eyes never pleaded like a deer's eyes. They challenged. No, it wasn't defiance. It was just a calm assumption of equality. And I

don't think it was deliberate. My belief is that it was unconscious on his part. It was there because it was there, and it couldn't help shining out. No, I don't mean shine. It didn't shine; it *moved*. I know I'm talking rot, but if you'd look into that animal's eyes the way I have, you'd understand. Steve was affected the same way I was. Why, I tried to kill that Spot once—he was no good for anything; and I fell down on it. I led him out into the brush, and he came along slow and unwilling. He knew what was going on. I stopped in a likely place, put my foot on the rope, and pulled my big Colt's. And that dog sat down and looked at me. I tell you he didn't plead. He just looked. And I saw all kinds of incomprehensible things moving, yes, *moving*, in those eyes of his. I didn't really see them move; I thought I saw them, for, as I said before, I guess I only sensed them. And I want to tell you right now that it got beyond me. It was like killing a man, a conscious, brave man who looked calmly into your gun as much as to say, "Who's afraid?" Then, too, the message seemed so near that, instead of pulling the trigger quick, I stopped to see if I could catch the message. There it was, right before me, glimmering all around in those eyes of his. And then it was too late. I got scared. I was trembly all over, and my stomach generated a nervous palpitation that made me seasick. I just sat down and looked at that dog, and he looked at me, till I thought I was going crazy. Do you want to know what I did? I threw down the gun and ran back to camp with the fear of God in my heart. Steve laughed at me. But I noticed that Steve led Spot into the woods, a week later, for the same purpose, and that Steve came back alone, and a little later Spot drifted back, too.

At any rate, Spot wouldn't work. We paid a hundred and ten dollars for him from the bottom of our sack, and he wouldn't work. He wouldn't even tighten the traces. Steve spoke to him the first time we put him in harness, and he sort of shivered, that was all. Not an ounce on the traces. He just stood still and wobbled, like so much jelly. Steve touched him with the whip. He yelped, but not an ounce. Steve touched him again, a bit harder, and he howled—the regular long wolf howl. Then Steve got mad and gave him half a dozen, and I came on the run from the tent.

I told Steve he was brutal with the animal, and we had some words—the first we'd ever had. He threw the whip down in the snow and walked away mad. I picked it up and went to it. That Spot trembled and wobbled and cowered before ever I swung the lash, and with the first bite of it he howled like a lost soul. Next he lay down in the snow. I started the rest of the dogs, and they dragged him along, while I threw the whip into him. He

rolled over on his back and bumped along, his four legs waving in the air, himself howling as though he was going through a sausage machine. Steve came back and laughed at me, and I apologized for what I'd said.

There was no getting any work out of that Spot; and to make up for it, he was the biggest pig-glutton of a dog I ever saw. On top of that, he was the cleverest thief. There was no circumventing him. Many a breakfast we went without our bacon because Spot had been there first. And it was because of him that we nearly starved to death up the Stewart. He figured out the way to break into our meat-cache, and what he didn't eat, the rest of the team did. But he was impartial. He stole from everybody. He was a restless dog, always very busy snooping around or going somewhere. And there was never a camp within five miles that he didn't raid. The worst of it was that they always came back on us to pay his

board bill, which was just, being the law of the land; but it was mighty hard on us, especially that first winter on the Chilcoot, when we were busted, paying for whole hams and sides of bacon that we never ate. He could fight, too, that Spot. He could do everything but work. He never pulled a pound, but he was the boss of the whole team. The way he made those dogs stand around was an education. He bullied them, and there was always one or more of them fresh-marked with his fangs. But he was more than a bully. He wasn't afraid of anything that walked on four legs; and I've seen him march, single-handed, into a strange team, without any provocation whatever, and put the *kibosh* on the whole outfit. Did I say he could eat? I caught him eating the whip once. That's straight. He started in at the lash, and when I caught him he was down to the handle, and still going.

But he was a good looker. At the end of the first week we sold him for seventy-five dollars to the Mounted Police. They had experienced dog drivers, and we knew that by the time he'd covered the six hundred miles to Dawson he'd be a good sled dog. I say we *knew,* for we were just getting acquainted with that Spot. A little later we were not brash enough to know anything where he was concerned. A week later we woke up in the morning to the dangedest dog-fight we'd ever heard. It was that Spot come back and knocking the team into shape. We ate a pretty depressing breakfast, I can tell you; but cheered up two hours afterward when we sold him to an official courier, bound in to Dawson with government despatches. That Spot was only three days in coming back, and, as usual, celebrated his arrival with a rough-house.

We spent the winter and spring, after our own outfit was across the pass, freight-ing other people's outfits, and we made a fat stake. Also, we made money out of Spot. If we sold him once, we sold him twenty times. He always came back, and no one asked for their money. We didn't want the money. We'd have paid handsomely for anyone to take him off our hands for keeps. We had to get rid of him, and we couldn't give him away, for when we tried everybody became suspicious. But he was such a fine looker that we never had any difficulty in selling him. "Unbroke," we'd say, and they'd pay any old price for him. We sold him as low as twenty-five dollars, and once we got a hundred and fifty for him. That particular party returned him in person, refused to take his money back, and the way he abused us was something awful. He said it was cheap at the price to tell us what he thought of us; and we felt he was so justified that we never talked back. But to this day I've never quite regained all the old self-respect that was mine before that man talked to me.

When the ice cleared out of the lakes and river, we put our outfit in a Lake Bennett boat and started for Dawson. We had a good team of dogs, and of course we piled them on top the outfit. That Spot was along—there was no losing him; and a dozen times, the first day, he knocked one or another of the dogs overboard in the course of fighting with them. It was close quarters, and he didn't like being crowded.

"What that dog needs is space," Steve said the second day. "Let's maroon him."

We did, running the boat in at Caribou Crossing for him to jump ashore. Two of the other dogs, good dogs, followed him; and we lost two whole days trying to find them. We never saw those two dogs again; but the quietness and relief we enjoyed made us decide, like the man who refused his hundred and fifty, that it was cheap at the price. For the first time in months Steve and I laughed and whistled and sang. We were as happy as clams. The dark days were over. The nightmare had been lifted. That Spot was gone.

Three weeks later, one morning, Steve and I were standing on the river-bank at Dawson. A small boat was just arriving from Lake Bennett. I saw Steve give a start, and heard him say something that was not nice and that was not under his breath. Then I looked; and there, in the bow of the boat, with ears pricked up, sat Spot. Steve and I sneaked immediately, like beaten curs, like cowards, like absconders from justice. It was this last that the lieutenant of police thought when he saw us sneaking. He surmised that there were law-officers in the boat who were after us. He didn't wait to find out, but kept us in sight, and in the M. & M. saloon got us in a corner. We had a merry time explaining, for we refused to go back to the boat and meet Spot; and finally he held us under guard of another policeman while he went to the boat. After we got clear of him, we started for the cabin, and when we arrived, there was that Spot sitting on the stoop waiting for us. Now how did he know we lived there? There were forty thousand people in Dawson that summer, and how did he *savve* [2] our cabin out of all the cabins? How did he know we were in Dawson, anyway? I leave it to you. But don't forget what I have said about his intelligence and that immortal something I have seen glimmering in his eyes.

There was no getting rid of him any more. There were too many people in Dawson who had bought him up on Chilcoot, and the story got around. Half a dozen times we put him on board steamboats going down the Yukon; but he merely went ashore at the first landing and

trotted back up the bank. We couldn't sell him, we couldn't kill him (both Steve and I had tried), and nobody else was able to kill him. He bore a charmed life. I've seen him go down in a dog fight on the main street with fifty dogs on top of him, and when they were separated, he'd appear on all his four legs, unharmed, while two of the dogs that had been on top of him would be lying dead.

I saw him steal a chunk of moose-meat from Major Dinwiddie's cache so heavy that he could just keep one jump ahead of Mrs. Dinwiddie's squaw cook, who was after him with an ax. As he went up the hill, after the squaw gave out, Major Dinwiddie himself came out and pumped his Winchester into the landscape. He emptied his magazine twice, and never touched that Spot. Then a policeman came along and arrested him for discharging firearms inside the city limits. Major Dinwiddie paid his fine, and Steve and I paid him for the moose meat at the rate of a dollar a pound, bones and all. That was what he paid for it. Meat was high that year.

I am only telling what I saw with my own eyes. And now I'll tell you something, also. I saw that Spot fall through a water-hole. The ice was three and a half feet thick, and the current sucked him under like a straw. Three hundred yards below was the big water-hole, used by the hospital. Spot crawled out of the hospital water-hole, licked off the water, bit out the ice that had formed between his toes, trotted up the bank, and whipped a big Newfoundland belonging to the Gold Commissioner.

In the fall of 1898, Steve and I poled up the Yukon on the last water, bound for Stewart River. We took the dogs along, all except Spot. We figured we'd been feeding him long enough. He'd cost us more time and trouble and money and grub than

---

[2] *savve*, know

we'd got by selling him on the Chilcoot—especially grub. So Steve and I tied him down in the cabin and pulled our freight. We camped that night at the mouth of Indian River, and Steve and I were pretty facetious over having shaken him. Steve was a funny cuss, and I was just sitting up in the blankets and laughing when a tornado hit camp. The way that Spot walked into those dogs and gave them what-for was hair-raising. Now how did he get loose? It's up to you. I haven't any theory. And how did he get across the Klondike River? That's another facer. And anyway, how did he know we had gone up the Yukon? You see, we went by water, and he couldn't smell our tracks. Steve and I began to get superstitious about that dog. He got on our nerves, too; and, between you and me, we were just a mite afraid of him.

The freeze-up came when we were at the mouth of Henderson Creek, and we traded him off for two sacks of flour to an outfit that was bound up White River after copper. Now that whole outfit was lost. Never trace nor hide nor hair of men, dogs, sleds, or anything was ever found. They dropped clean out of sight. It became one of the mysteries of the country. Steve and I plugged away up the Stewart, and six weeks afterward that Spot crawled into camp. He was a perambulating skeleton, and could just drag along; but he got there. And what I want to know is, who told him we were up the Stewart? We could have gone a thousand other places. How did he know? You tell me, and I'll tell you.

No losing him. At the Mayo he started a row with an Indian dog. The buck who owned the dog took a swing at Spot with an axe, missed him, and killed his own dog. Talk about magic and turning bullets aside—I, for one, consider it a blamed sight harder to turn an axe aside with a big buck at the other end of it. And I saw him do

it with my own eyes. That buck didn't want to kill his own dog. You've got to show me.

I told you about Spot breaking into our meat-cache. It was nearly the death of us. There wasn't any more meat to be killed, and meat was all we had to live on. The moose had gone back several hundred miles and the Indians with them. There we were. Spring was on, and we had to wait for the river to break. We got pretty thin before we decided to eat the dogs, and we decided to eat Spot first. Do you know what that dog did? He sneaked. Now how did he know our minds were made up to eat him? We sat up nights laying for him, but he never came back, and we ate the other dogs. We ate the whole team.

And now for the sequel. You know what it is when a big river breaks up and a few billion tons of ice go out, jamming and milling and grinding. Just in the thick of it, when the Stewart went out, rumbling and roaring, we sighted Spot out in the middle. He'd got caught as he was trying to cross up above somewhere. Steve and I yelled and shouted and ran up and down the bank, tossing our hats in the air. Sometimes we'd stop and hug each other, we were that boisterous, for we saw Spot's finish. He didn't have any chance at all. After the ice-run, we got into a canoe and paddled down to the Yukon, and down the Yukon to Dawson, stopping to feed up for a week at the cabins at the mouth of Henderson Creek. And as we came in to the bank at Dawson, there sat that Spot, waiting for us, his ears pricked up, his tail wagging, his mouth smiling, extending a hearty welcome to us. Now how did he get out of that ice? How did he know we were coming to Dawson, to the very hour and minute, to be out there on the bank waiting for us?

The more I think of that Spot, the more I am convinced that there are things in this world that go beyond science. On no scientific grounds can that Spot be explained. It's psychic phenomena, or mysticism, or something of that sort, I guess, with a lot of theosophy thrown in. The Klondike is a good country. I might have been there yet, and become a millionaire, if it hadn't been for Spot. He got on my nerves. I stood him for two years altogether, and then I guess my stamina broke. It was the summer of 1899 when I pulled out. I didn't say anything to Steve. I just sneaked. But I fixed it up all right. I wrote Steve a note, and enclosed a package of "rough-on-rats," telling what to do with it. I was worn down to skin and bone by that Spot, and I was that nervous that I'd jump and look around when there wasn't anybody within hailing distance. But it was astonishing the way I recuperated when I got quit of him. I got back twenty pounds before I arrived in San Francisco, and by the time I'd crossed the ferry to Oakland I was my old self again, so that even my wife looked in vain for any change in me.

Steve wrote to me once, and his letter seemed irritated. He took it kind of hard because I'd left him with Spot. Also, he said he'd used the "rough-on-rats," per directions, and that there was nothing doing. A year went by. I was back in the office and prospering in all ways—even getting a bit fat. And then Steve arrived. He didn't look me up. I read his name on the steamer list, and wondered why. But I didn't wonder long. I got up one morning and found that Spot chained to the gatepost and holding up the milkman. Steve went north to Seattle, I learned, that very morning. I didn't put on any more weight. My wife made me buy him a collar and tag, and within an hour he showed his gratitude by killing her pet Persian cat. There is no getting rid of that Spot. He will be with me until I die, for he'll never die. My appetite is not so good since he arrived, and my wife says I am looking peaked. Last night that Spot got into Mr. Harvey's henhouse (Harvey is my next-door neighbor) and killed nineteen of his fancy-bred chickens. I shall have to pay for them. My neighbors on the other side quarreled with my wife and then moved out. Spot was the cause of it. And that is why I am disappointed in Stephen Mackaye. I had no idea he was so mean a man.

The man who wrote this story

JACK LONDON   1876–1916

Born in poverty, Jack London learned early what it meant to work and fight. Before he was sixteen, London had become a young tough, working at night with the oyster pirates on the Oakland, California, waterfront. At seventeen, he shipped out on a sealing vessel and cruised the Pacific off the coasts of Siberia and Japan. He returned to roam around the United States and Canada. Suddenly aware of his ignorance, he went back to Oakland to complete an entire high-school course in three desperate months.

Because Jack London was never content to remain in one place, he rushed off to the Klondike to seek gold. He came back with his pockets empty but his mind full of experiences. From these experiences he wrote his first novels and stories. It took time for his writing to receive public attention, but within a few years he was one of America's favorite authors. He wrote wildly. Stories and novels poured from his pen and made him the nation's highest-paid author.

Jack London's most popular novels, like *The Call of the Wild* and *White Fang,* describe the adventures of wild or half-wild animals. His stories are still being read all over the world.

Let's consider . . .

1. Jack London used the following words to describe Spot:

> pig-glutton of a dog
> cleverest thief
> strongest-looking brute
> restless
> intelligent

Find incidents in the story which show that Spot had each of these qualities. Can you think of other words to describe Spot?

2. What were Jack London's feelings when he looked into Spot's eyes? Why couldn't he shoot the dog?

3. Why weren't Jack London and Steve through with Spot when they sold him to the Mounties? After that, Spot was sold many times. Were Steve and Jack being dishonest?

4. Describe several incidents that explain why London wrote that Spot had a charmed life.

5. Explain how Spot broke up the friendship between Jack and Steve. How great an effect do you think animals can have upon the lives of their masters? Illustrate your answer from your own experience with animals.

6. What would *you* have done with Spot?

7. Do you think Jack London expected you to believe every word of his story?

How can you tell? Which incidents—if any—do you think could not really have happened?

The writer's craft . . .

Short-story writers usually try to arouse your interest in the first few paragraphs because there just isn't time for a slow, leisurely beginning. "That Spot" began with Jack London telling you how he felt about Steve Mackaye. At one time he had loved Steve like a brother, but he had come to think of him as the meanest man in the world. Here was an attention-getting opening paragraph. It made you wonder what had happened to destroy the friendship of these two men. You looked forward to the rest of the story for an explanation.

1. List the events in the story which explained how and why the friendship was broken.

2. Now look at the last two sentences in the story. In what way do they bring you back to the opening paragraph?

3. Do you think "That Spot" is a good title for this story? How does it relate the opening paragraph to the closing one?

Knowing words . . .

Many English words are borrowed from other languages. Latin, in particular, has contributed to the English language. When Jack London wrote that there was no *circumventing* Spot, he used a word built from Latin roots. *Circum* means "around." *Vent* is a form of the Latin word meaning "to go." The sentence, "There was no circumventing him," means "There was no getting around him."

Use the word *circumventing* in a sentence of your own.

The Ghost of Benjamin Sweet

FREDERICK and PAULINE GILSDORF

Poor Benjamin Sweet did not enjoy being a ghost. To him the whole business was just plain silly. Then he was assigned to haunt Mr. Tubb, and things began to pick up. Reading a radio script may seem a little strange at first, but you'll soon get the knack of it. *Up* signifies an increase in volume; *down,* a decrease. *On filter* indicates that a mechanical device is being used to alter tones. Sometimes, as in a play, there are suggestions about the way the actors should read their lines. Try to hear the play as you read it. Imagine the music and background effects. The more actively you read any radio play, the more fun it will be. Without your cooperation, the print won't come to life.

CHARACTERS

Voice	Mrs. Hightreble
Benjamin Sweet	The Count
Dismal Ghost	Spinsterish Woman
Another Voice	Clerk
Mr. Tubbs	A Man
Mrs. Tubbs	Chairman

Chorus of Men and Women

Voice (*dead booth*): Bolt the doors. Fasten the windows. Turn out the lights. Sit down quietly in the dark. (*Long pause*) And meet the ghost of Benjamin Sweet.

Music: *Weird sequence ending in chime sounding twelve.*

Sound: *Wind.*

Voice: It is midnight of All Hallow's Eve, in the dark of the moon. Cold, faint starlight picks out a silent graveyard. Around the graveyard is a high, sharp, spiked fence. On the top of the fence sits the tired ghost of Mr. Benjamin Sweet.

Music: *Up for wind gust.*

Sweet: It's a thankless job. . . . (*Sighing deeply*) A thankless job. No rest, no relaxation . . . (*A show of rebellion*) I'm tired of it, I am! It's haunt here, haunt there, chase around on silly errands night

157

after night. And Halloween's worst of all.
. . . Overtime . . . Meet your quota. . . .
End of the year . . . (*Abruptly*) I wish I
had a pipeful of good tobacco. (*With
pathos*) I wish I had a pipeful of any kind
of tobacco!

SOUND: *An owl hoots.*

SWEET (*annoyed*): Don't hoot at me,
you brainless bag of feathers! (*Pause, then
angrily*) Any minute now they'll be after
me—the whole bony, chain-rattling crew of
them. "Brother!" they'll say, "Down off
that fence and get to work! Moan and
groan and rattle your chains."

SOUND: *Clanking of chains. A gust of
wind ushers in*

DISMAL GHOST (*a very sour individual*): Brother, get to work!

SWEET (*startled*): Don't sneak up be-

hind me like that! I never have gotten
used to it.

DISMAL: Move over. There's room for
both of us on that fence.

SWEET: What's the matter with you?
Fed up, too?

DISMAL: Fed up? Why the night's just
beginning. I feel fine.

SWEET (*disgust*): Oh, nuts.

SOUND: *Owl hoots.*

DISMAL (*approvingly*): That's a very
fine-sounding owl.

SWEET: All owls sound alike.

DISMAL: What are your plans for tonight, brother, if I may ask?

SWEET: Oh, I've got a terrible night
ahead of me. That's another thing that
makes me mad. When there's a dirty job
that nobody else wants, what do they do?
"Just give it to Sweet," they say. "He
doesn't matter." I've got a good mind not
to do this job at all.

DISMAL (*solemnly*): Brother, do you
want a word of warning?

SWEET: No!

DISMAL: I'll give it to you anyway.

SWEET (*absently*): I wish I had my old
briar pipe.

DISMAL (*severely*): Ghost of Benjamin
Sweet, . . . you're slipping. Slipping fast.

SWEET (*petulantly*): I don't care if I
am! I'm tired of being a ghost. I haven't
had a vacation since I died. And look at
the job they give me tonight! "Go and
scare Theobald Tubbs," they say. Do you
know who Theobald Tubbs is, brother?

DISMAL: Everyone knows Theobald
Tubbs.

SWEET: Why, he's the worst old fogey
in this country. Nothing in the earth, the
air, or the water can scare him. It's been
tried before by experts.

DISMAL: Well, all I know is they've got
their eye on you at Headquarters.

SWEET: Oh, they have, have they?

DISMAL: Yes . . . and I was sent to warn you. They don't like your attitude. You aren't making your quota this year. They say you don't haunt worth a nickel any more.

SWEET (*belligerently*): And what can those transparent nobodies do to me if I don't?

DISMAL: Don't forget you're a transparent nobody yourself. And there's always a cupboard.

SWEET: Cupboard? . . . what cupboard?

DISMAL: Did you never hear of the skeleton in the cupboard? Every family must have one, and with a click of their bony fingers the Powers That Be can switch you into a skeleton and stuff you into somebody's cupboard. How would you like that?

SOUND: *Someone whistling is heard approaching from a distance. Footsteps on gravel.*

SWEET: Poof! That's just talk. (*With less bravado*) Headquarters, hm?

DISMAL (*stage whisper*): Somebody's coming up the road.

SWEET (*easily*): Let him go by this time.

DISMAL (*severely*): Never! There's a penalty for that. Amendment 13, Section 13: No human may be permitted to pass a graveyard unmolested on Halloween night.

SWEET: All right, . . . all right. Get it over with, then. I feel like a fool every time I do this.

DISMAL: He's getting close. Now he's looking over his shoulder. (*Whistling by this time has grown loud.*) Ready, brother!

SOUND: *Loud clanking of chains. The two ghosts set up a hullabaloo. Soul-shattering moans. The owl hoots. Whistling stops abruptly. A voice yells, and footsteps run rapidly off.*

SWEET (*without any great satisfaction*): Well, that's that!

DISMAL (*enthusiastically*): And it was a good job, too. Did you see him take to his heels? A good beginning. Now what next?

SWEET: I suppose I'd better be getting on to Theobald Tubbs.

DISMAL: Do you want some company, brother?

SWEET: Not you, . . . sour face.

DISMAL (*injured*): No need for you to take offense, brother Sweet. I was warning you for your own good—just wanted to help you.

SWEET: When the ghost of Benjamin Sweet needs help, he'll ask for it.

DISMAL (*calling*): Wait a minute. Do you want me to take that back as a message from you to Headquarters?

SWEET (*a little off mike*): You can tell Headquarters for me that I don't like their attitude. I'm fed up. And the way I feel right now . . . anything might happen tonight!

MUSIC: *Swells for bridge.*

SOUND: *Wind fades. Door slams.*

TUBBS (*on filter until otherwise indicated*): My good woman, must you slam doors? I'm concentrating on a speech for the National, mind you, Association of Curtain Rod Manufacturers.

MRS. TUBBS (*same*): If you were concentrating, Theobald Tubbs, you wouldn't hear a door slam. And anyway, I didn't slam the door. There must be a draught in here. That doorknob blew right out of my hand.

TUBBS: What was the matter in the kitchen?

MRS. TUBBS: Sam thought he saw a ghost coming down the road by the cemetery. I told him not to be silly.

TUBBS (*thunderously*): That's the trouble with people nowadays. They believe anything they hear. They have no minds of their own. (*In his soapbox manner*)

Nobody looks for facts. Give me the facts, and I can prove . . .

Mrs. Tubbs: You don't need to make a speech to me about it.

Tubbs: Oh, yes, the speech. Would you like to hear what I've written so far?

Mrs. Tubbs (*sarcastically*): No, thank you, Theobald. It'll be just like all the others.

Tubbs: The trouble with you, Matilda, is that you have no imagination.

Mrs. Tubbs: How did this get in here?

Tubbs: What?

Mrs. Tubbs: This box with my name on it from the dressmaker's—oh, yes, Sam was to bring it home with him tonight. (*Strangely*) How did it get in here?

Tubbs: Don't ask me. I've been concentrating on my speech. Somebody must have brought it in, that's all.

Mrs. Tubbs: This box wasn't here when I left five minutes ago. Sam couldn't have brought it. The cook couldn't have brought it—how did it get in here?

Tubbs (*angrily*): I don't know. Quit bothering me. Where's my pipe?

Mrs. Tubbs: I hope you've lost the smelly thing.

Tubbs (*extremely annoyed*): I was smoking it a minute ago. I laid it right here at my elbow. It's a fine thing when a man can't lay down a pipe . . .

Mrs. Tubbs (*scared, in a weak voice*): Theobald! Look!

Tubbs: Look? What? Where?

Mrs. Tubbs: Beside you, . . . up . . . higher.

Tubbs: Say, . . . what is this?

Mrs. Tubbs: Your pipe . . . (*weakly*) hanging in the air!

Tubbs: I'll be hornswoggled. . . . It's smoking by itself!

Mrs. Tubbs: (*Screams*)

Sound: *A chair pushed back. A door opened and shut with a bang.*

Sweet (*calmly*): Well, that's a good riddance. Your wife, Mr. Tubbs, is as sour as your pipe.

Tubbs (*trying to put on a good bluff*): What's going on here? Where are you? Who in thunder . . .

Sweet: I'm the ghost of Benjamin Sweet . . . Benjamin C. Sweet, . . . and I'm right here beside you, Mr. Tubbs. Don't you ever clean this pipe, man? It's sour. . . . Ugh!

Tubbs: You're . . . what?

Sweet (*patiently*): I'm the ghost of a man named Benjamin Sweet. A spirit, . . . (*impressively*) a spook, Mr. Tubbs.

Tubbs (*uneasily*): Ghost? Stuff and nonsense!

Sweet (*a little injured*): I guess I know who I am. And there's very little stuff and practically no nonsense about me.

Tubbs (*gulping*): Whoever—whatever you are, get out of here.

Sweet (*sighing*): They were right about you.

Tubbs: Who was right about me? See here . . .

Sweet: They all said you couldn't be scared, Mr. Tubbs. We . . . spooks sometimes talk these things over together.

Tubbs: See here, . . . you Voice, . . . you Fake, . . . go away. (*Nervously*) Go away!

Sweet: I'll have you know I'm not a fake. And you can have your sour pipe.

Sound: *A clack as the pipe is thrown on a table.*

Tubbs (*in great agitation*): You are a fake. I can't see you. You . . . aren't . . . there.

Sweet: I'm not a fake, and I can prove it. Let's see . . . where is the switch!

Sound: *Click of an electric light switch.*

Tubbs: Hey! Turn those lights on again. What are you?

Sweet: Now, can you see me, Mr.

Tubbs? I don't show up in a bright light. (*Pause*) Can you see me, Mr. Tubbs?

TUBBS (*strangely*): Yes. I can see you. I can see . . . right through you.

SWEET: That's the way we are. (*Sadly*) The way we are. You can read a newspaper through us, . . . right through us.

TUBBS: What . . . do . . . you . . . want with me? (*With more bravado than before*) See here, you can't scare Theobald Tubbs with tricks like this.

SWEET: It's no trick. Anybody can be a ghost. All you do is . . . just die.

TUBBS: Are you . . . dead?

SWEET (*impatiently*): Of course I am. I'm a ghost, I tell you.

TUBBS (*a little frantically*): I don't believe in ghosts! I'm a sane man—a reasonable man. I don't believe in ghosts!

SWEET (*mildly*): Then how do you account for me?

TUBBS (*more frantically*): I don't have to account for you. Go away from here. Get out. Get out or I'll put you out!

SWEET: You can't get rid of me, Mr. Tubbs. I was told to haunt you tonight, and if I don't, I'm going to get in trouble.

TUBBS: For the last time, are you going to get out of my house?

SWEET: Nope . . . I've just got an idea . . . about you . . . and I want time to think it over.

SOUND: *Heavy drawer jerked open.*

TUBBS: Look here! Do you see this?

SWEET: Say! . . . (*with interest*) I haven't seen a gun like that for a long time. I used to have a little thirty-two myself. A beauty it was.

TUBBS (*shouting*): Keep away from this gun. (*Warningly*) This is your last chance . . . I'm warning you. . . . Are you going to get out of here?

SWEET (*suddenly understanding and amused*): Oh, I see. . . . You're going to shoot me!

TUBBS: I'll give you till I count five. . . . One, two . . .

SWEET (*delighted*): Say this is something out of the ordinary.

TUBBS: Three, four. . . . (*Pause*)

SWEET: Well? Five?

TUBBS: Did you hear me?

SWEET (*chuckling*): Haven't heard you say "five" yet.

TUBBS: A man has the legal right to shoot anybody who forces entry into his house.

SWEET: Yes, indeed. You're perfectly right. You can't be too careful these days.

TUBBS: Five!

SWEET: Well?

SOUND: *Revolver shot. Glass breaks as if shattered by the bullet.*

SWEET: Now, that's a shame. Right into that mirror.

TUBBS (*awed*): It didn't hurt you?

SWEET: No. I think it went through my head . . . or maybe it was my shoulder. No it was my head, all right. But you certainly ruined that mirror.

MRS. TUBBS (*screaming, off mike, behind a door*): Theobald! Theobald?

SWEET: I think I'll just lock that door. I don't like your wife, Mr. Tubbs.

SOUND: *A key clicks in a lock. Rattling doorknob and pounding on door.*

MRS. TUBBS: Theobald! Let me in!

TUBBS (*calling with effort*): There's nothing wrong, Matilda. My . . . gun . . . just went off.

MRS. TUBBS: I heard glass. What broke? (*Pause*) Was that (*ominously*) my good mirror? (*Pause*)

MRS. TUBBS (*loudly, still off mike*): Theobald! . . . Was that my good mirror?

TUBBS (*whispering angrily*): There'll be the deuce to pay when she finds out.

SWEET: I'll fix her up for a while. (*In his most spectral tones*) Matilda Tubbs! Matilda Tubbs! Do you hear me?

MRS. TUBBS (*scared*): What is that?

SWEET (*still in a chilling voice*): Your time is coming, Matilda Tubbs! (*Laughs*)

MRS. TUBBS: (*Retreats, screaming*)

SWEET: There! She's gone.

TUBBS (*admiringly*): Say, you aren't a bad sort, there . . . er—Mr. . . . er . . .

SWEET: Sweet is the name. Benjamin C. Sweet.

TUBBS: I think I was . . . maybe a little hasty, Mr. Sweet.

SWEET: Oh, don't mention it. A natural mistake, Mr. Tubbs. You know, Mr. Tubbs, I admire you. I can't tell you how much I admire a man like you.

TUBBS (*beginning to expand*): Well!

SWEET: You have gumption . . . spirit, . . . fight. You'd make a good ghost yourself.

TUBBS: Well, I daresay I can handle most situations.

SWEET (*going on*): Yes, Mr. Tubbs . . .

TUBBS: Call me Tubbs. Just plain Tubbs.

SWEET: Yes, well, Tubbs, if you were a ghost, you'd go out and really do things. What I mean is . . . well, say, if you didn't like the way things were run, you'd run them to suit yourself and to Heaven with Headquarters. . . .

TUBBS: Theobald Tubbs is his own boss —dead or alive!

SWEET (*thoughtfully*): Yes, I believe you and I would see eye to eye.

TUBBS (*expanding still more*): Let me tell you, Sweet, nobody ever put anything over on Theobald Tubbs.

SWEET (*warmly*): No, I knew that the minute I met you. By the way, when that screeching wife of yours quiets down, she might want whatever's in that package I brought along with me. Something I picked up on the road. Knew I was coming here. Had her name on it.

TUBBS (*still expanding*): No sir, no-body ever put over any fast deals on Theobald Tubbs. I tell them, "Give me the facts. Give me the facts and let the conclusions take care of themselves." Yes, yes, the package. Thanks.

SWEET (*still warmly*): I'd put my trust in you any day, Tubbs. In fact, I'd like to be associated with a man like you. (*Casually*) Say, suppose you let me have a look at that revolver.

TUBBS: What? . . . Oh, yes, sure . . . (*Resuming pompously*) I'm a business man, Sweet. And I might say, a successful one, in my line. It takes gumption. . . . It means getting there ahead of the next man. . . . It means . . .

SWEET (*interrupting casually*): Did you ever think of dying, Tubbs?

TUBBS: Dying? Nonsense. Why, my calendar is always filled up for six months ahead!

SWEET: There isn't much to it . . . and it has great possibilities for a man of your caliber.

TUBBS (*blandly*): Well, it's something I'll take care of . . . when the time comes.

SWEET: Of course. Of course.

TUBBS: Now, I make a lot of speeches one place and another. I am, I might say, in demand as a speaker. I'm working right now on a speech for the National Association of Curtain Rod Manufacturers next week—er . . . would you like to hear as much as I've written?

SWEET (*hastily*): I tell you, Tubbs, I've some business to transact tonight . . .

TUBBS: Oh, it'll take no time at all. (*Rustling papers, clearing his throat pompously*) This is good advice . . . even for a man in your . . . er . . . position. By the way, sit down. That's a comfortable chair there. Since you're here . . .

SWEET: All right . . . but I don't think I'll be here much longer. This gun of yours—don't suppose you happen to have another cartridge handy? I'll load it up for you . . . have nothing . . . else to do. While I'm listening to your speech, that is.

TUBBS: What? Oh, yes, to be sure. (*Fumbling in drawer*) Here.

SWEET: Thanks.

TUBBS: Now, the subject of this talk is "Quick Action for Quick Results."

SWEET (*enthusiastically*): Good idea!

TUBBS: I might explain, Sweet, that "Quick Action" is my motto in life. I believe too many people stop to think.

SWEET: I believe you're right there.

TUBBS: Well, . . . "Gentlemen and members of the curtain rod profession: It is a privilege to address you this evening. . . ."

SWEET: Pardon me, but would you mind sitting over a little to the right . . . so I can . . . hear you better.

TUBBS: Certainly.

SWEET: That's better. Thanks.

TUBBS: ". . . to address you this evening. We're all working toward the same goal . . ."

SWEET (*aside*): That's another way of putting it.

TUBBS: ". . . we all want a change for the better . . ."

SWEET: Right.

TUBBS: ". . . we all want to know what the future holds for us . . ."

SWEET (*getting excited*): There's a sure way of finding out.

TUBBS: ". . . we're all going places together . . ."

SWEET: Tubbs, you're right. You and I are going places together right now!

SOUND: *A revolver shot. Long pause.*

TUBBS (*coming from filter to straight mike*): Why, Sweet, you've shot . . . you've killed me.

SWEET (*calmly*): Yes. I meant to.

TUBBS: Why . . . (*pause, then a burst of laughter*) . . . why, man, you've put

something over on Theobald Tubbs. (*Great roar of laughter*) Why, I'm a ghost myself now.

SWEET (*beginning to laugh, now that things are going all right*): And you didn't believe in ghosts!

TUBBS: No. Funny, isn't it? (*Trying to control his mirth*) What do we do next?

SWEET (*enthusiastically*): Whatever we want. Come on! (*They both howl with laughter.*)

MUSIC: *Ghostly music up. Hold ten seconds, then fade into street noises.*

SOUND: *The usual Halloween street revelry: bells, whistles, shouts, clackers, and occasional snatches of band music. Create the impression that the two ghosts are strolling along through the crowded streets. Fade down street effects, but hold underneath.*

SWEET (*happily*): Lots of people out tonight, eh, Tubbs?

TUBBS (*with great geniality*): Halloween's a big night for this town, I guess. Never had time to think much about it before. Lots of parties, too, I suppose.

SWEET (*wistfully*): I'd kind of like to go to a party tonight. What d'you say we do?

TUBBS: All right with me. Say, I feel light as a feather.

SWEET (*chuckling*): You'll get used to that after while.

TUBBS: Are you sure nobody can see us?

SWEET: Not a chance. Too many street lights. You can only see ghosts in the dark.

TUBBS: Strange business. Well. (*Dismissing the thought airily*) . . . This is a fine little town we have here. One of the best street-lighting systems in the state. (*Falling into his soapbox manner*) A town needs push . . . spirit . . . go-aheadness. . . . Give a town those . . .

SWEET (*firmly*): Hey, wait a minute, brother Tubbs. You don't have to make speeches any more. Besides, I don't want to hear 'em.

TUBBS (*suddenly quashed*): No more speeches?

SWEET (*with an air of settling the matter once for all*): No more speeches.

TUBBS: I used to get a lot of pleasure out of my speeches. Wonder if I'll miss them much.

SWEET: You're going to hear plenty of them after while . . . when Headquarters start checking up on the two of us. They're great on speech making.

TUBBS (*enthusiastically*): Say, Sweet, I won't have to take my pills tonight. And say! My diet! I can give it up!

SWEET (*relieved*): I was just a little

afraid you'd . . . hold it against me. My shooting you like that.

TUBBS (*warmly*): Now, don't let that worry you, Sweet. I never felt so good in my life!

SWEET (*poking fun to cover his relief*): I must say, for a spook with a bay window like yours, you're stepping along pretty lively there.

TUBBS (*entering into the spirit of the thing*): Careful, brother! First you shoot me. Then you insult me. Maybe we'll have to have one of those duels they have in Europe.

SWEET: Good idea! (*Cheerfully*) Only trouble is . . . we've already shot each other once tonight. (*They both laugh heartily.*)

TUBBS: Sweet, you're a good guy.

SWEET (*embarrassed*): Oh, well, I'm just an old fellow. Don't have any business running around playing the fool. But, tarnation, I've been leading a dull life for a long time.

TUBBS: We'll keep things stirred up together now.

SWEET: Yes, you're the kind of fellow I always wanted to be. Smarter than the next one . . . not scared of anything . . .

TUBBS (*embarrassed*): Aw, forget all that. Where's this party we're going to?

SOUND: *Loud blast of tin horns. Laughter and talk off mike.*

SWEET (*whisper*): Let's try this house on the corner.

TUBBS: Say, I never did like the woman who lives in here. Maybe . . .

SWEET: Then I'll tell you what we'll do . . . (*Fade out*)

(*Fade out street noises*)

MUSIC: *Swells up for bridge and joins.*

SOUND: *Party noises. Fade in Mrs. Hightreble's laughter. All "humans" on filter.*

MRS. HIGHTREBLE (*a "dowagerish" voice; very coyly silly, much pointless gig-*

gling): Now, I throw the apple peel over my left shoulder . . . no, my right shoulder. There!

THE COUNT (*a very affected English accent*): Oh, I say, Mrs. Hightreble. It looks like a "C."

MRS. HIGHTREBLE: Oh, let's look. I believe it is a "C." My next husband's first initial will be "C"! Who . . . no, it isn't "C" after all.

COUNT: I swear it isn't. It's changing. The wind must be blowing.

MRS. HIGHTREBLE: It's an "F." My next husband's first initial will be "F."

ANOTHER WOMAN (*nasty spinsterish voice*): Throw another peel, Mrs. Hightreble. Better get his full name so you don't make any more mistakes.

MRS. HIGHTREBLE (*coolly*): Indeed? Where did I put my paring knife? Oh, yes, thank you, Count. Now . . . over my left shoulder. There!

CHORUS: "O."

MRS. HIGHTREBLE (*gaily*): "F." . . . "O." Another one . . . there.

CHORUS OF VOICES: Another "O."

COUNT: "F." . . . "O." . . . "O." Strange initials, what?

SPINSTERISH WOMAN: You must throw one more, Mrs. Hightreble. I think it's going to be his full name.

MRS. HIGHTREBLE: Oh, no. Let's not play this game any more. Won't you all have some more cider?

COUNT: Now, Mrs. Hightreble . . . for me . . . one more apple peeling. Here, . . . I've cut it for you.

MRS. HIGHTREBLE (*crossly*): All right. . . . There.

CHORUS: "L." (*Laughter*)

COUNT: "F . . . O . . . O . . . L" Why . . . (*The idea gets across*) Why, it spells "fool," Mrs. Hightreble. Queer, eh, what?

MRS. HIGHTREBLE: Very stupid game. It doesn't mean anything at all, Count.

Where is my cider? Somebody has been drinking it out of my glass!

COUNT: Here's your glass. I filled it up for you just a moment ago. Why, it's empty. That's extraordinary!

MRS. HIGHTREBLE: I'll have to have another one, then. Oh, thank you so much. (*Pause*) Now, shall we tell ghost stories?

SOUND: *Somebody runs a finger up the piano keys. Little squeaks of surprise from the women.*

COUNT: What an unearthly noise! I say, somebody's playing tricks. There's nobody near the piano at all.

MRS. HIGHTREBLE: Maybe it's a spook, Count. (*Laughing gaily*) Bother! Something's happened to my glass of cider again. Did you fill it, Count?

COUNT (*gallantly*): I'll replenish it for you, Mrs. Hightreble. A pleasure.

A MAN: Let's have a ghost story.

MRS. HIGHTREBLE: Yes, . . . and I'll tell it. I know a perfectly blood-curdling one.

CHORUS: *Voices urging her to tell it.*

MRS. HIGHTREBLE: Well, . . . there was once a captain on a ship who murdered one of his sailors . . .

SWEET (*earnestly*): It was the sailor who murdered the captain. Tell it right or don't tell it at all.

MRS. HIGHTREBLE: Who was that? Now, I'll tell this story the way I know it. . . . Oh, I guess it was the sailor who murdered the captain—gracious! My cider! It's gone again.

COUNT: Allow me, Mrs. Hightreble. (*Making a joke*) I say, I believe you're somewhat of a cider drinker.

MRS. HIGHTREBLE: Well, the sailor wrapped the captain up in a quilt.

SWEET (*impatiently*): In a tarpaulin, not a quilt!

MRS. HIGHTREBLE (*firmly*): In a quilt, and dropped him overboard on a dark night.

SWEET: There was a full moon that night!

MRS. HIGHTREBLE: Somebody's being very impolite. But I guess there was a moon that night. Well, the sailor went to his bedroom . . .

SWEET: His bunk in the fo'castle.

MRS. HIGHTREBLE (*getting rattled*): But he couldn't sleep. He pitched and tossed.

SWEET (*patiently*): It was the boat that pitched and tossed, for there wasn't any captain to steer it.

MRS. HIGHTREBLE: Who's interrupting me? (*Upset*) Where's my cider?

COUNT: I say, Mrs. Hightreble. Perhaps you've had just a drop too much.

MRS. HIGHTREBLE: Too much? I haven't had a bit!

COUNT: That's a strange circumstance. There isn't any cider left in the bowl at all.

MRS. HIGHTREBLE: Let me finish my story!

SWEET: I'll finish it. Then suddenly all the lights in the boat went out.

SOUND: *An electric switch clicks. Screams: "Who turned out that light? Put it on!"*

SWEET: And a wind swept across the deck.

SOUND: *Wind. Glass breaking. Furniture upset. Confusion.*

SWEET: And the captain and his mate sailed through the air, singing. (*He and Tubbs sing lustily but not tunefully a few bars of "Sailing, Sailing, over the Bounding Main."*)

SOUND: *More confusion. Someone yells, "Look over there by the door. There are two of them." Door slams.*

MUSIC: *Up for ten seconds. Fade into Sweet and Tubbs still singing their song. They have both had a considerable quantity of cider.*

TUBBS (*breathing heavily*): Say, that's more exercise than I've had in forty years.

SWEET: How do you feel now, brother? Good?

TUBBS: I feel marvelous. But can't we sit down somewhere and have a little rest? Where are we?

SWEET (*singing a few bars*): Good idea I had—going to that party.

TUBBS: Say, where are we?

SWEET: This is my favorite graveyard.

TUBBS: Pleasant spot you pick out!

SWEET: Come on. . . . Sit down on the fence. One of the best fences in this country!

TUBBS: It's got spikes on it.

SWEET: You won't notice them now. . . . Try it.

TUBBS (*grunting*): Umph. . . . Yes, quite comfortable, quite comfortable.

SOUND: *Owl hoots.*

TUBBS: What's that?

SWEET: That's a beautiful little owl. She lives here all the year round.

TUBBS: Say, it's been a good evening, Sweet. You sure are a grand guy. This is the life!

SWEET (*suddenly*): Tubbs, I just remembered something.

TUBBS: What?

SWEET (*sadly*): Tubbs, they're going to shut me up in a cupboard.

TUBBS (*sharply*): Who is?

SWEET: Headquarters. They've got their eye on me. Tonight's the end of our ghostal year, Tubbs. And I haven't been working hard enough. They're going to check up on me. They sent a long-faced fellow around to warn me a little while ago.

TUBBS (*firmly*): Listen here, Sweet. You're a friend of mine. And no friend of Theobald Tubbs ever got into trouble he couldn't get out of.

SWEET: Oh, it's a thankless job, brother. A thankless job. It wouldn't be bad . . .

being a ghost . . . if they didn't check up on you so close. They aren't going to like what I did at your house tonight.

TUBBS: If it's all right with me, it ought to be all right with them. Who runs this outfit anyhow?

SWEET: There's a Board of Management. You got to follow orders.

TUBBS: Brother, you've got nothing to worry about when Theobald Tubbs is on your side!

SWEET (*mournfully*): Why, they won't even let you sit down and rest a minute. Soon as you do, somebody's around.

SOUND: *A gust of wind ushers in the Dismal Ghost again. Same as in opening scene.*

DISMAL GHOST: Brothers, get to work!

SWEET: What'd I tell you?

DISMAL: Oh, ho! So it's you again, brother Sweet! Oh, ho! (*Direly*) Oh, ho!

SWEET (*aside to Tubbs*): This is the one I was telling you about.

TUBBS: Melancholy cuss, isn't he?

DISMAL: Brother, you're in trouble now. You're in bad trouble.

SWEET (*snappishly*): All right, but it's nothing for you to croak about!

DISMAL: I warned you. They sent me to warn you, and I did!

TUBBS: Say, how about your scuttling along? We don't like your company.

DISMAL: Oh, no! I know who you are, too! You're the new ghost of Theobald Tubbs.

SWEET (*sighing*): I suppose the word's got around by now.

DISMAL: The word's got around to Headquarters, all right. And you're going to have plenty of company here in a minute. They're on their way.

SWEET (*pathetically*): I suppose they're . . . pretty . . . mad?

TUBBS: Here, here, Sweet. Where's your spirit? Buck up!

SWEET: Oh, you don't know these guys.

SOUND: *In the distance a great rhythmic clanking of chains and a chorus chanting in march time, "Benjamin Sweet . . . Benjamin Sweet." They chant monotonously over and over as the chorus grows louder and nearer.*

TUBBS: Say, what is this . . . ?

DISMAL (*sharply*): Silence, brother Tubbs! The Board of Management approaches!

SWEET (*stage whisper*): That's Headquarters.

SOUND: *Chorus still chanting and clanking. Louder. The wind howls. Owl hoots. Chorus on mike.*

CHAIRMAN (*a fussy, nasal-voiced old man*): Halt!

SOUND: *Marching and chanting stops abruptly.*

CHAIRMAN (*triumphantly*): I see the ghost of Benjamin Sweet. He sits on the fence by yonder tombstone.

SOUND: *Murmur of voices: "There's the culprit." "He'll pay for this." "Get him." "Get Sweet. . . . Get Sweet. . . . Get Sweet."*

CHAIRMAN: Silence! Ghost of Benjamin Sweet, stand up! (*Pause*) There are two of you. Who's the other one?

TUBBS: I used to be Theobald Tubbs. (*Warming up for a speech*): And before you begin on my friend here, I'd like to say a few words.

SOUND: *Murmur of ghostly voices: "That's Tubbs." "There he is."*

CHAIRMAN (*shouting*): Silence! (*You can almost see him adjusting his spectacles.*) Shade! We know who you are. Your case will be taken up in its proper order. In the meanwhile, may I give you a friendly word of warning? You've fallen into the hands of one of the macabre [1] members of our company.

---

[1] *macabre,* gruesome

TUBBS: Now, see here . . .

CHAIRMAN: Ghost of Theobald Tubbs, sit down!

TUBBS (*aside to Sweet*): What's the law on this, Sweet?

SWEET (*aside*): When Headquarters says, "Sit down," they expect you to sit down!

TUBBS: Mister Chairman, I'm a newcomer here. I've been a practicing attorney in my time, but I don't know your code. May I have a look at your law?

CHAIRMAN: Clerk, hand the ghost of Theobald Tubbs the law. He can sit on the fence and read it while we proceed.

TUBBS: Now we're beginning to get somewhere.

CLERK: Here you are, brother. The law! Don't drop it.

SOUND: *Rustle of paper.*

TUBBS: Cheer up, brother Sweet. If there's a way out of this, depend on Theobald Tubbs to find it.

CHAIRMAN: Now, brother Sweet. We have just finished adding up your account for the year. (*Direly*) It doesn't look good.

SWEET: I know all about that. Go ahead. . . . (*Irritably*) What's the verdict?

TUBBS (*off mike, loud stage whisper*): Psst! Stall for time, Sweet. These pages are all mixed up.

CHAIRMAN: Listen to your report for the year, Benjamin Sweet. (*Pompously*) Total number of errands sent on?

CLERK: Three hundred sixty-five.

CHAIRMAN: Total number of successful finishes?

CLERK (*his replies always sound ominous*): Two hundred fifty.

CHAIRMAN: Total number of opportunities to transact disreputable business?

CLERK: One thousand five hundred eighty-three.

CHAIRMAN: Total number of opportunities let slip?

CLERK: One thousand.

CHAIRMAN: Total number of people scared?

CLERK: Sixty-four.

CHAIRMAN: And what is his quota?

CLERK: Four hundred two.

CHAIRMAN: Total number of hours spent haunting?

CLERK: Thirty-six.

CHAIRMAN: And his quota?

CLERK: One hundred fifty.

CHAIRMAN: Most unsatisfactory. What have you to say for yourself, Brother Sweet?

SWEET (*exploding wrathfully*): Nuts! That's what I say, . . . nuts!

SOUND: *Loud murmur of shocked voices.*

CHAIRMAN (*going on steadily*): Shade, not only is your record for the year a blot on our fair name . . . but tonight . . . on Halloween . . . you were given one last chance. You were sent on an important mission. (*Sternly*) Your orders were to scare Theobald Tubbs—not to shoot him!

SOUND: *Ghostly voices murmur excitedly.*

CHAIRMAN (*continuing*): Brother Sweet, you overstepped your authority!

SWEET (*hopelessly*): All right, . . . go on.

CHAIRMAN: To make bad matters worse, you took the ghost of Theobald Tubbs on a round of frivolity. You neglected your duties. (*Very sternly*) You drank cider!

SWEET (*flaring up a little*): A ghost needs a little relaxation now and then. I haven't had a vacation since I died. I'm sick and tired of all this routine . . . it's a bore.

CHAIRMAN: When a shade needs rest, the answer is simple. Every family needs a skeleton in its cupboard. The demand exceeds the supply. It will be very simple to make a skeleton out of you and lock you up for a century or two. Brother Sweet, the verdict in your case . . .

TUBBS (*shouting off mike and running up excitedly*): Stop! Wait! Hold on a minute!

SOUND: *Murmur of surprised voices.*

SWEET (*breathlessly*): Have you found something in the law, Tubbs?

TUBBS (*commanding*): Every ghost here will kindly turn toward and facing the East!

CHAIRMAN: What's the matter? I'm about to pronounce a verdict.

TUBBS: Look at the sky, Mister Chairman.

CHAIRMAN: Why (*with a start of alarm*) . . . it's dawn! Why didn't somebody tell me?

CLERK: You'll have to postpone the verdict till tonight.

TUBBS (*triumphantly*): You'll have to postpone the verdict forever, Mister Chairman.

CHAIRMAN AND SWEET: What?

SOUND: *Buzz of voices.*

TUBBS: I've just found a clause in the law. Amendment 456, Section 89. The page was out of place in the book.

CHAIRMAN (*anxiously*): Read it quick. Daylight's coming. We can't stay here.

TUBBS (*reading*): "Offenders against the law must be dealt with and verdict pronounced up to and including the end of the current year on Halloween night."

CHAIRMAN (*agitated*): Well?

TUBBS: That's an old law . . . ten centuries or so . . . but it's never been repealed. Therefore, you have no authority to pronounce a verdict on a crime committed last year. The new year began one minute ago.

SOUND: *Shouts: "Watch out." "The sun's coming up."*

CHAIRMAN (*screaming*): A curse on you, Theobald Tubbs!

SOUND: *More shouting and a scattering of voices. "Run for it."*

CHAIRMAN: Everybody run for it! The sun's coming up!

SWEET (*shouting*): Tubbs, I'm a free spirit. I knew you could do it!

MUSIC: *Sneaks under.*

TUBBS (*running*): "Quick Action for Quick Results," brother Sweet . . . that's me! There'll be (*fading*) quite a few changes made after I've been here for a while. . . . I can see where we can make a lot of improvements in the general management. . . . Of course, that will mean a new board of directors and certain other replacements . . .

MUSIC: *Up full to finish.*

The people who wrote this radio script

FREDERICK GILSDORF 1903–

and

PAULINE GIBSON GILSDORF 1908–

Born in Montana and raised in the Far West, Mr. Gilsdorf has led a varied and interesting life. He was at different times a sheep herder, a printer's devil, a reporter, and a motion picture projectionist. When he met Pauline Gibson, a young girl from Pennsylvania who was then working for a magazine, he decided that they should pool their talents. This worked so well that they decided to get married too.

Since then, always working together, the Gilsdorfs have written a number of radio and television plays. Whenever they are not actually writing, they are probably traveling and meeting new people—their favorite occupation. In their foot-loose and free way, they travel all over America.

Let's consider . . .

1. Benjamin Sweet wasn't a typical ghost. How was he different from most ghosts you have read about?

2. Dismal was a more traditional ghost. Describe *his* personality.

3. Why was Benjamin Sweet in trouble with the Board of Directors? What was his opinion of the Board members? How did Dismal probably get along with them?

4. Benjamin Sweet thought that being a ghost was a thankless job. How can you explain his enjoyment of the haunting expedition with Tubbs?

5. What tricks did the two ghosts play on the human beings at the party? What other tricks can you think of that might have been fun?

6. Look again at the scene in which Benjamin Sweet was about to shoot Tubbs. Tubbs made these statements:

"'Quick Action' is my motto in life."

"We all want a change for the better."

"We're all going places together."

In each case, Benjamin Sweet readily agreed with him. What was Tubbs referring to when he made these statements? How was Benjamin Sweet interpreting them?

7. How did Tubbs save Benjamin Sweet from having to spend a few centuries in a cupboard?

8. Act out your own production of "The Ghost of Benjamin Sweet." Before you assign any of the parts, study the cast of characters. Be sure you know what kind of person each character is. Since this is a radio play, try to match the voice of each actor with the part he is taking. Use a real microphone, if one is available. Plan your sound effects carefully. Decide in advance how to make each sound.

The writer's craft . . .

The writer of a radio play faces certain problems which do not trouble other playwrights. For one thing, he must remember that his audience can only hear what is happening. It cannot see any of the action. Therefore, what the characters in the radio play *say* is more important than what they *do*. The writer must bring his story to life through his use of narration, dialogue, music, and sound effects.

1. Look again at the beginning of "The Ghost of Benjamin Sweet." What purpose does *The Voice* serve? If this were a stage or television play, why would *The Voice* be unnecessary?

2. What sound effects were suggested at the beginning of the play? How would these sounds help to create the mood of a graveyard at night? What other sound effects were suggested in the play?

3. What kind of music was suggested for the opening scene? How would this music add to the effectiveness of the scene?

4. Explain how the dialogue in a radio play can make up for the absence of action.

5. If you were going to describe one of the characters in this radio play, you would look at two things: (1) what he said, and (2) what the writer told you about him in the comments printed in italics and enclosed in parentheses. Which of these two gave you the best idea of a character's personality? Choose one character and describe him to the class. Refer to both the dialogue and the writer's comments.

The Most Dangerous Game

RICHARD CONNELL

General Zaroff was bored. Hunting lions, tigers, or even the ferocious Cape buffalo no longer held any challenge for him. No wonder he welcomed Rainsford's visit. Would they merely swap yarns, or would the world-famous hunter be able to revive the general's zest for the hunt?

"Off there to the right—somewhere—is a large island," said Whitney. "It's rather a mystery—"

"What island is it?" Rainsford asked.

"The old charts call it 'Ship Trap Island,'" Whitney replied. "A suggestive name, isn't it? Sailors have a curious dread of the place. I don't know why. Some superstition—"

"Can't see it," remarked Rainsford, trying to peer through the dank tropical night that was palpable as it pressed its thick warm blackness in upon the yacht.

"You've good eyes," said Whitney, with a laugh, "and I've seen you pick off a moose moving in the brown fall bush at four hundred yards, but even you can't see four miles or so through a moonless Caribbean night."

"Nor four yards," admitted Rainsford. "Ugh! It's like moist black velvet."

"It will be light enough in Rio," promised Whitney. "We should make it in a few days. I hope the jaguar guns have come from Purdey's. We should have some good hunting up the Amazon. Great sport, hunting."

"The best sport in the world," agreed Rainsford.

"For the hunter," amended Whitney. "Not for the jaguar."

"Don't talk rot, Whitney," said Rainsford. "You're a big-game hunter, not a philosopher. Who cares how a jaguar feels?"

"Perhaps the jaguar does," observed Whitney.

"Bah! They've no understanding."

"Even so, I rather think they understand one thing—fear. The fear of pain and the fear of death."

"Nonsense," laughed Rainsford. "This hot weather is making you soft, Whitney. Be a realist. The world is made up of two classes—the hunters and the hunted. Luckily, you and I are hunters. Do you think we've passed that island yet?"

"I can't tell in the dark. I hope so."

"Why?" asked Rainsford.

"The place has a reputation—a bad one."

"Cannibals?" suggested Rainsford.

"Hardly. Even cannibals wouldn't live in such a God-forsaken place. But it's gotten into sailor lore, somehow. Didn't you notice that the crew's nerves seemed a bit jumpy today?"

"They were a bit strange, now you mention it. Even Captain Nielsen—"

"Yes, even that tough-minded old Swede, who'd go up to the devil himself and ask him for a light. Those fishy blue eyes held a look I never saw there before. All I could get out of him was: 'This place has an evil name among seafaring men, sir.' Then he said to me, very gravely: 'Don't you feel anything?'—as if the air about us was actually poisonous. Now, you mustn't laugh when I tell you this—I did feel something like a sudden chill.

"There was no breeze. The sea was as flat as a plate-glass window. We were drawing near the island then. What I felt was a—a mental chill; a sort of sudden dread."

"Pure imagination," said Rainsford. "One superstitious sailor can taint the whole ship's company with his fear."

"Maybe. But sometimes I think sailors have an extra sense that tells them when they are in danger. Sometimes I think evil is a tangible thing—with wave lengths, just as sound and light have. An evil place can, so to speak, broadcast vibrations of evil. Anyhow, I'm glad we're getting out of this zone. Well, I think I'll turn in now, Rainsford."

"I'm not sleepy," said Rainsford. "I'm going to smoke another pipe up on the afterdeck."

"Good night, then, Rainsford. See you at breakfast."

"Right. Good night, Whitney."

There was no sound in the night as Rainsford sat there but the muffled throb of the engine that drove the yacht swiftly through the darkness, and the swish and ripple of the wash of the propeller. Rainsford, reclining in a steamer chair, indolently puffed on his favorite brier. "It's so dark," he thought, "that I could sleep without closing my eyes; the night would be my eyelids—"

An abrupt sound startled him. Off to the right he heard it, and his ears, expert in such matters, could not be mistaken. Again he heard the sound, and again. Somewhere, off in the blackness, someone had fired a gun three times. Rainsford sprang up and moved quickly to the rail, mystified. He strained his eyes in the direction from which the reports had come, but it was like trying to see through a blanket. He leaped upon the rail and balanced himself there, to get greater elevation; his pipe, striking a rope, was knocked from his mouth. He lunged for it; a short, hoarse cry came from his lips as he realized he had reached too far and had lost his balance. The cry was pinched off short as the blood-warm waters of the Caribbean Sea closed over his head.

He struggled up to the surface and tried to cry out, but the wash from the speeding yacht slapped him in the face and the salt water in his open mouth made him gag and strangle. Desperately he struck out with strong strokes after the receding lights of the yacht, but he stopped before he had swum fifty feet. A certain cool-headedness had come to him; it was not the first time he had been in a tight place. There was a chance that his cries could be heard by someone aboard the yacht, but that chance was slender, and grew more slender as the yacht raced on. He wrestled himself out of his clothes, and shouted with all his power. The lights of the yacht became faint and ever-vanishing fireflies; then they were blotted out entirely by the night.

Rainsford remembered the shots. They had come from the right, and doggedly he swam in that direction, swimming with slow, deliberate strokes, conserving his strength. For a seemingly endless time he fought the sea. He began to count his strokes; he could do possibly a hundred more, he thought, and then—

Rainsford heard a sound. It came out of the darkness, a high, screaming sound, the sound of an animal in an extremity of anguish and terror. He did not recognize the animal that made the sound; he did not try to; with fresh vitality he swam toward the sound. He heard it again; then it was cut short by another noise, crisp, staccato.

"Pistol shot," muttered Rainsford, swimming on.

Ten minutes of determined effort brought another sound to his ears—the most welcome he had ever heard—the muttering and growling of the sea breaking on a rocky shore. He was almost on the rocks before he saw them; on a night less calm he would have been shattered against them. With his remaining strength he dragged himself from the swirling waters. Gasping, his hands raw, he reached a flat place at the top. Dense jungle came down to the very edge of the cliffs. What perils that tangle of trees and underbrush might hold for him did not concern Rainsford just then. All he knew was that he was safe from his enemy, the sea, and that utter weariness was on him. He flung himself down at the jungle edge and tumbled head-long into the deepest sleep of his life.

When he opened his eyes he knew from the position of the sun that it was late in the afternoon. Sleep had given him new vigor; a sharp hunger was picking at him. He looked about him, almost cheerfully.

"Where there are pistol shots, there are men. Where there are men, there is food," he thought. But what kind of men, he wondered, in so forbidding a place? An unbroken front of snarled and ragged jungle fringed the shore.

He saw no sign of a trail through the closely knit web of weeds and trees; it was easier to go along the shore, and Rainsford floundered along by the water. Not far from where he had landed, he stopped. Some wounded thing, by the evidence a large animal, had thrashed about in the underbrush; the jungle weeds were crushed down and the moss was lacerated; one patch of weeds was stained crimson. A small glittering object not far away caught Rainsford's eye and he picked it up. It was an empty cartridge.

"A twenty-two," he remarked. "That's odd. It must have been a fairly large animal, too. The hunter had his nerve with him to tackle it with a light gun. It's clear that the brute put up a fight."

He examined the ground closely and found what he had hoped to find—the print of hunting boots. They pointed along the cliff in the direction he had been going. Eagerly he hurried along, now slipping on a rotten log or a loose stone, but making headway; night was beginning to settle down on the island.

Bleak darkness was blacking out the sea and jungle when Rainsford sighted the lights. He came upon them as he turned a crook in the coast line, and his first thought was that he had come upon a village, for there were many lights. But as he forged his way along he saw to his astonishment that all the lights were in one enormous building—a lofty structure with pointed towers plunging upward into the gloom. His eyes made out the shadowy outlines of a palatial chateau; [1] it was set on a high bluff, and on three sides of it cliffs dived down to where the sea licked greedy lips in the shadows.

---

[1] *palatial chateau,* large, palace-like house

"Mirage," thought Rainsford. But it was no mirage, he found, when he opened the tall spiked iron gate. The stone steps were real enough; the massive door with a leering gargoyle for a knocker was real enough; yet about it all hung an air of unreality. He lifted the knocker, and it creaked up stiffly as if it had never before been used. He let it fall, and it startled him with its booming loudness. He thought he heard steps within; the door remained closed. Again Rainsford lifted the heavy knocker, and let it fall. The door opened then, opened as suddenly as if it were on a spring, and Rainsford stood blinking in the river of glaring gold light that poured out. The first thing his eyes discerned was the largest man Rainsford had ever seen—a gigantic creature, solidly made and black-bearded to the waist. In his hand the man held a long-barreled revolver, and he was pointing it straight at Rainsford's heart. Out of the snarl of beard two small eyes regarded Rainsford.

"Don't be alarmed," said Rainsford, with a smile which he hoped was disarming. "I'm no robber. I fell off a yacht. My name is Sanger Rainsford of New York City."

The menacing look in the eyes did not change. The revolver pointed as rigidly as if the giant were a statue. He gave no sign that he understood Rainsford's words, or that he had even heard them. He was dressed in uniform, a black uniform trimmed with gray astrakhan.

"I'm Sanger Rainsford of New York," Rainsford began again. "I fell off a yacht. I am hungry."

The man's only answer was to raise with his thumb the hammer of his revolver. Then Rainsford saw the man's free hand go to his forehead in a military salute, and he saw him click his heels together and stand at attention. Another man was coming down the broad marble steps, an erect, slender man in evening clothes. He advanced to Rainsford and held out his hand. In a cultivated voice marked by a slight accent that gave it added precision and deliberateness, he said: "It is a very great pleasure and honor to welcome Mr. Sanger Rainsford, the celebrated hunter, to my home. I've read your book about hunting snow leopards in Tibet, you see," explained the man. "I am General Zaroff."

Rainsford's first impression was that the man was singularly handsome; his second was that there was an original, almost bizarre quality about the general's face. He was a tall man past middle age, for his hair was a vivid white; but his thick eyebrows and pointed military mustache were as black as the night from which Rainsford had come. His eyes, too, were black and very bright. He had high cheek bones, a sharp-cut nose, a spare, dark face, the face of a man used to giving orders, the face of an aristocrat. Turning to the giant in uniform, the general made a sign. The giant put away his pistol, saluted, withdrew.

"Ivan is an incredibly strong fellow," remarked the general, "but he has the misfortune to be deaf and dumb. A simple fellow, but, I'm afraid, like all his race, a bit of a savage."

"Is he Russian?"

"He is a Cossack," said the general, and his smile showed red lips and pointed teeth. "So am I."

"Come in," he said, "we shouldn't be chatting here. We can talk later. Now you want clothes, food, rest. You shall have them. This is a most restful spot. Follow Ivan, if you please, Mr. Rainsford. I was about to have my dinner when you came. I'll wait for you. You'll find that my clothes will fit you, I think."

It was to a huge beam-ceilinged bedroom with a canopied bed big enough for six men that Rainsford followed the silent giant. Ivan laid out an evening suit, and Rainsford, as he put it on, noticed that it came from a London tailor who ordinarily cut and sewed for none below the rank of duke.

The dining room to which Ivan conducted him was in many ways remarkable. It suggested a baronial hall of feudal times with its oaken panels, its high ceiling, its vast refectory table where two score men could sit down to eat. About the hall were the mounted heads of many animals—lions, tigers, elephants, moose, bears; larger or more perfect specimens Rainsford had never seen. The table appointments were of the finest—the linen, the crystal, the silver, the china.

Half apologetically General Zaroff said: "We do our best to preserve the amenities of civilization here. Please forgive any lapses. We are well off the beaten track, you know."

The general seemed a most thoughtful and affable host, a true cosmopolite. But whenever he looked up from his plate Rainsford found the general studying him, appraising him narrowly.

"Perhaps," said General Zaroff, "you were surprised that I recognized your name. You see, I read all books on hunting published in English, French, and Russian. I have but one passion in my life, Mr. Rainsford, and it is the hunt."

"You have some wonderful heads here," said Rainsford. "That Cape buffalo is the largest I ever saw. I've always thought that the Cape buffalo is the most dangerous of all big game."

For a moment the general did not reply; he was smiling his curious red-lipped smile. Then he said slowly: "No. You are wrong, sir. The Cape buffalo is not the most dangerous big game." He sipped his wine. "Here in my preserve on this island," he said, in the same slow tone, "I hunt more dangerous game."

Rainsford expressed his surprise. "Is there big game on this island?"

"Oh, it isn't here naturally, of course. I have to stock the island."

"What have you imported, General?" Rainsford asked. "Tigers?"

The general smiled. "No," he said. "Hunting tigers ceased to interest me some years ago. No thrill left in tigers, no real danger. I live for danger, Mr. Rainsford. We will have some capital hunting, you and I. I shall be most glad to have your society."

"But what game—" began Rainsford.

"I'll tell you," said the general. "You will be amused, I know. I think I may say, in all modesty, that I have done a rare thing. I have invented a new sensation."

The general continued: "God makes some men poets. Some He makes kings, some beggars. Me He made a hunter. My hand was made for the trigger, my father said. When I was only five years old he gave me a little gun, specially made in Moscow for me, to shoot sparrows with. I killed my first bear when I was ten. My whole life has been one prolonged hunt. I went into the army and for a time commanded a division of Cossack cavalry, but my real interest was always the hunt. I have hunted every kind of game in every land. It would be impossible for me to tell you how many animals I have killed.

"After the debacle in Russia I left the country, for it was imprudent for an officer of the Tsar to stay there. Luckily, I had invested heavily in American securities, so I shall never have to open a tea room in Monte Carlo or drive a taxi in Paris. Naturally, I continued to hunt—grizzlies in your Rockies, crocodiles in the Ganges, rhinoceroses in East Africa. I went to the Amazon to hunt jaguars, for I had heard that they were unusually cunning. They weren't." The Cossack sighed. "They were no match at all for a hunter with his wits about him, and a high-powered rifle. I was bitterly disappointed. I was lying in my tent with a splitting headache one night when a terrible thought pushed its way into my mind. Hunting was beginning to bore me! And hunting, remember, had been my life. I asked myself why the hunt no longer fascinated me. You are much younger than I am, Mr. Rainsford, and have not hunted as much, but you perhaps can guess the answer."

"What was it?"

"Simply this: hunting had ceased to be what you call 'a sporting proposition.' It had become too easy. I always got my quarry. Always. There is no greater bore than perfection."

The general lit a fresh cigarette. "No animal had a chance with me any more. That is no boast; it is a mathematical certainty. The animal had nothing but his legs and his instinct. Instinct is no match for reason. When I thought of this it was a tragic moment for me, I tell you."

Rainsford leaned across the table, absorbed in what his host was saying.

"It came to me as an inspiration what I must do," the general went on.

"And that was?"

The general smiled the quiet smile of one who has faced an obstacle and surmounted it with success. "I had to invent a new animal to hunt," he said.

"A new animal? You're joking."

"Not at all," said the general. "I never joke about hunting. I bought this island, built this house, and here I do my hunting. The island is perfect for my purposes— there are jungles with a maze of trails in them, hills, swamps—"

"But the animal, General Zaroff?"

"Oh," said the general, "it supplies me with the most exciting hunting in the world. Every day I hunt, and I never grow bored now, for I have a quarry with which I can match my wits."

Rainsford's bewilderment showed in his face.

"I wanted the ideal animal to hunt," explained the general. "So I said: 'What are the attributes of an ideal quarry?' And the answer was, of course: 'It must have courage, cunning, and above all, it must be able to reason.'"

"But no animal can reason," objected Rainsford.

"My dear fellow," said the general, "there is one that can."

"But you can't mean—" gasped Rainsford.

"And why not?"

"I can't believe you are serious, General Zaroff. This is a grisly joke."

"Why should I not be serious? I am speaking of hunting."

"Hunting? Good God, General Zaroff, what you speak of is murder."

The general laughed. He regarded Rainsford quizzically. "I refuse to believe that so modern a man harbors romantic ideas about the value of human life. Surely your experiences in the war—"

"Did not make me condone cold-blooded murder," finished Rainsford, stiffly.

Laughter shook the general. "How extraordinarily droll you are!" he said. "One does not expect nowadays to find a young man of the educated class, even in America, with such a naive, and, if I may say so, mid-Victorian point of view. It's like finding a snuffbox in a limousine. I'll wager you'll forget your notions when you go hunting with me. You've a genuine new thrill in store for you, Mr. Rainsford."

"Thank you, I'm a hunter, not a murderer."

"Dear me," said the general, quite unruffled, "again that unpleasant word. But I think I can show you that your scruples are quite ill-founded."

"Yes?"

"Life is for the strong, to be lived by the strong, and, if needs be, taken by the strong. The weak of the world were put here to give the strong pleasure. I am strong. Why should I not use my gift? If I wish to hunt, why should I not? I hunt the scum of the earth—sailors from tramp ships—lascars, blacks, Chinese, whites, mongrels—a thoroughbred horse or hound is worth more than a score of them."

"But where do you get them?"

"This island is called Ship Trap," he answered. "Sometimes an angry god of the high seas sends them to me. Sometimes, when Providence is not so kind, I help Providence a bit. Come to the window with me."

"Watch! Out there!" exclaimed the general, pointing into the night. As the general pressed a button, far out to sea Rainsford saw the flash of lights.

The general chuckled. "They indicate a channel," he said, "where there's none: giant rocks with razor edges crouch like a sea monster with wide-open jaws. They can crush a ship as easily as I crush this nut." He dropped a walnut on the hardwood floor and brought his heel grinding down on it. "Oh, yes," he said, casually, as if in answer to a question, "I have electricity. We try to be civilized here."

"Civilized? And you shoot down men?"

A trace of anger was in the general's black eyes, but it was there for but a second, and he said, in his most pleasant manner: "Dear me, what a righteous young man you are! That would be barbarous. I treat these visitors with every consideration. They get plenty of good food and exercise. They get into splendid physical condition. You shall see for yourself tomorrow."

"What do you mean?"

"We'll visit my training school," smiled the general. "It's in the cellar. I have about a dozen pupils down there now. They're from the Spanish bark *Sanlucar* that had the bad luck to go on the rocks out there. A very inferior lot, I regret to say. Poor specimens and more accustomed to the deck than to the jungle."

He raised his hand, and Ivan brought thick Turkish coffee. Rainsford, with an effort, held his tongue in check.

"It's a game, you see," pursued the general, blandly. "I suggest to one of them that we go hunting. I give him a supply of food and an excellent hunting knife. I give him three hours' start. I am to follow, armed with a pistol of the smallest caliber and range. If my quarry eludes me for three whole days, he wins the game. If I find him,"—the general smiled—"he loses."

"Suppose he refuses to be hunted?"

"Oh," said the general, "I give him his option, of course. If he does not wish to hunt, I turn him over to Ivan. Ivan once had the honor of serving as official knouter [2] to the Great White Tsar, and he has his own ideas of sport. Invariably, Mr. Rainsford, invariably they choose the hunt."

"And if they win?"

The smile on the general's face widened. "To date I have not lost," he said. Then he added, hastily, "I don't wish you to think me a braggart, Mr. Rainsford. Many of them afford only the most elementary sort of problem. Occasionally I strike a tartar. One almost did win. I eventually had to use the dogs."

The general steered Rainsford to a window. The lights from the windows sent a flickering illumination that made grotesque patterns on the courtyard below, and

---

[2] *knouter,* one who beats criminals with a special kind of whip (formerly in Russia)

Rainsford could see moving about there a dozen or so huge black shapes; as they turned toward him, their eyes glittered greenly.

"A rather good lot, I think," observed the general. "They are let out at seven every night. If anyone should try to get into my house—or out of it—something extremely regrettable would occur to him." He hummed a snatch of a song.

"And now," said the general, "I want to show you my new collection of heads. Will you come with me to the library?"

"I hope," said Rainsford, "that you will excuse me tonight, General. I'm really not feeling at all well."

"Ah, indeed?" the general inquired, solicitously. "Well, I suppose that's only natural, after your long swim. Tomorrow, you'll feel like a new man, I'll wager. Then we'll hunt, eh? I've one rather promising prospect—"

Rainsford was hurrying from the room.

"Sorry you can't go with me tonight," called the general. "I expect rather fair sport—a big, strong black. He looks resourceful—Well, good night, Mr. Rainsford; I hope you have a good night's rest."

The bed was good, and the pajamas of the softest silk, and he was tired in every fiber of his being, but nevertheless Rainsford could not quiet his brain with the opiate of sleep. He lay, eyes wide open. Once he thought he heard stealthy steps in the corridor outside his room. He sought to throw open the door; it would not open. He went to the window and looked out. His room was high up in one of the towers. The lights of the chateau were out now and it was dark and silent, but there was a fragment of sallow moon, and by its light he could see, dimly, the courtyard; there, weaving in and out in the pattern of shadow, were black, noiseless forms; the hounds heard him at the window and looked up

expectantly, with their green eyes. Rainsford went back to the bed and lay down. He had achieved a doze when just as morning began to come, he heard, far off in the jungle, the faint report of a pistol.

General Zaroff did not appear until luncheon. He was dressed faultlessly in the tweeds of a country squire. He was solicitous about the state of Rainsford's health.

"As for me," sighed the general, "I do not feel so well. I am worried, Mr. Rainsford. Last night I detected traces of my old complaint. The hunting was not good last night. The fellow lost his head. He made a straight trail that offered no problems at all. That's the trouble with these sailors; they have dull brains to begin with, and they do not know how to get about in the woods. It's most annoying."

"General," said Rainsford, firmly, "I wish to leave this island at once."

The general raised his thickets of eyebrows; he seemed hurt. "But, my dear fellow," the general protested, "you've only just come. You've had no hunting—"

"I wish to go today," said Rainsford. He saw the dead black eyes of the general on him, studying him. General Zaroff's face suddenly brightened.

"Tonight," said the general, "we will hunt—you and I."

Rainsford shook his head. "No, General," he said, "I will not hunt."

The general shrugged his shoulders. "As you wish, my friend," he said. "The choice rests entirely with you. But may I not venture to suggest that you will find my idea of sport more diverting than Ivan's?"

"You don't mean—" cried Rainsford.

"My dear fellow," said the general, "have I not told you I always mean what I say about hunting? This is really an inspiration. I drink to a foeman worthy of my steel—at last."

The general raised his glass, but Rainsford sat staring at him.

"You'll find this game worth playing," the general said, enthusiastically. "Your brain against mine. Your woodcraft against mine. Your strength and stamina against mine. And the stake is not without value, eh?"

"And if I win—" began Rainsford huskily.

"I'll cheerfully acknowledge myself defeated if I do not find you by midnight of the third day," said General Zaroff. "My sloop will place you on the mainland near a town. I will give you my word as a gentleman and a sportsman. Of course, you, in turn, must agree to say nothing of your visit here."

"I'll agree to nothing of the kind," said Rainsford.

"Oh," said the general, "in that case— But why discuss that now?" Then a businesslike air animated him. "Ivan," he said to Rainsford, "will supply you with hunting clothes, food, a knife. I suggest you wear moccasins; they leave a poorer trail. I suggest, too, that you avoid the big swamp in the southeast corner of the island. We call it Death Swamp. There's quicksand there. One foolish fellow tried it. The deplorable part of it was that Lazarus followed him. I loved Lazarus; he was the finest hound in my pack. Well, I must beg you to excuse me now. I always take a siesta after lunch. You'll hardly have time for a nap, I fear. You'll want to start, no doubt. I shall not follow till dusk. Hunting at night is so much more exciting than by day, don't you think? Au revoir, Mr. Rainsford, au revoir."

General Zaroff, with a deep, courtly bow, strolled from the room. From another door came Ivan. Under one arm he carried khaki hunting clothes, a haversack of food, a leather sheath containing a long-bladed hunting knife; his right hand rested on a cocked revolver thrust in the crimson sash about his waist.

Rainsford had fought his way through the bush for two hours. "I must keep my nerve. I must keep my nerve," he said, through tight teeth.

He had not been entirely clear-headed when the chateau gates snapped shut behind him. His whole idea at first was to put distance between himself and General Zaroff, and to this end, he had plunged along, spurred on by panic. Now he had got a grip on himself, had stopped, and was taking stock of himself and the situation.

He saw that straight flight was futile; inevitably it would bring him face to face with the sea. "I'll give him a trail to follow," muttered Rainsford, and he struck off from the rude path he had been following into the trackless wilderness.

He executed a series of intricate loops; he doubled on his trail again and again, recalling all the lore of the fox hunt, and all the dodges of the fox. Night found him leg-weary with hands and face lashed by the branches, on a thickly wooded ridge. A big tree with a thick trunk and outspread branches was near by, and taking care to leave not the slightest mark, he climbed up into the crotch, and stretching out on one of the broad limbs, after a fashion, rested. Rest brought him new confidence and almost a feeling of security. Even so zealous a hunter as General Zaroff could not trace him there, he told himself; only the devil himself could follow that complicated trail through the jungle after dark.

Toward morning, when a dingy gray was varnishing the sky, the cry of some startled bird focused Rainsford's attention. Something was coming by the same winding way Rainsford had come. He flattened himself down on the limb, and through a screen of leaves almost as thick as tapestry, he watched. The thing that was approaching was a man.

It was General Zaroff. He made his way along with his eyes fixed in utmost concentration on the ground before him. He paused almost beneath the tree, dropped to his knees, and studied the ground. Rainsford's impulse was to hurl himself down like a panther, but he saw that the general's right hand held something metallic—a small automatic pistol.

The hunter shook his head several times, as if he were puzzled. Then he straightened up and took from his case one of his black cigarettes; its pungent smoke floated up to Rainsford's nostrils.

Rainsford held his breath. The general's eyes had left the ground and were traveling inch by inch up the tree. Rainsford froze there, every muscle tensed for a spring. But the sharp eyes of the hunter stopped before they reached the limb where Rainsford lay; a smile spread over his face. Very deliberately he blew a smoke ring into the air; then he turned his back on the tree and walked carelessly away, back along the trail he had come. The swish of the underbrush against his hunting boot grew fainter and fainter.

The pent-up air burst hotly from Rainsford's lungs. His first thought made him feel sick and numb. The general could follow a trail through the woods at night; he could follow an extremely difficult trail; only by the merest chance had the Cossack failed to see his quarry.

Rainsford's second thought was even more terrible. Why had the general smiled? Why had he turned back? Rainsford did not want to believe what his reason told him was true. The general was playing with him! The Cossack was saving him for another day's sport! The Cossack was the cat; he was the mouse. Then it

was that Rainsford knew the full meaning of terror.

"I will not lose my nerve. I will not."

He slid down from the tree, and struck off again into the woods. His face was set and he forced the machinery of his mind to function. Three hundred yards from his hiding place he stopped where a huge dead tree leaned precariously on a smaller, living one. Throwing off his sack of food Rainsford took his knife from its sheath and began to work with all his energy.

The job was finished at last, and he threw himself down behind a fallen log a hundred feet away. He did not have to wait long. The cat was coming again to play with the mouse.

Following the trail with the sureness of a bloodhound came General Zaroff. Nothing escaped those searching black eyes, no crushed blade of grass, no bent twig, no mark, no matter how faint, in the moss. So intent was the Cossack on his stalking that he was upon the thing Rainsford had made before he saw it. His foot touched the protruding bough that was the trigger. Even as he touched it, the general sensed his danger and leaped back with the agility of an ape. But he was not quite quick enough; the dead tree struck the general a glancing blow on the shoulder as it fell; he staggered, but did not fall, nor did he drop his revolver. He stood there, rubbing his injured shoulder, and Rainsford, with fear again gripping his heart heard the general's mocking laugh ring through the jungle.

"Rainsford," called the general, "if you are within sound of my voice, as I suppose you are, let me congratulate you. Not many men know how to make a Malay mancatcher. Luckily for me, I too have hunted in Malacca. You are proving of interest, Mr. Rainsford. I am going now to have my wound dressed; it's only a slight one. But I shall be back. I shall be back."

When the general, nursing his bruised shoulder, had gone, Rainsford took up his flight again. It was flight now, a desperate, hopeless flight. Dusk came, the darkness, and still he pressed on. The ground grew softer under his moccasins, the vegetation grew ranker, denser; insects bit him savagely. Then, as he stepped forward, his foot sank into the ooze. He tried to wrench it back, but the muck sucked viciously at his foot. With a violent effort he tore his foot loose. He knew where he was now. Death Swamp and its quicksand. The softness of the earth gave him an idea. He stepped back from the quicksand a dozen feet or so and began to dig. The pit grew deeper; when it was above his shoulders, he climbed out and from some hard saplings cut stakes and sharpened them to a fine point. These stakes he planted in the bottom of the pit with the points sticking up. With flying fingers he wove a rough carpet of weeds and branches and with it he covered the mouth of the pit. Then, wet with sweat and aching with tiredness, he crouched behind the stump of a lightning-charred tree.

He knew his pursuer was coming; he heard the padding sound of feet on the soft earth, and the night breeze brought him the perfume of the general's cigarette. Rainsford, crouching there, lived a year in a minute. Then he felt an impulse to cry aloud with joy, for he heard the sharp crackle of the breaking branches as the cover of the pit gave way; he heard the sharp scream of pain as the pointed stakes found their mark. He leaped up from his place of concealment. Then he cowered back. Three feet from the pit a man was standing, with an electric torch in his hand.

"You've done well, Rainsford," the voice of the general called. "Your Burmese tiger pit has claimed one of my best dogs. Again your score. I think, Mr. Rainsford, I'll see what you can do against my whole pack. I'm going home for a rest now. Thank you for a most amusing evening."

At daybreak Rainsford, lying near the swamp, was awakened by a sound that made him know that he had new things to learn about fear. It was the baying of a pack of hounds. For a moment he stood there, thinking. An idea that held a wild chance came to him, and tightening his belt, he headed away from the swamp.

The baying of the hounds drew nearer, then still nearer, nearer, ever nearer. On a

ridge Rainsford climbed a tree. Down a watercourse, not a quarter of a mile away, he could see the bush moving. Straining his eyes, he saw the lean figure of General Zaroff; just ahead of him, Rainsford made out another figure whose wide shoulders surged through the tall jungle weeds; it was the giant Ivan, holding the pack in leash.

They would be on him any minute now. His mind worked frantically. He thought of a native trick he had learned in Uganda. He slid down the tree. He caught hold of a springy young sapling and to it he fastened his hunting knife, with the blade pointing down the trail; with a bit of wild grapevine he tied back the sapling. Then he ran for his life. The hounds raised their voices as they hit the fresh scent.

He had to stop to get his breath. The baying of the hounds stopped abruptly, and Rainsford's heart stopped, too. They must have reached the knife.

He shinned excitedly up a tree and looked back, but the hope in his brain died, for he saw in the shallow valley that General Zaroff was still on his feet. Ivan was not. The knife, driven by the recoil of the springing tree, had not wholly failed.

Rainsford had hardly tumbled to the ground when the pack took up the cry again.

"Nerve, nerve, nerve," he panted, as he dashed along. A blue gap showed between the trees dead ahead. Rainsford forced himself on toward that gap. It was the shore of the sea. Across a cove he could see the gloomy gray stone of the chateau. Twenty feet below him the sea rumbled and hissed. Rainsford hesitated. He heard the hounds. Then he leaped far out into the sea. . . .

When the general and his pack reached the place by the sea, the Cossack stopped. For some minutes he stood regarding the blue-green expanse of water. He shrugged his shoulders. Then he sat down, took a drink of brandy from a silver flask, and hummed a bit from "Madame Butterfly."

General Zaroff had an exceedingly good dinner in his great paneled dining hall that evening. Two slight annoyances kept him from perfect enjoyment. One was the thought that it would be difficult to replace Ivan; the other was that his quarry had escaped him. In his library he read, to soothe himself, from the works of Marcus Aurelius. At ten he went up to his bedroom. He was deliciously tired, he said to himself, as he locked himself in. There was a little moonlight, so before turning on his light he went to the window and looked down at the courtyard. He could see the great hounds, and he called: "Better luck another time," to them. Then he switched on the light.

A man who had been hiding in the curtains of the bed was standing there.

"Rainsford!" cried the general. "How in God's name did you get here?"

"Swam," said Rainsford. "I found it quicker than walking through the jungle."

The general sucked in his breath and smiled. "I congratulate you," he said. "You have won the game."

Rainsford did not smile. "I am still a beast at bay," he said in a low, hoarse voice. "Get ready, General Zaroff."

The general made one of his deepest bows. "I see," he said. "Splendid! One of us is to furnish a repast for the hounds. The other will sleep in this very excellent bed. On guard, Rainsford. . . ."

He had never slept in a better bed, Rainsford decided.

The man who wrote this story

RICHARD CONNELL 1893–1949

Of his early days as a writer, Connell said, "My first writing was done for the daily newspaper my father edited in Poughkeepsie, N. Y. I covered baseball games. I was ten years old and got ten cents a game. I have been a professional writer ever since." At sixteen, he was city editor of his father's paper. Later, when he attended Harvard, he was editor of both the *Daily Crimson* and the *Lampoon*.

When America entered the First World War, Connell quit his job as copy writer for a large advertising agency and enlisted. He served a year with the A. E. F.

After the war he earned his living as a free-lance writer and was best known for his short stories. He also wrote a few novels, motion picture stories, and screen plays.

Let's consider . . .

1. What were Rainsford's first clues that the island was a place of danger?

2. What forces led the general to begin hunting men? How could he have turned his passion for hunting into channels that would benefit man rather than destroy him?

3. How did Rainsford finally outwit the general?

4. On what did the general base his ideas of fair play? What was wrong with his sense of values?

5. This story would make a good radio or television program. Would it be more frightening on radio or television? What would be the advantages of *seeing* it on television? What would be the advantages of *hearing* it on radio?

The writer's craft . . .

The author made "The Most Dangerous Game" an exciting adventure story. Explain how his use of each of the following items helped to build a feeling of suspense.

The dogs
Ivan
The chateau
The name, "Ship Trap Island"
The character and appearance of the general
The duel
The general's hunt for Rainsford
The Death Swamp
The rock-bound coast

Which of the above items made you most anxious to find out what would happen next?

Knowing words . . .

Below are several sentences taken from the selection. Each of the sentences has one word written in italics. After you are sure of the meaning of the italicized word, use it in a sentence of your own.

1. Sometimes I think evil is a *tangible* thing—with wave lengths, just as sound and light have.

2. Desperately he struck out with strong strokes after the *receding* lights of the yacht.

3. The island is perfect for my purposes —there are jungles with a *maze* of trails in them.

4. "I can't believe you are serious, General Zaroff. This is a *grisly* joke."

5. The general laughed. He regarded Rainsford *quizzically*.

6. Three hundred yards from his hiding place he stopped where a huge dead tree leaned *precariously* on a smaller, living one.

The Rime of the Ancient Mariner

SAMUEL TAYLOR COLERIDGE

A man hurrying to a joyful wedding feast is stopped by a strange old Mariner. The tale this Mariner tells is filled with beauty, fantasy, and horror. At the story's end, the Mariner departs, leaving the Wedding Guest to reflect on the wisdom which the Mariner could learn only through suffering:

> "He prayeth best, who loveth best
> All things both great and small."

PART I

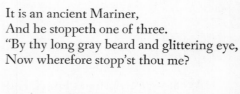

It is an ancient Mariner,
And he stoppeth one of three.
"By thy long gray beard and glittering eye,
Now wherefore stopp'st thou me?

"The Bridegroom's doors are opened wide,
And I am next of kin;
The guests are met, the feast is set;
May'st hear the merry din."

He holds him with his skinny hand;
"There was a ship," quoth he.
"Hold off! unhand me, graybeard loon!"
Eftsoons [1] his hand dropped he.

He holds him with his glittering eye—
The Wedding Guest stood still,
And listens like a three years' child;
The Mariner hath his will.

---

[1] *eftsoons,* soon afterwards

The Wedding Guest sat on a stone;
He cannot choose but hear;
And thus spake on that ancient man,
The bright-eyed Mariner.

"The ship was cheered, the harbor cleared,
Merrily did we drop
Below the kirk,[2] below the hill,
Below the lighthouse top.

"The sun came up upon the left,
Out of the sea came he—
And he shone bright, and on the right
Went down into the sea.

"Higher and higher every day,
Till over the mast at noon—"
The Wedding Guest here beat his breast,
For he heard the loud bassoon.

The bride hath paced into the hall,
Red as a rose is she;
Nodding their heads before her goes
The merry minstrelsy.

The Wedding Guest he beat his breast,
Yet he cannot choose but hear;
And thus spake on that ancient man,
The bright-eyed Mariner.

"And now the Storm blast came, and he
Was tyrannous and strong.
He struck with his o'ertaking wings,
And chased us south along.

"With sloping masts and dipping prow,
As who pursued with yell and blow
Still treads the shadow of his foe,
And forward bends his head,
The ship drove past, loud roared the blast,
And southward aye we fled.

"And now there came both mist and snow,
And it grew wondrous cold;

---

[2] *kirk,* church

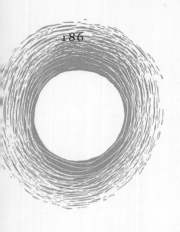

And ice, mast-high, came floating by,
As green as emerald.

"And through the drifts the snowy clifts
Did send a dismal sheen;
Nor shapes of men nor beasts we ken—
The ice was all between.

"The ice was here, the ice was there,
The ice was all around;
It cracked and growled, and roared and howled
Like noises in a swound!

"At length did cross an Albatross,
Thorough the fog it came;
As if it had been a Christian soul,
We hailed it in God's name.

"It ate the food it ne'er had eat,
And round and round it flew.
The ice did split with a thunder fit;
The helmsman steered us through!

"And a good south wind sprung up behind;
The Albatross did follow,
And every day, for food or play,
Came to the mariners' hollo!

"In mist or cloud, on mast or shroud,
It perched for vespers nine;
Whiles all the night, through fog-smoke white,
Glimmered the white moonshine."

"God save thee, ancient Mariner!
From the fiends, that plague thee thus!—
Why look'st thou so?"—"With my crossbow
I shot the Albatross!"

The poet's art . . .

1. The poem began as the ancient Mariner stopped the Wedding Guest who was hurrying to a joyous wedding feast. Why did the Guest stop and listen to the Mariner's tale?

2. In a few phrases, Coleridge described the physical features of the Mariner. Which of these features made the most

vivid impression on you? Explain why.

3. The Mariner began his tale by speaking of the strong winds that blew the ship far out to sea. Later he described the ice which kept the ship from moving: "It cracked and growled, and roared and howled." Actually, only living things can growl, roar, and howl. What effect did Coleridge achieve by speaking of the ice as "growling" and "roaring"?

4. Coleridge used personification when he described the ice as growling and roaring. **Personification** is the figure of speech in which lifeless objects are given human characteristics. You use personification in your daily speech when you speak of a roaring waterfall or of an angry storm. Think of three other examples of personification which you use in your everyday language.

5. Keep in mind not only that the Albatross came to the ship for food and play, but also that the crew believed the bird was somehow responsible for freeing the ship. Why, then, is the last line of Part I particularly dramatic?

PART II

"The Sun now rose upon the right,
Out of the sea came he,
Still hid in mist, and on the left
Went down into the sea.

"And the good south wind still blew behind,
But no sweet bird did follow,
Nor any day for food or play
Came to the mariners' hollo!

"And I had done a hellish thing,
And it would work 'em woe;
For all averred, I had killed the bird
That made the breeze to blow.
Ah wretch! said they, the bird to slay,
That made the breeze to blow!

"Nor dim nor red, like God's own head,
The glorious Sun uprist;
Then all averred, I had killed the bird
That brought the fog and mist.
'Twas right, said they, such birds to slay,
That bring the fog and mist.

"The fair breeze blew, the white foam flew,
The furrow followed free;
We were the first that ever burst
Into that silent sea.

"Down dropped the breeze, the sails dropped down,
'Twas sad as sad could be;
And we did speak only to break
The silence of the sea!

"All in a hot and copper sky,
The bloody Sun, at noon,
Right up above the mast did stand,
No bigger than the Moon.

"Day after day, day after day,
We stuck, nor breath nor motion;
As idle as a painted ship
Upon a painted ocean.

"Water, water, everywhere,
And all the boards did shrink;
Water, water, everywhere,
Nor any drop to drink.

"The very deep did rot; O Christ!
That ever this should be!
Yea, slimy things did crawl with legs
Upon the slimy sea.

"About, about, in reel and rout
The death fires danced at night;
The water, like a witch's oils,
Burnt green and blue and white.

"And some in dreams assurèd were
Of the Spirit that plagued us so;
Nine fathom deep he had followed us
From the land of mist and snow.

"And every tongue, through utter drought,
Was withered at the root;
We could not speak, no more than if
We had been choked with soot.

"Ah! welladay! what evil looks
Had I from old and young!
Instead of the cross, the Albatross
About my neck was hung.

The poet's art . . .

1. At first, how did the crew react to the killing of the Albatross? When the breezes continued to blow, the members of the crew changed their opinion. At this time, what did they say the bird had brought?

2. Then the winds stopped blowing, and the men suffered from heat and thirst. Why do you think they were forced to undergo this suffering?

3. Part II ends with the Mariner saying,

"Instead of the cross, the Albatross
About my neck was hung."

What might the bird's weight represent?

PART III

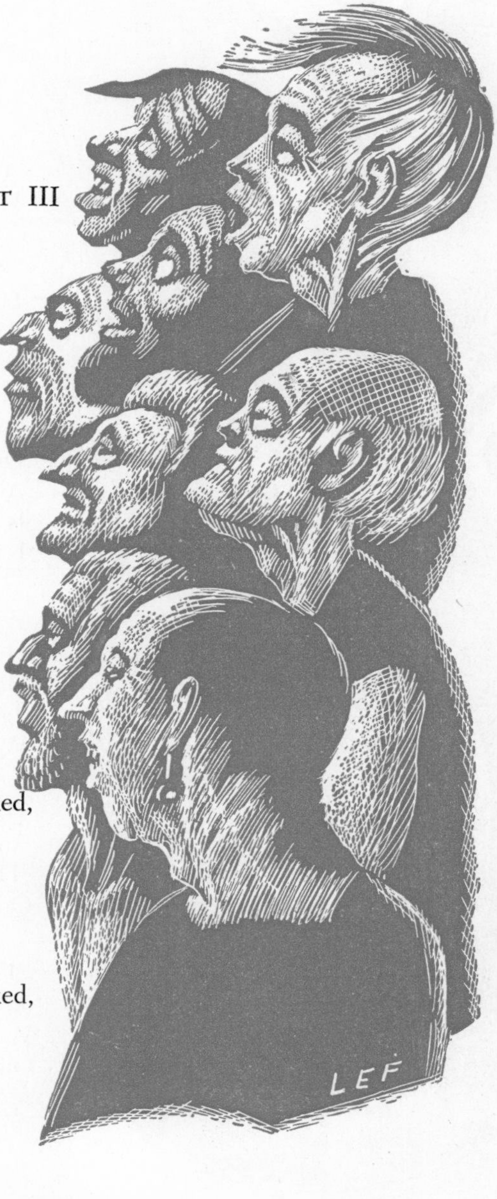

"There passed a weary time. Each throat
Was parched, and glazed each eye.
A weary time! a weary time!
How glazed each weary eye,
When looking westward, I beheld
A something in the sky.

"At first it seemed a little speck,
And then it seemed a mist;
It moved and moved, and took at last
A certain shape, I wist.

"A speck, a mist, a shape, I wist!
And still it neared and neared;
As if it dodged a water sprite,
It plunged and tacked and veered.

"With throats unslaked, with black lips baked,
We could nor laugh nor wail;
Through utter drought all dumb we stood!
I bit my arm, I sucked the blood,
And cried, A sail! A sail!

"With throats unslaked, with black lips baked,
Agape they heard me call;
Gramercy! they for joy did grin,
And all at once their breath drew in,
As they were drinking all.

"See! see! (I cried) she tacks [3] no more!
Hither to work us weal;
Without a breeze, without a tide,
She steadies with upright keel!

"The western wave was all aflame.
The day was well-nigh done!
Almost upon the western wave
Rested the broad bright Sun;
When that strange shape drove suddenly
Betwixt us and the Sun.

"And straight the Sun was flecked with bars,
(Heaven's Mother send us grace!)
As if through a dungeon grate he peered
With broad and burning face.

"Alas! (thought I, and my heart beat loud)
How fast she nears and nears!
Are those her sails that glance in the Sun,
Like restless gossameres?

"Are those her ribs through which the Sun
Did peer, as through a grate?
And is that Woman all her crew?
Is that a Death? and are there two?
Is Death that woman's mate?

"Her lips were red, her looks were free,
Her locks were yellow as gold.
Her skin was as white as leprosy,
The Nightmare Life-in-Death was she,
Who thicks man's blood with cold.

"The naked hulk alongside came,
And the twain were casting dice;
'The game is done! I've won! I've won!'
Quoth she, and whistles thrice.

"The Sun's rim dips; the stars rush out;
At one stride comes the dark;
With far-heard whisper, o'er the sea,
Off shot the specter bark.

[3] *tacks,* changes her course

190

"We listened and looked sideways up!
Fear at my heart, as at a cup,
My lifeblood seemed to sip!
The stars were dim, and thick the night,
The steersman's face by his lamp gleamed white;
From the sails the dew did drip—
Till clomb above the eastern bar
The hornèd Moon, with one bright star
Within the nether tip.

"One after one, by the star-dogged Moon,
Too quick for groan or sigh,
Each turned his face with a ghastly pang,
And cursed me with his eye.

"Four times fifty living men,
(And I heard nor sigh nor groan)
With heavy thump, a lifeless lump,
They dropped down one by one.

"The souls did from their bodies fly—
They fled to bliss or woe!
And every soul, it passed me by,
Like the whizz of my crossbow!"

The poet's art . . .

1. The Mariner described the desolate weariness of the men. What aroused their hopes?

2. Why were their hopes crushed by what they saw?

3. "Death" and "Life-in-Death" appeared on the specter ship. They were casting dice. "Life-in-Death" won the Mariner, but "Death" won the rest of the crew. Do you think that the crew deserved to die? In what way was the Mariner's existence a "life-in-death"? Was his punishment worse than the crew's? Give the reasons for your answer.

PART IV

"I fear thee, ancient Mariner!
I fear thy skinny hand!
And thou art long, and lank, and brown,
As is the ribbed sea sand.

"I fear thee and thy glittering eye,
And thy skinny hand, so brown."—
"Fear not, fear not, thou Wedding Guest!
This body dropped not down.

"Alone, alone, all, all alone,
Alone on a wide, wide sea!
And never a saint took pity on
My soul in agony.

"The many men, so beautiful!
And they all dead did lie;
And a thousand thousand slimy things
Lived on! and so did I.

"I looked upon the rotting sea,
And drew my eyes away;
I looked upon the rotting deck,
And there the dead men lay.

"I looked to heaven, and tried to pray;
But or ever a prayer had gushed,
A wicked whisper came, and made
My heart as dry as dust.

"I closed my lids, and kept them close,
And the balls like pulses beat;
For the sky and the sea, and the sea and the sky
Lay like a load on my weary eye,
And the dead were at my feet.

"The cold sweat melted from their limbs,
Nor rot nor reek did they;
The look with which they looked on me
Had never passed away.

"An orphan's curse would drag to hell
A spirit from on high;
But oh! more horrible than that
Is a curse in a dead man's eye!
Seven days, seven nights, I saw that curse,
And yet I could not die.

"The moving Moon went up the sky,
And nowhere did abide;
Softly she was going up,
And a star or two beside—

"Her beams bemocked the sultry main,
Like April hoarfrost spread;
But where the ship's huge shadow lay,
The charmèd water burnt alway
A still and awful red.

"Beyond the shadow of the ship,
I watched the water snakes.
They moved in tracks of shining white,
And when they reared, the elfish light
Fell off in hoary flakes.

"Within the shadow of the ship
I watched their rich attire;
Blue, glossy green, and velvet black,
They coiled and swam, and every track
Was a flash of golden fire.

"Oh happy living things! no tongue
Their beauty might declare.
A spring of love gushed from my heart,
And I blessed them unaware;
Sure my kind saint took pity on me,
And I blessed them unaware.

"The selfsame moment I could pray;
And from my neck so free
The Albatross fell off, and sank
Like lead into the sea.

The poet's art . . .

1. After the Wedding Guest heard of the Mariner's encounter with "Death," he said, "I fear thee, ancient Mariner." How did the Mariner's appearance add to the Guest's fears?

2. What did the Guest fear? How did the Mariner ease the fears of the Guest?

3. The Mariner discovered that he could not pray. How did his reaction to the water snakes make it possible for him to pray?

4. The curse in the dead men's eyes tormented the Mariner. How large a part did his own conscience play in causing this torment?

PART V

"O sleep! it is a gentle thing,
Beloved from pole to pole!
To Mary Queen [4] the praise be given!
She sent the gentle sleep from Heaven,
That slid into my soul.

"The silly buckets on the deck,
That had so long remained,
I dreamt that they were filled with dew;
And when I awoke, it rained.

"My lips were wet, my throat was cold,
My garments all were dank;
Sure I had drunken in my dreams,
And still my body drank.

"I moved, and could not feel my limbs;
I was so light—almost
I thought that I had died in sleep,
And was a blessèd ghost.

"And soon I heard a roaring wind.
It did not come anear;
But with its sound it shook the sails,
That were so thin and sere.

"The upper air burst into life!
And a hundred fire flags sheen,
To and fro they were hurried about!
And to and fro, and in and out,
The wan stars danced between.

[4] *Mary Queen*, the Virgin Mary

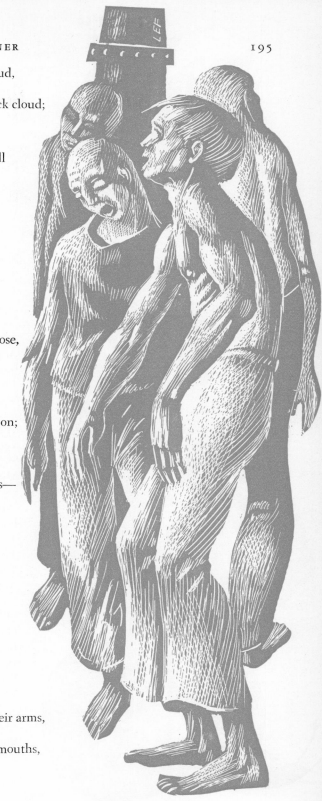

"And the coming wind did roar more loud,
And the sails did sigh like sedge;
And the rain poured down from one black cloud;
The Moon was at its edge.

"The thick black cloud was cleft, and still
The Moon was at its side;
Like waters shot from some high crag,
The lightning fell with never a jag,
A river steep and wide.

"The loud wind never reached the ship,
Yet now the ship moved on!
Beneath the lightning and the Moon
The dead men gave a groan.

"They groaned, they stirred, they all uprose,
Nor spake, nor moved their eyes;
It had been strange, even in a dream,
To have seen those dead men rise.

"The helmsman steered, the ship moved on;
Yet never a breeze up-blew;
The mariners all 'gan work the ropes,
Where they were wont to do;
They raised their limbs like lifeless tools—
We were a ghastly crew.

"The body of my brother's son
Stood by me, knee to knee:
The body and I pulled at one rope,
But he said nought to me."

"I fear thee, ancient Mariner!"
"Be calm, thou Wedding Guest!
'Twas not those souls that fled in pain,
Which to their corses came again,
But a troop of spirits blest;

"For when it dawned—they dropped their arms,
And clustered round the mast;
Sweet sounds rose slowly through their mouths,
And from their bodies passed.

"Around, around, flew each sweet sound,
Then darted to the Sun;
Slowly the sounds came back again,
Now mixed, now one by one.

"Sometimes adropping from the sky
I heard the skylark sing;
Sometimes all little birds that are,
How they seemed to fill the sea and air
With their sweet jargoning! [5]

"And now 'twas like all instruments,
Now like a lonely flute;
And now it is an angel's song,
That makes the heavens be mute.

"It ceased; yet still the sails made on
A pleasant noise till noon,
A noise like of a hidden brook
In the leafy month of June,
That to the sleeping woods all night
Singeth a quiet tune.

"Till noon we quietly sailed on,
Yet never a breeze did breathe;
Slowly and smoothly went the ship,
Moved onward from beneath.

"Under the keel nine fathom deep,
From the land of mist and snow,
The Spirit slid; and it was he
That made the ship to go.
The sails at noon left off their tune,
And the ship stood still also.

"The Sun, right up above the mast,
Had fixed her to the ocean;
But in a minute she 'gan stir,
With a short uneasy motion—
Backward and forward half her length
With a short uneasy motion.

"Then like a pawing horse let go,
She made a sudden bound;

---

[5] *jargoning,* sounds which cannot be understood

It flung the blood into my head,
And I fell down in a swound.

"How long in that same fit I lay,
I have not to declare;
But ere my living life returned,
I heard, and in my soul discerned,
Two voices in the air.

" 'Is it he?' quoth one, 'Is this the man?
By him who died on cross,
With his cruel bow he laid full low
The harmless Albatross.

" 'The Spirit who bideth by himself
In the land of mist and snow,
He loved the bird that loved the man
Who shot him with his bow.'

"The other was a softer voice,
As soft as honeydew;
Quoth he, 'The man hath penance done,
And penance more will do.' "

The poet's art . . .

1. After the Mariner prayed, how was his suffering lessened?

2. The Mariner heard a voice saying, "He loved the bird that loved the man. . . ." Who loved the Albatross?

3. Which incidents in Part V seemed to be supernatural? What was your reaction to these supernatural incidents?

4. How do the following lines foreshadow the fate of the Mariner?

"The man hath penance done,
And penance more will do."

PART VI

First Voice
" 'But tell me, tell me! speak again,
Thy soft response renewing—
What makes that ship drive on so fast?
What is the ocean doing?'

Second Voice
" 'Still as a slave before his lord,
The ocean hath no blast;
His great bright eye most silently
Up to the Moon is cast—

" 'If he may know which way to go;
For she guides him smooth or grim.
See, brother, see! how graciously
She looketh down on him.'

First Voice
" 'But why drives on that ship so fast,
Without or wave or wind?'

Second Voice
" 'The air is cut away before,
And closes from behind.

" 'Fly, brother, fly! more high, more high!
Or we shall be belated;
For slow and slow that ship will go,
When the Mariner's trance is abated.'

"I woke, and we were sailing on
As in a gentle weather;
'Twas night, calm night, the Moon was high;
The dead men stood together.

"All stood together on the deck,
For a charnel dungeon fitter;
All fixed on me their stony eyes,
That in the Moon did glitter.

"The pang, the curse, with which they died,
Had never passed away;
I could not draw my eyes from theirs,
Nor turn them up to pray.

"And now this spell was snapped; once more
I viewed the ocean green,
And looked far forth, yet little saw
Of what had else been seen—

"Like one, that on a lonesome road
Doth walk in fear and dread,
And having once turned round, walks on,
And turns no more his head;
Because he knows a frightful fiend
Doth close behind him tread.

"But soon there breathed a wind on me,
Nor sound nor motion made;
Its path was not upon the sea,
In ripple or in shade.

"It raised my hair, it fanned my cheek
Like a meadow gale of spring—
It mingled strangely with my fears,
Yet it felt like a welcoming.

"Swiftly, swiftly flew the ship,
Yet she sailed softly too;
Sweetly, sweetly blew the breeze—
On me alone it blew.

"Oh! dream of joy! is this indeed
The lighthouse top I see?
Is this the hill? Is this the kirk?
Is this mine own countree?

"We drifted o'er the harbor bar,
And I with sobs did pray—
O let me be awake, my God!
Or let me sleep alway.

"The harbor bay was clear as glass,
So smoothly it was strewn!
And on the bay the moonlight lay,
And the shadow of the Moon.

"The rock shone bright, the kirk no less,
That stands above the rock;
The moonlight steeped in silentness
The steady weathercock.

"And the bay was white with silent light
Till, rising from the same,
Full many shapes, that shadows were,
In crimson colors came.

"A little distance from the prow
Those crimson shadows were;
I turned my eyes upon the deck—
Oh, Christ, what saw I there!

"Each corse lay flat, lifeless and flat,
And, by the holy rood!
A man all light, a seraph-man,
On every corse there stood.

"This seraph band, each waved his hand;
It was a heavenly sight!
They stood as signals to the land,
Each one a lovely light;

"This seraph band, each waved his hand;
No voice did they impart—
No voice; but oh! the silence sank
Like music on my heart.

"But soon I heard the dash of oars,
I heard the Pilot's cheer;
My head was turned perforce away,
And I saw a boat appear.

"The Pilot and the Pilot's boy,
I heard them coming fast;
Dear Lord in Heaven! it was a joy
The dead men could not blast.

"I saw a third—I heard his voice;
It is the Hermit good!
He singeth loud his godly hymns
That he makes in the wood.
He'll shrieve [6] my soul, he'll wash away
The Albatross's blood.

---

[6] *shrieve*, free from guilt

The poet's art . . .

1. Describe the Mariner's feelings when he realized that he was back in his native country. What happened aboard ship?

2. What did the Mariner believe that the Hermit would have the power to do? Was the Mariner right?

PART VII

"This Hermit good lives in that wood
Which slopes down to the sea.
How loudly his sweet voice he rears!
He loves to talk with mariners
That come from a far countree.

"He kneels at morn, and noon, and eve—
He hath a cushion plump;
It is the moss that wholly hides
The rotted old oak stump.

"The skiff boat neared; I heard them talk,
'Why, this is strange, I trow!
Where are those lights so many and fair,
That signal made but now?'

" 'Strange, by my faith!' The Hermit said—
'And they answered not our cheer!
The planks look warped! and see those sails,
How thin they are and sere!
I never saw aught like to them,
Unless perchance it were

" 'Brown skeletons of leaves that lag
My forest brook along,
When the ivy tod is heavy with snow,
And the owlet whoops to the wolf below,
That eats the she-wolf's young.'

" 'Dear Lord! it hath a fiendish look'—
(The Pilot made reply)
'I am afeared'—'Push on, push on!'
Said the Hermit cheerily.

"The boat came closer to the ship,
But I nor spake nor stirred;

The boat came close beneath the ship,
And straight a sound was heard.

"Under the water it rumbled on,
Still louder and more dread;
It reached the ship, it split the bay;
The ship went down like lead.

"Stunned by that loud and dreadful sound,
Which sky and ocean smote,
Like one that hath been seven days drowned
My body lay afloat;
But swift as dreams, myself I found
Within the Pilot's boat.

"Upon the whirl, where sank the ship,
The boat spun round and round;
And all was still, save that the hill
Was telling of the sound.

"I moved my lips—the Pilot shrieked
And fell down in a fit;
The holy Hermit raised his eyes,
And prayed where he did sit.

"I took the oars; the Pilot's boy,
Who now doth crazy go,
Laughed loud and long, and all the while
His eyes went to and fro.
'Ha! ha!' quoth he, 'full plain I see,
The Devil knows how to row.'

"And now, all in my own countree,
I stood on the firm land!
The Hermit stepped forth from the boat,
And scarcely he could stand.

" 'O shrieve me, shrieve me, holy man!'
The Hermit crossed his brow.
'Say quick,' quoth he, 'I bid thee say—
What manner of man art thou?'

"Forthwith this frame of mine was wrenched
With a woeful agony,

Which forced me to begin my tale;
And then it left me free.

"Since then, at an uncertain hour,
That agony returns;
And till my ghastly tale is told,
This heart within me burns.

"I pass, like night, from land to land;
I have strange power of speech;
That moment that his face I see
I know the man that must hear me;
To him my tale I teach.

"What loud uproar bursts from that door!
The wedding guests are there;
But in the garden bower the bride
And bridemaids singing are;
And hark the little vesper bell,
Which biddeth me to prayer!

"O Wedding Guest! this soul hath been
Alone on a wide, wide sea;
So lonely 'twas, that God himself
Scarce seemèd there to be.

"O sweeter than the marriage feast,
'Tis sweeter far to me,
To walk together to the kirk
With a goodly company!—

"To walk together to the kirk,
And all together pray,
While each to his great Father bends,
Old men, and babes, and loving friends,
And youths and maidens gay!

"Farewell, farewell; but this I tell
To thee, thou Wedding Guest!
He prayeth well, who loveth well
Both man and bird and beast.

"He prayeth best, who loveth best
All things both great and small;

For the dear God who loveth us,
He made and loveth all."

The Mariner, whose eye is bright,
Whose beard with age is hoar,
Is gone; and now the Wedding Guest
Turned from the bridegroom's door.

He went like one that hath been stunned,
And is of sense forlorn;
A sadder and a wiser man,
He rose the morrow morn.

The man who wrote this poem

SAMUEL TAYLOR COLERIDGE
1772–1834

When he was a schoolboy, Samuel Coleridge spent most of his spare time either writing poems, reading, or day-dreaming. He won several prizes at Cambridge but left the university without a degree. Soon he met and befriended another young poet, Robert Southey. They were filled with the ideas about freedom, equality, and liberty that were then flooding over Europe and England from the French Revolution. Together the two planned an ideal colony in America. Unfortunately, they could not raise enough money to get the colony started.

Then Samuel Coleridge met a neighbor, William Wordsworth, one of England's greatest poets. This meeting resulted in one of the most famous friendships in English literature. Together they wrote and published a book of poems, *Lyrical Ballads,* in 1798. "The Rime of the Ancient Mariner" was one of the poems included in it. The book attracted wide attention, and marked a new movement in poetry, the so-called "romantic" movement. Readers were astonished that poems about common people in everyday language could be effective.

Coleridge had to force himself to write. He still day-dreamed as he did when he was a child, and he was wracked with rheumatic pains. In his effort to ease this pain, he became addicted to opium, which destroyed the little will power he had. Although his poetic career was over almost as soon as it began, few poets have been so respected and praised for so few poems.

The poet's art . . .

1. How did the Pilot, the Hermit, and the Pilot's Boy react when each of them saw the Mariner?

2. Can you explain why these three men reacted so violently when they saw the Mariner?

3. After the Mariner had landed, his body became wracked with agony. How was he able to ease the pain?

4. The Mariner told the Wedding Guest that whenever the agony returned, he was forced to tell his ghastly story.

"I know the man that must hear me;
To him my tale I teach."

Why do you suppose the Mariner used the word *teach*? What did his tale teach you?

5. As the Mariner departed, he spoke these final words:

"He prayeth best, who lovest best
All things both great and small;
For the dear God who loveth us,
He made and loveth all."

How do these words sum up what the Mariner had learned?

6. There was a great deal of the supernatural in this poem. Do you think these fantastic incidents actually happened, or were they only the products of the Mariner's tortured mind? Give several reasons to support your answer.

7. "The Rime of the Ancient Mariner" is a poem that readers seldom forget. Explain why this poem makes such a vivid impression on readers. What parts of it will you remember?

NOW THINK BACK

THINK FOR YOURSELF

Select one story from FAIR PLAY AND FOUL that you particularly liked. Imagine that it is a case being tried in court. You're a witness to what happened. What kind of witness would you make?

1. Who is the *plaintiff* in the case, the person making the complaint? Jabez Wilson, for example, reported the disappearance of the Red-headed League. He was the plaintiff in the case called "The Red-headed League."

2. Who is the *defendant*—the person or persons accused of acting unfairly?

3. What is the complaint? Tell exactly what happened.

4. Do you think the complaint is serious? Not too important? Funny? Explain why.

5. Were there any witnesses to what happened?

a. Who will testify for the plaintiff—that is, speak in favor of the one making the complaint? What would this witness say?

b. Who will testify for the defendant? What would this witness say?

6. What could the defendant offer in his own defense?

7. If you were on a jury deciding this case, in whose favor would you decide? Why?

8. Whose point of view does the author seem to take? How can you tell?

9. Were you satisfied with the way the author handled this case? Why? If not, how would you have handled it?

SHARE YOUR IDEAS

Deciding what's right and what's wrong in some cases isn't as easy as it may seem at first. Now share your ideas with your classmates about all the stories in this part. Discussion will help you gain many new understandings.

1. Which of these cases do you consider most serious? Why? Is this kind of case serious enough to be brought into a regular court of law?

2. Which case might make a good subject for a movie short or comic cartoon? Why?

3. People judge you in one or more of these ways:

a. By what you say (your words)

b. By what you do (your actions)

c. By how you look (your appearance)

d. By what others say about you (your reputation)

How do *you* judge other people? How would you want them to judge you? Why?

4. You formed opinions about many of the characters in this part. Some you admired; others you disliked. An author helps you to understand and judge a character by telling you

a. What the character thinks or says

b. What the character does

c. How the character looks

d. What others say or think about the character (Sometimes the author gives you his opinion, too.)

Choose a character from one of the selections in this part. Which of these devices did the author use to help you judge that character? Find at least one example of each device used.

5. Some people that you know always seem to play fair. Others seem to have a mean or selfish streak in them. How do you explain this difference among people?

6. Do you consider yourself a "fair-minded" person? Did you ever treat someone unfairly? What happened? (Perhaps you'd rather not talk about it, but keep in mind what happened as you discuss the next question.)

7. Are people either 100% good, or 100% bad? Are you? Think of a character in this part that you admired or liked very much. Was there anything about this person that you could dislike?

WIDEN YOUR EXPERIENCE

Things to do . . .

1. Conduct a mock trial of one of the characters in this part. Remember that in England and America the accused person is considered innocent until he is *proved* guilty. Use the facts you found in the selection, and be sure to let the accused state his own side of the case.

Your class may wish to plan a series of trials covering several of the selections. If so, set up a number of committees, each of which will handle a trial of its own.

2. Make a drawing, cartoon, stage set, or other project to illustrate an important incident in one of the selections.

3. Organize special committees to carry out one or more of these activities:

a. Choose a game or sport that is popular in your school or community. Study the rules. Pick out some of the rules that help to guarantee fair play and good sportsmanship. Discuss these in a report to the class.

b. Report on current radio programs, television programs, and movies that deal with some aspect of fair play. Which of these do you recommend most highly?

c. Is there anything unfair about conditions in your school or community? In your report to the class, discuss the steps you think should be taken to improve the situation.

d. Organize a bulletin board display of news items on the theme of this part. Display items that deal with both school and community life. Try to provide time in class to discuss these news items from day to day.

4. Investigate the possibilities of starting an honor system in your school. Many colleges and high schools are proud of their honor systems and would be glad to offer advice. Some of these systems have been written up in magazines and newspapers where you can readily track them down.

5. Draw up a *Code of Fair Conduct* for the members of your class or the students of your school.

6. Perhaps, during your turn as a witness at one of the mock trials, you were thwarted by an attorney who shouted "Objection!" before you had a chance to speak your mind. Now you have an opportunity to get a few opinions off your chest without being interrupted. Choose one of the following questions, and answer it to your heart's content—on paper. No one will stifle you until you have said all you care to, and your answer will get a fair hearing. Don't expect all your classmates to agree with your point of view. You may have to have *more* trials, or perhaps an informal debate, to secure a consensus of opinion. Try to present your case as convincingly as possible. Don't sit on the fence. Adopt a point of view and keep it consistent throughout your composition.

Is Cheating Ever Justified?
Are Marks Necessary?
Are Teenagers Snobs?
Are Athletic Scholarships Fair?
Was the Umpire (*or* Referee) Blind?

More to read . . .

The Complete Sherlock Holmes by SIR ARTHUR CONAN DOYLE. If you liked "The Red-Headed League," you will enjoy reading about the other cases solved by the famous Holmes and his friend Dr. Watson. Doubleday & Company, Inc., 1936.

"The Murders in the Rue Morgue" in *Complete Tales and Poems of Edgar Allen Poe.* Like Sherlock Holmes, Poe's detective Dupin sets out to solve a mystery. This is difficult reading in spots but well worth the effort. Modern Library, Inc., 1938.

Treasure Island by ROBERT LOUIS STEVENSON. Jim Hawkins and a pirate crew search for buried treasure. It is hard to decide whether the old pirate, Long John Silver, deserves sympathy or scorn. Try *Kidnapped,* also, a story of Scotland's uprisings in 1745. Charles Scribner's Sons, 1911, 1913.

The Tattooed Man by HOWARD PEASE. The author is well known for his tales of mystery and dangerous adventure. If you like this book, try another exciting sea story, *Jinx Ship.* Doubleday & Company, Inc., 1926, 1946.

"A Retrieved Reformation" in *Complete Works of O. Henry.* Suspense runs high in this story about the fabulous gentleman crook, Jimmy Valentine. If you are a fan of O. Henry's surprise endings, you will greatly enjoy the other stories in this collection too. Doubleday & Company, Inc., 1953.

The Enchanted by ELIZABETH COATSWORTH. Young David Ross settles a farm in Maine on the edge of an "enchanted" wood and solves the mystery surrounding his wife, Molly. Pantheon Books, Inc., 1951.

The Lady or the Tiger? and Other Stories by FRANK STOCKTON. Everyone should know this famous story with the puzzling ending. Charles Scribner's Sons, 1907.

The Call of the Wild by JACK LONDON. The wolf-dog Buck is stolen from his California home and taken to the wilds of the Klondike. The Macmillan Company, Inc., 1903.

The Devil and Daniel Webster by STEPHEN VINCENT BENÉT. In this story, the famous lawyer and orator battles with a clever opponent for the soul of a New England farmer. Rinehart & Co., Inc., 1937.

Chad Hanna by WALTER D. EDMONDS. A lad from the Erie canal joins a circus where all is fair that fools the customers. Grosset & Dunlap, Inc., 1944.

Rootabaga Stories by CARL SANDBURG. For you who like a mixture of nonsense and imagination, with just a touch of seriousness, these stories will be a real treat. Harcourt, Brace and Company, Inc., 1922.

Go, Team, Go! by JOHN TUNIS. The B team has to make good when the varsity basketball squad is disqualified. What happens makes an absorbing story. William Morrow & Company, Inc., 1954.

FACING LIFE

When you were a young child, your parents tried to shield you from many of the harsh realities of life. Now as you approach adulthood, you want to make your own decisions and solve your own problems. But learning how to live with yourself and others isn't easy. Neither are you always sure what your goal in life should be.

The selections in FACING LIFE show you how other young people worked toward their own particular goals. Some of these selections are autobiographical—drawn directly from the lives of the authors. Others, though presented as fiction, seem just as real. All of them suggest answers to your question, "Where do I go from here?"

PART FOUR

FACING LIFE

Bombardier

PAUL GALLICO

Everyone makes mistakes. It is what you learn from these mistakes that
matters. Salvo Jenkins, a young bombardier, made a blunder so big that
the whole Air Force knew about it.

Second Lieutenant Salvo Jenkins
crouched on his knees in the greenhouse [1]
of the big B-31 bomber as the ship, shaking, trembling, and complaining, swiveled
into the wind and thundered down the
runway for the take-off. This, then, was it
at last. The practice days were over. The
hunt was on. And he was miserable.

The concrete strip, streaked like scratchy
film, reeled interminably beneath the glass
nose of the bombardier's bay. *Lumbering
Annie*, wing and belly heavy with her load
of gasoline, demolition bombs, and depth
charges, took her own sweet time about getting into the air. Of the dangers that
might be encountered on the mission, this
was the worst moment, the leap into the
sky. The B-31 had a reputation for cranki-
ness at the end of the runway.

But Bombardier Salvo Jenkins—aged
twenty-two, blue-eyed, slight; his face, beneath the short-cut tawny hair, the face of
a child; quick and nervous as a cat in his
movements—was not entertaining visions
of what would befall *Lumbering Annie* if
she failed to shake loose at the end of the
field—the crashing green of stripped trees,

the red bricks of the barracks, white faces
staring upward, and the final holocaust of
flame. His fears and doubts reached far
ahead to that moment which might come
upon him out over the blue wastes of water, when the success or failure of the mission and all that it meant to his crew
would depend upon him alone.

What if he should let them down? He
fought off the sickish feeling his thoughts
brought on and swallowed to get the dry-
ness out of his throat. This was for keeps.
The pilot and navigator would bring him
to the target. They could do no more. He
was the bombardier. It would be he who
must make the kill. Must make it . . . must
make it . . . must make it. . . . The words
throbbed to the engines beating slightly
out of synchronization.

Runway, fence, trees, barracks, and sand
waste fell away beneath them. They
crossed the white edge of the Atlantic as
they climbed into the sky. In ten minutes
the target area would begin. To ease his
nerves, Salvo Jenkins reached into his data
kit for his computer. Pilot Captain Strame
had given him his bombing instructions before the take-off. "We'll bomb at X feet
altitude and zero-zero-zed speed."

---

[1] *greenhouse,* glass-enclosed section of an airplane
where the bombardier sits

You bombed at low altitude and in a hurry on those sub hunts. You had just so many seconds to lay your eggs from the moment the tin shark was sighted until it vanished to safety beneath the sea. Salvo made his computations, ground speed, temperature, true altitude, checked and re-checked them, and set his Rube Goldberg, the Flanick hand sight used for low-level bombing. He loved the Flanick. It was like pointing and sighting a fine gun. If your computations were right, steady eye, steady hand, finger ready on the solenoid switch for firing, you couldn't miss. You dared not miss.

He knew that his figures were correct, but it gave him no feeling of ease or re-laxation. If and when the emergency came, he might have to discard them in an instant, and in the trembling space of ticking seconds recalculate entirely for dif-ferent height and speed. No one could in-struct or help him. A fractional error, and chance and prey would be gone. The men upstairs trusted him. If he failed, he could never face them. So this was what it meant to be a bombardier.

But fearful and anguished of nerves as he was, Salvo would not have traded places with any of those above in the ship. The thought of his name in the crew list, chalked up on the blackboard in the squad room, filled him with pride: "Bombardier: Sec. Lt. Horace Jenkins."

He had found excuses to go in there more often than was necessary, so that he could glance up at it. He would catch himself sneaking those glances and would say to himself, "Dawgone it, Jenkins; you're actin' just like a kid. Ain't you evah goin' tuh grow up?"

But the line kept bringing a glow to his heart. There it was, up with the finest crew on the field—Pilot Captain: John (Cappy) Strame; Navigator: Lt. Carl Jor-gens; Copilot: Lt. Ed Hammond; Engi-neer: Sgt. James Bradley; the radioman and the gunners. But how his own name stood out—"Bombardier: Sec. Lt. Horace Jenkins." Why, that was himself. That line was the end of a long-ago dream come true—or at least almost the end.

The altimeter needle settled at 1000 feet and stayed there. Automatically, Salvo checked the centigrade thermometer and inspected the green lights glowing on his bomb-indicator panel. Below him rolled the Atlantic, calm, capless and shimmering in the afternoon sunlight.

The earphones of the intercommunica-tion system crackled, and he heard, "Navi-gator from pilot: What is the course?"

When the navigator gave it, Salvo checked it with his own compass.

He heard the pilot's brief acknowledge-ment, "Roger."

"Roger." Salvo savored the word. It was the airman's response and meant "Received order." Jenkins used it whenever he could in his everyday talk. It was one of the things that set you apart, like the title "Bombardier" in front of your name. In-stead of saying "Okay," or "That's right," or "You're darn tootin'," you said "Roger." It was Air Forces.

They were ten minutes out and flying south over the water, paralleling the yel-low-and-green strip of shore in the star-board haze. The mission was yet young and there was a moment's kidding on the interphone.

"What'll you bet the lunch is ham sand-wiches again?"

"Copilot from navigator: You'd holler if it was caviar."

"Shut up! You'll wake the bombardier."

Something seemed to choke the throat of Salvo Jenkins. He was so proud to be kidded by them.

Yes, that was his gang up above. He belonged to them and they to him. He had become a member of the greatest team in the world. In school, at the outbreak of the war in Europe, he had dreamed of some day becoming a bombardier. But he had not imagined that it would be like this.

As a boy, back on his father's farm in the Great Smokies of North Carolina, he had yearned for the day when he would go to college and play on a team—when he would belong. But he had been far too slight for football at State University. He could run and play a little ball, but he had never made anything. He had been a wistful wanderer on the fringes of the great who belonged. He admired the football men who had their own talk and fellowship of play and strategy and bruises. Young Jenkins thought the finest thing in the world was the friendship between the star halfback, Swifty Morgan, Ted Jones, who ran interference for him, and Sparky Slade, the quarterback. They did everything together. It was all for one and one for all, and everything for the team.

The pilot called for a crew check-in over the intercommunication, and in his turn Salvo barked, "Bomber, Roger!" and listened to the others, "Navigator, Roger! . . . Copilot, Roger! . . . Radio, Roger! . . . Engineer, Roger!"

This was a real team. How they worked together. Each trusting in and dependent on the other. Only this was such a game as none of them had ever played before. And, at the thought, the old pang returned to the bombardier, and his nerves quivered again. He was the only member of the crew as yet untried. He was still Salvo Jenkins.

His mind turned back to that awful moment during a patrol flight over the California coast two months ago, when, in one sickening moment of error, confusion, and a momentarily jammed level, he had gone

to "Salvo" instead of "Selective," and had dumped two thousand, five hundred pounds of expensive demolition bombs into the Pacific Ocean. And he had picked the time to do it when the general was on board and at the controls of the ship. There had been a truly magnificent explosion, but outside of killing all the fish in the vicinity, it had accomplished nothing but to pin a nickname on him. From that moment on, he was known as "Salvo" Jenkins.

It had got around, this really Gargantuan [2] blunder. They knew of it in Texas the same night, in Louisiana, New Mexico, and the Atlantic seaboard the next day, and in Australia, India, and Java the following week; in the primary and advanced schools, the flying fields, the bombing grounds, and the fighting squadrons. News moved swiftly in the Air Forces. The radio would talk, a transfer would carry the story, or an outward-bound pilot of the Ferry Command, hot with the latest home news, would squat down in Africa, or South America, or the Near East, and say to the gang, "Did you hear about that kid Jenkins from the Eighteenth? Salvoed a ton on a turtle. Had the general riding with him."

The earphones came alive. "Target at ten o'clock. Eight miles."

The left wing dropped slightly and *Lumbering Annie* turned and then slid downhill a little. Salvo crouched and strained his eyes in the direction indicated. The sparkling water rushed beneath them. "Target" to the Army Air Forces Bomber Command was anything that floated above or beneath the waves. Only after it identified itself did it become a ship. They were still hours away from the area designated by Intelligence as possibly harboring a

[2] *Gargantuan,* huge; Gargantua is a giant king in French literature

U-boat, but Salvo's fingers were itching for his levers.

The intercommunication clicked, "Sub-chaser!"

"Roger!"

She looked like a greyhound, long, lean, slim of flank, blue-gray in color, and flecked with the white hats of her crew. A curving white wake boiled out behind her. The racing ship changed course and charged on as the lumbering bomber dipped her left wing and staggered around her in a wide circle. The hairs at the back of Salvo's neck bristled. The Navy was on the hunt too. Was she following a scent with her instruments? If so, there might be work for him to do. In a heap, he tried to remember everything he had been taught.

He saw the subchaser's blinker light flash, and read the code. Up above, Cappy Strame was talking to her with his blinker, too, probably querying whether they were following a trail of sinister submerged engines, distantly beating.

The firefly light from below winked, "n-o."

"Huh," said Salvo Jenkins to himself. "They probably wouldn't tell us if they had one treed," and then, in an onrush of loyalty, corrected himself with, "Jenkins, ain't you ever a-goin' tuh grow up? You know the Navy's been co-operatin' a hundred per cent. But I sure wish she was on a sub."

The black ball of the compass jogged around until they were on their course again, southward. "Just one sub," prayed Salvo Jenkins; "just a conning tower." How he'd like to lay an egg right alongside. In his mind he saw the upheaval of the depth charge, the crushed U-boat lurching to the bottom. His imagination took him further. Now he stood on the field, his head cocked a little to one side, and watched the technical sergeant in charge of the ground crew proudly painting a tiny submarine on the fuselage of *Lumbering Annie* near the tail. One for the team. Once for Cappy Strame, the best pilot and the greatest guy who ever lived. One for—the dream broke. What if Salvo Jenkins lost his head and missed?

Again the imagining of failure brought that cold horror to his stomach. So terribly much was at stake. He was just Salvo Jenkins, the kid who had gummed things up the day the general was aboard.

He thought back to the third day after his arrival at Humphrey Field, from the West, discouraged and miserable, and his summons to the office of the commanding officer. The C.O. was a great lanky stalk of a man, six foot six, with a craggy face, beak nose, and an abrupt manner that covered his absorbing passion for his command.

He said, "Lieutenant Jenkins, there is a vacancy for a bombardier in the crew of Captain Strame. I am assigning you to that crew."

"Yes, sir. Did you say 'Captain Strame'?" It was no wonder he had asked. Strame's was the crack bombing crew of the squadron. It had been together for more than a year. It was like the coach calling up a third-string substitute and saying, "O.K., son. You're on the varsity. Go in there and score."

The C.O. sucked at a pipe carved in the shape of a skull, and said, "Captain Strame asked for you, Lieutenant Jenkins. I don't mind telling you that I questioned his judgement. He could have had any man he wanted. I made that plain. I am going to repeat to you his exact words. He said, 'I'll take the kid, if you don't mind, sir. He's a bombardier. I know all about that Salvo stuff, but it doesn't cut any ice. He's got hunting blood. He signed up for bombardier from way back. He's no washed-out pilot or flop navigator. Ever since he's come into the Air Forces he's done nothing but eat, sleep, live, and dream bombing. He just wants to bomb. When we get over a target, that's the kind of kid I want at the sights.' "

The C.O. blew a wisp of smoke, studied Jenkins a moment, and then concluded, "That's all, lieutenant."

The big bomber droned along on its mission. The men in her watched their instruments and the surface of the sea. Thinking back over what the C.O. had said, Salvo Jenkins knew that he would never want to succeed for anyone as much as he wanted to succeed for John Strame, not even for Mary Lou Allen, who was pledged to him back at State University at Raleigh. And he loved Mary Lou with all his youth and yearning and imagination.

Strame was a pink-cheeked, black-haired, black-eyed boy from Alabama who was a born pilot the way Jenkins felt he was a born bombardier. He radiated love for his work, his ship, and his crew. He was as trim and fiery as a Derby race horse. His specialty was flying. The other specialties he left to the various members of his crew. But he expected and accepted nothing short of perfection.

It wasn't the job Jenkins worshiped, but the man, his spirit and his friendship. It seemed as if Strame was the first person who had ever understood him and had faith in him. Jenkins' fear of letting Strame down became a sweating nightmare that never wholly left him.

He remembered that not even Mary Lou had quite understood him when he explained his great ambition to her. They had sat one night in the rear booth of Mason's drugstore. She wore a muslin dress that was soft and inexplicably thrilling to touch. It smelled of a mixture of warm cloth and flowers. Her presence brought pangs of sweetness to his heart that were nearly unbearable. When he put his fingers beneath her chin and turned her head to him, she gave him her mouth without restraint. It was that night that he told her that he had passed his preliminary examinations and was going to try for a commission as a bombardier.

She looked at him with her wide, serious eyes, contemplating what he had told her. She was not a lion hunter, but, womanlike, she wanted her man to have the best. She said, "It sounds teh'bly exciting, honey." But it was not exciting the way she said it. Then she added, "Swifty and Ted and Sparky are going to be pilots. I mean—"

"Let 'em." Jenkins leaned forward on the table top wet with circles of their glasses, his face flushing, his young blue eyes shining with enthusiasm. "Anybody can fly a plane. But when they get where they're agoin' to, the bombardier pulls the trigger. That's me."

She had continued to stare at him strangely. He could not decide whether it was because she did not quite understand what a big job the bombardier had, or because she was surprised at him for wanting to be one. He hadn't meant to boast, but the ambition had burned so long inside him, unexpressed, that he had to talk about it.

"It's the most wonderful job in the war, Mary Lou. You've got to have a good bombardier. And it ain't as though anybody can do it. Why, if you know how, you can knock out a battleship from over twenty thousand feet in the air. It's the shooting part, Mary Lou. That's why I know I can do it better'n anybody else. I'm goin' to be the best bombardier they evah had. I'm goin' to sink a battleship."

Of course, he was only a kid of twenty then, or he wouldn't have talked like that.

He knew a lot more now. Well, if Mary Lou had not quite grasped the significance of his ambition, she had divined the enthusiasm and the yearning behind it. Her loyal attitude was that if he said so, it must be all right. She had taken his hand and said, "I know you will, honey, a big one."

What children they had been, and how different it all was, now that he was no longer a boy, but a second lieutenant and a bombardier. It was one thing sitting with your girl in a booth and telling her what a big shot you were going to be, and another to be squatting in the nose of a flying ice wagon, out over the Atlantic Ocean, desperately afraid of making a botch of dropping a bomb on an enemy submarine, if you ever saw one.

The heavy ship hit a bump in the air and jarred Jenkins back to reality. Somebody clicked a microphone and said, "Oh-oh!" which wasn't regulations, but got over the idea. Ahead and slightly to the east, a pillar of black smoke boiled up into the sky, a furious, volcanic, writhing thing, as though the ocean were erupting at that point.

Talk crackled on the intercommunication. "Tanker! Got it last night!"

"Roger!"

"Engineer from pilot: Get a picture of her."

"Engineer, Roger!"

They came down to within fifty feet of the surface of the water to let Bradley, the engineer, who doubled as photographer, get a shot. Only the stern of the tanker was visible. The rest was smoke threaded with orange flames. She was already down by the bow and the water around her was burning too. Salvo Jenkins stared hard. It was the first torpedoed ship he had ever seen. Somewhere beneath the surface of the sea, miles away by now, crept the enemy that had done this. And he, Horace Jenkins, was hunting him now, to wipe him out if he could. Somehow it was like being back on the farm when a wildcat would come down from the mountains and

get into the chickens. Then you would go out with dog and gun and track him down and kill him.

He remembered suddenly what his father had told him when he taught him to shoot.

"Yuh got to be able to hit what you aimin' at, son," his father had said, "or it ain't no use goin' out with a gun. The dogs kin git you tuh where the cat's at, an' yore legs cain carry yuh there, but it don't do yuh no good if yuh miss."

Here in this strange element, the air, out over the endless wastes of water, the same held true. Pilot, navigator, and radioman would find the quarry if it was humanly possible, and would carry him to it. But once there, they were helpless. Their work was done. He must aim the deadly charge and send it straight to the target.

He remembered the day he had decided to be a bombardier. It was when a British bomber pilot had come to State University to lecture. There had been questions permitted after the talk, and everybody stared when young Jenkins asked, "Who pushes the button that lets the bomb go, sir? I mean is there anyone special who has to—"

"Rather! That's the bombardier. He's the top card in the deck. I fancy we've got the keenest chap in the whole push in our crew. We caught a Nazi supply ship off the coast of Norway once, a big one. He put one right down her funnel from ten thousand. That's bombing, you know. He got a medal for it, and dashed well deserved it. We called him Dead-Eye Dick."

Jenkins' heart beat faster. Dead-Eye Dick! Right down the funnel from ten thousand! Top card in the deck! "That's for me," said young Horace Jenkins under his breath, and from that moment on had hardly thought of anything else.

And all the time these thoughts were racing through his head he was crouching on his knees in the glass nose, straining his eyes onto the glittering surface of the sea to catch the first glimpse of a rising periscope, fingering his instruments, rechecking his calculations, mentally making his selection of depth charges from the indicator panel, working, studying, fretting, worrying, thinking of Strame and his crew mates and the wonderful team of which they were all a part, and how terribly he wanted to make good for them, to make them as proud of him as he was of them.

They passed over a convoy escorted by a busy destroyer. Abeam of the lighthouse, the navigator set a new course and they wheeled left and headed out to sea, away from the sheltering land.

They saw nothing for a hundred miles but a broad oil slick from sunken tankers, and then they came upon a stubby freighter, all gray under war paint, terribly lonely and nervous, pushing her way eastward. She changed her course as they circled her, and then changed it twice more, rapidly.

Salvo recognized the symptoms of her jitters. Those lone freighters got to thinking, whenever they saw a bomber hovering about them, that there must be a submarine in the vicinity, and immediately began cutting semi-panicky patterns to avoid possible torpedoes.

He felt a sudden pity for the solitary vessel. He wanted to call down to her, "It's all right. Don't you worry. We're here." The big bomber spread her wings protectively over the hysterical ship. Salvo's heart went out to her; she seemed so helpless. That was why they were flying around out there, to watch over wanderers like her, to blast to the bottom of the sea the steel sharks that lay in wait.

Then the ship was gone from beneath them as *Lumbering Annie* clattered on, sniffing the sea lanes. Salvo understood better now the whys and wherefores of the long training grind that aimed only at perfection. Ground school, long sieges of physics, mathematics, navigation, meteorology, sighting and theory of bombing, the arithmetic of falling bodies, followed by the long weeks of practice with hundreds upon hundreds of missiles dropped from every altitude. He thought of all the mil errors made, never to be recovered, of the fractions miscalculated in the mind, the hundredth part of an infinitesimal error that magnified itself to a hundred yards off the target below and failure. Inevitably his mind returned once more to the culmination of his frailty—the day he had salvoed and wasted his whole load.

Again close to panic at the awesome picture of responsibility that had opened itself out, he reviewed his time from student to bombardier, and wished desperately that he had applied himself even more to his studies.

Legs appeared at the hatchway and descended the short iron ladder, bringing after them Hammond, the copilot. He carried a cup of grapefruit juice and a sandwich wrapped in wax paper.

"It's ham again," he said. "I thought we'd plowed all those pigs under years ago." He made himself comfortable in the narrow bay crammed with instruments, levers, tubing, cable leads, pet cocks, wiring, and aluminum. "Nice place you have here, provided you've got a can opener to get out of it with," he commented. "Best view in the house."

Salvo munched on his sandwich. The fruit juice felt good in his dry throat. He was glad to have company for a moment.

The copilot retailed the gossip from above. "Carl's going to have a fine shiner in the morning. He was taking drift[3]

[3] *taking drift,* determining how much an aircraft has been blown off course

when we hit that bump a way back. Good old navigator's driftmeter eye. Cappy's fidgety. He thinks he smells a sub. Say, I wish I had your job. Why didn't I think of putting in for bombardier? Ride around like an air-line passenger all day and when a target pops up, push a button and bloo-o-o-ey! Pretty soft."

Salvo said, "Oh, it is, is it?" Of course Hammond was kidding, but through his mind there flashed all the other myriad duties of a bombardier besides hitting his target—the loading of bombs, repair and cleaning of guns, repair of his equipment in the air, knowledge of Morse code, blinker code, flag code, flare code, hydraulic, fuel and fire-extinguisher systems of the ship, as well as a working knowledge of how to fly and land her in emergency.

As he looked at Hammond, Salvo had an instant's temptation to unburden himself of all the doubts and fears and worries that had assailed him since the take-off, to rid his mind somehow of the nightmare of failure that haunted him. But he held it back. That was kid stuff, shooting off your mouth. The Air Forces didn't care about what you thought or how you felt. There was only one thing you could do for it— deliver.

"Guess I'll be getting back upstairs to the club," said the copilot. "The carburetors want to ice up. In June. So long, kid. If we flush something, don't miss."

Don't miss! Don't miss! That awful refrain. Earlier in the flight, Salvo had prayed for a target, had asked to be allowed to see just one sub. Now his jangled nerves cried for a reprieve. If they would only complete this mission without sighting a target, it would give him another chance— for more study, more practice. Just two hours, just an hour more on the training tower. The next time he would be ready.

He looked at his watch. Four hours under way. They would be turning back soon. He heard Cappy Strame on the interphone, "Navigator from pilot: Turning back. What is the new course?"

"New course, two-nine-zero, turn now."

"Roger!" Then, informally, "We'll have another look at that freighter on the way in."

"Roger!"

Salvo saw the big starboard wing dip. The sun, already low on the horizon, floated in an arc around them as they made their turn. The wind had freshened and occasional whitecaps frothed on the sea below.

He was glad, in a way, that they were going to pay another visit to the lonely freighter pushing its way eastward. It might make it cut those frantic circles again, but it would be a comfort to it, too, when those friendly wings flew overhead, watching over it.

An hour passed, and another. Salvo's eyes ached from straining to the sea. The white patches of froth made observation more difficult. His duty was never to take his eyes from the sea below.

The impersonal, colorless, metallic voice of the interphone said, "Ship at one o'clock. Ten miles."

Salvo crouched low in his bay to see ahead out from under the glass nose. She was ahead and a little to starboard, a tiny speck on the darkening sea, growing larger as the thundering motors ate up the misty miles. She looked lonelier than ever. One tiny ship, an endless waste of water and sky, a tiring sun swelling and yellow as it neared the horizon and—

"Bomber from pilot: Open bomb-bay doors!"

"Roger!"

"Submarine three o'clock five miles."

With what seemed like a single lightning movement, Salvo hit the three steel levers to his left, one after the other, but faster than the eye could follow. "Doors open!" "Selective!" "Depth charges armed!"

"Pilot from bomber: Bomb-bay doors open! Hey! We've got something!"

He did not even know he had yelled the last into the interphone. The surface of the sea was rising up to meet him with incredible speed as the big bomber descended, her air-speed indicator leaping forward.

There she lurked, the sub's black form, barely at surface. Already she was tilting forward for the crash dive. A matter of seconds and she would be gone. Salvo Jenkins was as cold as a glacier. His fingers had already pressed the selector switch —depth charges "Two" and "Five" one from each side, two in reserve. He crouched like a cat waiting to spring, his nostrils spread, eyes staring, his rear end waggling catlike as he got himself set.

There were only seconds, but his mind was so clear and keyed and ready that he seemed to know everything that was needed to be known at the same instant, as though there were different compartments in his head, and all of them were functioning independently. He knew altitude, air speed, ground speed, temperature, and time. And he knew at once—had known it from the first instant he had sighted the diving sub and while his fingers were pressing the selector switch— that they would not be able to bomb at the predetermined level. By the time they got there the target would be gone.

He had eyes in the back of his head, in his knees and elbows and in the seat of his pants. Inside his brain a computer worked like a machine. In the time that the swooping ship dropped fifty feet he knew at what level Strame would make the run, and recalculated. The figures popped up and leaped into place as though he were seeing them on a gigantic screen.

"Bombardier from pilot: On course! Level!"

No time for a verbal answer. Salvo double-clicked his mike. His right hand held the hand sight, swung from its steel shaft, the ring and bead centered on the vanishing conning tower. The fingers of his left hand quivered over the firing switch, hovering, barely touching, moving slightly to keep the barest contact.

Half the conning tower and periscope was still visible, tilting forward. . . . Breath held. . . . Steady aim! Like shooting a gun at a treed wildcat.

The bead lifted inexorably from the sea to the black steel poised there, held—

Just a tightening of the fingers on the solenoid firing switch.

"Bomb away! Okay to turn!"

Two legless gray pigs appeared beneath the glass nose of the ship and drifted downward lazily, shrinking in size like deflating toy balloons. They kept forward pace with the hurtling ship as it raced across the line straight to the sub. The wing had already dipped for turning.

At the precise moment that the bombs met water, the nose of the ship passed over the target and Salvo's vision was cut off.

"Engineer from pilot: Prepare to take picture left side!"

"Engineer: Roger!"

Then the intercommunication seemed to go haywire for an instant as somebody up above yelled "Yahooo!" into it.

Salvo had already selected two more depth charges.

He was a split second ahead of Strame with a new set of calculations when the order came, "Bombardier from pilot: Stand by for second run! We've got him!"

"Bomber: Roger!"

Lumbering Annie swung heavily into a

diving turn. The freighter hove into sight again, veering frantically away, black smoke belching from her single funnel. Then into Salvo's view came an expanse of tumbled white froth, as though there had been a sub-sea eruption. In the center of it bubbled a thick yellowish slick from which something black was upthrust. It was the bow of the stricken submarine, poised there for an instant.

Salvo felt no elation. He was too busy. Computations checked, bombs armed, fingers gentling the firing switch, bead drifting onto target, steady—

"Bomb away!"

"Pilot from engineer: Picture taken okay! Oh, baby!"

Salvo Jenkins tried to remember what had happened, what he had done, what his calculations had been, whether he had left anything out. He couldn't. He remembered nothing. *Lumbering Annie* circled and circled. The yellow oil patch grew in size and length, bits and pieces of unidentifiable things appeared in the center. The freighter was stuttering hysterical cheers with her blinker.

Someone came down through the hatch from above and began to beat Salvo on the back, yelling, "Wow! Wow! Wow! Wow!" in tune with the thrumming motors.

Salvo Jenkins went back to the orderly room of the squadron to pick up his data kit, which he had left there in the excitement. He felt very tired and a little queer in his insides.

Voices came drifting through from the partitioned office of the C.O. The door was shut, but he recognized the speech of Ed Hammond, the copilot, "Say, Cappy. We've got a bombardier, haven't we?"

The hard, crackling voice of the C.O. broke in. "He's your man, John. I was wrong. And glad of it."

Salvo Jenkins wanted to get his brief case and get out of there. But his hands were trembling so, he fumbled it.

Captain Strame said, "That kid's a honey. Say, Ed, that Salvo stuff is gonna be out. From now on we're calling him Bull's-Eye."

Bull's-Eye Jenkins got his brief case, but found suddenly that he could not see his way clearly to the door until he stopped and brushed the tears away from his eyes.

"Dawgone it, Jenkins," he said to himself. "There you go, actin' just like a kid again. Ain't you evah goin' tuh grow up?"

The man who wrote this story

PAUL GALLICO 1897–

Paul Gallico was born and educated in New York City. After he finished college at Columbia University, he went to work as a newspaperman. Soon he was writing a sports column for the New York *Daily News*. He wrote about every kind of sport, from archery to wrestling. He not only knew his sports but loved them as well. Once he let himself be knocked out by Jack Dempsey. Another time, after only a short skiing course in a department store, he almost killed himself on an expert's trail.

Shortly before the Second World War, Mr. Gallico gave up sports reporting to be a free-lance writer. He wrote movie scripts, books, and many short stories for popular magazines like the *Saturday Evening Post*. During the war he served as a war correspondent for *Cosmopolitan Magazine*. "Bombardier" shows how carefully and sympathetically he observed men and machines in battle.

Let's consider . . .

1. Salvo loved being part of a team. Explain why good teamwork was so important to the members of the crew. Why is working as part of a team often more satisfying than working alone?

2. Salvo was given his nickname after he had made an enormous blunder. Describe the blunder.

3. After his blunder, Salvo still loved his job but was haunted by the fear of failure. How did his anxiety help him become a better bombardier? On the other hand, how might a lack of confidence have kept him from doing the best possible job?

4. Even though the bombing missions were dangerous, the members of the crew enjoyed kidding one another:

"What'll you bet the lunch is ham sandwiches again?"

"You'd holler if it was caviar."

"Shut up! You'll wake the bombardier."

Why do you think they joked in this manner?

5. The crew knew of Salvo's blunder,

yet they included him in their jokes and treated him as an equal. How did their acceptance make Salvo feel?

6. As Salvo made the bombing mission, he recalled telling Mary Lou what it meant to be a bombardier. In what ways was his actual experience different from what he had thought it would be?

7. Why did Strame ask for Salvo as his bombardier? Why was the choice a good one?

8. Strame expected perfection from his crew. Explain why anything short of perfection could lead to disaster.

9. At the end of the story, Salvo said to himself, "Dawgone it, Jenkins, there you go, actin' just like a kid again. Ain't you evah goin' tuh grow up?" Why did he make this remark? In what ways had he "grown up" during the story?

The writer's craft . . .

You recall that writers of short stories often use the opening sentences to arouse your interest. Look again at the first paragraph of "Bombardier." Paul Gallico not only stimulated your interest with this opening; he did several other things as well.

1. He introduced you to the leading character.

2. He told you the feelings of the leading character.

3. He gave you the setting of the story.

4. He began the action.

5. He aroused your interest.

Number your paper from one to five. After each number, give the information that shows he did each of the things listed above. For example, after number one you would write, "The leading character is Salvo Jenkins, a young bombardier."

Knowing words . . .

In "Bombardier" you found many words which pertained to flying. Since you live in an air age, it's a good idea to know some of the words used in aviation. Below there are several sentences from the story. In each sentence one or two words are italicized. When you are sure of the meaning of each italicized word, use it in a sentence of your own.

1. The *altimeter* needle settled at 1000 feet and stayed there.

2. *Abeam* of the lighthouse, the *navigator* set a new course and they wheeled left and headed out to sea.

3. In the time that the swooping ship dropped fifty feet he knew at what level Strame would make the run, and *recalculated*.

The Road Not Taken

ROBERT FROST

Two roads diverged in a yellow wood,
And sorry I could not travel both
And be one traveler, long I stood
And looked down one as far as I could
To where it bent in the undergrowth;

Then took the other, as just as fair,
And having perhaps the better claim,
Because it was grassy and wanted wear;
Though as for that the passing there
Had worn them really about the same,

And both that morning equally lay
In leaves no step had trodden black.
Oh, I kept the first for another day!
Yet knowing how way leads on to way,
I doubted if I should ever come back.

I shall be telling this with a sigh
Somewhere ages and ages hence:
Two roads diverged in a wood, and I—
I took the one less traveled by,
And that has made all the difference.

The man who wrote this poem

ROBERT FROST   1875–

Robert Frost was born in San Francisco but has lived in New England since he was ten. After his father died, his mother took the children back to that part of the country where the Frost family had lived for nine generations. Robert Frost attended school in Massachusetts and proved a good student. He went to college for a while, but left to work as a mill hand, to tramp through the South, to teach, and to work on a newspaper. When he was older and more experienced, he returned to study at Harvard for two years.

When Frost's aunt died and left him a farm, he became a farmer. He would go into the fields and stand and think instead of pulling weeds. Although his thoughts became poems, the farm was not profitable. Therefore he also taught. Suddenly, courageously, he moved with his whole family to England. Poetry had been his special talent since his teens. Now, at thirty-six, he would give his talent a chance. A chance was all it needed. When Frost returned to America in 1915, he was famous.

Again he took up farming. The open, brave life of the country was as much a part of him as his interest in poetry. He returned to the universities as a teacher and poet. He was known to students as a man with a farmer's face and hands, and with a heart and mind as delicate as the first ice on a New England pond. He has many honors and prizes now, but he continues to live simply on his farm, still teaching, still writing.

The poet's art . . .

1. Robert Frost told you about a decision he once made. Why did he choose one path instead of the other?

2. On what basis do you make decisions? How do your reasons for making decisions differ from Robert Frost's?

3. If people could live their lives over again, do you think they would make the same decisions a second time? Give your reasons.

4. Poems usually suggest more than they actually say. In "The Road Not Taken" Frost was actually describing his choice between two roads in the woods. Yet the poem may suggest much more to you. It may suggest choices you will have to make between different vocations or political beliefs, or between remaining at home or seeking new surroundings. List all the different things the paths could stand for. After you have made your list, read the poem again. Decide which of the possible meanings on your list is closest to what the poem suggests to you.

Modern Ode to the Modern School

JOHN ERSKINE

Just after the Board had brought the schools up to date
To prepare you for your Life Work
Without teaching you one superfluous thing,
Jim Reilly presented himself to be educated.
He wanted to be a bricklayer.
They taught him to be a perfect bricklayer.
And nothing more.

He knew so much about bricklaying
That the contractor made him a foreman.
But he knew nothing about being a foreman.
He spoke to the School Board about it,
And they put in a night course
On how to be a foreman
And nothing more.

He became so excellent a foreman
That the contractor made him a partner.
But he knew nothing about figuring costs
Nor about bookkeeping
Nor about real estate,
And he was too proud to go back to night school.
So he hired a tutor
Who taught him these things
And nothing more.

Prospering at last
And meeting other men as prosperous,
Whenever the conversation started, he'd say to himself
"Just wait till it comes my way—
Then I'll show them!"
But they never mentioned bricklaying
Nor the art of being a foreman
Nor the whole duty of contractors,
Nor even real estate.
So Jim never said anything.

The man who wrote this poem

JOHN ERSKINE 1879–1951

John Erskine was born in New York City and received his education at the various schools of Columbia University. Except for a few years of teaching at Amherst and a year in France during the First World War, Erskine spent his adult life as a professor of English at Columbia.

During the day he lectured on novelists and poets, speaking of the authors as though they were his next door neighbors. The students loved his easy manner and wide knowledge; they jammed his classes.

Erskine's writing had to be done in his spare time, whenever he was not reading. His verses were written late at night or in the grey hours before breakfast.

The poet's art . . .

1. Jim Reilly knew everything about his trade. But what else did he need to know?

2. Explain whether or not you think Jim was a successful man. Use lines from the poem to support your answer.

3. Many of the school subjects you are now taking are not directly related to your future work, and yet these subjects do have value. What are these subjects? What value do they have for you *now*? How will they serve you in the *future*?

4. What kind of schooling did John Erskine favor? How much vocational training should boys and girls get in high school?

5. The author of this poem spoke of the disadvantages of vocational training. What are some of its advantages?

Boy Gets Job

BENJAMIN FRANKLIN

Finding the right career is seldom an easy task. As a young boy Benjamin Franklin wanted to become a sailor. When he grew older he wished to work in a printer's shop. Unfortunately, in 1720 only two newspapers were published in America, and printer's jobs were hard to find. Let Benjamin Franklin tell you how he solved the problem.

My elder brothers were all put apprentices to different trades. I was put to the grammar-school at eight years of age, my father intending to devote me, as the tithe [1] of his sons, to the service of the Church. My early readiness in learning to read (which must have been very early, as I do not remember when I could not read), and the opinion of all his friends, that I should certainly make a good scholar, encouraged him in this purpose of his. My uncle Benjamin, too, approved of it, and proposed to give me all his shorthand volumes of sermons, I suppose as a stock to set up with, if I would learn his character. I continued, however, at the grammar-school not quite one year, though in that time I had risen gradually from the middle of the class of that year to be the head of it, and farther was removed into the next class above it, in order to go with that into the third at the end of the year. But my father, in the meantime, from a view of the expense of a college education, which having so large a family he could ill afford, and the mean

living many so educated were afterwards able to obtain—reasons that he gave to his friends in my hearing—altered his first intention, took me from the grammar-school, and sent me to a school for writing and arithmetic, kept by a then famous man, Mr. George Brownell, very successful in his profession generally, and that by mild, encouraging methods. Under him I acquired fair writing pretty soon, but I failed in the arithmetic, and made no progress in it. At ten years old I was taken home to assist my father in his business, which was that of a tallow-chandler and sope-boiler; [2] a business he was not bred to, but had assumed on his arrival in New England, and on finding his dyeing trade would not maintain his family, being in little request. Accordingly, I was employed in cutting wick for the candles, filling the dipping mold and the molds for cast candles, attending the shop, going of errands, etc.

I disliked the trade, and had a strong inclination for the sea, but my father de-

[1] *tithe,* voluntary share

[2] *tallow-chandler and sope-boiler,* candle and soap maker

227

clared against it. . . . I continued thus employed in my father's business for two years, that is, till I was twelve years old; and my brother John, who was bred to that business, having left my father, married, and set himself at Rhode Island, there was all appearance that I was destined to supply his place, and become a tallow-chandler. But my dislike to the trade continuing, my father was under apprehensions that if he did not find one for me more agreeable, I should break away and get to sea, as his son Josiah had done, to his great vexation. He therefore sometimes took me to walk with him, and see joiners, bricklayers, turners, braziers, etc., at their work, that he might observe my inclination, and endeavor to fix it on some trade or other on land. It has ever since been a pleasure to me to see good workmen handle their tools; and it has been useful to me, having learnt so much by it as to be able to do little jobs myself in my house when a workman could not readily be got, and to construct little machines for my experiments, while the intention of making the experiment was fresh and warm in my mind. My father at last fixed upon the cutler's trade,[3] and my uncle Benjamin's son Samuel, who was bred to that business in London, being about that time established in Boston, I was sent to be with him some time on liking. But his expectations of a fee with me displeasing my father, I was taken home again.

From a child I was fond of reading, and all the little money that came into my hands was ever laid out in books. . . .

This bookish inclination at length determined my father to make me a printer, though he had already one son (James) of that profession. In 1717 my brother James returned from England with a press and letters to set up his business in Boston. I liked it much better than that of my father,

but still had a hankering for the sea. To prevent the apprehended effect [4] of such an inclination, my father was impatient to have me bound to my brother. I stood out some time, but at last was persuaded, and signed the indentures when I was yet but twelve years old. I was to serve as an apprentice till I was twenty-one years of age, only I was to be allowed journeyman's wages [5] during the last year. In a little time I made great proficiency in the business, and became a useful hand to my brother. . . .

My brother had, in 1720 or 1721, begun to print a newspaper. It was the second that appeared in America, and was called the *New England Courant*. The only one before it was the *Boston News-Letter*. I remember his being persuaded by some of his friends from the undertaking, as not likely to succeed, one newspaper being, in their judgment, enough for America. At this time (1771) there are not less than five-and-twenty. He went on, however, with the undertaking, and after having worked in composing the types and printing off the sheets, I was employed to carry the papers thro' the streets to the customers.

He had some ingenious men among his friends, who amus'd themselves by writing little pieces for this paper, which gain'd it credit and made it more in demand, and these gentlemen often visited us. Hearing their conversations, and their accounts of the approbation [6] their papers were received with, I was excited to try my hand among them; but, being still a boy, and suspecting that my brother would object to printing anything of mine in his paper if he knew it to be mine, I contrived to disguise my hand, and, writing an anonymous paper, I put it in at night under the door of the printing-

---

[3] *cutler's trade,* making and repairing knives
[4] *apprehended effect,* feared result
[5] *journeyman's wages,* experienced man's wages
[6] *approbation,* praise

house. It was found in the morning, and communicated to his writing friends when they call'd in as usual. They read it, commented on it in my hearing, and I had the exquisite pleasure of finding it met with their approbation, and that, in their different guesses of the author, none were named but men of some character among us for learning and ingenuity. I suppose now that I was rather lucky in my judges, and that perhaps they were not really so very good ones as I then esteem'd them.

Encourag'd, however, by this, I wrote and convey'd in the same way to the press several more papers which were equally approv'd; and I kept my secret till my small fund of sense for such performances was pretty well exhausted, and then I discovered it, when I began to be considered a little more by my brother's acquaintance, and in a manner that did not quite please him, as he thought, probably with reason, that it tended to make me too vain. And, perhaps, this might be one occasion of the differences that we began to have about this time. Though a brother, he considered himself as my master, and me as his apprentice, and accordingly, expected the same services from me as he would from another, while I thought he demean'd [7] me too much in some he requir'd of me, who from a brother expected more indulgence. Our disputes were often brought before our father, and I fancy I was either generally in the right, or else a better pleader, because the judgment was generally in my favor. But my brother was passionate, and had often beaten me, which I took extreamly amiss; and, thinking my apprenticeship very tedious, I was continually wishing for some opportunity of shortening it. . . .

I then thought of going to New York, as the nearest place where there was a printer; and I was rather inclin'd to leave Boston

[7] demean'd, debased, lowered

when I reflected that I had already made myself a little obnoxious to the governing party, and, . . . it was likely I might, if I stay'd, soon bring myself into scrapes; and farther, that my indiscreet disputations about religion began to make me pointed at with horror by good people as an infidel or atheist. I determin'd on the point, but my father now siding with my brother, I was sensible that, if I attempted to go openly, means would be used to prevent me. My friend Collins, therefore, undertook to manage a little for me. He agreed with the captain of a New York sloop for my passage. . . . So I sold some of my books to raise a little money, was taken on board privately, and as we had a fair wind, in three days I found myself in New York, near 300 miles from home, a boy of but 17, without the least recommendation to, or knowledge of any person in the place, and with very little money in my pocket.

My inclinations for the sea were by this time worne out, or I might now have gratify'd them. But, having a trade, and supposing myself a pretty good workman, I offer'd my service to the printer in the place, old Mr. William Bradford, who had been the first printer in Pennsylvania, but removed from thence upon the quarrel of George Keith. He could give me no employment, having little to do, and help enough already; but says he, "My son at Philadelphia has lately lost his principal hand, Aquila Rose, by deathe; if you go thither, I believe he may employ you." Philadelphia was a hundred miles further; I set out, however, in a boat for Amboy, leaving my chest and things to follow me round by sea.

In crossing the bay, we met with a squall that tore our rotten sails to pieces, prevented our getting into the Kill, and drove us upon Long Island. In our way, a drunk-

en Dutchman, who was a passenger too, fell overboard; when he was sinking, I reached through the water to his shock pate, and drew him up, so that we got him in again. His ducking sobered him a little, and he went to sleep. . . .

When we drew near the island, we found it was a place where there could be no landing, there being a great surff on the stony beach. So we dropt anchor, and swung round towards the shore. Some people came down to the water edge and hallow'd [8] to us, as we did to them; but the wind was so high, and the surff so loud, that we could not hear so as to understand each other. There were canoes on the shore, and we made signs, and hallow'd that they should fetch us; but they either did not understand us, or thought it impracticable, so they went away, and night coming on, we had no remedy but to wait till the wind should abate; and, in the meantime, the boatman and I concluded to sleep, if we could; and so crowded into the scuttle, with the Dutchman, who was still

[8] *hallow'd*, shouted

wet, and the spray beating over the head of our boat, leak'd thro' to us, so that we were soon almost as wet as he. In this manner we lay all night, with very little rest; but, the wind abating the next day, we made a shift to reach Amboy before night, having been thirty hours on the water, without victuals, or any drink but a bottle of filthy rum, and the water we sail'd on being salt.

In the evening I found myself very feverish, and went into bed; but, having read somewhere that cold water drank plentifully was good for a fever, I follow'd the prescription, sweat plentiful most of the night, my fever left me, and in the morning, crossing the ferry, I proceeded on my journey on foot, having fifty miles to Burlington, where I was told I should find boats that would carry me the rest of the way to Philadelphia.

It rained very hard all the day; I was thoroughly soak'd, and by noon a good deal tired; so I stopt at a poor inn, where I staid all night, beginning now to wish that I had never left home. I cut so miserable a figure, too, that I found, by the questions ask'd me,

I was suspected to be some runaway servant, and in danger of being taken up on that suspicion. However, I proceeded the next day, and got in the evening to an inn, within eight or ten miles of Burlington, kept by one Dr. Brown. He entered into conversation with me while I took some refreshment, and, finding I had read a little, became very sociable and friendly. Our acquaintance continu'd as long as he liv'd. He had been, I imagine, an itinerant doctor, for there was no town in England, or country in Europe, of which he could not give a very particular account. He had some letters, and was ingenious, but much of an unbeliever, and wickedly undertook, some years after, to travestie the Bible in doggrel verse, as Cotton had done Virgil. By this means he set many of the facts in a very ridiculous light, and might have hurt weak minds if his work had been published; but it never was.

At his house I lay that night, and the next morning reach'd Burlington, but had the mortification to find that the regular boats were gone a little before my coming, and no other expected to go before Tuesday, this being Saturday; wherefore I returned to an old woman in the town, of whom I had bought gingerbread to eat on the water, and ask'd her advice. She invited me to lodge at her house till a passage by water should offer; and being tired with foot travelling, I accepted the invitation. She understanding I was a printer, would have had me stay at that town and follow my business, being ignorant of the stock necessary to begin with. She was very hospitable, gave me a dinner of ox-cheek with great good will, accepting only of a pot of ale in return; and I thought myself fixed till Tuesday should come. However, walking in the evening by the side of the river, a boat came by, which I found was going towards Philadelphia, with several people

in her. They took me in, and, as there was no wind, we row'd all the way; and about midnight, not having yet seen the city, some of the company were confident we must have passed it, and would row no farther; the others knew not where we were; so we put toward the shore, got into a creek, landed near an old fence, with the rails of which we made a fire, the night being cold, in October, and there we remained till daylight. Then one of the company knew the place to be Cooper's Creek, a little above Philadelphia, which we saw as soon as we got out of the creek, and arriv'd there about eight or nine o'clock on the Sunday morning, and landed at the Market-street wharf.

I have been the more particular in this description of my journey, and shall be so of my first entry into that city, that you may in your mind compare such unlikely beginnings with the figure I have since made there. I was in my working dress, my best clothes being to come round by sea. I was dirty from my journey; my pockets were stuff'd out with shirts and stockings, and I knew no soul nor where to look for lodging. I was fatigued with travelling, rowing, and want of rest, I was very hungry; and my whole stock of cash consisted of a Dutch dollar, and about a shilling in copper. The latter I gave the people of the boat for my passage, who at first refus'd it, on account of my rowing; but I insisted on their taking it. A man being sometimes more generous when he has but a little money than when he has plenty, perhaps thro' fear of being thought to have but little.

Then I walked up the street, gazing about till near the market-house I met a boy with bread. I had made many a meal on bread, and, inquiring where he got it, I went immediately to the baker's he directed me to, in Second-street, and ask'd for bisket, intending such as we had in Boston; but they, it seems, were not made in Philadelphia. Then I asked for a three-penny loaf, and was told they had none such. So not considering or knowing the difference of money and the greater cheapness nor the names of his bread, I bad him give me three-penny worth of any sort. He gave me, accordingly, three great puffy rolls. I was surpriz'd at the quantity, but took it, and, having no room in my pockets, walk'd off with a roll under each arm, and eating the other. Thus I went up Market-street as far as Fourth-street, passing by the door of Mr. Read, my future wife's father; when she, standing at the door, saw me, and thought I made, as I certainly did, a most awkward, ridiculous appearance. Then I turned and went down Chestnut-street and part of Walnut-street, eating my roll all the way, and, coming round, found myself again at Market-street wharf, near the boat I came in, to which I went for a draught of the river water; and, being filled with one of my rolls, gave the other two to a woman and her child that came down the river in the boat with us, and were waiting to go farther.

Thus refreshed, I walked again up the street, which by this time had many clean-dressed people in it, who were all walking the same way. I joined them, and thereby was led into the great meeting-house of the Quakers near the market. I sat down among them, and, after looking round awhile and hearing nothing said, being very drowsy thro' labor and want of rest the preceding night, I fell fast asleep, and continued so till the meeting broke up, when one was kind enough to rouse me. This was, therefore, the first house I was in, or slept in, in Philadelphia.

Walking down again toward the river, and, looking in the faces of people, I met a young Quaker man, whose countenance I

lik'd, and, accosting him, requested he would tell me where a stranger could get lodging. We were then near the sign of the Three Mariners. "Here," says he, "is one place that entertains strangers, but it is not a reputable house; if thee wilt walk with me, I'll show thee a better." He brought me to the Crooked Billet in Water-street. Here I got a dinner; and, while I was eating it, several sly questions were asked me, as it seemed to be suspected from my youth and appearance, that I might be some runaway.

After dinner, my sleepiness return'd, and being shown to a bed, I lay down without undressing, and slept till six in the evening, was call'd to supper, went to bed again very early, and slept soundly till next morning. Then I made myself as tidy as I could, and went to Andrew Bradford the printer's. I found in the shop the old man his father, whom I had seen at New York, and who, travelling on horseback, had got to Philadelphia before me. He introduc'd me to his son, who receiv'd me civilly, gave me a breakfast, but told me he did not at present want a hand, being lately suppli'd with one; but there was another printer in town, lately set up, one Keimer, who, perhaps, might employ me; if not, I should be welcome to lodge at his house, and he would give me a little work to do now and then till fuller business should offer.

The old gentleman said he would go with me to the new printer, and when we found him, "Neighbor," says Bradford, "I have brought to see you a young man of your business; perhaps you may want such a one." He ask'd me a few questions, put a composing stick in my hand to see how I work'd, and then said he would employ me soon, though he had just then nothing for me to do; and, taking old Bradford, whom he had never seen before, to be of the town's people that had a good will for him, enter'd into a conversation on his present undertaking and prospects; while Bradford, not discovering that he was the other printer's father, on Keimer's saying he expected soon to get the greatest part of the business into his own hand, drew him on by artful questions, and starting little doubts, to explain all his views, what interest he reli'd on, and in what manner he intended to proceed. I, who stood by and heard all, saw immediately that one of them was a crafty old sophister, and the other a mere novice. Bradford left me with Keimer, who was greatly surprised when I told him who the old man was.

Keimer's printing-house, I found, consisted of an old shatter'd press, and one small, worn-out font of English, which he was then using himself, composing an Elegy on Aquila Rose, before mentioned, an ingenious young man, of excellent character, much respected in the town, clerk of the Assembly, and a pretty poet. Keimer made verses too, but very indifferently. He could not be said to write them, for his manner was to compose them in the types directly out of his head. So there being no copy, but one pair of cases, and the Elegy likely to require all the letter, no one could help him. I endeavor'd to put his press (which he had not yet us'd, and of which he understood nothing) into order fit to be work'd with; and, promising to come and print off his Elegy as soon as he should have got it ready, I return'd to Bradford's, who gave me a little job to do for the present, and there I lodged and dieted. A few days after, Keimer sent for me to print off the Elegy. And now he had got another pair of cases, and a pamphlet to reprint, on which he set me to work.

[Abridged]

The man who wrote this autobiography

BENJAMIN FRANKLIN 1706–1790

Benjamin Franklin geared himself to make the most of each day and thus made a tremendous success of his entire life. During the course of his eighty-four years, he was an outstanding author, publisher, statesman, scientist, and philosopher. His warmth, humor, and common sense won him friends the world over. The achievements of his very active life still influence the world—and particularly America.

Franklin first made a name for himself as a printer in Philadelphia, and like other printers of his time, he wrote much of the material which came off his presses. In a homely, folksy manner he gave practical suggestions on the best way to live. Such quotes from his *Poor Richard's Almanac* as "Early to bed and early to rise makes a man healthy, wealthy, and wise" are now American proverbs. Franklin also commented on the problems of the day, supporting many different causes—from organizing a fire department to providing fairer treatment for the Indians.

Always a student, Franklin worked hard in his print shop all day and went home at night to study. Science fascinated him; he became so absorbed in it that he turned his business over to his foreman and planned to devote the rest of his life to his experiments. Bifocal spectacles, lightning rods, a stove, and a harmonica are just a few of the products of Franklin's creative mind. These inventions won him fame in both the United States and England.

Franklin's status as a public figure grew rapidly as his good sense and practical method were recognized. For eighteen years he represented the American colonies in England and was listened to with respect. At the beginning of the American Revolution, Franklin returned home to help the colonists in their fight for freedom. His efforts made him one of the great figures in the days of the new nation. He was a delegate to the Continental Congress, worked on the Declaration of Independence, and served as an ambassador of good will in Europe after the war. His last great contribution to America was his participation in the Federal Constitutional Convention. By this time he was an old man, tired in body but still keen in mind. He kept the spirited delegates calm and pointed the way out of many difficulties. His signature on the Constitution is one more evidence of his wisdom and importance.

Let's consider . . .

1. Benjamin Franklin's father did not want his son to become a sailor. Describe the way he helped Benjamin learn about other trades. What did Franklin gain from this experience? Would you enjoy using the same technique to learn about different kinds of work? What are the advantages of this technique?

2. Do you think Franklin's father was wise in not letting Benjamin become a sailor? Remember that the boy was only twelve years old.

3. Even though Franklin was only twelve, he wished to write for his brother's newspaper. How did he manage to get several letters published?

4. When Franklin spoke of a grammar school, he meant a Latin grammar school, one in which Latin and Greek were stressed. Only those boys planning to attend college and to study for the profes-

sions were admitted. How does your school differ in meeting the needs of the students?

5. Which of Franklin's experiences did you find the most interesting? Tell the class why you enjoyed this episode.

6. Describe Franklin as he entered Philadelphia. From this humble beginning he rose to become a leader in colonial America. Would such a rise to fame be possible today? Why, or why not?

The writer's craft . . .

1. "Boy Gets Job" was taken from the *Autobiography of Benjamin Franklin*. An **autobiography** is the life story of a person written by himself. Reading an autobiography is like listening to a friend tell you about his experiences. As Benjamin Franklin told you about his boyhood, you came to know him as a real person rather than as just another name in a history book. How was "Boy Gets Job" different from accounts you have read of Franklin in history books?

2. Below are a list of words often used to describe Franklin. Select incidents from "Boy Gets Job" which illustrate each of these qualities.

courage	skillful writer
kindness	interest in others
inventiveness	humility

Knowing words . . .

Benjamin Franklin wrote that he found his apprenticeship very *tedious*. If you are not sure of the meaning of this word, check it with your glossary.

1. What things do *you* find tedious?

2. Explain why *tedious* is a good word to express your feelings about these things.

3. What other words could you use in place of *tedious*?

A Start in Life

RUTH SUCKOW

Daisy Switzer is about to leave home for her first job. She is thrilled at the idea of living and working in a modern farmhouse, so different from the meager surroundings she has always known. But as she says good-bye to her family, she begins to understand for the very first time what it means to be facing life.

The Switzers were scurrying around to get Daisy ready by the time that Elmer Kruse should get through in town. They had known all week that Elmer might be in for her any day. But they hadn't done a thing until he appeared. "Oh, it was so rainy today, the roads were so muddy, they hadn't thought he'd get in until maybe next week."

It would have been the same any other day.

Mrs. Switzer was trying now at the last moment to get all of Daisy's things into the battered telescope [1] that lay on the bed. The bed had not "got made"; and just as soon as Daisy was gone, Mrs. Switzer would have to hurry off to the Woodworths, where she was to wash today. Daisy's things were scattered over the dark brown quilt and the rumpled sheet that were dingy and clammy in this damp weather. So was the whole bedroom with its sloping ceiling and old-fashioned square-paned windows, the commode that they used for a dresser littered with pin trays, curlers, broken combs, ribbons,

smoky lamp, all mixed up together; the door of the closet open, showing the confusion of clothes and shabby shoes. . . . They all slept in this room—Mrs. Switzer and Dwight in the bed, the two girls in the cot against the wall.

"Mama, I can't find the belt to that plaid dress."

"Oh, ain't it somewheres around? Well, I guess you'll have to let it go. If I come across it I can send it out to you. Someone'll be going past there."

She had meant to get Daisy all mended and "fixed up" before she went out to the country. But somehow . . . oh, there was always so much to see to when she came home. Gone all day, washing and cleaning for other people; it didn't leave her much time for her own home.

She was late now. The Woodworths liked to have her get the washing out early so that she could do some cleaning too before she left. But she couldn't help it. She would have to get Daisy off first. She had already had on her wraps ready to go, when Elmer came—her cleaning cap, of a blue faded almost gray, and the ancient black coat with gathered sleeves that she wore

---

[1] *telescope,* traveling bag made of two cases, one slipping inside the other

235

over her work dress when she went out to
wash.

"What's become of all your under-
clothes? They ain't all dirty, are they?"

"They are, too. You didn't wash for us
last week, mama."

"Well you'll just have to take along what
you've got. Maybe there'll be some way of
getting the rest to you."

"Elmers come in every week, don't
they?" Daisy demanded.

"Yes, but maybe they won't always be
bringing you in."

She jammed what she could into the
telescope, thinking with her helpless, anxious fatalism that it would have to do somehow.

"Daisy, you get yourself ready now."

"I am ready, mama, I want to put on my
other ribbon."

"Oh, that's 'way down in the telescope
somewhere. You needn't be so anxious to
fix yourself up. This ain't like going visiting."

Daisy stood at the little mirror preening
herself—such a homely child, "all Switzer,"
skinny, with pale sharp eyes set close together and thin, stringy, reddish hair. But
she had never really learned yet how
homely she was. She was the oldest, and
she got the pick of what clothes were given
to the Switzers. Goldie and Dwight envied
her. She was important in her small world.
She was proud of her blue coat that had
belonged to Alice Brooker, the town lawyer's daughter. It hung unevenly above
her bony little knees, and the buttons came
down too far. Her mother had tried to
make it over for her.

Mrs. Switzer looked at her, troubled, but
not knowing how she could tell her all the
things she ought to be told. Daisy had
never been away before except to go to
her Uncle Fred's at Lehigh. She seemed
to think that this would be the same. She

had so many things to learn. Well, she
would find them out soon enough—only
too soon. Working for other people—she
would learn what that meant. Elmer and
Edna Kruse were nice young people. They
would mean well enough by Daisy. It was
a good chance for her to start in. But it
wasn't the same.

Daisy was so proud. She thought it was
quite a thing to be "starting in to earn."
She thought she could buy herself so much
with her dollar and a half a week. The
other children stood back watching her,
round-eyed and impressed. They wished
that they were going away, like Daisy.

They heard a car come splashing
through the mud on low. "There he is
back! Have you got your things on?
Goldie—go out and tell him she's coming."

"No, me tell him, me!" Dwight shouted
jealously.

"Well—both of you tell him. Land! . . ."

She tried hastily to put on the cover of
the bulging telescope and to fasten the
straps. One of them broke.

"Well, you'll have to take it the way
it is."

It was an old thing, hadn't been used
since her husband, Mert, had "left off canvassing" before he died. And he had worn
it all to pieces.

"Well, I guess you'll have to go now.
He won't want to wait. I'll try and send
you out what you ain't got with you." She
turned to Daisy. Her face was working.
There was nothing else to do, as everyone
said. Daisy would have to help, and she
might as well learn it now. Only, she
hated to see Daisy go off, to have her starting in. She knew what it meant. "Well—
you try and work good this summer, so
they'll want you to stay. I hope they'll
bring you in sometimes."

Daisy's homely little face grew pale with
awe, suddenly, at the sight of her mother

crying, at something that she dimly sensed in the pressure of her mother's thin strong arms. Her vanity in her new importance was somehow shamed and dampened.

Elmer's big new Buick, mud-splashed but imposing, stood tilted on the uneven road. Mud was thick on the wheels. It was a bad day for driving, with the roads a yellow mass, water lying in all the wheel ruts. The little road that led past these few houses on the outskirts of town, and up over the hill, had a cold, rainy loneliness. Elmer sat in the front seat of the

Buick, and in the back was a big box of groceries.

"Got any room to sit in there?" he asked genially. "I didn't get out, it's so muddy here."

"No, don't get out," Mrs. Switzer said hastily. "She can put this right on the floor there in the back." She added, with a timid attempt at courtesy, "Ain't the roads pretty bad out that way?"

"Yes, but farmers get so they don't think so much about the roads."

"I s'pose that's so."

He saw the signs of tears on Mrs. Switzer's face, and they made him anxious to get away. She embraced Daisy hastily again. Daisy climbed over the grocery box and scrunched herself into the seat.

"I guess you'll bring her in with you some time when you're coming," Mrs. Switzer hinted.

"Sure. We'll bring her."

He started the engine. It roared, half died down as the wheels of the car spun in the thick wet mud.

In that moment, Daisy had a startled view of home—the small house standing on a rough rise of land, weathered to a dim color that showed dark streaks from the rain; the narrow sloping front porch whose edge had a soaked, gnawed look; the chickens, grayish-black, pecking at the wet ground; their playthings, stones, a wagon, some old pail covers littered about; a soaked, discolored piece of underwear hanging on the line in the back yard. The yard was tussocky and overhung the road with shaggy long grass where the yellow bank was caved in under it. Goldie and Dwight were gazing at her solemnly. She saw her mother's face—a thin, weak, loving face, drawn with neglected weeping, with its reddened eyes and poor teeth . . . in the old coat and heavy shoes and cleaning cap, her work-worn hand with its big

knuckles clutching at her coat. She saw
the playthings they had used yesterday,
and the old swing that hung from one of
the trees, the ropes sodden, the seat in
crooked. . . .

The car went off, slipping on the wet
clay. She waved frantically, suddenly understanding that she was leaving them.
They waved at her.

Mrs. Switzer stood there a little while.
Then came the harsh rasp of the old black
iron pump that stood out under the box
elder tree. She was pumping water to leave
for the children before she went off to
work.

Daisy held on as the car skidded going
down the short clay hill. Elmer didn't
bother with chains. He was too used to the
roads. But her eyes brightened with scared
excitement. When they were down, and
Elmer slowed up going along the tracks in
the deep wet grass that led to the main
road, she looked back, holding on her hat
with her small scrawny hand.

Just down this little hill—and home was
gone. The big car, the feel of her telescope
on the floor under her feet, the fact that
she was going out to the country, changed
the looks of everything. She saw it all
now.

Dunkels' house stood on one side of the
road. A closed-up white house. The windows stared blank and cold between the
old shutters. There was a chair with a
broken straw seat under the fruit trees.
The Dunkels were old Catholic people
who seldom went anywhere. In the front
yard was a clump of tall pines, the rough
brown trunks wet, the green branches,
dark and shining, heavy with rain, the
ground underneath mournfully sodden and
black.

The pasture on the other side. The
green grass, lush, wet and cold, and the
outcroppings of limestone that held little
pools of rain water in all the tiny holes.
Beyond, the low hills gloomy with timber
against the lowering sky.

They slid out onto the main road. They
bumped over the small wooden bridge
above the swollen creek that came from
the pasture. Daisy looked down. She saw
the little swirls of foam, the long grass that
swished with the water, the old rusted tin
cans lodged between the rocks.

She sat up straight and important, her
thin, homely little face strained with excitement, her sharp eyes taking in everything. The watery mud holes in the road,
the little thickets of plum trees, low and
wet, in dark interlacings. She held on
fiercely, but made no sound when the car
skidded.

She felt the grandeur of having a ride.
One wet Sunday, Mr. Brooker had driven
them all home from church, she and Goldie
and Dwight packed tightly into the back
seat of the car, shut in by the side curtains,
against which the rain lashed, catching the
muddy scent of the roads. Sometimes they
could plan to go to town just when Mr.
Pattey was going to work in his Ford.
Then they would run out and shout eagerly, "Mr. Pattey! Are you going through
town?" Sometimes he said, with curt good
nature, "Well, pile in"; and they all hopped
into the truck back. "He says we can go
along with him."

She looked at the black wet fields
through which little leaves of bright green
corn grew in rows, at showery bushes of
sumac along the roadside. A gasoline engine pumping water made a loud desolate
sound. There were somber-looking cattle
in the wet grass, and lonely, thick-foliaged
trees growing here and there in the pas-
tures. She felt her telescope on the floor
of the car, the box of groceries beside her.
She eyed these with a sharp curiosity.

There was a fresh pineapple—something the Switzers didn't often get at home. She wondered if Edna would have it for dinner. Maybe she could hint a little to Edna.

She was out in the country. She could no longer see her house even if she wanted to—standing dingy, streaked with rain, in its rough grass on the little hill. A lump came into her throat. She had looked forward to playing with Edna's children. But Goldie and Dwight would play all morning without her. She was still proud of being the oldest, of going out with Elmer and Edna; but now there was a forlornness in the pride.

She wished she were in the front seat with Elmer. She didn't see why he hadn't put her there. She would have liked to know who all the people were who lived on these farms; how old Elmer's babies were; and if he and Edna always went to the movies when they went into town on Saturday nights. Elmer must have lots of money to buy a car like this. He had a new house on his farm, too, and Mrs. Metzinger had said that it had plumbing. Maybe they would take her to the movies, too. She might hint about that.

When she had gone to visit Uncle Fred, she had had to go on the train. She liked this better. She hoped they had a long way to go. She called out to Elmer.

"Say, how much farther is your place?"

"What's that?" He turned around. "Oh, just down the road a ways. Scared to drive in the mud?"

"No, I ain't scared. I like to drive most any way."

She looked at Elmer's back, the old felt hat crammed down carelessly on his head, the back of his neck with the golden hair on the sunburned skin above the blue of his shirt collar. Strong and easy and slouched a little over the steering wheel that he handled so masterly. Elmer and Edna were just young folks; but Mrs. Metzinger said that they had more to start with than most young farmers did, and that they were hustlers. Daisy felt that the pride of this belonged to her too, now.

"Here we are!"

"Oh, is this where you folks live?" Daisy cried eagerly.

The house stood back from the road, beyond a space of bare yard with a little scattering of grass just starting—small, modern, painted a bright new white and yellow. The barn was new, too, a big splendid barn of frescoed brick, with a silo of the same. There were no trees. A raw, desolate wind blew across the back yard as they drove up beside the back door.

Edna had come out on the step. Elmer grinned at her as he took out the box of groceries, and she slightly raised her eyebrows. She said kindly enough:

"Well, you brought Daisy. Hello, Daisy, are you going to stay with us this summer?"

"I guess so," Daisy said importantly. But she suddenly felt a little shy and forlorn as she got out of the car and stood on the bare ground in the chilly wind.

"Yes, I brought her along," Elmer said.

"Are the roads very bad?"

"Kind of bad. Why?"

"Well, I'd like to get over to mama's some time today."

"Oh, I guess they aren't too bad for that."

Daisy pricked up her sharp little ears. Another ride. That cheered her.

"Look in the door," Edna said in a low fond voice, motioning with her head.

Two little round, blond heads were pressed tightly against the screen door. There was a clamor of "Daddy, daddy!" Elmer grinned with a bashful pride as he stood with the box of groceries, raising his eyebrows with mock surprise and demanding, "Who's this? What you shoutin' 'daddy' for? You don't think daddy's got anything for you, do you?" He and Edna were going into the kitchen together, until Edna remembered and called back hastily:

"Oh, come in, Daisy!"

Daisy stood, a little left out and solitary, there in the kitchen, as Billy, the older of the babies, climbed frantically over Elmer, demanding candy, and the little one toddled smilingly about. Her eyes took in all of it. She was impressed by the shining blue-and-white linoleum, the range with its nickel and enamel, the bright new woodwork. Edna was laughing and scolding at Elmer and the baby. Billy had made his father produce the candy. Daisy's sharp little eyes looked hungrily at the lemon drops and Edna remembered her.

"Give Daisy a piece of your candy," she said.

He would not go up to Daisy. She had to come forward and take one of the lemon drops herself. She saw where Edna put the sack, in a dish high in the cupboard. She hoped they would get some more before long.

"My telescope's out there in the car," she reminded them.

"Oh! Elmer, you go and get it and take it up for her," Edna said.

"What?"

"Her valise—or whatever it is—out in the car."

"Oh, sure," Elmer said with a cheerful grin.

"It's kind of an old telescope," Daisy said conversationally. "I guess it's been used a lot. My papa used to have it. The strap broke when mama was fastening it this morning. We ain't got any suitcase. I had to take this because it was all there was in the house, and mama didn't want to get me a new one."

Edna raised her eyebrows politely. She leaned over and pretended to spat the baby as he came toddling up to her, then rubbed her cheek against his round head with its funny fuzz of hair.

Daisy watched solemnly. "I didn't know both of your children was boys. I thought one of 'em was a girl. That's what there is at home now—one boy and one girl."

"Um-hm," Edna replied absently. "You can go up with Elmer and take off your things, Daisy," she said. "You can stop and unpack your valise now, I guess, if you'd like to. Then you can come down and help me in the kitchen. You know we got you to help me," she reminded.

Daisy, subdued, followed Elmer up the bright new stairs. In the upper hall, two strips of very clean rag were laid over the shining yellow of the floor. Elmer had put her telescope in one of the bedrooms.

"There you are!"

She heard him go clattering down the stairs, and then a kind of murmuring and laughing in the kitchen. The back door slammed. She hurried to the window in time to see Elmer go striding off toward the barn.

She looked about the room with intense curiosity. It, too, had a bright varnished floor. She had a bed all her own—a small, old-fashioned bed, left from some old furnishings, that had been put in this room that had the pipes and the hot water tank. She had to see everything, but she had a stealthy look as she tiptoed about, started to open the drawers of the dresser, looked out of her window. She put her coat and hat on the bed. She would rather be down in the kitchen with Edna than unpack her telescope now.

She guessed she would go down where the rest of them were.

Elmer came into the house for dinner. He brought in a cold, muddy, outdoor breath with him. The range was going, but the bright little kitchen seemed chilly, with the white oilcloth on the table, the baby's varnished high chair and his little fat mottled hands.

Edna made a significant little face at Elmer. Daisy did not see. She was standing back from the stove, where Edna was at work, looking at the baby.

"He can talk pretty good, can't he? Dwight couldn't say anything but 'mama' when he was that little."

Edna's back was turned. She said meaningly:

"Now, Elmer's come in for dinner, Daisy, we'll have to hurry. You must help me get on the dinner. You can cut bread and get things on the table. You must help, you know. That's what you are supposed to do."

Daisy looked startled, a little scared and resentful. "Well, I don't know where you keep your bread."

"Don't you remember where I told you to put it this morning? Right over in the cabinet, in that big box. You must watch, Daisy, and learn where things are."

Elmer, a little embarrassed at the look that Edna gave him, whistled as he began to wash his hands at the sink.

"How's daddy's old boy?" he said loudly, giving a poke at the baby's chin.

As Edna passed him, she shook her head and her lips just formed, "Been like that all morning!"

He grinned comprehendingly. Then both their faces became expressionless.

Daisy had not exactly heard, but she looked from one to the other, silent and dimly wondering. The queer ache that had kept starting all through the morning, under her interest in Edna's things and doings, came over her again. She sensed something different in the atmosphere than she had ever known before—some queer difference between the position of herself and of the two babies, a faint notion of what mama had meant when she had said that this would not be visiting.

"I guess I'm going to have the toothache again," she said faintly.

No one seemed to hear her.

Edna whisked off the potatoes, drained the water. . . . "You might bring me a dish, Daisy." Daisy searched a long time while Edna turned impatiently and pointed. Edna put the rest of the things on the table herself. Her young, fresh, capable mouth was tightly closed, and she was making certain resolutions.

Daisy stood hesitating in the middle of the room, a scrawny, unappealing little figure. Billy, fat, blond, in funny dark blue union-alls—was trotting busily about the kitchen. Daisy swooped down upon him and tried to bring him to the table. He set up a howl. Edna turned, looked astonished, severe.

"I was trying to make him come to the table," Daisy explained weakly.

"You scared him. He isn't used to you. He doesn't like it. Don't cry, Billy. The girl didn't mean anything."

"Here, daddy'll put him in his place," Elmer said hastily.

Billy looked over his father's shoulder at Daisy with suffused, resentful blue eyes. She did not understand it, and felt strangely at a loss. She had been left with Goldie and Dwight so often. She had always made Dwight go to the table. She had been the boss.

Edna said in a cool, held-in voice, "Put these things on the table, Daisy."

They sat down. Daisy and the other children had always felt it a great treat to eat away from home instead of at their own scanty, hastily set table. They had hung around Mrs. Metzinger's house at noon, hoping to be asked to stay, not offended when told that "it was time for them to run off now." Her pinched little face had a hungry look as she stared at the potatoes and fried ham and pie. But they did not watch and urge her to have more, as Mrs. Metzinger did, and Mrs. Brooker when she took pity on the Switzers and had them there. Daisy wanted more pie. But none of them seemed to be taking more, and so she said nothing. She remembered what her mother had said, with now a faint comprehension. "You must remember you're out working for other folks, and it won't be like it is at home."

After dinner Edna said, "Now you can wash the dishes, Daisy."

She went into the next room with the children. Daisy, as she went hesitatingly about the kitchen alone, could hear Edna's low contented humming as she sat in there rocking, the baby in her lap. The bright kitchen was empty and lonely now. Through the window, Daisy could see the great barn looming up against the rainy sky. She hoped that they would drive to Edna's mother's soon.

She finished as soon as she could and went into the dining room where Edna was sewing on the baby's rompers. Edna went on sewing. Daisy sat down disconsolately. That queer low ache went all through her. She said in a small dismal voice:

"I guess I got the toothache again."

Edna bit off a thread.

"I had it awful hard awhile ago. Mama come pretty near taking me to the dentist."

"That's too bad," Edna murmured politely. But she offered no other condolence. She gave a little secret smile at the baby asleep on a blanket and a pillow in one corner of the shiny leather davenport.

"Is Elmer going to drive into town tomorrow?"

"Tomorrow? I don't suppose so."

"Mama couldn't find the belt of my plaid dress and I thought if he was, maybe I could go along and get it. I'd like to have it."

Daisy's homely mouth drooped at the corners. Her toothache did not seem to matter to anyone. Edna did not seem to want to see that anything was wrong with her. She had expected Edna to be concerned, to mention remedies. But it wasn't toothache, that strange lonesome ache all over her. Maybe she was going to be terribly sick. Mama wouldn't come home for supper to be told about it.

She saw mama's face as in that last glimpse of it—drawn with crying, and yet trying to smile, under the old cleaning cap, her hand holding her coat together . . .

Edna glanced quickly at her. The child was so mortally unattractive, unappealing even in her forlornness. Edna frowned a little, but said kindly:

"Now you might take Billy into the

kitchen out of my way, Daisy, and amuse him."

"Well, he cries when I pick him up," Daisy said faintly.

"He won't cry this time. Take him out and help him play with his blocks. You must help me with the children, you know."

"Well, if he'll go with me."

"He'll go with you, won't he, Billy boy? Won't you go with Daisy, sweetheart?"

Billy stared and then nodded. Daisy felt a thrill of comfort as Billy put his little fat hand in hers and trotted into the kitchen beside her. He had the fattest hands, she thought. Edna brought the blocks and put the box down on the floor beside Daisy.

"Now, see if you can amuse him so that I can get my sewing done."

"Shall you and me play blocks, Billy?" Daisy murmured.

He nodded. Then he got hold of the box with one hand, tipped out all the blocks on the floor with a bang and a rattle, and looked at her with a pleased proud smile.

"Oh no, Billy. You mustn't spill out the blocks. Look, you're too little to play with them. No, now—now wait! Let Daisy show you. Daisy'll build you something real nice—shall she?"

He gave a solemn nod of consent. Daisy set out the blocks on the bright linoleum. She had never had such blocks as these to handle before. Dwight's were only a few old, unmatched broken ones. Her spirit of leadership came back, and she firmly put away that fat hand of Billy's whenever he meddled with her building. She could make something really wonderful with these blocks.

"No, Billy, you mustn't. See, when Daisy's got it all done, then you can see what the lovely building is."

She put the blocks together with great interest. She knew what she was going to

make—it was going to be a new house, no, a new church. Just as she got the walls up, in came that little hand again, and then with a delighted grunt Billy swept the blocks pellmell about the floor. At the clatter, he sat back, pursing his mouth to give an ecstatic "Ooh!"

"Oh, Billy—you mustn't, the building wasn't done! Look, you've spoiled it. Now, you've got to sit 'way off here while I try to build it over again."

Billy's look of triumph turned to surprise and then to vociferous protest as Daisy picked him up and firmly transplanted him to another corner of the room. He set up a tremendous howl. He had never been set aside like that before. Edna came hurrying out. Daisy looked at Edna for justification, but instinctively on the defense.

"Billy knocked over the blocks. He spoiled the building."

"Wah! Wah!" Billy gave loud heart-broken sobs. The tears ran down his fat cheeks and he held out his arm piteously toward his mother.

"I didn't hurt him," Daisy said, scared.

"Never mind, lover," Edna was crooning. "Of course he can play with his blocks. They're Billy's blocks, Daisy," she said. "He doesn't like to sit and see you put up buildings. He wants to play, too. See, you've made him cry now."

"Do' wanna stay here," Billy wailed.

"Well, come in with mother then." She picked him up, wiping his tears.

"I didn't hurt him," Daisy protested.

"Well, never mind now. You can pick up the blocks and then sweep up the floor, Daisy. You didn't do that when you finished the dishes. Never mind," she was saying to Billy. "Pretty soon daddy'll come in and we'll have a nice ride."

Daisy soberly picked up the blocks and got the broom. What had she done to Billy? He had tried to spoil her building.

She had always made Dwight keep back until she had finished. Of course it was Daisy, the oldest, who should lead and manage. There had been no one to hear her side. Everything was different. She winked back tears as she swept, poorly and carelessly.

Then she brightened up as Elmer came tramping up on the back porch and then through the kitchen.

"Edna!"

"She's in there," Daisy offered.

"Want to go now? What? Is the baby asleep?" he asked blankly.

Edna gave him a warning look and the door was closed.

Daisy listened hard. She swept very softly. She could catch only a little of what they said—"Kind of hate to go off . . . I know, but if we once start . . . not a thing all day . . . what we got her for . . ." She had no real comprehension of it. She hurried and put away the broom. She wanted to be sure and be ready to go.

Elmer tramped out, straight past her. She saw from the window that he was backing the car out from the shed. She could hear Edna and Billy upstairs, could hear the baby cry a little as he was wakened. Maybe she ought to go out and get on her wraps, too.

Elmer honked the horn. A moment later Edna came hurrying downstairs in her hat and coat, and Billy in a knitted cap and a red sweater crammed over his union-alls, so that he looked like a little brownie. The baby had on his little coat, too.

Edna called out, "Come in and get this boy, daddy." She did not look at Daisy, but said hurriedly, "We're going for a little ride, Daisy. Have you finished the sweeping? Well, then, you can pick up those pieces in the dining room. We won't be gone very long. When it's a quarter past five, you start the fire, like I showed you

this noon, and slice the potatoes that were left, and the meat. And set the table."

The horn was honked again.

"Yes! Well, we'll be back, Daisy. Come, lover, daddy's in a hurry."

Daisy stood looking after them. Billy clamored to sit beside his daddy. Edna took the baby from Elmer and put him beside her on the back seat. There was room—half of the big back seat. There wasn't anything, really, to be done at home. That was the worst of it. They just didn't want to take her. They all belonged together. They didn't want to take anyone else along. She was an outsider. They all—even the baby—had a freshened look of expectancy.

The engine roared—they had started; slipping on the mud of the drive, then forging straight ahead, around the turn, out of sight.

She went forlornly into the dining room. The light from the windows was dim now in the rainy, late afternoon. The pink pieces from the baby's rompers were scattered over the gay rug. She got down on her hands and knees, slowly picking them up, sniffing a little. She heard the Big Ben clock in the kitchen ticking loudly.

That dreadful ache submerged her. No one would ask about it, no one would try to comfort her. Before, there had always been mama coming home, anxious, scolding sometimes, but worried over them if they didn't feel right, caring about them. Mama and Goldie and Dwight cared about her—but she was away out in the country, and they were at home. She didn't want to stay here, where she didn't belong. But mama had told her that she must begin helping this summer.

Her ugly little mouth contorted into a grimace of weeping. But silent weeping, without any tears; because she already had the cold knowledge that no one would notice or comfort it.

The woman who wrote this story

RUTH SUCKOW 1892–

As the daughter of an Iowa minister, Ruth Suckow moved from parish to parish and knew the lives of many people. After attending colleges in Iowa, Boston, and Denver, she managed an apiary (bee farm) for six summers, an arrangement that allowed her to write as she pleased during the winter months.

Her reputation was established when H. L. Mencken, the "Dean of American Literature" in the 1920's, published some of her stories. Soon she was writing for many magazines and able to support herself entirely through her earnings as a writer.

She writes of the things that she knows best. Frequently, her characters are German immigrants. Her stories are always set in one area, the Middle West. For this reason, Ruth Suckow is known as a regional writer.

Let's consider . . .

1. Mrs. Switzer was troubled because she knew that Daisy had so many things to learn. In what ways was Daisy poorly prepared to meet her new situation?

2. How is working for other people much different from helping out at home? Should Daisy's mother have given her some idea of what it would be like?

3. What home training is necessary to equip young people to meet their first jobs gracefully? What role should the school play in this preparation?

4. Describe the way in which Daisy handled Billy. Why did she act this way toward him? How would you have treated Billy?

5. List several incidents from the story that show how Mrs. Kruse treated Daisy. Do you think that she was always fair? Did she expect too much of such a young girl? Explain your answers.

6. How might Mrs. Kruse have made Daisy's first day easier?

7. Why did Daisy develop such a strong ache? Have you ever had similar aches and pains? Tell the class about an incident in your life that reminds you of Daisy's ache. (Remember the headache that developed on the day of an important test?)

The writer's craft . . .

People who want all stories to have happy endings forget that life is not all happiness. A realistic story, such as "A Start in Life," is written to reflect life as it really is. When the characters and experiences are true-to-life, you have to expect a true-to-life ending. A harsh experience may end happily, but just as often it will not.

It may have seemed unfair to you that this story didn't promise success for Daisy in her job and a better life for the Switzer family. But Ruth Suckow wasn't writing a "soap-opera" script in which some unexpected good fortune nearly always saves the day. She was presenting the hardships and lack of understanding which really exist in the world.

1. Make a list of the most popular daytime radio or television serials which feature a family, a married couple, or a man or woman seeking a career.

Discuss the problems these people face in life and the way they solve their problems. What seems *real* and what seems made-up about these people? In what ways are their problems the same or different from the problems of people you know? In what ways are their solutions more like those in a storybook than in real life?

2. Which kind of story, radio or television program, or movie do you like best? What are your reasons?

a. The happy-ending story, even if the people, problems, and solutions aren't very true to life

b. The realistic story in which the people and the experiences seem true to life, even though the ending may be disappointing

Knowing words . . .

The sentences below are taken from "A Start in Life." Each sentence contains one or two italicized words which in some way reflect the story's somber tone. Explain the meaning of each italicized word.

1. That *dreadful* ache *submerged* her.

2. A raw, *desolate* wind blew across the back yard as they drove up beside the back door.

3. The child was so mortally unattractive, *unappealing* even in her *forlornness*.

Poverty

I met her on the street today and she
Just turned her lovely eyes away from me.
But oh! I can forgive her, for I know,
If she seems dull, what things have made her so.
She is so closely wrapped in costly fur
No tingling wind has ever quickened her;
She never felt warm rain upon her face,
(Her motor takes her round from place to place).
That slender hand, bright with its jewelled ring,
Has never searched the sweet damp earth in Spring

For little growing things, nor have those eyes
Been tender with the light of sacrifice;
She may not laugh nor weep nor cry aloud
(The vogue is to be blasé in her crowd).
She thrills not to the promise of the Dawn;
She greets the hush of starlight with a yawn;
And Life has sheltered her, poor thing!
From all the holy joy of suffering.

Perhaps she feels the sting of poverty
And that is why she does not bow to me.

Anne Sutherland

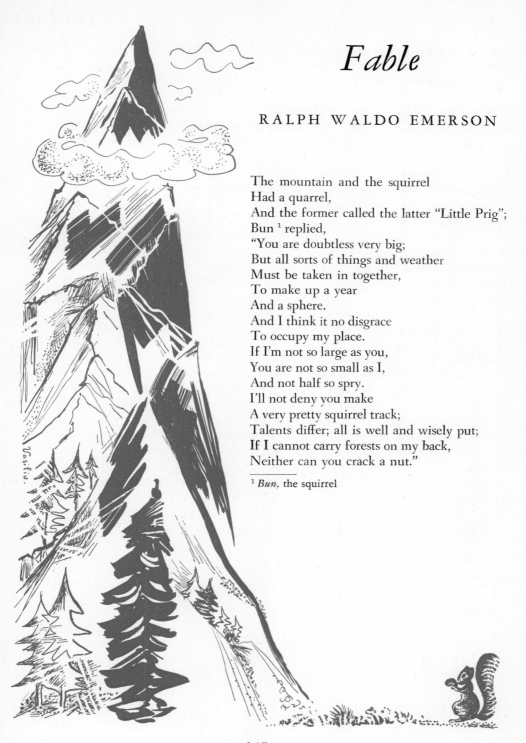

Fable

RALPH WALDO EMERSON

The mountain and the squirrel
Had a quarrel,
And the former called the latter "Little Prig";
Bun [1] replied,
"You are doubtless very big;
But all sorts of things and weather
Must be taken in together,
To make up a year
And a sphere.
And I think it no disgrace
To occupy my place.
If I'm not so large as you,
You are not so small as I,
And not half so spry.
I'll not deny you make
A very pretty squirrel track;
Talents differ; all is well and wisely put;
If I cannot carry forests on my back,
Neither can you crack a nut."

[1] *Bun,* the squirrel

The man who wrote this poem

RALPH WALDO EMERSON   1803–1882

Seven generations of Puritan ministers preceded the birth of Ralph Waldo Emerson, and it was in the same tradition of the stern, hard, honest life that he was raised. His father died while Emerson was still a child, and the family of eight children was left very poor. Emerson worked his way through Harvard, graduating when he was only eighteen. For a while he taught at his brother's school for young ladies, but he returned to college to study for the ministry. Emerson was not happy as a minister and soon resigned to become a lecturer and essayist.

On his first visit to England, Emerson met several famous authors, one of whom was Thomas Carlyle, a lifelong friend. Emerson was so stimulated by his journey that he wrote his first book, *Nature*. This book was not popular, but it did provide the beginning for his later essays. Even then he was expressing these beliefs about life: that man should depend upon himself; that each person can find sources of power and inspiration within himself; and that "the highest revelation is that God is in every man."

In his time Emerson was one of the best lecturers in the United States. When he completed a lecture tour, he would return to his small home town where thoughtful men from all over the world would come to sit at the feet of the "Sage of Concord." His ideas were soon influencing people's thinking on both sides of the Atlantic.

The poet's art . . .

1. In your opinion, who won the argument? Why?

2. What kind of person does the squirrel represent? What kind does the mountain represent? Which kind of person contributes more to the world? Could we do without either?

3. As a child, you enjoyed Aesop's *Fables*. Then you were content to believe the story of the hare and the tortoise, the fox and the crow. Now that you are older, you will enjoy these fables even more because you can understand the idea beneath the surface of the story. Emerson called his poem "Fable." What *idea* did you find expressed in the poem?

4. Most fables end with a moral, the lesson which the fable teaches. Emerson's "Fable" does not have a moral at the end. Compose your own moral for this fable. If you can, write it in rhyme.

Polonius' Advice to His Son

WILLIAM SHAKESPEARE

And these few precepts in thy memory
Look thou character. Give thy thoughts no tongue,
Nor any unproportion'd thought his act.
Be thou familiar, but by no means vulgar.
Those friends thou hast, and their adoption tried,
Grapple them unto thy soul with hoops of steel;
But do not dull thy palm [1] with entertainment
Of each new-hatch'd, unfledg'd comrade. Beware
Of entrance to a quarrel; but, being in,
Bear't that the opposed may beware of thee.
Give every man thy ear, but few thy voice;
Take each man's censure, but reserve thy judgment.
Costly thy habit [2] as thy purse can buy,
But not expressed in fancy; rich, not gaudy;
For the apparel oft proclaims the man,
And they in France of the best rank and station
Are most select and generous, chief in that.
Neither a borrower nor a lender be;
For loan oft loses both itself and friend,
And borrowing dulls the edge of husbandry.
This above all: to thine own self be true,
And it must follow, as the night the day,
Thou canst not then be false to any man.
Farewell: my blessing season this in thee!

[1] *dull thy palm,* make your hand callous
[2] *habit,* clothing

The man who wrote this selection

WILLIAM SHAKESPEARE   1554–1616

William Shakespeare is undoubtedly the most famous author in English literature. For over three centuries his poems and plays have been read in hundreds of languages, and the thousands of books about him and his characters would fill a library. Such phrases from his plays as "To be or not to be" or "It was Greek to me," have become common sayings.

The selection which you have just read was taken from *Hamlet,* one of Shakespeare's best known plays. Hamlet was the Prince of Denmark. Polonius was the Lord Chamberlain (chief advisor) at the court of Hamlet's uncle, the King of Denmark. In this selection, Polonius is advising his son, Laertes, who is about to depart for France. It was the custom for young nobles like Laertes to live in France a while in order to learn the culture and manners of that country. France, and particularly Paris, was considered the center of European culture. Therefore, it was the best place for Laertes to learn how to be a gentleman.

Shakespeare wrote histories, comedies, and tragedies, but his plays are much more than stories. Each contains comments on life, bits of philosophy, and advice on how to live.

The poet's art . . .

1. Polonius is a character in the play, *Hamlet.* As his son is preparing to leave for France, Polonius gives him advice on how to act. Using your own words, "translate" this advice into a set of practical rules of conduct.

2. Which of these rules have value for the job seeker? For the new employee? Which apply in social situations?

3. Explain why you agree or disagree with the following pieces of advice:

"Take each man's censure, but reserve thy judgment."
"Neither a borrower nor a lender be."

4. Are teenagers most likely to take advice from parents, teachers, or friends? Explain. How can you profit from listening to your parents when they give advice which is similar to Polonius' advice to his son?

Years Ago

RUTH GORDON

Curtain going up . . . If you were seated in a theater, this would be the hushed moment when the curtain rose and the stage was suddenly revealed before your eyes. You would see at a glance the many details of the New England sitting room where the action takes place.

As a fireside play-goer, however, you must try a little harder to "see" the setting. In the first few pages, Ruth Gordon describes the set for you and introduces you to her family. Read these pages carefully and try to visualize the setting and the people. Your reward will be a greater enjoyment of the play.

THE CAST

MY FATHER, Clinton Jones
MY MOTHER, Annie Jones
ME, Ruth Gordon Jones
KATHERINE FOLLETT, my best friend
ANNA WITHAM, my next best friend

FRED WHITMARSH, a beau
MR. SPARROW, a man who owned a wagon
MR. BAGLEY, from the Y.M.C.A.
MISS GLAVIN, from out to Brookline

PUNK, our cat

SYNOPSIS OF SCENES

The scene is our dining room-sitting room at 14 Elmwood Avenue, Wollaston, Massachusetts.

ACT ONE: An evening in January, years ago.

ACT TWO
SCENE ONE: The next evening.
SCENE TWO: The next afternoon.

ACT THREE: Five months later, June. About eleven o'clock in the morning.

ACT ONE

An evening in January, years ago. Our dining room-sitting room at 14 Elmwood Avenue, Wollaston, Massachusetts. It is a small room, but there is nothing small in it. The paper is patterned with prize apples, grapes, and roses, all grown to an outlandish size, and in the center of the room is a large oblong table spread with a white damask cloth, fresh on Sunday. There is a fern basket in the middle of the table. On the left-hand side of the room is a door to the entry, and in this entry are the cellar door and the kitchen door. Also on the right-hand wall of the dining room is a small sliding wooden arrangement that opens like a window and through which dishes may be passed to the kitchen. Alongside this is a heavy golden-oak sideboard with a looking-glass back. On it My Mother has set out the most presentable of her cut glass; a pewter fruit dish, won at a whist party, in which she keeps a few elastic bands, a post-card or two, and any stray button or key; a Bavarian-ware stein for her change purse and anything precious like a receipted bill; and all the aforementioned are set out on hand-embroidered doilies. Next to this sideboard is an insecure bamboo table which holds old *Saturday Evening Posts*. Against the center wall is a straight-backed dining-room chair, golden oak, with a black leather seat held down with black leather-covered nails. Next is the oval-topped reading table with a faded tapestry cover that Miss Turner brought us from Liberty's, London. On My Mother's side of this table are piled *Mental Science* magazines, *Unity,* give-away samples of *Butterick Fashions,* and *McCall's* and *The Ladies' Home Journal* borrowed from our neighbor Mrs. Litchfield. The green-shaded gasolier pours its light down from the center of the table. On My Father's side is *The Saturday Evening Post,* the new one, and the latest *McClure's Magazine,* which no one but he is supposed to touch. Drawn up to this side of the table is My Father's rattan armchair which has leaned so long toward the light when My Father is sitting in it that even when it is not occupied it still continues to lean. Between it and the table is a Dresden china cuspidor that had been a bargain. Beyond My Father's chair is a black mission chafing-dish stand which my Uncle George had unaccountably made for My Father and which had never ceased to irk him. My Father said we had no chafing dish and George Gage knew it and he had no earthly reason to give it other than to annoy. So he uses it for his pipes and tobacco and sundries like pipe cleaners and disreputable odds and ends. There are two windows out onto the front porch, where three rockers can be seen; and beyond the porch are the maple trees of Elmwood Avenue. On the left-hand wall is a mantelpiece for our black marble clock, over which is a steel engraving of something or other, a forest presumably, out of which a stag is peering, startled apparently by our dining room. My Father's golden-oak dining-room chair is drawn up against the wall. There is a door out into the front hall where one can see our stairs and square oak newel post. Across the hall are our parlor and our front door.

As the curtain rises, I am standing on a gold bamboo side chair. My Mother is pinning up the hem of the dress I am wearing, a dress made out of some thin wool material, brick red—the color is called "Tango." One sleeve has not been sewed in and my arm is bare. The hem of the skirt, which My Mother is adjusting, is basted with cotton. The skirt is three tiered. There is a white net vest and revers embroidered in self-toned birds about the size of sparrows. Around the neck is a narrow strip of bear fur. This also appears again in decoration around the wrists to finish off the long sleeves. The belt is broad, of the same material, and is clasped together by two simple German-silver cherubs. The material of my clothes may be hand-me-down but the designs are strictly my own—copies from actresses' pictures, from peeking into *Bon Ton* and *The Elite,* fifty-cent magazines which I see for a fraction of a moment at Mr. Shunk's, our newsdealer's, while I am buying the Quincy *Patriot* for My Mother, or a mortifying box of Dill's Square Cut Tobacco for My Father. My dress of course comes decently to my ankles and more than conceals the top half of my tan laced boots. For jewelry I am confined by circumstances to a narrow plain gold bracelet hoop, a gold signet ring, a very small opal ring, and a little-finger ring, gold also, with a sliver of something dark which on close observation turns out to be a garnet. I have on a spun-silver butterfly brooch, and a string of dull amber beads which My Father had brought back on a voyage from Russia. I do not admire them much but I would feel naked without a necklace and this is the only one I have. All in all, I look like someone who has not given in to conditions, and though this is not my very ideal of how I should look, I am satisfied that I do not look like Wollaston. My Mother wears a white embroidered shirt-waist, with a high-boned collar and buttons down the back. She wears a gray wool skirt that sweeps the floor—rather its dust braid does. She too wears boots, but hers are buttoned boots and black. To My Mother's right is a wicker sewing stand where she keeps notions. My Father is sitting across the room at left beside the oval reading table, absorbed in his *McClure's Magazine*. My Father looks like no one in Wollaston. It is hard to tell why. He just doesn't. He wears a suit, non-descript as to color and stuff. It comes from Leopold Morse and it is too large for him. So is his stiff collar, which stands away from his Adam's apple and juts out along his chin. A locomotive whistle is heard in the distance, then a chug of cars along the New York, New Haven, and Hartford Railroad tracks near by.

ME: I *hate* Jones for a name. I wish our name was something else.

MY MOTHER (*Finishing pinning up the hem*): Why, Jones is a good name . . . easy to remember . . . short to write.

ME: It's too plain. Papa, do you think our name is *really* Jones? (*My Father makes no reply and I continue my attack.*) I wish you were a changeling,[1] Papa, and our name was somethin' else.

MY FATHER: Don't go through life looking for changelings! Aim to *amount* to something! Then it won't matter if your name is Jones or Finnegan or Andrew J. Forepaugh. Good wine needs no bush.

MY MOTHER (*Finished with the hem*): All right now. You can get down.

ME (*Getting down and noticing my skirt*): No, Mama—!

MY MOTHER (*Hastily interrupting me*): Ruth, hand me my hug-me-tight off that chair. . . . (*Indicating it hanging on the back of the dining-room armchair.*)

ME (*As I do so*): But, Mama . . .

MY MOTHER (*Cutting me off*): Clinton, do you think you could get the furnace to give out a little more heat?

MY FATHER (*Takes off his glasses, puts his magazine down, and rises*): It ain't the *furnace!* It's the coal they sent us. We order a ton of half nut and half egg and what we get is a ton full of clinkers. (*The cellar door slams after him.*)

MY MOTHER (*In an exasperated whisper, slipping into the hug-me-tight which I'm holding for her*): I had to get your father to go *do* that so I could tell you about this skirt.

ME (*In despair*): It's all *wrong*, Mama!

MY MOTHER: No, it is *not* all wrong. It's the way it's going to *be!* I am *not* going to let you wear any skirt like that actressy picture you showed me.

ME: Oh, Mama . . . slit skirts are all the rage!

MY MOTHER: Well, let them be! But I'm certainly not going to have you walking round Wollaston in a skirt slit halfway up past all decency!

ME: Oh Mama!

[1] *changeling,* child secretly exchanged for another

My Mother: You want people to think you live in a harem?

Me: It's how the dress *has* to be. It *has* to, Mama. It's what gives it the *Frenchy* touch.

My Mother: Has to or *not* has to . . . I *will not!* Why, all you'd have to do is walk up Newport Avenue *once* in that dress and everyone in Wollaston would know you wanted to be an actress. If you don't feel able to tell your own father, then please don't flaunt it out to *everybody else.* You can't go round dressed like Gaby Deslys. This is Wollaston, Massachusetts, please remember, not Gay Paree!

Me (*In despair*): It doesn't cost any more to have it stylish, does it?

My Mother (*near the end of her patience*): Ruth, do you or do you not want your father to know you want to be an actress?

Me: *No.*

My Mother: Well, then don't go appearing before him in a hobble skirt with a slit! . . . Let me make your skirt *pretty* and I'll talk to Papa about letting us have a telephone.

Me (*In despair*): You'll just ruin all my looks!

My Mother: No, I won't. Go in the parlor and get on your other dress.

Me (*Reluctantly giving in*): Well, then, you ask him about the telephone. You *promised.*

My Mother: I will if the *furnace* hasn't made him mad. (*I disappear into the parlor.*)

My Father (*Coming in*): Thermometer says four above but a' course ours ain't a reputable thermometer. No one's is . . .

My Mother (*Enthusiastically*): Oh, it's warmer in here already.

My Father (*Returning to his magazine with considerable satisfaction*): Good magazine, *McClure's.*

My Mother: I'm glad you got something to enjoy, Clinton, and if you say so it *must* be good, because you don't like to read just any old thing. And I'm sure Mrs. Litchfield will be glad to lend you next month's, too. (*She picks up her* Unity Magazine *and sits down at the reading table.*) You know I been thinking, Clinton, everybody else has got one and we ought to have a telephone.

My Father (*Amiably*): Wouldn't have one if you gave it to me!

My Mother: Why, Clinton? What have you got against it? (*My father sits still as a statue for a moment, then gives a loud sneeze.*)

My Father (*Indignantly*): Get that cat off the register! Hot air comin' up through cat fur'll give me back my old malaria. (*My Mother hurries over to the sideboard.*)

My Mother: Here, Punk.

My Father: Get him off there! I ain't goin' to have him layin' around warmin' up all his germs!

My Mother: Punk's clean and healthy and hasn't any germs! (*She gets him out from under the sideboard and starts for the kitchen.*) Clinton, please try not to be against a telephone. (*She puts Punk into the kitchen and closes the door.*)

My Father: I *ain't* against it, so long as we don't have to have one.

Me (*Enthusiastically, from the parlor*): The kind of telephone *we* want, Papa, won't cost anythin' at all to speak of except just one old nickel a day.

My Mother: And that's only for when *we* telephone.

Me: When people telephone *us* it's *free!*

My Mother: So what *we* want is to get a coin-in-the-slot one . . .

Me: All you have to do is every day put in a nickel.

My Mother (*Happily*): And that way

makes the bills be all paid. Isn't that lovely? (*A soothing afterthought*) And, Clinton, if you don't want to, you don't personally have to have a thing to do with it; it can just be Ruth's and mine.

MY FATHER (*Genially*): It can be Shem and Japheth's so long's I don't have to pay for it. (*He gives another sneeze.*) What good's a cat anyway? What about throwin' him away?

MY MOTHER: Clinton, you just like to hear yourself talk but you don't fool anyone, not even Punk.

ME: I wish we could have a dog; a cat's so tacky lookin'.

MY MOTHER: Punk loves you best of *anyone,* Clinton. And well he might, because you *taught* that cat every single blessed thing he knows!

ME: Papa, you'd have felt awful that day President Cleveland died if you couldn't have called up Mrs. Litchfield to tell Mama to hang out our flag at half mast!

MY FATHER: Well, how often do you think *that* occasion is likely to arise?

MY MOTHER: What was just a blessing of course was Eaton's iceman happening by!

MY FATHER (*Ruminatively*): That feller lashed them ropes to the halliards like he'd took lessons from Corticelli's cat! [2] How people handle rope and string is oftentimes characteristic.

MY MOTHER (*Tolerantly*): Well, now, Clinton, just because *you* happen to have been a sailor doesn't mean *everyone* can knot a rope right!

MY FATHER: People don't *happen* to be sailors. There's quite a knack to it.

ME: I wish our name was *Cleveland.* There's a girl goes to Quincy Mansion School named Fentress Serene Kerlin.

MY FATHER: And the Queen of the

---

[2] *Corticelli's cat,* a cat entangled in thread, seen in advertisements in the early part of this century

Hawaiian Islands is named Liliuokalani. What's *that* got to do with anythin'? (*My Father returns to his* McClure's *and I surreptitiously take a large magazine out from under some tablecloths in the sideboard drawer and start upstairs. My Mother, not looking up from her reading of* Unity, *hears me leaving.*)

MY MOTHER: You read or whatever you're going to do down here, Ruth. It's too cold upstairs.

ME (*Continuing on my way and hiding the magazine behind me*): I'll be all right.

MY MOTHER: Besides, it'll save electric light.

MY FATHER (*Not glancing up from his magazine*): Every time you turn on an electric light it costs a penny. Bear that in mind. You can leave a light *burning* for six and one-half minutes, for the *same* price it costs to turn it on. (*It is clear I have to give in. I cautiously enclose my large magazine in a copy of* The Saturday Evening Post *and reluctantly sit down to read.*)

MY FATHER: Got your grocery list ready for Pierce's? (*He puts down his* McClure's Magazine *and looks up at My Mother.*)

MY MOTHER: Oh, Clinton, you want to do that *now*? (*She puts aside* Unity *and hurries over to the sideboard.*) Now what did I do with Pierce's catalogue? Something tells me I put it in here. (*She pulls open a drawer.*)

ME: I *hate* Ruth for a name. I wish my name was Zoe.

MY MOTHER (*Searching intently*): Why, Ruth Gordon Jones is a pretty name.

ME: But it just sounds like any old name. I wish you'd thought of *Hortense.*

MY MOTHER: And Papa and I thought it had a lovely meaning. Ruth for little Ruthie Cleveland that died when she was only twelve years old. And the Gordon for dear old Dr. Gordon that when *everyone* thought you were born dead somehow got you to breathing, and of course there was no choice about Jones. Oh, *here* it is! I got it, Clinton.

My FATHER: Didn't they send no order sheet?

My MOTHER: Isn't it there with the catalogue? I declare I don't know where that gets to!

My FATHER: It don't get to *no* place. A order sheet stays where it's put!

My MOTHER: Yes, I know it does, but where's *that*?

My FATHER: Can't you get up and *help* your mother, Gwendolyn-Genevieve?

ME: What?

My FATHER (*With a fair amount of force*): Get up and do somethin' *useful*! (*I get up with a veiled look of disgust.*)

My MOTHER (*Shouting triumphantly*): Here it is in the stein! (*She puts it down by My Father, then reaches into the cut-glass pitcher for a torn brown paper bag.*) Just have patience, do, Clinton, while I get a pencil. (*She pulls open the drawer with a jerk and the gasolier shivers.*) Ruth, pull up your skirt. A gored skirt gets stretched sitting on it. Papa won't mind.

ME: Mama, *please!* Don't be *disgustin'!*

My FATHER: Look out you don't set us afire with that lamp!

My MOTHER (*Reassuringly*): I won't, Clinton.

ME: If we had a telephone to call up the fire station, it'd be a whole lot safer if we ever caught fire.

My MOTHER (*Pulling out a magazine with a jerk*): It's my *Unity* got caught in the top.

My FATHER: Your what?

My MOTHER: My Mental Science magazine. I wish you'd read it, Clinton. It helps me a good deal . . . (*My Father notices a pink card in the magazine.*) That's just to keep my place with. Mental

Science is *awful* hard to follow if you ever lose your place.

My FATHER: Come on! Did you have a grocer's bill at Backus' this week?

My MOTHER (*Reluctantly*): Well, yes I did . . . one or two little things I ran short of.

My FATHER (*Puts down his pen and regards My Mother with considerable annoyance*): Well, it beats the Dutch! Every two weeks we get a order of groceries sent out from Boston from S. S. Pierce! I bring home the eggs and the meat every Saturday from Faneuil Hall Market! Friday I get us a fish at T Wharf! And yet each week comes dribblin' out a Backus grocery bill!

My MOTHER (*Humbly*): I know it. But I'm just not a *wizard*. Now, you *know* I'm not! I can't tell exactly, absolutely, two weeks *ahead*, just what I'm going to use for the next two weeks to *come*!

My FATHER (*Warming to the subject*): Well, it beats the Dutch, *why* you can't! A cook on a vessel can do it. If you're in the Straits of Singapore and you want a can of lard, there's just two things you can do. You can have it with you or you can go without!

My MOTHER (*Earnestly*): I know it, Clinton, don't think I don't.

My FATHER: So I got to look at Backus and his whole family drive around in a two-seated carriage *every Sunday afternoon!*

My MOTHER: Oh dear . . .

My FATHER (*Interrupting*): Well, a bill ain't goin' to disappear regrettin' it! Get it out! (*My Mother hands it to him reluctantly. He studies it for a moment.*) What about this butter? I thought Ruth went and got that stuff that farmer sends the Brighams every week?

My MOTHER: Well, no, Clinton, she *started* to, but . . .

ME (*Plaintively*): The Brighams live way up on Prospect!

MY MOTHER: And climbing that hill and all, Ruth says it hurts her back.

MY FATHER: She climbs up there all right to go coastin', don't she?

MY MOTHER: Well, it's carrying *butter* tires her out.

MY FATHER: Why, we don't take but three pounds a week!

MY MOTHER: Now, Clinton, you know yourself . . . (*Her voice drops to a delicate whisper.*) She's just at the growing age.

MY FATHER (*Studies me morosely*): Lazy as a louse! How old is she anyway? Fourteen? Fifteen?

ME (*With displeasure*): I'm *sixteen*, Papa.

MY FATHER: At that age, I'd had nine years before the mast and *one* of 'em was spent sailin' under Captain Dermot out of Rockland Harbor, totalin' up that nine years to seem more like thirteen!

ME (*Eagerly*): Papa, can't you remember just a *little* what Maxine Elliott looked like?

MY FATHER: Why should I? She was just old man Dermot's daughter, Jessie, stoppin' off from High School to see her father's ship set sail. Why *should* I remember her? No one knew she was goin' on the stage and be Maxine Elliott, did they? (*Glancing down at the bill again*) What's this cat meat? Was that the steak we had last night?

MY MOTHER: Of *course* not! That was called Louisiana steak! It was a receipt I got out of the Boston *Globe* and you ate it like you liked it, too!

MY FATHER: Well, if it was so good, why'nt you give some to Punk? What's he got to have special cat meat for? What's good enough for *me* is good enough for *him!*

MY MOTHER: No, dear, you've got it all wrong . . .

MY FATHER (*Roaring*): You mean it *ain't* good enough for him. Why I'll kick that cat clear to Gibraltar and back home again!

MY MOTHER (*Soothingly*): No, dear, no. You're so hasty, Clinton! You got the dates all wrong. The day I bought the cat meat was the day *we* had baked beans and there wasn't anything else left in the house. You can't feed a cat *beans!* And when he's hungry he's doleful and it makes me feel bad.

MY FATHER: I don't care how doleful he is, there's no call to lay out money on a cat.

MY MOTHER: Oh, *poor* Punk!

MY FATHER: Dribble, dribble, dribble, that's where the money goes. The Mellin's Food Company pays me thirty-seven dollars and fifty cents a week to be foreman of their factory and you got me runnin' up bills like I was D. W. Dollaber sittin' over in the State Street office at a rolltop mahogany desk.

MY MOTHER (*Gently reproachful*): Oh, Clinton, saying we live like Mr. Dollaber, president of the whole Mellin's Food Company!

ME: I should think the *Mellin's Food Company*'d want you to have a telephone . . .

MY FATHER: What we got to have a *cat* for?

MY MOTHER: Oh well now, Clinton, Punk's a lot of company when Ruth isn't home. Dan Weymouth thinks he's a bright cat, and he loves you, Clinton.

MY FATHER: Who? Dan Weymouth?

MY MOTHER: Clinton! Punk, of course . . . Punk loves you!

MY FATHER: A cat's a animal ain't any use to man. Boston *Globe* may not say so, but it's so all the same. Germ carriers every one of 'em. Layin' in at Singapore one time, bubonic plague broke out and everyone said it was brought aboard ship by the second mate's cat.

MY MOTHER: Dear, dear!

MY FATHER: Malay cook we had at that time tossed him right off the poop deck.

MY MOTHER: Oh, my! Whatever did the poor thing do?

MY FATHER: What the . . . What would *you* do? He swam, of course.

MY MOTHER (*Full of sympathy for the whole world of cats*): Oh, that's *dreadful*, treating a dumb animal like that!

MY FATHER: Don't know what's dumb about 'em. Don't do no work, gets a fair-to-middlin's place to live in and upwards and onwards of anywheres from three to forty square meals a day! (*My Father's eyes drift back despondently to the bill.*) What was we doin' with four tangerines?

MY MOTHER: Well now, Clinton, the child took one a day to high school, in her box of lunch . . .

MY FATHER: Can't she eat just simple plain oranges like the rest of us or is her back too weak to *lug* a piece of fruit that large? Lask week's bill was a dollar ninety-

eight and this week it's over *two dollars!*

MY MOTHER (*Gently*): Only twenty-two cents!

MY FATHER: And then there's that Dr. Adams' bill I got to pay somethin' on, and January twenty-third the North Western premium's due. I'd like to go to sleep and not come to till *January twenty-fourth!*

MY MOTHER (*In a mild reproof*): What a way to talk, dear. Why, suppose that premium slid . . . what would Ruth and I do if anything happened to you?

MY FATHER: I guess you wouldn't starve!

MY MOTHER (*With just the faintest amount of asperity*): Well, I'd like to know *why* we wouldn't!

MY FATHER (*Good and loud*): Because you'd be so stuffed full of food I'd bought you from S. S. Pierce and George Backus!

MY MOTHER: Oh dear! I know the Claflins' bill is bigger than ours . . .

MY FATHER: I don't give a . . . *what* Claflins' bill is. Claflin may be a millionaire for all I know! I just know I ain't and never *will* be, so long as I got all these bills. Why, we can't get along on thirty-seven dollars and fifty cents a week even! And what if the time came they ever had to lay me off? What would we live on *then?*

MY MOTHER: Well now, Clinton . . .

MY FATHER: I'm fifty-two years old and I've worked at the Mellin's Food Company for twenty-four years . . . And I got sixty dollars in the bank to show for it! If they ever went and laid me off, then runnin' up bills the way we do, how would we live on *that?*

MY MOTHER: Clinton, you exaggerate so; The Mellin's Food Company would *never* lay you off.

MY FATHER: How do you *know?*

MY MOTHER: Why, where could they ever get anyone like you?

MY FATHER: You can always get a foreman.

MY MOTHER: You appreciate your schooling, Ruth. It's what Papa had to do without . . . But besides, the thirty-seven dollars and fifty cents, Clinton, don't forget there's your bonus.

MY FATHER: What's that to count on? There ain't nothin' certain about a bonus till they actually hand it over—A man has to grovel and curtsey three hundred and sixty-four days a year, then the three hundred and sixty-fifth day you might offend Dollaber and a whole year's bonus is gone!

MY MOTHER: Oh well, I guess money isn't everything.

MY FATHER: Well, poverty is! Poverty's everything there is in my whole world!

MY MOTHER (*Gently reproving*): Clinton, you can't call us poverty!

MY FATHER (*Vehemently*): Yes, I can too! I even know what color it is; it's a rotten, dark brown. And it's everywhere I am, every day of the year in every kind of weather. . . . It's in my hair and eyes and nose and ears and feet. It's in my front walk when I come home at night and in *The Saturday Evening Post!*

MY MOTHER (*With a little gasp*): Clinton, you're just crazy! You're just all tired out!

MY FATHER (*Hollering*): Yes, and if I'm crazy, I'm crazy because I'm *poor!* Seems like there isn't *anything* you mention that I can afford! Not one anything! I can't even afford to take a *cold!* If Waterhouse, up on the hill, feels like it, he can have one week in, week out! Why, even when I sit down on our furniture, especially the stuff in the parlor, I sit *careful* so it won't wear out! I buy *The Saturday Evening Post* and I wish it was *The Scientific American* but I buy *The Saturday Evening Post!* Why? Because it costs just a weasely five cents and *The Scientific*

American . . . Well, what's the use talkin' . . . I got the brains and the inclination but I *ain't* got the thirty-five sou markees! (*Bitterly*) And we live on hash and stew and Louisiana cat meat for all I know, when I got a taste for oysters and curry, like they make it in Bombay, and birds' nest soup, and cheese fondoo the way that French girl fixed it in Wiscasset where I went with Fred Gee, and a good ripe custard apple they pretty near give away for nothin' at Mozambique!

MY MOTHER (*Distracted*): Oh, I don't know what to do! I *don't* know what to do, Clinton, I *really* don't!

MY FATHER (*With a world of meaning*): Don't trouble! I'm goin' out!

MY MOTHER (*Aghast*): Why, Clinton, you *can't!* It must be nine o'clock!

MY FATHER (*In a thundering tone*): Don't try to stop me! I been out every hour of the night there is!

MY MOTHER: Oh, Clinton, where are you going? (*Beseeching him*) Don't do anything rash, Clinton! *Please,* Clinton, for all our sakes!

MY FATHER (*Filled with determination and high purpose*): Nothin' rasher than to just go lay down on the New York, New Haven, and Hartford railroad tracks!

MY MOTHER (*Wringing her hands*): Oh, Clinton, you wouldn't! (*My Father stops a minute and gives a furious sneeze; his indignation reaches a new high.*)

MY FATHER (*Wrathfully*): And what's more I'm going to take that cat *with* me!

MY MOTHER (*Fervently*): Oh, Clinton, *please!!*

MY FATHER: He's gone and sneaked back on that register again! Look at him! It's a wonder he ain't fricasseed! (*To Punk*) You get out from under here!

MY MOTHER: Oh, Clinton, I'll never give him anything again, I don't care *how* he looks at me, I won't. Only *don't* go out,

Clinton, don't go out for me! Think of all I've done, dear. Think of Ruth!

MY FATHER (*Regards me with considerable irritation*): What are you readin' that you can't *stop!*

MY MOTHER: Put your book down, Ruth, and talk to Papa.

ME: (*Hastily closing my* Saturday Evening Post *over the other magazine*): It's a magazine.

MY MOTHER: Well, put it down and pay attention. Papa wants to talk. You're a *bad cat* to crawl back under there. From now on you just make up your mind to eat anything that's left over. (*Once more she shoves him out into the kitchen. Just then the doorbell rings. My Father assumes an expression of considerable displeasure. My Mother hurries to My Father; anxiously*) Sh, Clinton, they can hear you!

MY FATHER: Hear me *what?*

MY MOTHER: Go see who it is, Ruth, and if it's anyone, they can't stay long. It's nine o'clock!

MY FATHER (*Takes out his big gold watch and consults it*): You say nine o'clock every time you happen to feel like it and it ain't nine o'clock *yet!*

MY MOTHER: Pull your skirt down in back, Ruth; it shows your Equipoise.

ME (*Coming forward*): Mama, *please!* (*I go out to the hall and open the front door. From outside we hear,* "Hello, Ruth, hello." "Hello, Anna; hello, Katherine.")

MY MOTHER (*Relieved*): Oh, it's just Anna Witham and Katherine Follett.

KATHERINE: Hello, Mrs. Jones. Hello, Mr. Jones.

MY MOTHER: Hello, Katherine.

ANNA: Hello, Mrs. Jones. Hello, Mr. Jones.

MY FATHER: Hello.

MY MOTHER: Come stand by the side-board. The register'll warm you up. . . . Hello, Anna.

MY FATHER (*Motions Katherine away from the register*): No, don't get near the hot air or you'll get chilblains. If your feet are cold, don't never put 'em near the *fire*, stick 'em in cold water.

KATHERINE: Oh, I won't get chilblains, Mr. Jones. I stand by the register all the time.

MY MOTHER: Lay your coats in the hall, girls. My, Katherine, you've *grown* some more.

ME: Mama, *please!*

MY MOTHER: What?

ME (*Patiently*): People don't want to be talkin' about how tall they are.

MY MOTHER: Katherine, do you keep telling *your* mother what to say all the time?

KATHERINE (*Amiably*): Well, quite a *lot* of the time.

ME (*Making a start for the stairs*): We have to do Latin, Mama.

MY MOTHER: Well, sit down here in the dining room. Papa and I'll take our things out in the kitchen.

MY FATHER (*Clears his throat, feeling the inclination come upon him to give a short talk*): Chilblains are an awful thing! We was headin' into Halifax one time. December it was. December takes a toll of more vessels than any other month. . . .

ME (*Patiently*): Papa . . . No one's got *chilblains!*

MY FATHER: They *will* if they stand by a register . . . or get your feet wet with snow! Chilblains not only attack the hands and feet . . . in some instances they been known to cause damage to the nose. Sailin' through the Northern Straits one time, 'board a vessel answerin' to the name of *Star of Malta*—That was the first voyage out I had my spyglass. Hand it in, Ruth. The girls might like a look at her. Bought her while we was takin' on cargo at Liverpool.

MY MOTHER: Here it is. (*She starts for the parlor briskly, glad to seize this opportunity to humor My Father.*)

MY FATHER: Good as she ever was; best glass to be had for the money!

KATHERINE (*Somewhat nonplussed*): Uh huh . . .

MY FATHER: The lens is ground by Karl and Rausch of Hamburg . . . I set great store by that glass.

KATHERINE: Mmm . . .

MY MOTHER: Put it back on the parlor mantel, Ruth, right where it was. (*I do so.*)

MY FATHER: If you ever have occasion—

MY MOTHER: Clinton, the daily slips from Backus are out on the kitchen spindle. You take Pierce's order sheet and I'll go light the lamp. Close the door after Papa, Ruth, so's not to be disturbing. (*My Mother goes out. My Father takes the catalogue and order sheet and his fountain pen and glasses.*)

MY FATHER (*Genially, to Katherine*): Don't never make port in Halifax in wintertime, if you can make some other arrangements! (*He goes out.*)

KATHERINE (*Pleasantly consoling*): Goodness, Ruth, your *father!*

ANNA (*As though she was speaking of something a little bit shady*): Was he a sailor long?

ME: Oh sure, but of course it was quite a while ago. (*I get* The Theatre Magazine *from inside* The Saturday Evening Post.)

ANNA (*In terrific excitement*): There it *is!*

KATHERINE (*Equally excited*): Let's see!

ME (*In alarm*): Sh!!

ANNA: What's the matter?

ME: I don't want Papa to see it.

ANNA: Why not?

ME: He'd kill me!

ANNA: Why?

ME: Because it costs thirty-five cents.

ANNA (*Excitedly*): Did it have the Hazel Dawn pictures?

ME (*Perfectly radiant*): A whole *page!*

KATHERINE (*All agog*): Scenes from *The Pink Lady?*

ME: One is. The others are all her in *private life!*

ANNA (*Thrusting* The Theatre Magazine *at me*): Find it, Ruth, *hurry!*

ME (*I have by now looked at the pictures so often, I am able to turn to the page at once*): Here!

KATHERINE (*Rapturous*): Look at her in her auto . . .

ANNA (*Overwhelmed*): It's a *Pierce-Arrow!*

ME (*Happily*): A Pierce-Arrow runabout!

ANNA (*Eagerly*): Where does it say she lives at?

ME (*Impressed*): At her home in Rutherford, New Jersey.

ANNA: Ruth, if Hazel Dawn hadn't answered *your* letter, do you think you would *still* be going to be an actress?

ME (*Proudly*): Seein' *The Pink Lady* changed my whole life.

ANNA: But did you think right there in the Colonial Theatre you'd go be an actress yourself?

ME: I don't know if I did exactly, I mean at the matinee. Of course I knew right off I'd rather be like Hazel Dawn than anybody else in the world, but then when *I* got the letter from her and *you didn't* . . . well . . . I knew then I must be different. *Before* that I thought I was just only peculiar. Katherine, open your Latin book, so if Papa comes in . . .

KATHERINE (*Doing as requested*): Ruth . . . when do you think you're going to ever tell your father?

ANNA: Tell him what?

KATHERINE: About going on the stage?

ANNA (*Astonished*): Ruth, haven't you told your own father you're going to be an actress?

ME (*With a good deal of expression*): Mercy . . . No!

KATHERINE (*Placidly, turning the pages of her Latin book*): He'd kill her. (*Guardedly*) Oh, Mr. Jones has a terrible disposition. Why, when Ruth only went and looked in the Waterhouses' window the night Gertrude Waterhouse got married, Mr. Jones grabbed Ruth by the ear when she came home and kept banging her head down *right there* on this dining-room table. (*She reaches over and designates the exact spot.*)

ANNA: *Golly!*

KATHERINE: And hollering at her, "You old *goat!*"

ANNA: Ruth, why should your father get so mad at you rubbering at the Waterhouses? We were all up there doing it.

KATHERINE: It's just Mr. Jones's *disposition!*

ME: He was mad because he and Mama got invited but he didn't have a dress suit.

ANNA: I suppose he got that way being a sailor.

KATHERINE (*Disapprovingly*): He wants her to be a Physical Culture instructor!

ME (*Briefly*): I would rather be *dead!*

KATHERINE (*Loyal even to handing me the hemlock*): Oh, Ruth'd just as soon kill herself.

ME (*Threateningly*): I certainly *would!*

ANNA: Well, why does your father think you should be a Physical . . .

ME: Anna, open *your* Collar and Daniels, too.

KATHERINE (*Turning the pages of* The Theatre Magazine): Here's a picture of Edith Wynne Matthison with her own fox terrier.

ANNA (*Opening her Latin book as requested*): Why does he want you to be a Physical . . .

ME (*Very disgusted, poring over my Latin book*): Oh, because he goes in Boston to that evenin' gymnastic class at the Y.M.C.A.

KATHERINE (*Equally disgusted, turning the pages of the magazine*): To keep from having a cold or something . . .

ME: And he's wild about the director of it, Mr. Bagley, and Mr. Bagley has a friend, Miss Glavin, that's a Physical Culture instructor.

KATHERINE (*To Anna*): Out to Brookline . . .

ME: And she's so healthy, Papa wants *me* to be one . . .

KATHERINE (*Admiringly, to Anna*): Ruth'd rather be dead.

ANNA: But you couldn't be an actress, could you, without telling your father?

KATHERINE: You have to tell him *some* time!

ME: But no matter what he says I'm goin' to be an actress. I'm goin' to be somebody wonderful like you *read* about. I don't want to be just *people.*

ANNA: Well, but . . .

ME: And I want to have everythin' around me gorgeous and no *scrimpin'* and *plannin'.* But have things be all rich and careless. And I want to have stunnin' clothes and travel around in parlor cars and ocean liners. Sometimes in the South Station, when the Merchants' Limited is next track, I see the pink lights on in the dinin' car and the parlor cars all mahogany and green velvet with fringe and not one person on the whole train looks economical.

KATHERINE: Gosh!

ME: *Everyone* looks extravagant . . . and that's how I want to be. If I have to be rich, I will be, but what I *want* is to be *extravagant!* It's disgustin' to be normal.

And I want to meet famous people and see what they look like close to. Hazel Dawn and Woodrow Wilson and Willie K. Vanderbilt . . .

KATHERINE: Oh, Ruth, *they* wouldn't want to meet *you*!

ME: They have to if *I* get wonderful. They got to meet *somebody*!

ANNA: Ruth, could I see your *own* Hazel Dawn picture again? The one she sent you herself?

ME (*Jumping up and going up on the landing*): All right. And I'm goin' to have a Pierce-Arrow car and a country place of my own in some gorgeous place like Rutherford, New Jersey. Or some other gorgeous place just as good! And I'm goin' to have Mama and Papa be livin' in a house up on the hill with a hired girl and *another* Pierce-Arrow car and a thoroughbred fox terrier. And of course we'll run up terrible grocery bills and *never* look at the price! And every single thing we don't like, the minute it wears out we'll just give it away! I'm goin' to get everythin' great for *everybody*! It's disgustin' to live just to support yourself!

KATHERINE: Gorry!

ME (*Hurrying upstairs*): I'll get my Hazel Dawn.

KATHERINE (*Ecstatically, carried away*): Oh, *get* it! (*Looking around perfectly delightedly*) It's like reading *Green Book Magazine* to hear Ruth talk!

ANNA: I wonder if an actress *could* come from a place like here.

KATHERINE: They always come from more like San Francisco.

ANNA: Or Utah.

KATHERINE: Or where Ethel Barrymore comes from . . .

ANNA: And a lot come from convents. (*The kitchen door opens and My Mother comes in.*)

MY MOTHER: Here's some marble cake . . . Why, where's Ruth gone to? (*Anna and Katherine both stand up politely.*)

ANNA (*Delicately*): She had to go upstairs.

KATHERINE: Oh, *thank* you, Mrs. Jones. (*I come rushing downstairs with the picture, which I quickly put behind my back.*)

MY MOTHER (*Affably*): What you got, Ruth?

ME: Nothin'.

MY MOTHER: Well, put it away where Papa can't see it. (*She goes back to the kitchen and closes the door. We each take a piece of cake and some of the ensuing conversation is kind of full-mouthed. I display the picture guardedly in front of my Collar and Daniels.*)

ME: Here it is!

ANNA (*Rapturous*): Oh!

ME: I'll keep it back of my Latin book in case of Papa.

ANNA (*Fervently*): Aren't her furs gorgeous!

KATHERINE: Ruth! . . . If you're an actress, *you* might have furs!

ME: I'm goin' to! Squirrel for every day and plain white tailless ermine for night life. I should think everyone in this whole *world* would want to be an actress!

ANNA: I know it!

KATHERINE: I think more people would if they didn't have to act in *front* of everybody.

ME (*Looking at the picture and at the same time managing to sing softly through some cake*): "To you, Beautiful Lady, I raise my eyes!" (*Anna and Katherine join in—softly so the sound won't seep out into the kitchen.*)

ALL THREE OF US:
"My heart, Beautiful Lady . . .
To your heart cries . . ."

(*I, with the Hazel Dawn picture in my hands, waltz down beyond the dining-room table.*)

KATHERINE: Oh, Ruth, you're the limit!
(*Anna doesn't know any more of the words
and Katherine is temporarily halted by a
fresh mouthful of cake. Nothing halts
me.*)
ME: "Dream, dream . . . Dream and
      forget! . . .
      Care, pain, useless regret . . ."
ANNA (*Breaking in*): Oh, and "Flow,
River, flow! . . ."
ALL THREE OF US:
      "Down to the sea,
        Bright sea . . ."
KATHERINE: Oh, I'm wild about this!
ALL THREE OF US:
". . . bring my loved one home to me.
True, dear one, true,
   I'm trying hard to be
But hear me say:
   It's a very long, long way,
From the banks of the Seine,
   For a girl to go and stay
By the banks of the Saskatchewan.

By the banks of the Seine,
With girls so beautiful—"
(*The kitchen door flies open and My Father comes in.*)
MY FATHER (*Indignantly*): Do you
have to *sing out* your lessons? Your mother
and I went and moved our stuff out here
because you said you had to *study!*
ME (*Very meek*): We're just goin' to,
Papa.
MY FATHER: Well, get at it and don't
combine it with nothin'! A education is
denied to *most* people, so treat it with some
respect. Given *your* opportunities . . .
(*Noticing* Theatre Magazine's *gaily col-
ored cover*) Why, what the—What's this?
ME: It's nothin', just a magazine.
MY FATHER: *The Theatre Magazine!*
Why, where'd this come from?
ME (*Frightened*): It's nothin' at all. I
just happened to have it.

MY FATHER (*Reading from the cover*):
Thirty-five cents! Did you get stung thirty-
five cents for this?
ME (*In a very small voice*): No.
MY FATHER: Well, where the—Where
did you get it?
ME: I . . .
MY FATHER: Did you go fling *money*
away on this trash?
ME: It's Katherine's. I borrowed it.
MY FATHER: Oh . . . Well, stow it away.
(*Out he goes.*)
ANNA: Gosh!
ME: Excuse me sayin' it was your *The-
atre Magazine*, Katherine.
ANNA: Oh, you *had* to.
KATHERINE: *That* was all right.
ANNA (*Distressed*): But, Ruth, if you
can't even tell your father about *Theatre
Magazine*, how could you ever actually tell
him you're going to be an actress yourself?
ME: He can't stop me.
KATHERINE: I don't know, Ruth. Your
father's very *firm*.
ME: Nobody can stop me. You want to
know somethin'? Somethin' so *great* I
thought maybe I'd *never* tell *anyone*?
KATHERINE: What?
ANNA: *What*, Ruth?
ME (*My fingers trembling with excite-
ment, I remove a letter pinned by a large
safety pin to the inner side of my corset
cover*): Look!
ANNA: What is it?
ME: Look! I walked down to the Post
Office tonight just like any old night and
there *this* was, right there in the Wollaston
Post Office, just like it might have been
nothin'!
KATHERINE: Is it a letter from *Hazel
Dawn?*
ME: It's a letter from Miss Doris Olsson,
leadin' lady of the whole John Craig Castle
Square stock company invitin' me to come
to see her *tomorrow!*

KATHERINE (*In terrific excitement*): What?

ANNA: *Ruth!*

ME: To come see her *behind the scenes!*

ANNA (*So excited she stands right up*): *Ruth!!*

KATHERINE (*Gets up, too*): Oh, *mercy!*

ME: I wrote her about how to start goin' on the stage and she wrote me back to come *see* her.

KATHERINE: Oh, *read it!*

ME: Right in her own dressin' room!

ANNA: Oh, *I'll die!* (*Katherine reaches for the letter.*)

ME: Don't *touch* it. I'm goin' to get it framed.

KATHERINE: Oh, *Ruth!*

ANNA: *Hurry!*

ME (*Transported*): "Castle Square Theatre—Castle Square—Boston, Mass. January 19, Dear Miss Jones: . . ."

KATHERINE: Read it slowly!

ME: "Castle Square Theatre—Castle Square—Boston, Mass. January, 19, Dear Miss Jones: Thank you for your letter. I think it is fine that you want to be an actress. If you ever come to a matinee perhaps you would like to come to my dressing room and meet me. . . ."

KATHERINE (*Half a moan—half a suppressed shriek*): Oh!

ANNA (*Almost equally wrenched by events*): Oh, *mercy!*

KATHERINE: Oh, Ruth, read it *again!*

ME (*Calm outwardly, but obviously uplifted*): *Wait*, I didn't *finish* yet. (*An appropriate pause*) "Sincerely yours, Doris Olsson."

KATHERINE (*Speaking from her very soul*): Oh, she must be *beautiful!* (*Anna just wags her head in inarticulate corroboration.*)

ME (*Almost mystical*): Does it really seem as though a thing like that can happen to anyone in Wollaston? (*We all three sit lost in wonder at the magic of fate.*)

KATHERINE (*Recovering a little bit*): But, Ruth, you said *tomorrow.*

ME: Well, the next matinee *is* tomorrow.

ANNA (*Distressed*): But tomorrow's a school day.

ME (*Adamant*): Then I'll say I'm sick. I'll say I have a headache.

ANNA (*Worried*): Miss O'Neill'll *never* let you go home for that.

ME: Well, then, I'll throw up!

KATHERINE: Oh, that'll be *wonderful!* What do you think you'll wear?

ME: My new red tango-color dress. Some of it's only basted, but it's the only thing stylish I've got.

ANNA: Oh, you'll look stunning! Will you do your hair any different?

KATHERINE: Ruth, do it like Hazel Dawn's! (*She picks up the photograph.*) Here, stand up. Let me try it.

ME: All right.

ANNA: I'll hold the picture for you. (*As I jump up I catch sight of myself in the sideboard mirror and suddenly feel discouraged.*)

ME: I look funny.

KATHERINE (*Loyally*): No, you don't. You'll look darling with your hair like Hazel Dawn.

ME: I don't mean my hair! I mean all over.

KATHERINE: You do not! You know what Clark Boynton told Gladys Bain . . .

ME (*Embarrassed*): Katherine!

ANNA: What?

ME: If you tell that . . .

ANNA: Go on. What'd he say?

KATHERINE (*To me*): You went and told Anna I was crazy about Herbert Mann!

ME: Well, that's nothin'.

KATHERINE (*To Anna*): Clark Boynton

went and told Gladys Bain, Ruth had a cute *shape!*

ANNA (*Quite shocked*): Why, that's repulsive!

ME (*Mortified*): I'm goin' to tell everyone Herbert Mann's cousin says she wouldn't be surprised if when the *proper time* comes you and he get married!

KATHERINE (*Delighted*): Oh, she's a pill!

ANNA (*Thoughtfully*): He's asked you to go to Harvard Class Day with him.

KATHERINE (*Happily sarcastic*): Well, does that mean I'm going to *marry* him?

ANNA: It most always does at Harvard.

KATHERINE (*Simply bursting with pleasure*): Heavens! He's five years older than me!

ME: Ellen Terry was only seventeen and *she* married a man old enough to be her grandfather.

ANNA: That's repulsive!

ME: Oh, I don't mean *I* would.

KATHERINE: Fred Whitmarsh is older than you are! *Ha! Ha!*

ME (*Disdainfully*): Fred Whitmarsh!!! *Mercy!*

ANNA: He's cute, though.

ME: Oh, he's all right; he's nothin'.

ANNA: He's rich.

ME: I probably'll *never* get married. On the stage you don't have to. Actresses aren't *ever* old maids.

KATHERINE: But say you went and fell in love?

ME: I can't let myself. (*Just then the doorbell rings. Hastily I snatch up* Theatre Magazine *and thrust it back in the sideboard drawer. To Katherine*) Your father goin' to call for you?

KATHERINE (*Disdainfully*): Perish the thought!

ME (*Fiercely*): Don't say anythin' about anythin' to *anybody!*

MY MOTHER (*Coming in from the kitchen*): Who's that, do you suppose? (*I hastily close up Hazel Dawn's picture in my Latin book lest my father should come in, too. Some blocks away, the factory whistle blows the curfew and My Mother calls back to the kitchen.*) Well, now it's nine o'clock, Clinton. There's the curfew. Ruth, see who's at the door.

MY FATHER (*From the kitchen doorway*): Who is it? (*I open the door.*)

ME: Oh, hello—it's nine o'clock . . .

MY MOTHER: Who is it, Ruth?

MY FATHER: Who'd you say it was?

MY MOTHER: Mercy! . . . Why, hello, Fred. You're out late! (*Calling back to My Father*) It's just Fred Whitmarsh.

FRED: Well . . . er . . . I saw the light on so I knew you were still sitting up. . . .

MY MOTHER (*Cordially*): Well, we're not sitting up *long,* Fred, but you can come in for a minute. . . .

MY FATHER (*Trying to place him*): I thought *you* were at Harvard College.

FRED: I was. I mean I *am,* but tonight's my sister Lillian's birthday, so I came out home to supper.

MY FATHER (*Finding himself uninterested*): Oh . . . well . . . (*And he goes back to the kitchen, followed by My Mother.*)

ANNA: Hi, Fred.

FRED: Hello.

ME: Want to take your coat off?

FRED: All right. (*To Katherine*) Where's Herbert?

KATHERINE (*Elaborately*): Gracious! How should I know? (*To me*) Anna and I have to go . . .

ME (*Nonchalantly*): No, you don't. . . .

KATHERINE: Ruth, after you finish with *Theatre Magazine* could I borrow it if I give it right back?

ANNA: After Katherine, could *I?*

ME: Uh huh.

ANNA: Meet you in front of Brooks' seven-thirty tomorrow?

KATHERINE: And if it's awful, I got three school trip tickets left over and we can take the trolley.

ME: I'd rather walk. . . .

ANNA: If it's not zero . . .

KATHERINE: They won't be good next month. . . . Well, good night.

ANNA: Good night.

FRED: Good night.

ME: Good night. (*And down the walk we hear the crunch of their feet through the snow. There is a pause, then Fred picks up the book I have left on the table.*)

FRED: I don't think Latin trains your bean. I've forgot it already.

ME: Oh sure.

MY MOTHER (*Out in the kitchen, calling to our pet*): Here, Punk . . . Here, Punk . . . Here, good Punkie, Punkie, Punk. . . . He's back of the stove! (*My Mother has raised her voice to attract Punk's attention and in doing so has also attracted Fred's and mine. We listen for a moment, then, with no acknowledgment that we have been listening, Fred continues.*)

FRED: Latin never seemed to be *about* anything. They were all kind of bughouse . . . er . . . Caesar and Cicero and Virgil . . .

ME: Oh sure. . . .

FRED: Ever read *Ben Hur*?

ME: In Latin?

FRED: No, just in a book.

MY FATHER (*From the kitchen*): Why, he's gone and wedged himself back under the boiler. . . . Come here! Come here, worse-than-useless. (*Fred and I have halted, our attention automatically distracted.*)

MY MOTHER (*In the kitchen*): Here, Punkie . . . (*Apparently her efforts are successful.*) There! I'll put him out, Clinton. You go fix the furnace. . . .

FRED: Ben Hur was Roman like those others but it was a *good* book.

ME: None of the books in *Latin* are good or anythin'. They're not supposed to be. You just have to take it for the college course. Not that I'm goin' to college, but I didn't know I wasn't goin' when I took the college course. . . . (*Suddenly the kitchen door opens, My Father goes through the entry and out the cellar door. My Mother follows him with Punk in her arms, stiff with revolt. She opens the front door and pushes Punk out on the porch.*)

MY MOTHER: Punk's just like me, doesn't like cold weather. Did you offer Fred a piece of cake, Ruth? There's some more. . . .

ME: Mama, he doesn't want cake!

MY MOTHER: Oh, doesn't he? Well, it's right there. (*She goes into the kitchen.*)

FRED: I thought you were going to Radcliffe.

ME: *Radcliffe!* They're all suffragettes. At school today—(*Downstairs there is a rumbling and shaking. My Father is bedding down the furnace.*) At school today, Mr. Collins had me down in his office to ask if I was registerin' for college and I said I wasn't.

FRED: Oh, college doesn't cut any ice with *me!*

ME: When I told Mr. Collins I *wasn't* goin' he looked sort of funny. I felt as though I'd cut off the last ties of respectability.

FRED: Why?

ME (*Having said more than I meant to*): Oh . . . no particular reason . . .

FRED: What *will* you do?

ME (*Airily*): Oh, I don't really know.

FRED: Be kind of bum just sitting around Wollaston. (*My Mother comes in with a square, open-top wooden box with a handle on it. It is divided into partitions.*)

ME (*Patiently*): Mama, do you have to do that *now*?

MY MOTHER: Well, I should think I

did! Look what time it is. Papa and I have to go to bed.

ME (*Mortified*): Mama!

MY MOTHER: Well, Fred doesn't mind me saying that. (*She opens the sideboard drawer and starts putting away silver in the box.*)

ME: I mean do you have to do that with the *silver?*

MY MOTHER (*Indignantly*): Well, of course I do. This is solid silver. I can't leave it around! (*She holds up a small silver cream pitcher and sugar bowl for Fred to see.*) Mr. Edward F. Atkins gave me these for a wedding present. I was his stenographer. . . .

ME: Secretary, Mama!

MY MOTHER: Secretary. I'd been his . . . er . . . secretary for three years and the day I left to get married, his wife, *Mrs.* Atkins came all the way in from Hopedale and gave me these. They're from Bigelow Kennard's, and she said, "I just want to tell you how much Mr. Atkins is going to mind losing you because I know Mr. Atkins is never going to tell you so himself."

ME: Mama, Fred isn't . . .

MY MOTHER: Well, I don't suppose he is. But I'm certainly not going to leave things like these down here for anyone to just walk in and help themselves to. They go right in this box, right under my bed. (*There is a gentle thud at the window connecting with the front porch. My Mother puts her silver down and goes to open the window.*) There's Punk! . . . After I'm gone and they're yours, then you do as you see fit, but I . . . (*She lifts the cat in and dusts some snow off his fur.*) Put him down cellar, Ruth.

ME: Oh, Mama, now I'll get all fur!

MY MOTHER (*Exasperated*): Why, his fur's not coming off in January; don't be so notional. (*As I take Punk to the entry and thrust him through the cellar door, she calls in a good loud voice*) Oh, Clinton! (*But the furnace is giving out such rumbles, My Father cannot hear.*) Sing out to your father, Ruth. I don't want him to let Punk up again.

ME: Oh, he won't, Mama.

MY MOTHER (*To Fred*): Punk could just as well as not stay right here all night, but he gets up on the piano in the parlor and eats my Boston fern.

FRED: He does?

MY MOTHER: And I wouldn't mind if he enjoyed it but he doesn't. He just loves to jump up and bite the leaves off, then all he does is chew 'em around for a while and drop 'em out on the floor. . . .

MY FATHER (*Opening the cellar door*): Get back there, Punk!

MY MOTHER: Ruth, step out in the kitchen and hand me the alarm clock and don't drop it bringing it in.

MY FATHER (*Winding up his big gold watch with the key hanging from his chain*): Well . . . good night.

MY MOTHER: Hurry up, Ruth. Papa's saying good night.

ME (*Coming in with the battered tin alarm clock*): Good night. (*My Father and I give each other a withering New England kiss and My Mother and I the same. My Mother adds a little hug.*) Mama, please!

MY MOTHER: Good night, Fred. Don't sit up all night, Ruth. You go to bed by nine-thirty, and, Fred, *you* come again.

MY FATHER (*Halfway up the stairs*): And when you're through with it, put the lamp out. (*He disappears.*)

MY MOTHER: Yes. Good night. (*And she, too, goes off upstairs. There is a pause of a moment for us to shake off their presence.*)

FRED: I dropped by because I been thinking about something I thought I'd like to get settled. . . .

ME: What?

FRED: Well, I don't know how you feel about it and I don't know even if there's anyone you'd rather go with.... (*Upstairs a door slams.*)

ME: Where?

FRED: And of course it isn't for several *months*. . . .

MY MOTHER'S VOICE (*From upstairs*): Oh, Clinton!

ME: Uh huh.

FRED: But I know there's no one else I . . .

MY MOTHER'S VOICE: Oh, Clinton! (*Upstairs a door opens.*)

MY FATHER'S VOICE: Did you sing out?

MY MOTHER'S VOICE: The alarm clock says nine-seventeen. Is that right?

MY FATHER'S VOICE: Close enough. (*The door closes.*)

FRED: It's kind of noisy in here. Would you want to go into the kitchen and maybe make some cocoa?

ME: Perish the thought!

FRED: Oh. (*Upstairs there is a rush of water into the tin-lined bathtub.*)

ME: Where did you mean for me to go to?

MY MOTHER'S VOICE (*Startled*): Why, Clinton, you going to take a *bath*?

MY FATHER'S VOICE: No. I was just testin' her out to see the pipes hadn't froze.

FRED (*After a decent pause*): If you don't feel like cocoa . . .

ME: Uh uh!

FRED: Then, would you want to go in the kitchen and get a glass of water?

ME: No thanks.

MY MOTHER'S VOICE: Let me know when you're through, Clinton. I want to come in.

FRED (*After a mild nervous reaction, points to the kitchen*): Cocoa or water or *anything*?

ME: Nope. (*Upstairs a door opens.*)

MY FATHER'S VOICE: All right, come ahead.

FRED: I just thought maybe you might be thirsty.

MY MOTHER'S VOICE (*Upstairs, gently singing as she goes down the hall*):
"Sweet hour of prayer, sweet hour of prayer
   That leads me from this world of care."
(*The door shuts.*)

FRED: The only thing is . . . I just thought in the kitchen . . .

ME (*Sternly*): No, Fred, I'm not ever goin' in the kitchen.... That is, not ever with a fellow....

FRED: Oh, I don't care anything about it *personally*. I just thought maybe you . . .

ME: Even if it was *President Taft* asked me to make cocoa, I wouldn't go in the kitchen with *him!*

FRED: President Taft's married.

ME (*Fervently*): I can't help it!

FRED: Oh. . . . Well, anyway what I came to ask you about—and the reason I came to ask you *tonight* is, the Harvard Class Day Invitations Committee got elected today and I'm on the committee....

ME: Oh, Fred, that's *dandy!*

FRED: And you're the only girl I feel like this about, so would you go to Harvard Class Day with me?

ME: *Fred!*

FRED: Well, would you? It's not till June, of course.

ME: Oh gee, Fred!!!

FRED: June the *fifteenth*.

ME: Harvard Class Day! . . . Oh *gorry*. . . . Oh, Fred. Oh, that's *wonderful!!!* Harvard Class Day! . . . *Golly!* You know sometimes how you get thinkin' about things? You know? How no fellow will ever send you flowers? Or take you to the Harvard and Yale football game: Or ask you to—well, I just soon say it—ask you to get married? Well, look, Fred, I really never *did* think anyone would ever, so long as I lived, ask me to Class Day at Harvard College. And here I am and I *did* get invited. . . . Gee, Fred, even if I never *do* go, it's *dandy* bein' invited.

FRED: What do you mean, if you never *do* go? You're coming with me!

ME: Well, I'd like to only . . . only you know what Harvard Class Day sort of means . . . well, *you* know.

FRED (*Earnestly*): Yes, I *do* know and that's what I mean. I don't want you to think I just *said* that. . . . I mean without thinking. I *have* thought about it. I've thought about it quite a lot. I didn't know exactly if I'd *say* anything to you about it until after I graduate, but since the subject's come up, I'm *glad* it has. I'm kind of glad to get it off my *chest!*

ME: Oh, Fred, I really thought everyone in the whole *world* would get asked but me!!

FRED: I thought I'd wait till day after graduation and then I'd speak to your father about it . . .

MY FATHER'S VOICE: Has he gone yet?

FRED: I thought I'd maybe write him a *letter*.

ME: Fred, I guess you got to go. . . .

FRED: All right. I guess I better. Is it all right if I drop back tomorrow?

ME: Yes, only you better go *now*, Fred.

FRED: I'll see you tomorrow. I guess I better put my collar up. . . . It's cold out. . . . It's cold out to Cambridge. Somebody thought—I don't know if it will or not—the Charles River might freeze over.

MY FATHER'S VOICE: Good night.

MY MOTHER'S VOICE: Good night, Clinton. (*Two doors close. Fred picks up courage and turns back into the room.*)

FRED: Say! . . . Have you heard "Too Much Mustard"?

ME: No. . . .

FRED: Out to Cambridge everybody's dippy about it; they play it all the time.

(*He starts to hum it, softly, but still with quite a bit of zip.*) It's to do the maxixe to. . . . Here, let me show you. (*He takes my hand, puts his arm around me and humming softly we dance a few steps of a very mild maxixe, by the dining-room table. Fred, letting himself go, lets out his voice with quite a bit of volume. Suddenly—*)

MY FATHER'S VOICE (*Hollering out good and loud to My Mother*): Claflin's gone and got his Graphophone on again!

ME (*In alarm*): Look, Fred. You got to go. . . .

(*Fred suddenly leans down and plants a kiss on my mouth, then jumps as if he'd been stung, out into the hall and straight out through the front door.*)

Don't!!

(*But the door is closed and he is gone. I just stand kind of moody and transfixed. Something makes me drift over to the sideboard mirror where I look at myself and suddenly smile simply bewitchingly—at least as bewitchingly as a person can smile at herself. After a bit, I look at my right profile and, satisfied, I look at my left. Then I cast a glance over what appears in our sideboard mirror of my "cute shape." I seem gently pleased with all sides of myself and very softly hum a snatch of "Too Much Mustard," and resume a gentle maxixe. It is so dreamy that it is more like a maxixe done under water. . . . But as I float round I catch sight of the Hazel Dawn picture. I stop short, pick up the picture and look at it long and hard. Just then the train rattles by; the whistle sounds; the little room is full of clatter and rush. I stop and listen . . . look around the room. Then I take the letter from my corset cover, look at it rapturously, then back at the picture. I am safe. The train is going somewhere and so am I. Only a brief moment and the Hazel Dawn picture and the Doris Olsson letter have won me back. Without taking my eyes off them, I start singing softly again. Not "Too Much Mustard" this time. Cambridge can have it! "To You Beautiful Lady," I sing softly but fervently as I waltz over to turn out the gasolier and thoughtfully reach for the last piece of marble cake.*

On I waltz out into the front hall, try the outer door, all the time keeping step, put out the hall light, and, without ever stopping, waltz right upstairs to my own room and slam the door.)

CURTAIN

Let's consider . . .

1. Ruth Gordon called her play *Years Ago*. What incidents in this act could have happened only years ago? What things did people in those days miss? What things do you take for granted that were unheard of in those days?

2. Ruth and her friends were thrilled when they looked at the glamour photograph of Hazel Dawn. In the same way, many of you probably enjoy looking at photographs of your favorite stage, movie, or television stars. In what other ways were Ruth and her family and friends just like people today?

3. Punk was not very popular with Father. Is there a pet in your household? Is he equally popular with all members of the family? If not, tell the class why.

4. Father did not approve of *The Theatre Magazine*, particularly when he saw the price. What extravagance do you have that *your* parents do not approve of?

5. To the girls: Would you have treated Fred as casually as Ruth did? Explain.

To the boys: Would you have invited Ruth to a school dance? Explain.

ACT TWO

SCENE ONE

My Mother is laying the tablecloth on the dining-room table in great style. My Mother is full of hostess worries. I come downstairs, buttoning the back of my dress —carried away by my own excitement from the visit of this afternoon.

ME: Oh, Mama, nothin' can ever happen to me in my whole *life* like this afternoon!

MY MOTHER: Get the pink rose embroidered center piece Mrs. Brigham made me and put it right here on the table. Oh dear, Ruth, I *wish* you hadn't gone to see Miss Doris Olsson just the very day your father chooses to invite company.

ME: When I went in the stage door of the Castle Square Theatre, Mama, my knees shook and my eyes kind of felt all glazed over, and I think I kind of died right in the alley and then came to life as somebody else.

MY MOTHER: Ruth, please try not to look so *happy!* Your father'll know right *off* something's the matter.

ME: I should think you'd be *glad* I had somethin' lovely happen so I can bear this visit better.

MY MOTHER (*Worriedly*): It's one thing to write letters to actresses and get their pictures from them, but to go visit them in their dressing rooms and not have your own father know it!

ME: I can stand it, but oh, *why* did Mr. Bagley and Miss Glavin have to come out here *tonight?*

MY MOTHER: Because they're giving the

Baptist Church entertainment. Now set out the teaspoons.

ME: But why didn't you and Papa just go *see* the entertainment?

MY MOTHER: Oh, Ruth, you know as well as I do your father won't go inside a church!

ME: He's gone to the Baptist Church to bring 'em back here, hasn't he?

MY MOTHER: He's gone to *meet* them, at the front *walk* of the Baptist Church.

ME (*Sternly*): *They* can't talk me into bein' a Physical Culture instructress, Mama, and just meetin' Miss Glavin isn't goin' to get me interested. (*Relapsing into rapture again*) Oh, Mama, if you had just *seen* Miss Olsson! Her make-up was so *beautiful!* Bright blue paint on her eyelids and little red dots painted in each eye . . .

MY MOTHER: Now hand me Mr. Atkins' sugar bowl and pitcher. Oh, Ruth, I really think it would kill me if I ever saw *your* face painted red and blue.

ME: And Miss Olsson's costume was red silk *imported* panne velvet.

MY MOTHER: Just for curiosity once, I *priced* some panne velvet.

ME: It had two panniers edged with skunk fur edged with red chiffon rosebuds and a two-foot fork-ed train. Her sister made it for her. She makes *all* her costumes for her!

MY MOTHER: Look in that drawer and get out the cake knife.

ME: They live in a flat out to Back Bay.

MY MOTHER: Who does?

ME: Miss Doris Olsson, Mama! Miss Doris Olsson and her sister.

MY MOTHER: Put Papa's spyglass up here on the mantel. Papa might want to show it to Mr. Bagley and Miss Glavin.

ME: Oh, Mama, they won't want to see it.

MY MOTHER: Well, put it up there *any-*

way. . . . (I go into the parlor for it.) Papa'll like the look of it!

ME: If Mr. Bagley and Miss Glavin *already* had supper at the Baptist Church sociable, what do *we* have to give 'em anythin' for?

MY MOTHER (*Indignantly*): Why, you got to feed company *something!*

ME: And Miss Olsson noticed *my* dress, Mama. Oh, I *wished* you'd let me had the slit in it! She went and noticed it *several* times!

MY MOTHER: Then I'm happy she must have noticed you came from decent people!

ME: Anybody can be decent! I'd rather look like I had some *go!* Did you talk to the telephone company like you *promised?*

MY MOTHER (*In exasperation*): Oh, darn it! That's *another* thing! Ruth, you shouldn't have *made* me promise. . . .

ME: What did they say? It'll be all right, Mama. Papa didn't *exactly* say no.

MY MOTHER: Well, he didn't say *yes,* either. I really don't know how I get roped into these things. They went and said they'd put it in *tomorrow!*

ME (*Exuberantly*): *Tomorrow!* Oh, Mama!

MY MOTHER: I never thought they could bring a telephone so *soon!* (*In consternation*) Why, there's Fred Whitmarsh coming up the walk. He can't *stay,* Ruth! He wouldn't be appropriate. Papa wouldn't want him in the way. (*I open the door.*)

ME: Oh, hello, Fred.

FRED (*Stepping just inside the door*): Hello.

ME: You can't stay long. Papa's havin' company.

MY MOTHER: Hello, Fred. Mercy, Ruth, you're abrupt.

ME: Well, you said to be.

MY MOTHER: Well, I said—you see,

Fred, Mr. Jones is having some very special people here, so . . .

FRED (*Reassuringly*): Oh, I'm not going to *stay*.

MY MOTHER: Well then, *that's* lovely! Ruth, I'll just run upstairs and get on my dotted Swiss apron and my engagement ring.

ME: All right. (*She hurries up the stairs.*)

FRED (*Proffering me a package*): I brought you this. Did you get to think any more about—er—Class Day?

ME (*Taking the package*): What is it? No, I'm sorry, Fred. I really didn't.

FRED: Two pounds of Huyler's. I didn't think you'd have time yet.

ME: Oh, thank you—no, I just honestly didn't. I want to go, Fred. I want to a whole *lot!*

FRED: Well, why *can't* you, then? Herbert Mann's asked Katherine. . . . Gosh, what *is* it? Have you heard something *awful* about me?

ME: Oh, *no*, Fred, it's just that . . . Well, it's just that . . .

FRED: Someone *else?*

ME: No. . . . Not some*one* . . . some*thing!* (*The doorbell rings.*)

FRED: What?

ME: Oh mercy, maybe it's them. Mama! Oh *mercy!*

FRED (*Reassuringly*): I'm just going. Should I go out the back door? (*I fearfully open the door.*)

ME: Oh *mercy!* Oh, come in, Mr. Sparrow.

MR. SPARROW: What's happened to you? You got a telegram.

ME: Why I did *not!* Let me see it.

MR. SPARROW: You got a telegram all right. It come over Mr. Fay's pay station and I says *I* was *walkin'* this way, so I just soon carry it to you.

ME (*Taking the folded note paper from Mr. Sparrow*): Are you *sure* it's for me?

MR. SPARROW: That's what I say to *Mr. Fay,* but he says, "She's Ruth Gordon Jones, ain't she?"

ME: Oh, yes. Oh, I'm *her* . . . *she,* I mean. Oh, *thank you.*

MR. SPARROW: I hope it ain't nothin' dreadful. You better show it to your mama. Well, good-by.

ME: Good-by.

MR. SPARROW (*Noticing Fred*): Oh, how do. (*Mr. Sparrow leaves.*)

ME: Mama! Oh, Fred, get Mama. Oh, *hurry.* My knees are shakin'. *Hurry!*

FRED: Is it *bad* news?

ME: I don't know. I never *got* a telegram. (*He rushes to the stair landing. I sink down and unfold the note paper.*)

FRED (*Calling upstairs as politely as possible*): Oh, Mrs. Jones!

ME (*Leaping up with a start*): Oh, *mercy!* Oh . . . Oh . . . *Oh* . . . *mercy!* . . . Oh!!!

MY MOTHER (*Running downstairs, tying on her apron as she comes*): Why, what on earth is it?

ME: It's a telegram, Mama! For me to go on the stage!

MY MOTHER: *What!*

ME: It's from Miss Doris Olsson!

MY MOTHER: Inviting you to be an *actress?*

ME: Just as good as! Tellin' me Mr. John Craig'll see me in his office *tomorrow* at two-thirty P.M. Oh, *Mama!* (*I fling my arms around My Mother.*)

MY MOTHER: Oh, child!

FRED: Oh, *good night!*

ME (*Coming out of My Mother's arms in a hurry*): Oh, Fred. I forgot you were there. I forgot all about you. You better go, Fred. I can't talk to you any more tonight.

FRED (*Anxiously*): Well, what about the thing?

ME: What thing?

FRED: Well, you know . . . the thing we were talking about . . .

ME (*Distracted*): I don't know, Fred. See, that's just it . . .

MY MOTHER: Ruth!

ME (*Rapturously*): Oh, Mama . . . things happen to me the *greatest* of anyone in the whole *world!*

MY MOTHER (*Excited but firm*): Ruth, you *have* to tell your father. I will *not* take the sole responsibility of you receiving telegrams! Ruth, you *cannot* arrange about becoming an actress behind your father's back!

ME: Oh, Mama, tomorrow by two-thirty I might *be* an actress!

MY MOTHER: Don't *say* such a thing! Ruth, you have to tell him *now*. I won't take all the responsibility. You know your father's disposition! If he finds out you're going calling on this John Craig, why, I don't know *what* he'd do. You know how he threw the cantaloupes round when all I said was I wish they were *peaches. You* remember how those cantaloupes stuck on the kitchen wall with all the seeds and mush dripping down in the sink? Well, if he finds out about all this, dear only *knows* what he'd throw around!

ME: Oh, Fred, with all the people in the world to choose from, Mr. Craig went and chose *me!*

FRED: Well, so did I.

ME: What?

FRED: Choose you.

ME: Oh. . . . (*Just then My Father and his guests heave up to the front porch.*)

MY MOTHER: Oh, mercy, here they *are!* Put that darn thing away!

ME: Oh, Fred, it's them. I guess you better go maybe.

FRED: All right, but when do you think . . . ?

MY MOTHER: Yes, Fred, we are a little flustered. . . .

ME: I'll let you know, Fred. *Honest* I will.

MY MOTHER: Light the back-porch light, Ruth, so he doesn't break his neck.

FRED: I don't care if I *do,* Mrs. Jones.

MY MOTHER: Oh, Fred, please don't talk like that. God'll hear you.

FRED: I don't care if He *does*, Mrs. Jones. (*And he disappears into the kitchen just as the front door opens.*)

MY MOTHER (*Somehow managing a happy smile*): Come right *in!*

MY FATHER (*Proudly*): Annie, this lady is Miss Glavin from Sargent's School of Gymnastics out to Brookline, and this is Mr. Bagley from the Y.M.C.A. in Boston. (*I come in from the kitchen.*)

MY MOTHER: Well, this is *lovely!*

MY FATHER: Miss Glavin, be acquainted with Mrs. Jones.

MISS GLAVIN: How do.

MY MOTHER: How do. Ruth, this is Miss Glavin and this is Mr. Bagley. Miss Glavin and Mr. Bagley, this is our daughter, Ruth.

MISS GLAVIN: How do.

MR. BAGLEY: How do.

ME: How do.

MY FATHER: Miss Glavin has consented to size Ruth up, Annie, as to her chances of gettin' into Sargent's Physical Culture School.

MY MOTHER (*Flustered*): Oh my! . . . er . . . Ruth, draw up a chair for Miss Glavin. Let Mr. Bagley sit beside Papa. We didn't know just what time you'd be getting here but we saved our dessert to have it with you. Start bringing it in, Ruth, and don't drop it.

MR. BAGLEY: Well, this looks very enjoyable. Miss Glavin, I'm hanging your Indian clubs right here by my lantern slides, so please don't feel anxious. Miss Glavin's Indian clubs are made up specially for her out of selected tulip wood.

MY MOTHER: Well . . . er . . . sit right down, Mr. Bagley.

MY FATHER: Mr. Bagley's been showin' his lantern slides of gymnastics as practiced in the Scandinavian countries. . . .

MR. BAGLEY: Some of the lantern slides aren't clear from back a ways, so Miss Glavin kindly comes along and gives an *actual* representation of what goes on, *on* the slides.

MY MOTHER: And using her own actual Indian clubs. Oh, *my!*

MISS GLAVIN (*Amiably*): You could just as well've come.

MR. BAGLEY (*Cordially*): Yes, indeed. The Baptist Church permitted the sociable to be nonsectarian, and supper was thirty-five cents.

MY FATHER (*Expansively*): I don't doubt but what it was enjoyable, only we ain't much on church goin'. We leave *that* to our daughter Ruth. (*Cordially, to Miss Glavin*) Heave to, Miss Glavin. Don't wait! How many churches you been to so far, Snuggy? Episcopal? Congregational? Unitarian?

MY MOTHER (*Jumping to my rescue*): Oh, well now, Clinton, to outsiders it might sound funny, but it doesn't when you understand. Ruth, bring in the sponge cake. I was brought up Episcopalian and Mr. Jones and I were married at St. *Chrysostoms*—some people call it St. Chrysostoms—by the Reverend Skinner. . . . (*I come in, outwardly carrying cake but spiritually walking on air.*)

MY FATHER: Them days, if you wasn't married by Reverend Skinner, you wasn't legally hitched. His son is this Otis Skinner, now appearin' on the stage.

ME (*Ecstatically*): Mama, *you* never told me that!

MY MOTHER: Told you *what?*

ME: You and Papa were married by Otis Skinner's father!

MY FATHER (*In a hearty roar*): Reverend Skinner don't have to take a back seat to no *son!* He was the best sky pilot *around!*

MY MOTHER (*Ingratiatingly to Miss Glavin*): When he was a sailor, Mr. Jones got some picturesque expressions.

MISS GLAVIN (*Picks up her slice of cake and folds it over double. When she speaks, she gives the impression of addressing her class*): I been out here to Wollaston once, *walked* out from Boston! Speakin' of walkin' . . . every day of my—thank you—life I walk five miles out in the fenway, rain or shine, summer or winter, before I sit down to eat a *crumb!*

MY FATHER (*Full of admiration*): Listen to Miss Glavin, Ruth!

MR. BAGLEY (*To My Mother*): Miss Glavin's quite famous. She won the State Championship for Ladies' Broad Jump at Mechanics' Hall year before last.

MY MOTHER (*Enthusiastically*): Oh, *we* know Mechanics' Hall! They hold the Food Fair there. And the Mellin's Food Company always hands out free tickets.

MR. BAGLEY: And even with winning the championship she didn't do it good as she could. The judges went and made her wear track shoes, and she jumps best barefoot.

MISS GLAVIN (*Admonishing the whole table*): Speakin' of feet, feet could be improved fifty to sixty per cent if people'd give up shoes!

MY FATHER (*Delighted*): Give 'em up *altogether?*

MY MOTHER: Oh *my!*

MR. BAGLEY: A shoe isn't a natural encasement.

MISS GLAVIN: How's your feet goin' to breathe? Hmm?

MY FATHER: Why, that's so!

MISS GLAVIN (*Ruminatively*): Best pair of feet I ever saw belonged to a Carlisle

Indian that gave exhibitions so's to put himself through college, jumpin' barefoot on broken glass. It's all in *trainin'!*

My Mother: Oh *my!* Besides training, Miss Glavin, *that* must take a whole lot of *faith!* He must have *believed* he could.

My Father (*Enthusiastically*): Trainin' can work *wonders!* Well, now you seen her, Miss Glavin, how, in your opinion, you think Ruth'd make out?

Miss Glavin (*Shaking her head warningly at me*): Many are called but few are chosen.

My Father (*Earnestly*): Oh, Ruth's prepared to work.

Mr. Bagley: Mr. Jones is doing all right in our evening class.

My Mother (*Apprehensively*): Well, of course, it's different with different people. *Mr. Jones* enjoys it.

My Father (*To me*): Not only is gymnastics a *interesting* career, but you stay healthy while gettin' paid for it.

Me: My health's *fine,* Papa.

My Father: Well it won't be, if you go coverin' up your chest. (*To Mr. Bagley*) *Scientific American* says women's chest afflictions comes from wearin' furs around their necks. To *stay* healthy, *expose* the chest!

My Mother (*To Miss Glavin*): Mr. Jones is quite drastic.

My Father: Well, what do you think, Miss Glavin?

Miss Glavin (*Resting her spoon on her saucer with quite a clatter, and pushing her chair back from the table in a businesslike manner*): Stand up! Let's see what you look like, what sort of posture you got.

My Father: Heave anchor, Snuggy! (*I arise embarrassedly; Miss Glavin studies me with a good deal of concentration.*)

Miss Glavin: Throw your shoulders back . . . back . . . way back! (*Unfortunately Miss Glavin gives a rather unattrac-*

tive demonstration.) Chest up. Shoulders *back* and *down!*

Mr. Bagley (*To My Mother*): Miss Glavin is a bear on posture.

My Father: Stiffen up, Snuggy. What you think, Miss Glavin? Could she likely pass the requirements?

Miss Glavin: Well, she isn't *made* for it, but on the other hand she hasn't got anything the *matter*.

My Father: Well, *that's* a relief!

Mr. Bagley (*Warningly*): Of course, Physical Culture is a very demanding career.

Miss Glavin: It means givin' up all sorts of indulgences—wine, tobacco, late hours . . .

My Father: Oh, Ruth don't indulge. Of course, at her age, *I* give up wine, but I give it up for *hard liquor.*

My Mother: Mercy, Clinton!

Mr. Bagley: Physical Culture isn't for everyone.

Miss Glavin: You got to devote your whole twenty-four hours a day to it.

My Mother: Well—

My Father (*Earnestly*): Oh, Physical Culture ain't somethin' just happens to you layin' *down! Ruth* knows that!

Miss Glavin: Well, I know how she feels so I don't mind helpin' a little.

Mr. Bagley: A little help paves the way.

Miss Glavin: Mr. Bagley's told me how anxious you feel so before I dropped out here I made arrangements for her to come out to Sargent's School. And *if* she passes muster, then I fixed it so's she don't have to *wait* for the autumn course. She can begin the *summer* term startin' day after Fourth of July.

My Father: Miss Glavin, you're a *daisy!*

Mr. Bagley: Summer term is the hardest to get into.

My Father: Snuggy, you're sailin' in luck.

My Mother: Well . . . er . . .

Miss Glavin (*Looking at me with a friendly glare*): So you just hurry out to Sargent's School tomorrow afternoon at two o'clock, standin' up good and straight!

My Father: She'll be there with bells on!

Miss Glavin: And come equipped. They'll require a physical examination, so bring your serge bloomers along.

Me: Oh, I haven't any.

Miss Glavin: I'll lend you a pair of mine. They'll look kind of crazy on you, but you aren't comin' there to look stylish.

Mr. Bagley (*Encouragingly*): Most ladies find bloomers are *better* when they're not worn too skimpy.

My Father: Oh, Ruth don't care what she looks like. Good wine needs no bush!

Miss Glavin: And get you a pair of sneakers.

Mr. Bagley: Boys' sneakers give the best support.

My Father: Get the best pair of sneakers to be got, Snuggy. I'll take care of the financial end.

Miss Glavin: And between *now* and July fifth, go at your Indian clubs like *you* were goin' to give an exhibition at the Baptist Church *yourself*. Take the way you're sittin' *now* . . . That induces a lazy spine. When you sit, sit *upright* so's your spine isn't folded way down under. (*To me*) Anythin' you want to ask me?

My Mother (*Cutting in*): Well, Ruth isn't *ever* very talkative . . .

Miss Glavin (*With an approving nod*): No better way to learn than to listen. It's the still sow sucks the most swill.

My Mother: Well . . .

Miss Glavin: What sort of physical trainin' have you had up to now?

My Mother: Well, Ruth's a very lovely dancer . . .

Miss Glavin (*With grudging praise*): Dancin' exercises the rhythm.

Mr. Bagley: In Physical Culture rhythm is very important.

My Mother: Mrs. Percy Moorehouse, Ruth's piano teacher, always says she keeps time *very well*.

My Father: Mrs. Jones has had Ruth takin' piano instructions ever since she hit seven. Give us "The Pixies' Drill," Snuggy. (*Reassuringly to his guests*) This one's *all right!*

Me (*Miserable*): I forgot it, Papa.

My Father: What'd you want to go and forget it for? Next to "Sailin'," that was your best piece.

My Mother: Well, then give us "Sailing," Ruth. That's got a whole *lot* of rhythm.

Me (*Pleading*): Oh, Mama. It won't be any good.

My Mother (*Obdurate*): Go play it, good or not! (*I reluctantly go in to the piano.*)

My Father: And play it *loud!*

My Mother (*To our guests*): Our piano is quite interesting. It was used at the ball for King Edward the time he came to Boston as the Prince of Wales.

My Father: They had it at the old Revere House.

My Mother: And Ralph Waldo Emerson was there and Henry W. Longfellow.

My Father: But Thoreau wouldn't come.

My Mother (*Shouting to me in the parlor*): All right, Ruth. Go ahead. (*I start to play.*)

My Father (*Picking up the last half of the music*):

"Sailin', sailin', over the boundin' main,
For many a stormy wind will blow
Ere Jack comes home again."

(*I return embarrassedly to the dining room.*)

MY MOTHER (*Kindly*): That was lovely!

MR. BAGLEY (*Temperately*): I enjoyed that!

MY FATHER: Sometime when you get round to it, polish up "The Pixies' Drill."

MISS GLAVIN: Well, of course I'm more at home with dumbbells and Indian clubs than I am with songs. Why I nearly went and forgot. I brought you out this list of questions. You fill out the answers and bring it with you tomorrow. (*She extricates a sheaf of papers from her bulging pocketbook.*)

MY FATHER (*Accepting the papers*): We'll take care of that tonight. (*The clock starts to strike.*)

MR. BAGLEY: Miss Glavin, if we want to get that train you said, we got to get a wiggle on.

MY FATHER (*Getting out his watch*): Well, that clock ain't far off.

MR. BAGLEY: We'll just make a noise like a hoop and roll away.

MY MOTHER (*Laughs politely but without too much heart in it*): And come again when you can stay longer . . .

MY FATHER: Ruth'll be at Sargent's School at two P.M. tomorrow, all sails set.

MR. BAGLEY: Good-by, Mrs. Jones, and thank you. When we have our evening exhibition, you come see your husband do a running somersault and land on his two feet *upright.*

MY MOTHER (*Perfectly astonished*): Why, *Clinton!*

MR. BAGLEY: Yes, *ma'am!*

MY MOTHER: Well, please don't urge him on, Mr. Bagley, so's he goes and strains something. Mr. Jones is no chicken! Mr. Bagley, please bear that in mind.

MISS GLAVIN (*To me*): I'll be there to give you your goin' over tomorrow. (*To Mr. Bagley*) You comin'?

MY FATHER: Turn right at the foot of the walk and you'll hit the tracks beam on! And if anyone accosts you, lam 'em with the Indian clubs, then ask what they want, *after!*

MY MOTHER: Mercy, Clinton! Well, good-by. (*My Father steps out onto the porch with Mr. Bagley and Miss Glavin. We hear them call out "Good-by" as they go down the snowy walk.*)

MY MOTHER (*In a tense whisper*): Ruth, where are you? . . . Everybody isn't living their lives just to suit *you*. They may not have cared for you *either!*

ME (*Just as tensely*): If I ever see them again, I'll *kill* myself. I wouldn't live through this *twice!*

MY MOTHER: Remember, you promised me you could put up with anything.

ME: Bloomers and sneakers! I thought I would have to throw up!

MY MOTHER: Here, clear away the dishes. It'll relax you.

ME (*Outraged, doing as I am told, aided by My Mother*): Every single minute it got more disgustin'!

MY FATHER (*Coming in, extremely contented*): Orion's sword and belt's [3] standing out over Claflin's house, brighter'n a beacon. Fine man, Mr. Bagley. Happy you had the opportunity of meeting him, Annie.

MY MOTHER (*Anxiously*): He seemed a *very* lovely man.

MY FATHER: Of course, Miss Glavin, the minute I seen her, I liked the cut of her jib. (*He goes to the sideboard and takes the sheaf of school questions.*)

MY MOTHER (*Guardedly*): She seems very prepossessing. (*My Father unscrews his fountain pen with great ceremony and sits down to the dining-room table to write.*)

---

[3] *Orion's sword and belt,* certain stars in the constellation Orion, The Hunter

My Mother watches him anxiously. I have turned away.)

MY MOTHER (*Apprehension in her voice*): Clinton, couldn't you just wait till we clear away the dishes?

MY FATHER: Stow 'em away later.

MY MOTHER: Well, but . . .

MY FATHER (*Looking up proudly*): Dishes ain't vital, Mama! We got a daughter goin' to enroll tomorrow at Sargent's Physical Culture School! (*He studies the first question on the paper.*) Cast anchor, Snuggy. (*He indicates a dining-room chair.*)

MY MOTHER: Clinton . . .

MY FATHER: Well, now let's see . . . (*Reading off the first question*): Name? (*My Mother looks at me imploringly, but it is all right, for My Father is writing.*) Name of Ruth Gordon Jones.

MY MOTHER (*Imploringly to me*): Ruth . . .

MY FATHER (*Reading from the paper*): Age? (*This time My Mother prompts me with a smart shove.*)

MY MOTHER: Sixteen.

MY FATHER (*Writing*): Age: Sixteen.

MY MOTHER: Sixteen is very young, Clinton, to . . .

MY FATHER: Date of birth?

MY MOTHER: October thirtieth, 1896. Clinton, would you just . . .

MY FATHER (*Refusing to be interrupted*): Eighteen-nine-six. Sex? Female.

MY MOTHER: Er . . .

MY FATHER: Weight? You'd shift the scales at close to a hundred, with your duds on.

MY MOTHER: Now, Clinton . . .

MY FATHER: One hundred . . . Height?

MY MOTHER: Five feet. I know that from the length of her skirts. (*She motions to me to speak up and say something, but I am too distressed.*)

MY FATHER: Five feet . . . Past

Schoolin'? Wollaston Grammar School and Quincy High School. . . .

MY MOTHER: And Mrs. Farrington's Kindergarten. . . .

MY FATHER: That ain't schoolin'; that's just foolin' a child's time away. . . . (*Reading from the paper*) Sports in which you excel?

(*There is no reply. My Mother seems unable to go on answering for me and I cannot seem to speak. Studying his paper, he repeats the question without looking up.*)

What sports in which you excel? (*My Mother looks at me, but remains silent. Nothing in the way of an answer comes out.*) What sports in which you excel?

MY MOTHER (*Fearfully*): Clinton, Ruth is upset . . .

MY FATHER: What about?

MY MOTHER (*Miserably*): She doesn't want to be a Physical Culture teacher.

MY FATHER (*Looks up, startled*): Why the—Why not?

MY MOTHER (*Hurrying on anxiously*): Clinton, some people get inspired over some things, others over *others*. Now *you* got inspired to be a sailor. Not a carpenter, like you said your father was . . .

MY FATHER: Ruth doesn't know *what* she's inspired over, at *sixteen!*

MY MOTHER: Now be patient, Clinton . . .

MY FATHER (*Turning to me, with not too much patience*): Well, what *do* you think you're inspired over?

ME: I don't know—(*I stare miserably at the fern basket in the middle of the table.*)

MY MOTHER: Why yes you do too, Ruth. You tell Papa.

ME (*Feebly*): I don't want to be a Physical Culture teacher.

MY FATHER (*Sternly*): What *do* you want to do?

MY MOTHER (*Urgently*): Tell Papa, Ruth. He wants to know.

ME (*Even weaker than before*): I don't want to be a Physical Culture instructress.

MY FATHER: *Why* don't you?

ME (*In a tearful whisper*): Because I'd rather be dead.

MY MOTHER (*Earnestly*): Ruth, don't say that. God will hear you.

MY FATHER: God's listenin' to harps and trumpets and watchin' sparrows fall.

MY MOTHER: God's listening to *everybody. . . .*

MY FATHER (*Turning to me again*): God's listenin' to everybody, but *I'm* listening to *her!* (*I sit tensely, trying to get some courage.*)

MY MOTHER: Tell Papa!

ME: I have to do my home work.

MY MOTHER: Why no you don't, it's Friday night.

ME: Well . . .

MY MOTHER: *Ruth!*

MY FATHER: Don't sit there like a dyin' calf. If you got somethin' to say, spit it out!

ME (*All the misery in the world in my looks and tone*):

I want to go on the stage. (*This is said in such an agony of emotion, it is little more than a whisper. There is a long pause. My Father looks at me doing my best to hold back the tears. He knows, as anyone would to look at me, that this is not some childish whim. Right or wrong, here is a person with whole heart and soul in a cause. Looking at me, surprised at the violence and depth of my feeling, he finds himself looking at the little boy of eight that he had been, who had needed to do what he had to do. He sits and looks at me. It is a long time before he speaks.*)

MY FATHER (*Gravely*): What makes you think you got the stuff it takes?

ME (*Just barely audible*): I don't know. (*There is another long pause as My Father looks at me.*)

MY FATHER: What give you the idea?

ME: I don't know, Papa. Maybe I got to be rovin' like *you* felt.

MY MOTHER: And, Clinton, she has a chance to. Ruth got a telegram today. Well, tell Papa about it, Ruth. He wants to know.

ME: I got a telegram from Miss Doris Olsson, the leadin' lady of the whole Castle Square Theatre Stock Company, sayin' there's a part openin' up there and Mr. John Craig will see me *tomorrow . . .*

MY FATHER (*Startled*): John Craig of the Castle Square Theatre?

ME (*Radiantly*): Yes, Papa.

MY FATHER: He wants *you* to be in the company?

ME (*Almost in a state of exaltation*): There's a *chance!* . . . And Miss Olsson says for me to go see him at two-thirty in the afternoon. Oh, Papa, I *wish* I could be like what you want me to be, but it's like if you asked me to be a giant and I'm not a giant and I'm not a Physical Culture person *either!*

MY FATHER (*Considers for a moment; then gravely*): What makes you think you're a *actress?*

MY MOTHER (*Eagerly*): She's not statuesque, of course, but she looks all right when she remembers to stand up straight. And when she smiles and doesn't look like a thundercloud, Ruth can be very appealing. She has all *sorts* of artistic leanings. And *mercy,* Clinton, I guess *some* things, you got to trust in the Lord.

MY FATHER: Lord or no Lord, when you get up at a meetin', you got to deliver the goods. I know *that* from bein' a audience. I seen actors and actresses all my life pretty nearly, but I ain't see none looked like you. I can't deny but I always enjoyed theatres. Most every time I got ashore I took in whatever attraction was playin'. I been in some places where I wouldn't ask no lady to accompany me, and I also seen the best. I seen Booth and Barrett and Modjeska . . . And I seen Lotta. Once when the *Austria* was lyin' in at Frisco, I went and served as a stagehand so's I could see her close to . . . Fine woman, those associated with her told me, and I didn't see nothin' led me to believe different. But she nor *none* of 'em was anythin' like you.

MY MOTHER (*Gently*): Well, maybe Lotta's mother and father felt the same, Clinton, when *she* wanted to go on the stage.

ME (*Astonished and impressed*): Papa —I didn't know you ever worked in a theatre—

MY FATHER (*Thoughtfully*): I did it *another* time . . . I went and pushed stuff round for Booth. . . . His first wife lies buried over to Dorchester. Oh, I guess there's decent people on the stage same as anywheres. I ain't objectin' to it from *that* end.

MY MOTHER: Maude Adams, they say, is very lovely. But would you say *she* seemed very actressy?

ME (*Terribly excited*): Papa, please don't make up your mind against me. Would you just *please* give me a chance? I got somethin' I can recite to you. Some speeches from some plays I learned. Will you just please, please, Papa, listen to me, while I say 'em? Hasn't everybody got a right to a chance?

MY FATHER (*Looks at me thoughtfully before replying*): Some pieces you learned by heart?

ME: I learned *millions* of 'em, but I'll pick out just one comical and one tragical . . . (*I stand back between the sideboard and the reading table in a frenzy of nervous excitement, part terror, part exhilaration.*)

Mama, *please* sit over there by Papa! (*My Mother gets up to accommodate me, but just then I have a finer idea.*)

No, wait, let me stand on the landin'. That'll be more like a stage. (*I fly up the two steps to the landing and My Mother and My Father turn to watch me. I am really trembling with nerves and excitement. My voice is a shaky whisper.*)

"Make me a willow cabin at your gate,
  And call upon my soul within the house;
  Write loyal cantons of contemned love
  And sing them loud even in the dead of
      night—"

MY FATHER (*Interrupting*): Hold on a minute! Is this comical or tragical?

ME (*Feverishly*): That was comical, Papa, but I guess it doesn't sound so. Wait a minute—maybe I better do the tragical.

"Tell me not, Friar, that thou hear'st of this,
  Unless thou tell me how I may prevent it;
  If in thy wisdom, thou canst give no help,
  Do thou but call my resolution wise,
  And with this knife I'll help it presently.
  God join'd my heart and Romeo's, thou our hands;
  And ere this hand, by thee to Romeo sealed,
Shall be the label to another deed,
Or my true heart with treacherous revolt
Turn to another, this shall slay them both:
Therefore, out of thy long-experienc'd time,
Give me some present counsel, or, behold,
  'Twixt my extremes and me, this bloody knife
Shall play the umpire, arbitratin' that
Which the commission of thy years and art
Could to no issue of true honor bring.
Be not so long to speak; I long to die,
If what thou speak'st speak not of remedy."

It's really "remedy" but it has to be pronounced "die"—"reme-*die*." (*There is a long pause. I stand anxiously and My Father looks thoughtful.*)

MY FATHER (*Dubiously*): Do you think you could be *heard*?

ME (*Earnestly*): I can do it *louder.*
        "Tell me not, Friar—"
(*My Father interrupts me.*)

MY FATHER (*Gravely*): All right, say you *can* be heard. Do you think people'd shell out *money* for it?

ME (*With my heart and soul in my answer*): I can *learn* it if anybody'll teach it to me and Miss Doris Olsson says Mr. John Craig is a very *wonderful* director. . . .

MY MOTHER: This Miss Doris Olsson seems like a *very* lovely person, Clinton. She lives with her own sister in their flat out to Back Bay and her sister makes all her costumes.

ME: I wrote to her, Papa, how would *I* go about gettin' on the stage, and she wrote me back a letter . . .

MY MOTHER: Answered Ruth's letter, Clinton. Just think of that!

ME: And said I could come see her and . . . please don't get mad, Papa, but I *had* to see her close to, the same way you felt about Booth and Lotta. Papa, you say I'm not like actresses—but I'm not like Miss Glavin *either!*

MY MOTHER: Ruth is like you, Clinton, morning, noon, and *night!*

MY FATHER: When did *all this* go on?

ME: This afternoon, Papa. I *wish* I'd told you right off.

MY FATHER: So what took place?

ME: She said the *best* thing to do was to get a job and begin actin'. That way I could get experience *right away,* and—this was before she talked to Mr. Craig, of course—she said if I went to New York City to do it, I better live at a place there called the Three Arts Club.

MY MOTHER: It's like the Y.M.C.A.

ME (*Hastily correcting her*): Y.W.C.A., Mama.

MY MOTHER: Well, then, Y.W.C.A.

ME: But *then,* Papa, she said maybe there was a chance I could start right in actin' at the Castle Square Theatre Stock Company in Boston because there was a place openin' up and she would try to arrange for Mr. John Craig to give me an appointment to see if maybe *I* could get the place and the telegram proves she *did!*

My Mother: For Miss Doris Olsson to take this interest, *must* mean something, Clinton. And so did another actress, Miss Hazel Dawn in *The Pink Lady,* wrote to Ruth and never even so much as dropped Anna Witham a line. It must mean *something!* Actresses like that surely don't write to *everybody,* take for instance Anna Witham! (*Just then the train goes by. My Father sits and listens to it, somberly.*)

My Father: There goes Mr. Bagley and Miss Glavin . . .

My Mother (*Gently*): They were *very* lovely.

My Father (*Rousing himself*): Life on the stage isn't anythin' *near* so benefitin' as bein' a Physical Culture teacher. It ain't a healthy life nor a easy one. . . .

My Mother: Oh, Ruth, how *could* you go out *nights* to Castle Square? Why, it's one of the *worst* sections of Boston!

Me: Mama, you say that about a lot of places.

My Mother (*In a great state of alarm*): And I'm *right.* Girls walk out of their front doors and disappear *somewheres* every day in the week.

Me: But I'll be *careful,* Mama!

My Mother (*Not even hearing*): People offering them poison candy and saying they'll show them how to find the way. Don't ever inquire how to get somewheres from *anyone* but a policeman, Ruth! And it's not only *men* you have to worry about. Women are *worse* than men. Girls can disappear and never be seen again and end up ashamed all their life, in Rio, where *Papa's* been!

My Father: Bein' a Physical Culture instructor, you could lead a normal life. Bein' a actress means headin' out on a rough voyage.

My Mother: Oh dear, nobody has such problems as we have. John Craig *might* want you to commence acting *right away.*

Me (*Sternly*): Well, I *will* then.

My Father: Not finish your *schoolin'?*

Me: But, Papa, every minute counts! Why, Maude Adams started when she was only six weeks old and here I am goin' on *seventeen!*

My Father: A *education* is somethin' you can't afford not to *have!*

Me: But, Papa, I *got* my education practically! There's only a few months more!

My Father: But then you'd *graduate.*

Me (*Distractedly*): Well, what's *that?* It just means they give me an old diploma. . . . Well, what's *that,* for heaven's sakes? Nobody cared whether *Ethel Barrymore* or *Maude Adams* or *Booth* or *Lotta* got a diploma!

My Mother (*Urgently*): Oh, Ruth, it's different with them. They're different people altogether. People don't ask such things about them. But it would be *awful* when people ask you as they're *bound* to. Why, I wouldn't know *what* to say!

Me (*Earnestly*): I'm not goin' to *know* people that ask such questions.

My Mother: Oh dear! . . . Clinton, have some Moxie? If you have some, I'll take a glass.

My Father (*Sternly, with real feeling and intensity*): I ain't goin' to argue with you. I'm layin' down the law. You finish your schoolin'! It ain't like schoolin' was somethin' you could come back to later. I found *that* out! At eighteen I *left* the sea for a period and headed for Elmira in up-state New York, hired a room at the Rathbun House, and put in a whole winter attemptin' to pick up some learnin'. At *sea* my ratin' was that of Ship's Mate and I had made a considerable number of voyages, been round the world two times . . . and up at that school in Elmira, they put me in the fourth grade.

My Mother (*With a feeble effort to*

console him): But you got to know Mark Twain there, Clinton.

MY FATHER: But I missed what I set out to *get!* It was too late for a *education!*

ME (*With a faith that moves mountains and brooks no interference*): But, Papa, education *meant* somethin' to you. I've got all I *need!* And whatever Mr. John Craig says to, then I *got* to. I can't pick and choose my *chance!*

MY FATHER: Your chance can come later, when you're equipped to accept it.

ME: Papa, I *got* to do what Mr. John Craig tells me. I'm not a child! Maude Adams has acted all her *life* and didn't they have her come to Harvard College to put on *Joan of Arc* right in the *Stadium?* And Lotta Crabtree was *always* actin' and you said she was the *best!* And now she owns three hotels in Boston and the Lee Mansion down on Hancock Street! I'll never get *anywheres* if you don't let me *start!* This is my big opportunity. *Booth* never had a diploma!

MY FATHER: I ain't bringin' up Booth. But I am responsible for *you.* You send word to this feller, you ain't in a position to deal with him. You ain't *open* to a offer.

ME: Papa, I never stood up to you before. But this time I have to. You can hit me or throw cantaloupes around or *anythin'.* But I got a *right* to my opportunity.

MY FATHER: I'm affordin' you the luxury of a *education.* Don't take that luxury so lightly! If I *wanted* to I could send you into Jordan Marsh's tomorrow and put you to work behind the counter. Instead, I'm choosin' to *educate* you. *Your mother and I are choosin'* to do *without* so's you can be educated. So see you *respect* our efforts and fulfill your end of the obligation.

ME: Oh, *Papa!*

MY FATHER: No! Get the cat out and batten down the hatches. It's time to get to bed. (*He stamps down the cellar stairs.*)

ME (*In an imploring whisper*): Mama!

MY MOTHER (*Hastily drags Punk out from under the sideboard*): Ruth, you heard what your father said.

ME (*Whispering, but no longer imploring; the whisper is almost fierce*): Mama . . . Papa'll ruin my chances. . . . I can't tell John Craig what to do!

MY MOTHER (*Thrusting Punk out the front door*): You hurry up, Punk! (*To me*) Now just don't start raging round. Just be thankful he didn't put his foot down on your being an actress *at all.* (*She crosses over to lock the windows. We are both talking in loud whispers.*)

ME: Mama, could *you* talk to Papa?

MY MOTHER: No, I couldn't. I'm not going to tamper with your father, particularly when he's *right.* Oh dear, I never left the dishes before. (*Picking up Fred's gift*) Why, what's *this?*

ME (*Furiously*): Some old *candy!* Oh, Mama!

MY MOTHER: From Fred? (*I nod grimly.*) Oh, *why* couldn't you forget all this about being an actress, Ruth, and settle down with some good man?

ME: *Please don't be disgustin'!*

(*My Father stalks through the room, picks up his pen and glasses from the dining-room table, and disappears up the stairs.*)

MY MOTHER: Oh, dear, you had to go and be so *different!* (*A thud at the door. It is Punk. My Mother puts him briskly down cellar.*)

ME: Oh, Mama, when two-thirty comes tomorrow afternoon, I'll never live through it.

MY MOTHER: Yes, you will. (*She closes the cellar door.*) I'm not even going to bother with the silver.

MY FATHER'S VOICE: Douse the glim and don't be chewin' the rag all night. Electric light costs money.

My Mother: Come to bed, Ruth, or your father'll have a fit.

Me: I'll go ravin' mad, Mama!

My Mother: Oh dear! When I'm quietly reading my *Unity,* life seems so simple and it's easy to have faith, but *Unity* never seems to take into consideration there's people like you and your father!

Oh dear! I suppose it's no use asking you because you know all about *everything,* but for the last time, before I turn out this light, wouldn't you, just for *all* our sakes, Ruth, please *consider* being normal? (*My only answer is to stomp up the stairs.*)

CURTAIN

Let's consider . . .

1. Father wanted Ruth to become a Physical Culture teacher. How did Ruth feel about this? Do you think parents should choose careers for their children? Why, or why not? To what extent should young people agree to their parents' plans?

2. How did you *expect* Father to act when he learned that Ruth wanted to become an actress? How *did* he act?

3. In what ways was Ruth's desire to go on the stage similar to her father's youthful dreams? Mother thought that Ruth was just like Father. What similarities did you find between them?

4. Ruth asked, "Hasn't everybody got a right to a chance?" In your own words, explain what she meant. Why do you agree, or disagree with her?

5. Father was not sure that Ruth had the appearance of an actress. What qualities are more important than physical appearance in any career? Did Ruth have these qualities? Find incidents from the play to support your answer.

6. Ruth laughed at the suggestion that a diploma was important for her. What is your opinion of her attitude? How necessary is a high school diploma today? A college degree?

7. Mother said that she was "roped into" getting a telephone. Can you think of an occasion when you used unusual pressure to get your parents to do something? Tell the class about it.

8. You have probably noticed that Ruth was a clothes-conscious young lady. How did Mother react to some of her daughter's ideas about clothes? What is the latest fashion in clothes for young people in your community? Are your parents in favor of it? If not, what steps have you taken to convert them?

ACT TWO

SCENE TWO

Late afternoon of the next day. The telephone rings. My Mother sits sewing. My Father sits gloomily smoking his unlit pipe. The telephone rings again.

MY MOTHER: I won't even answer it, Clinton, and I'll have the telephone company take it right out *tomorrow*.

MY FATHER (*Morosely*): Tomorrow's Sunday.

MY MOTHER: Well, Monday, then. Ruth shouldn't have talked me into it. I knew better all the time. (*Silence from My Father.*) So please don't be depressed any more, Clinton. This is Saturday afternoon and you ought to be enjoying it. (*Silence while My Father knocks the ashes out of his pipe.*) Is it that you're still upset about Ruth last night?

MY FATHER (*Morosely*): Where is she?

MY MOTHER (*Immensely encouraged at even this feeble rejoinder*): Up to Katherine Follett's. Why, on Saturday afternoon you always polish your spyglass and there's that good new chamois rag. Here, let me run get it.

MY FATHER: Never mind.

MY MOTHER: Clinton, there *is* something the matter! You'd never let your spyglass get dingy. (*Silence. My Father fills his pipe afresh, but doesn't bother to light it. She continues beseechingly*) Clinton?

MY FATHER (*After a pause*): What?

MY MOTHER: *Please* don't feel bad by *yourself*! (*My Father sits looking down at the backs of his hands. She says with finality*) I *know* it's about *last night* and *Ruth*!

MY FATHER: Well, you're wrong. It *ain't* about last night and it *ain't* about Ruth; it's about the factory and *me*. . . .

MY MOTHER: *Clinton!*

MY FATHER (*Despondently*): I didn't want to trouble you none. I *thought* I could keep it to myself.

MY MOTHER (*Gently*): What concerns you concerns me. You tell me, Clinton.

MY FATHER: Word went round the shippin' room this morning, Dan Weymouth's goin' to leave.

MY MOTHER: Dan Weymouth? Why, what for?

MY FATHER: That's what none of us *knows*.

MY MOTHER: Why, Dan Weymouth's been at the factory a little longer than *you* have! Why, Mr. Dollaber wouldn't *let* him go!

MY FATHER: Word is Dan's goin' to retire.

MY MOTHER (*Relieved*): Oh, you mean he's quitting and *wants* to!

MY FATHER: Who knows? If he's retirin' and *wants* to, that's *one* thing! But if they're *makin'* him retire and take a pension, well then, where's the axe goin' to fall next?

MY MOTHER: Clinton!

MY FATHER: See, if I *knew* Dan went and retired of his own free will and accord, *that* would be all right. All right for *Dan*, I mean. But if they asked me to go do likewise, the only answer I got is to go over and lay down on the New York, New Haven, and Hartford Railroad tracks!

MY MOTHER: *Clinton!*

MY FATHER: Of course with Dan, it ain't so drastic. He owns his own house in Mather Street and he's already got his G.A.R. pension. . . . So it's just possible he *ain't* bein' retired *forcibly*, but he's quittin' and *glad* to. But how am I goin' to know for *certain*, if someone don't cough up some facts?

MY MOTHER (*Anxiously*): Well, what about the others, Clinton? Are any more men leaving, too?

MY FATHER: Not's I know of, but a few hours ago I didn't know nothin' about Dan Weymouth, neither! Here *I* been worryin' if I'm goin' to get my bonus that ain't even *due* me, providin' they decide to give it to me, until July, and *now* it turns out it ain't my bonus I have to worry about. *It's my whole job!*

MY MOTHER: Clinton, won't you please, just to make me happy, call up Dan on our telephone and see what he *personally* has to say? We'll get rid of it on Monday, but couldn't we just let it be helpful *today?*

MY FATHER (*Miserably*): Oh, no. I guess it ain't as bad as all *that!*

MY MOTHER: Please, Clinton, call up Dan.

MY FATHER: What consolation is it goin' to be? If it's *bad* news, I'll just get to hear it sooner and have it cost me a nickel besides.

MY MOTHER: Clinton, is your peace of mind worth a nickel? Won't you please pay a nickel for *that?*

MY FATHER (*Glaring out the window*): Why this is Elmwood Avenue—full of *maple* trees!

MY MOTHER: *Clinton!*

MY FATHER (*Pulls the window shade up higher and peers gloomily out for a minute*): Oh, all right. You got to have money in your jeans to wait for bad news. (*My Mother waits to hear nothing further but hurries to the telephone book hanging beside our coin-in-the-slot telephone. My Father drops down in his reading chair and dejectedly studies the back of his hands.*) I ain't worryin' for a yacht nor a Oldsmobile. I'm worryin' if I can hold down a thirty-seven dollar and fifty-cent job. Due to maybe somebody's whim! (*Then from down deep in his innards*) There's two things takes the gimp out of a man. . . . One's injustice and one's no money. . . .

MY MOTHER (*In the entry, riffling the pages of the brand-new telephone book till she comes to the "w's" and conducting a conversation at the same time, brightly*): Don't I know it! Well, then, right this minute I don't know *what* state of mind I'd be in, if it wasn't for Mental Science. I wish I could get you to try it, Clinton, even if you never get any further than to just read *Unity*. (*Interrupting herself*) Here's Dan's number, Clinton, just back of my thumb. (*She keeps her thumb on the place while My Father takes out his glasses case, gets his glasses out, and carefully adjusts them to his nose.*) Here!

MY FATHER (*Gets up and moves reluctantly toward the telephone; he stands and looks at it for a minute*): I said I wasn't never goin' to use this telephone, and now here I am doin' it.

MY MOTHER (*Gently*): Well, Clinton, I guess every one of us makes statements we aren't always privileged to keep. (*She follows him into the entry.*) Look in the Clark's O.N.T. box. You'll find a nickel. (*With an effort to make this first occasion of My Father's using the telephone seem not to be anything in any way important*) You know what O.N.T. stands for? It stands for "Our New Thread." (*My Father refers once again to the telephone book, then drops a nickel in the slot. As he does so a bell rings faintly. My Father jerks the receiver away from his ear and looks into it. Then he clears his voice to be ready. He speaks very carefully.*)

MY FATHER: Oh, how do. I want to telephone to Ashmont two, seven, one, party J. (*He listens intently for a moment, then turns with a dismal sort of satisfaction to My Mother.*) She heard me all right!

MY MOTHER (*Heartily*): You got a *fine* speaking voice, Clinton. I have to *always* say a number twice.

MY FATHER (*Gives a little start, stands

rigid as a ramrod, then begins speaking very carefully): Hello? . . . Is that you, Dan? . . . Who? . . . Oh, is that you, *Fan?* . . . This is Jones . . . I'm telephonin' to you from Wollaston. . . . From *Wollaston.* . . . From *Wollaston—where—I—live!* . . . That's right. Clinton Jones. . . . Can you hear me all right? . . . What's that? . . . What? . . . Oh, yes, I can hear you *fine!* . . . I'm telephonin', Fan, because I'd like to speak to your father, that is, if it's convenient. . . . Oh. . . . Well, what's a likely time for him to be back home again. . . . I don't want to put him to no trouble but it's somethin' a little urgent. . . . All right, he can telephone me late as he's a mind to. Our telephone number is . . .

My Mother (*Prompting him eagerly*): Six, five, seven, R.

My Father: You got a pencil to write it down there? . . . All right, I'll go ahead. The number is six—five—seven . . . six, five, seven, party R . . . Quincy. . . . That's right! All right, now, Fan, if you're ready I'll hang up my end. (*He does.*)

My Mother: When's Dan coming back, did she say?

My Father (*Disconsolately*): Who knows? He's at a Lodge meetin' and I've spent a nickel.

My Mother (*Clutching at a straw*): Well, *that* seems like a good sign! A man wouldn't go to a Lodge meeting that's just been laid off on a pension!

My Father: I guess if you go to Lodge meetin's, you go under all conditions. (*The phone rings.*) (*Anxiously*) That'll be *Dan.* (*He hurriedly puts on his glasses.*) Hello, this is Jones. . . . What? . . . Who? . . . Why, this telephone's just a nuisance like I *knew* it was goin' to be!

My Mother: Sh-h-h! Clinton, they can hear you!

My Father: What's the matter with that galoot?

My Mother (*In an anxious whisper*): Who *is* it?

My Father (*Shouting*): That gink from Harvard College.

My Mother (*Hastily picking up the receiver and somehow managing an affable voice*): Oh, Fred, it's Ruth's mother. Ruth's up to Katherine Follett's. . . . She isn't? Well, then, I don't know where she is.

My Father: If she ain't at Katherine Follett's, then where in . . .

My Mother (*Hastily*): Good-by. (*She hangs up.*) She and Katherine probably stepped out somewhere. *Gracious!* Here, occupy yourself till Dan calls you. Look at this I found in my library book. (*She holds out a little tinseled paper lace valentine. My Father gives it only a half a glance.*) It's an old valentine someone must have had for a bookmark. It says "February 14, 1899. From Sue to little Mae." Someone must have forgot to take it out when they brought the book back to the library.

My Father (*Glancing at it disparagingly*): What's interestin' about a valentine?

My Mother: Well, a valentine means something to *most* people, but you're so unsentimental. . . .

My Father: *Why* am I?

My Mother: Well, you never think of sending valentines or . . .

My Father: I never sent no old thing like *that!* But I went and sent one once that set me back twenty-five dollars!

My Mother (*With a little shriek*): *Twenty-five dollars! Clinton!*

My Father: Or the equivalent. . . . Why ain't Ruth contented to *once* and a while stay home?

My Mother (*In blank astonishment*): Clinton, you mean to tell me you spent twenty-five whole dollars for just nothing but a *valentine?* (*My Father wishes he had not been quite so free with his memoirs.*)

MY FATHER (*Doggedly*): That's what I said. I felt ashamed havin' to let 'em know out to Sargent School, Ruth didn't know her own mind for two minutes.

MY MOTHER (*Sitting down as though she really needs to*): Why, Clinton Jones! Why, for pity's sake? What on earth was it *made* of?

MY FATHER: You sure she notified this Craig feller she wouldn't come there *neither?*

MY MOTHER: Clinton! I *asked* you something!

MY FATHER (*After quite a little pause*): *What?*

MY MOTHER: I asked you what it was made of?

MY FATHER (*Irascibly*): It was made of silk and lace and roses and ribbon and *how do you suppose I know?*

MY MOTHER: Why, Clinton, you never told me that!

MY FATHER (*Truthfully*): It never came up before! If Dan don't call up presently I'm a good mind to go over there. (*He picks up* McClure's Magazine.)

MY MOTHER: Who did you buy it for?

MY FATHER: For a lady that run a boardin' house in Le Havre, France, where our ship was takin' on gear and from where I went up to Paris and spent a day. (*My Father says all this looking into his magazine as though he were reading the words off the printed page. There is a pause, for My Mother says nothing. Apparently this irks My Father. He looks up at her.*) This only happened to me about thirty years ago. It don't seem as vital as why Ruth has to go galivantin' all over the whole town. Get in touch with the Folletts and find out where they went to. (*My Mother obediently picks up the telephone book.*)

MY MOTHER: What on earth was her name?

MY FATHER (*Roaring it out good and loud*): I may be without a job for all you know, and all you can find to worry about is . . . Her name was Madame Lynch!

MY MOTHER: Well, mercy, I don't think that's very *nice!*

MY FATHER: She ran a A-1 good boardin' house and if her name was Lynch it was *Lynch!*

MY MOTHER (*Into the phone*): Quincy nine, nine, one, M. (*Back to My Father, and very stiffly*) Oh, I wasn't talking about your *friend,* Clinton. . . . I mean I don't think it's nice to *shout!* I don't know how I can *help* being interested! Did *all* the sailors fling their money around?

MY FATHER: I don't know. I was only Second Mate, not their father confessor.

MY MOTHER: Oh, hello, Katherine. Is Ruth there? Oh. . . . Do you know where she went to? . . . Oh. . . . Well, she's probably up to Anna's. Good-by. (*She puts the receiver back on the hook.*) Well, Clinton, I *must* say I didn't know you had *that* side to your nature.

MY FATHER: Lots of things about me you don't know. Would you think I'd ever wore gold hoop earrings? And a sash for a belt? And I didn't like the name of Clinton for a sailor so I said my name was *Frank?*

MY MOTHER (*Giving a little shriek*): Clinton! . . . Are you just *crazy?* . . . Or irritable because Ruth's not home?

MY FATHER (*Staring morosely at the fern dish on our dining-room table*): When I think of Callao and all them ports I'll never see again . . . Get in touch with Anna Witham. I want to find out where she *is.* If I thought she went in town to see that Craig feller . . . (*There are steps on the porch and the front door opens slowly.*)

MY MOTHER (*Eagerly calling out*): Ruth?

ME (*In the forlornest voice imaginable*): Uh huh.

MY FATHER: Where you been all this time? Why, why you got on your best gear? (*Somehow I cannot say anything. I am too done in even to care. My Father's tone is angry.*) Did you go see this Craig feller? (*My look and appearance all say yes. The words just don't come. My Father starts across the room at me with considerable force. My Mother intervenes.*)

MY MOTHER: Now wait, Clinton. You let Ruth explain.

MY FATHER: I told her *not* to, didn't I?

MY MOTHER (*Alarmed but courageous*): Yes, you did, but you *hear* her, Clinton. She's got a right to *say*. (*She turns gently to me.*) Why did you do what Papa told you *not* to, Ruth?

ME (*Scarcely audible*): I had to.

MY FATHER: You had to go against my will? (*I nod. My Father comes at me again, but I just stand there.*)

MY MOTHER: Wait, Clinton. Why did you disobey your father, Ruth?

ME (*In the weakest of voices*): I thought if I didn't I'd kill myself. (*This has a kind of toneless beaten quality that arrests and maybe convinces even My Father.*)

MY FATHER: You didn't sign nothin'?

ME (*Feebly*): What?

MY FATHER (*Roaring*): What! What the . . .

MY MOTHER (*Remonstratingly*): Clinton! (*She turns to me.*) Papa wants to know what Mr. Craig said.

ME (*Haltingly*): Oh . . . er . . . he just wanted to see me . . . and . . . er . . . meet me . . . that was all.

MY FATHER (*Indignantly*): Is that worth disobeyin' your father for? . . . And

if all he wanted was to *see* you, then what were we sittin' up half the night for? And what was all this leavin' school talk?

ME (*Somehow managing to get it out*): Oh, that was just in case.

MY MOTHER (*Gently*): But didn't Miss Olsson tell you Mr. Craig could use you right away?

ME: If I was *right,* she said.

MY MOTHER (*Indignant*): Well, could he tell you *weren't,* from just only one glimpse?

ME (*Looking longingly at the stairs*): No, but it just wasn't *like* that!

MY FATHER (*Taking a little more controlled attack*): Well, what was the meetin' like?

ME: Well, I went into his office . . . (*I have to pause for a moment.*)

MY MOTHER (*Prompting me with encouragement and love in her voice*): Yes . . . and did you see Miss Olsson there?

ME (*Weakly*): No . . . she was actin' at the matinee. . . . And he sat there . . . Mr. Craig . . . (*I have trouble getting on with my story.*)

MY MOTHER: Go on, dear. (*For some reason it seems easier to look away off somewheres so I focus my gaze out the window, across the street, on the Rumrells' house.*)

ME: Well—he didn't seem like he was interested . . . very. . . . And I was sort of scared. . . . (*Glancing back into our dining room for a moment*) I didn't think I was goin' to be. . . . But I was. . . . (*I find it better looking at the Rumrells' so my gaze wanders across the street again.*) And he didn't ask me to sit down but I thought I better . . . so I wouldn't look so short. . . . And he just looked at me like he was quite busy. . . . And then he said: "What experience have you had?" . . . and I *know* Miss Olsson told him I was just goin' on the stage *now* and hadn't been on *yet* . . . so I got all mixed up and said: "No *amateur* experience, only professional." And then I had to go back and say: "I mean no *professional*, only amateur" . . . and then he just said he didn't think I'd fit into the company because I didn't seem like I was suited to hardly any parts.

(*It's too much for me. I slump into a chair and burst out in an awful fit of crying, with my head pressed down hard on the dining-room table. Nobody says anything. My Mother looks at me with a world of love and sympathy. I cry and cry. Some time passes. Then at last—*)

MY FATHER: He don't sound like much! . . . What'd you want to go see *him* for?

MY MOTHER (*Gently*): Miss Olsson recommended him. Will you take a glass of Moxie, Ruth? (*But I just sob on. The telephone rings. My Father walks over thoughtfully, takes off the receiver, and speaks very distinctly.*)

MY FATHER: Hello? . . . Is that you, Dan? (*A pause*) Yes, I thought it was; it sounds like you. This is *Jones*. Can you hear me or do you want me to speak up louder? (*Results are apparently satisfactory at Mr. Weymouth's end.*) I'm telephonin' to you, Dan, about a matter that's give me a whole lot of concern and what I'd like to do is find out about it without in no ways buttin' in. It's what's goin' on at the factory about you gettin' ready to leave. (*A short pause. My Father listens absorbedly. Suddenly his whole expression brightens.*) Just repeat that, Dan, so's I can make sure I got it *correct*. You done it because you *wanted to*. Mr. Dollaber didn't *ask* you to do it. In other words, the whole idea come from *your* end. (*Relief is in My Father's voice.*)

MY MOTHER (*Scarcely breathing lest it be disturbing*): There!

MY FATHER: Well, Dan, I'm glad to hear you say so. Fixed as I am, it's a relief!

You can appreciate I ain't askin' you all this out of idle curiosity. . . . You can start to hang up now. . . . I'm hanging up, Dan. Good-by. (*He puts the receiver back on the hook.*)

MY MOTHER (*With a world of relief*): Oh, isn't that just a *blessing*! Dan's a *very* lovely man! (*She turns to my bowed head.*) Papa had a worry, too, but his got straightened out. (*My Father, coming back into the dining room walks up and down between the sideboard and the dining-room table.*)

MY FATHER (*Gravely*): This Castle Square Company strikes me as kind of a *fresh-water* craft. . . . Next time you try, go after somethin' seaworthy. . . . Somethin' that has a A-1 ratin' in Lloyd's. . . . And don't sail from no rivermouth port. Back water ain't good for a sailor and it ain't good for theatrical personages neither. You got a kick in the pants. But that ain't fatal! A kick in the pants ain't never agreeable, but it don't dislocate your whole life. I *told* you to get a education. *Get it!* Then you're ready for a first-class ship. You better write to that place in New York City. Where was it you said to live at that was like the Y.W.C.A.?

ME (*With a muffled sob from under the brim of my hat*): The Three Arts Club.

MY MOTHER: They say it's a *very* lovely place, far *superior* to the Y.W.C.A.

MY FATHER: The Three Arts Club . . . (*He rolls the sound around.*) That don't sound like a bad anchorage. Write and get 'em to send their chart. . . . New York City's got the finest natural harbor of any city in the world. . . . From South Street on the end of Manhattan Island clear down the Hook to Ambrose Light. How much you figure it would take for you to start off with all your seams caulked?[4] How

---

[4] *seams caulked,* nautical expression meaning that a boat is made watertight, hence seaworthy

long would it likely take you to sign on to a job?

ME (*Fervently, raising a tear-stained face*): I'd get one *right off*, Papa. I *know* I could. . . . It mightn't be *good* or anythin', but I know I . . .

MY MOTHER (*To My Father*): Clinton, want that dish of ambrosia I saved from last night?

MY FATHER: Well, have you some notion of what it would take to get started? You can't set up a enterprise without some money in your jeans.

MY MOTHER: Oh, it might spoil your supper. Have it after.

ME: Eighteen dollars? (*I inquire rather than state it.*)

MY FATHER: I'll tell you what I'll do. I'll give you a wide berth. Go ahead and graduate from High School, then I'll give you two weeks' board at this Three Arts Club, *plus* which I'll see if I can get together fifty dollars to give you. Actin' or navigatin', first rule to steer by is *put money in your jeans!*

MY MOTHER (*Ecstatically*): Oh, Clinton, you're a splendid man! I don't care a thing about that old valentine you sent! Ruth, you got a splendid father!

ME: I wouldn't take fifty dollars, Papa. It'd just be wasteful.

MY FATHER (*Scornfully*): I know the world better'n you do. Have money in your jeans and just because you got it, don't mean you got to spend it . . . spondulix [5] don't grow on trees.

MY MOTHER (*Earnestly*): Oh, she *wouldn't* spend it, Clinton. You can trust Ruth.

MY FATHER: See, I ran away from the people that was in charge of bringin' *me* up. They were awful people!

MY MOTHER: Only one I ever met was your old Cousin Hartwell.

[5] *spondulix,* slang expression meaning money

MY FATHER: They were awful people. They worked me long and *hard*. If I went against their will, they beat me or locked me in the shed, and then when Sunday came, they went to church three times. The Christmas I was eight years old, they wrapped up my good suit I'd been wearin' all winter and hung it on the Sunday School Christmas tree. . . .

MY MOTHER: Oh, Clinton . . .

MY FATHER: I been to the Fiji Islands and I got along with *them people*; and I been up to the Baltic where I seen men catch fish with their hands and eat 'em raw, but they was pleasant spoken and agreeable . . . and I've ate many a bowl of rice with the heathen Chinee . . . but from one end of the world to the other I ain't never seen no one to equal them psalm-singin' *hypocrites,* my great-aunts Jerusha and Reliance Rogers of Orleans, Mass. So that Christmas night I set off for New Bedford and signed on as a cabin boy. . . . Vessel with a cargo of whale oil bound for Barcelona. I didn't care *where* she was bound for; I was eight and anythin' seemed better than my great-aunts Reliance and Jerusha, that was in charge of bringin' me up. . . .

MY MOTHER (*Gently*): If only your mother'd been alive, Clinton, everything'd have been different.

MY FATHER (*Grimly*): But she wasn't alive. . . . My mother wasn't alive because she killed herself in a Boston boardin' house. I was two years old and there she was, left with me. My father ran away. . . .

MY MOTHER: Oh, Clinton . . . (*I look at My Father wide-eyed.*)

MY FATHER: There wasn't nothin' much my mother *could* do but kill herself. She wasn't trained for no kind of labor. And with a small child to look after. *She* knew what mean folks them Rogerses was. . . . And I figure, rather than return to 'em, she . . . well, she done what she done.

ME: Gee, Papa. . . . Oh, *gee!* (*It had never occurred to me that My Father was someone to feel sorry for. I have to wink back the tears.*)

MY MOTHER: Oh, your poor mother! . . . Oh, Clinton, you never told me. . . .

MY FATHER: So now you know why I never see none of my people and why I wouldn't talk about 'em none. I'll feel bitter to 'em if I live to be a hundred. They was awful people. Till the day I *die,* I'll feel bitter! So when the time comes *my* child sets out, I'd like to try to grease the ways for her, about fifty dollars' worth.

ME (*Very near to crying*): Oh, *Papa!* (*Flinging my arms around him*) Oh, *Papa!*

MY FATHER: Only thing is I don't know where it's goin' to come from.

MY MOTHER: You'll get it, Clinton. Just *believe* you will. . . .

MY FATHER: Of course there's my bonus. That falls due first week of July. *That's* a hundred. So half of that you *could* consider to be yours. That is, if they'll advance it to me. . . . If it's goin' to be mine July third anyways, then they *could,* if they wanted to, advance it just as well in June. . . .

MY MOTHER: Oh, they *would,* Clinton. I just know they would. . . . Why, what difference would it make to anybody?

MY FATHER: Only difference is, Dollaber's a rich man. Only *poor* people know money is more valuable on certain days than it's ever goin' to be again.

MY MOTHER: You know what fifty dollars means to your father and I, Ruth? In my whole life I never saw fifty dollars together, not even *once.*

ME: Oh, Mama!

MY MOTHER: But money isn't everything. All we *really* need is faith!

MY FATHER: Well, you and Ruth grapple with the faith end of it and I'll tackle D. W. Dollaber. Faith is a wonderful thing all right, but I never was in no situation where havin' money made things any *worse!*

CURTAIN

Let's consider . . .

1. Father turned out to be something more than the comic, talkative man he was in Act One. Why did he insist that Ruth complete high school? What made him decide to help her become an actress? How has your opinion of him changed since Act One?

2. Why did Ruth fail in her interview with Mr. Craig? Of what value was the experience?

3. You may have been surprised at Father's allergy to the new telephone. To you it seems as basic as electric lights or plumbing. Yet, can you recall similar reactions in your own family to television, or to some other "new-fangled" invention? Share your family experience with the class.

4. In every crisis, Mrs. Jones recommended a glass of Moxie, a beverage that was as popular then as the cola drinks are today. What is your mother's special trick for getting the family out of low spirits? How effective is it?

ACT THREE

*June, five months later. About eleven
o'clock in the morning. The scene is the
same and there is a terrific bustle. This is
it! This is the day I am going to leave!
The dining-room table is stripped for action and at one side of it I am making peanut butter sandwiches to take on the train
with me. Fred Whitmarsh is sitting at a
chair drawn up alongside of the table,
watching me.*

FRED: But I still don't see why you have
to go to New York City the very day after
your graduation. It doesn't matter if you
start to be an actress this week or next,
does it? And with Class Day only day after
tomorrow . . .

ME: I *can't* wait till day after tomorrow,
Fred. Every minute counts.

FRED: The day after I graduate I don't
feel I have to hop right into the Shawmut
National Bank just because my uncle's got
me an opening there. I'm going to go to
Marblehead like always, then in September
I'll go to work. (*Shaking his head*) What's
the address of the Three Arts Club?

ME: Three forty West Eighty-fifth
Street, New York City. My room is number sixty-one. It's reserved beginnin' today!
Fred! In New York City, there's a room
waitin' for me to just unlock the door and
walk in!

FRED: Gosh! I wonder where three hundred and forty West Eighty-fifth Street is.
I went through New York City once on my
way to Buffalo . . .

MY MOTHER (*Coming through from the
kitchen*): Why, Fred, I never knew you'd
been out West . . . (*She holds up my graduation dress. It is white ruffled net with
short sleeves and a hand-embroidered collar. The skirt is long enough to sweep the
floor. She holds it up for my approval.*)
Look lovely? I pressed it where you got the

ruffles flat last night. I'll get it in the
trunk; Mr. Sparrow'll be here any minute
to cart it to the station. (*She goes upstairs
holding the dress aloft.*)

FRED (*Slightly mournful*): I'm not taking anyone to Class Day. I didn't ask
anyone else. . . . Will you miss me? I'm
going to miss you. . . .

ME (*Thoughtfully*): I don't *think* I
will. It sounds awful, but I want to *go* so,
I don't guess I'm goin' to miss *anybody*. I
don't mean to *ever* like anybody—a fellow,
I mean—that is, not unless they live in
New York City or just outside.

FRED (*Surprised*): Why?

ME: Because New York City is where
an actress has to live most of the time.

FRED: Well, but suppose you liked a fellow and he *didn't* live in New York City.
Suppose he lived in *Boston*.

ME (*Very definite*): I *couldn't*.

FRED (*Doggedly*): But how could you
help it if you *did* like him?

ME: Because I wouldn't let myself get to
like him in the *first* place. See, Fred, if I
ever got to fallin' in love with a fellow,
then I myself might not want to be an

actress, that's why, except that *one time*, I never would kiss anybody except of course in games of Post Office. Maybe I'll never kiss anybody, but if I do, it's either got to be Post Office or the fellow *has* to live in New York City.

FRED (*Gloomily*): Or just outside. (*Through the windows comes the rattle of wagon wheels. Over the sound comes a loud "Whoa" and the wagon stops.*)

ME (*Looking out the window*): There's Mr. Sparrow come for my trunk! . . . *Mama!* (*Hollering excitedly.*) Mama! Did you get my graduation dress in?

MY MOTHER'S VOICE (*Just as excited*): *Of course* I did. I'm doing it right now!

ME: Fred, I guess we're pretty busy here . . .

FRED: Yuh . . . Well, I'm just going.

ME (*At the door in great excitement*): Hullo, Mr. Sparrow.

MR. SPARROW (*In a peculiarly mournful voice*): Trunk ready?

ME: Yes. It's upstairs with Mama.

MR. SPARROW (*In the hall, sadly*): What you want to go 'way for?

ME (*Trying not to appear too boastful*): I'm goin' to New York City to go on the stage.

MR. SPARROW (*Startled, in a minor key*): You mean to be a actor?

ME: Yes.

MR. SPARROW: Well, you certainly are a dabster!

MY MOTHER (*From the top of the stairs*): Come right up, Mr. Sparrow. (*Mr. Sparrow gives me a sad look and starts upstairs.*)

MR. SPARROW (*To My Mother*): Ruth know what she's talking about? She says she's going on the stage?

MY MOTHER (*From upstairs*): Yes, she's made up her own mind. The trunk's right in here, Mr. Sparrow.

FRED: If I write to you . . .

MR. SPARROW (*Shouting sadly from upstairs*): That boy can give me a hand if he's got a mind to . . .

ME: No, he's got to go. *I'll* help you, Mr. Sparrow.

FRED (*Indignantly, stopping me at the landing*): Gosh, you sound like some kind of suffragette, hauling trunks around! (*He goes up the stairs.*)

MY MOTHER (*From upstairs*): Oh, that's nice of you, Fred.

MR. SPARROW (*From upstairs*): Here, boy, git her by the rear end.

MY MOTHER (*Hurrying downstairs*): Please don't ram the trunk into the wallpaper, Mr. Sparrow. Mr. Jones wouldn't like that. (*Outside on the front walk we hear Anna's voice.*)

ANNA: Yoo hoo . . .

ME (*Calling out to her*): Hello, Anna, come on in . . .

ANNA (*Comes in with a tissue-paper-wrapped package tied with pink ribbon*): I brought you something . . .

ME: Oh, Anna!!!

ANNA: It's half for last night's graduation present and half for today going away . . .

ME (*Undoing the tissue paper and ribbon*): Oh, *thank* you, Anna. . . . Oh, *Mama!* Anna's brought me somethin' . . .

MY MOTHER (*Rushing in*): Oh, hello, Anna . . . *Ruth,* what *is* it?

ANNA: Is it too late to go in the trunk?

MY MOTHER: Yes, here's Mr. Sparrow and Fred coming downstairs with it now. It'll go in Ruth's new straw suitcase her father gave her for graduation.

ME: Oh, *look,* Mama. Oh, *thank* you, Anna.

MY MOTHER: Oh, my! That'll be your very best corset cover, Ruth.

ME: Mama, please! Fred and Mr. Sparrow!

MY MOTHER: Yes, put it away.

ANNA: What time's your train go, Ruth?

ME (*Exuberantly*): One twenty-five from the South Station arrivin' in New York City at the Grand Central Station at eighteen minutes to seven.

MY MOTHER: I'm glad to think she'll be settled before it starts to get dark there. And please not go out nights, Ruth, unless accompanied by some older woman. . . . (MR. *Sparrow and Fred lumber down with an old-fashioned trunk.*)

ANNA: Hello, Fred. Hello, Mr. Sparrow.

FRED: Hello . . .

MR. SPARROW: Don't try to talk and carry a trunk downstairs. Come back and talk after.

FRED (*To Anna*): Wait a sec.

MR. SPARROW: Hang on, now, while I ease her round this corner. . . .

MY MOTHER: Don't trip on the landing, Mr. Sparrow . . . Ruth, kick that whale's tooth out from in front of the door. . . .

ANNA: I'll be down to the station . . .

MY MOTHER: Oh, won't that be lovely. . . . Here, let me move that rocking chair back out of the way, Mr. Sparrow. (*She goes out, holding the screen door open for Fred and Mr. Sparrow.*)

ANNA: I can't *wait* to see your dress!

ME: Oh, Anna! (*And in a great burst of emotion I fling my arms around my next best friend and she goes.*)

MY MOTHER (*Out on the porch*): Ruth, get my purse out of the stein on the mantelpiece and get a piece of last night's cherry pie for Mr. Sparrow.

ME (*Doing as directed*): All right. (*Glancing at the clock on the mantel*): Mama! Look what time it is! Shouldn't Papa be gettin' here by now?

MY MOTHER: Any minute . . .

ME: He isn't goin' to forget, you think?

MY MOTHER (*Painfully exasperated*): Now, how often does your father knock off work at ten o'clock in the morning to go bring home fifty dollars so his daughter can go on the stage?

ME: Well . . .

MY MOTHER: And get Mr. Sparrow a glass of Moxie while you're at it. (*Calling out to Fred*) Oh, Fred, have some Moxie? Ruth's getting some for Mr. Sparrow . . .

FRED: No thanks, Mrs. Jones.

MY MOTHER: Hello, Katherine . . . Ruth's out in the kitchen. (*Calling out to me*) Ruth, here's Katherine. I'll get Mr. Sparrow's pie. (*The screen door slams and Katherine bursts in in a great state of excitement.*)

KATHERINE: Look, Mrs. Jones. It's in the *paper!*

MY MOTHER: *What* is?

KATHERINE: About Ruth. *Read* it!

MY MOTHER: Oh mercy! (*She takes the paper from Katherine shouting to me at the same time.*) Ruth, quick! It's in the paper! (*To Katherine*) In the Quincy *Patriot?*

KATHERINE: Right under Wollaston news.

ME (*Coming in*): Hello, Katherine . . . What?

KATHERINE: Ruth, here it is! It says all about you right in the Quincy *Patriot!*

ME (*Nearly startled out of my wits*): Katherine!!! Oh, *where?*

MY MOTHER: Let me see, too!

ME (*Reading, with a perfectly blissful, broad, and absolutely unashamed smile, while My Mother reads over my shoulder*): "Miss Ruth Gordon Jones, daughter of Mr. and Mrs. Clinton Jones of 14 Elmwood Avenue, is leavin' Wollaston shortly" —oh, mercy—"to embark on a career of actin' in New York City where she hopes to make a name for herself on the Great White Way. She plans to appear under the name of Ruth Gordon." . . . *Oh, Mama!!!*

MY MOTHER: I *wonder* how they happened to put it in the paper?

ME: Look at my name in print! And Mr. Collins'll see it and Miss O'Neill and everyone at High School and everyone *everywhere!*

KATHERINE: It really kind of scared me, the Ruth Gordon part.

ME (*Suddenly disturbed*): Ruth Gordon looks *awfully* plain for an actress's name. (*In a beseeching tone*) Oh, Mama, I *wish* you'd let me have my way! Oh, *please!*

MY MOTHER (*Bridling*): Why, don't be so *silly!* I've put up with everything *else.* I've even talked Papa into letting you be just *Ruth Gordon* and give up the Jones. Papa's agreed to it, though he kicked like a steer. But if you aren't satisfied with that, then you can just not go on the stage and unpack your trunk and stay *home,* because I'm *not going* to *ever* agree to you calling yourself *Fentress Serene Kerlin!* (*She goes into the kitchen.*)

ME: And my trunk's really gone! Did you see it?

KATHERINE: Gosh! When you think of going to be an actress you never think of things like Mr. Sparrow having to come— Oh mercy! I brought you this. (*She offers a small package.*)

ME (*Tearing off the wrappings*): Oh, gosh! Oh, Katherine, *thank* you . . .

MY MOTHER (*Coming in from the kitchen with a piece of pie and a mug of Moxie*): Why, what's that, Ruth?

ME: "U-All-No After Dinner Mints." They have advertisements in the *Theatre Magazine.*

MY MOTHER: Oh my! Put 'em in your suitcase. They'll be nice to munch on on the train. (*In come Mr. Sparrow and Fred.*)

ME (*Thrusting the Quincy Patriot at Fred*): Look, Fred, it's in the *Patriot.*

MY MOTHER: Sit down there, Mr. Sparrow, no one's going to steal the trunk off your wagon, and eat up this good piece of pie. Have something, Katherine?

KATHERINE: No thanks, Mrs. Jones.

FRED (*Looking up from the paper*): Well, I'll write you . . .

ME: All right . . .

FRED: Three forty West Eighty-fifth Street.

MY MOTHER: New York City. Gracious, it doesn't seem possible. Mr. Sparrow, did *you* know that? She'll be there in New York City this very night.

MR. SPARROW: Well, she's likely to, goin' all the way by steam cars.

MY MOTHER: She just has to change once at Boston. (*Getting her purse*) I only have a fifty-cent piece, Mr. Sparrow.

MR. SPARROW (*Reaches down into his trouser pocket and brings up a change purse*): Well, I may have a quarter . . .

MY MOTHER: I won't *take* a quarter, Mr. Sparrow; you give me fifteen cents.

MR. SPARROW (*Suspiciously*): It's twenty-five cents to haul it. What's the extra ten for?

MY MOTHER (*Kindly*): For you to go across to Mr. Shunk's after you get the trunk on the station platform and buy two Cremo cigars!

MR. SPARROW (*Mournfully amiable*): Oh well, I don't mind that. A *present* ain't disagreeable; I thought you was goin' to offer me ten cents.

FRED: Well, good-by . . .

ME: I'll think about you Class Day.

FRED: Well, good-by . . .

ME: All right, Fred . . . good-by.

MY MOTHER: Oh dear, good-bys are sad. Well, good-by, Fred. Maybe she isn't going to go forever. People change their minds.

ME: Mama!

MY MOTHER: Oh, I know you're different. I'm just saying to Fred about *peo-ple*. (*Fred gives a wan smile and fades out. The screen door slams and we hear footsteps going down the gravel path. Mr. Sparrow brushes his whiskers with a convenient piece of cotton waste and rises from the table.*)

MR. SPARROW: I'll have your trunk check down at the station when you get there.

MY MOTHER: Mr. Jones will be with us; you can hand it over to him. (*Mr. Sparrow nods and goes out.*)

KATHERINE (*Starts to go*): I'll see you down to the station. Anna's coming of course. And Gladys Bain and Gladys Glover and . . . oh, a lot of people. I got to go to Backus's first.

MY MOTHER: All right, Katherine. See you at the station.

ME (*Fervently*): Oh, Katherine, did you ever *really* think I'd be goin'? *I* did! (*Katherine and I hug each other briefly but rapturously. She goes.*)

MY MOTHER (*Looking after Katherine*): Katherine's a lovely girl. Why, who sent you these, Ruth? (*She picks up some carnations wrapped up in a twist of tissue paper.*)

ME: Just Fred . . .

MY MOTHER: Oh dear . . . He's such a nice boy! With any encouragement at *all*, he'd—

ME (*Not caring for this trend*): Mama, where is *Papa*? Do you suppose anythin' awful happened, like the bank said he didn't *have* fifty dollars?

MY MOTHER: Why, of course he has, he must have.

ME: But goin' to the bank'll maybe make him miss the train! (*With a kind of wail*) Oh, *why* didn't he just ask Mr. Dollaber like he said he would, to just advance him his *bonus*?

MY MOTHER: Well, he was going to,

but Papa thought asking might make Mr. Dollaber think we were living beyond our means. . . . Your father doesn't want to give the impression he's unreliable and has to borrow past his salary!

ME: Mama, *please!* Couldn't we call up the factory? Just this once? Mama, please! Couldn't we? Papa said he'd *surely* be back here by now.

MY MOTHER: Well, all right. He may be going to change his mind and meet us at the South Station. I'll call Dan Weymouth at the factory.

ME: Mama, don't you remember? Dan Weymouth's gone and retired.

MY MOTHER (*Dropping in the nickel*): Not till the end of the month—Tremont eight, two, four—You know where to lay your hands on your railroad ticket to New York City if Papa says to come to Boston to meet him?

ME: It's under the corner of the straw mattin' between my shirtwaist box and the commode.

MY MOTHER: The shipping department—Papa was lovely to buy you that parlor-car seat. You'll be the very first one in this family to ever ride in a parlor car—Dan Weymouth, please—Go out in the kitchen and eat something.

ME (*Excitedly*): Oh, Mama, I *can't!*

MY MOTHER: How're you going to be an actress with nothing on your stomach?

ME (*Making a start for the kitchen*): Well, just a glass of milk.

MY MOTHER: Eat a pear, too. Fruit's nourishing. (*On the phone*) Hello, Dan? Oh, Dan this is Annie . . . yes . . . I was wondering about Clinton. He was coming home and he ought to be here by now. (*Relief in her voice*) Oh, he *did?* . . . What time did he leave, Dan? Did he tell you he was coming out here? (*Happily*) Oh, he *did?* . . . Well, then that means he'll be here any minute . . . Ruth was getting anxious. She's going to New York City today ... What? (*My Mother's voice suddenly gets quite stiff*) No, of course she's not. Well, good-by, Dan. (*She hangs up as I come in from the kitchen with a glass of milk.*) Dan *means* well, but sometimes ... !!! You know what Dan said? He said, "Ruth's not going to be one of them *high kickers,* is she?"

ME: Where'd he think Papa is?

MY MOTHER: Dan doesn't know. He'll be here any moment ... Papa ... so you go upstairs and start getting ready.

ME: Yes, I better. (*I rush up the first few steps, then come down again and just stare.*) Mama!

MY MOTHER: Hmm?

ME (*In a kind of awed whisper*): Mama!

MY MOTHER (*Turns, noticing my strained face*): Why, what's the matter, Ruth? Don't you feel well?

ME: Mama ... look at me ... I been goin' up these stairs since I was six years old and now when I come down *this* time, I'll be on the road to fame!

MY MOTHER (*Indignantly*): Oh, Ruth!

ME: Watch me go, Mama! When I come down I'll be somebody else! (*I start off, half awed and half excited, walking with care as though I were scaling a ladder. My mother in spite of herself, really does watch me. From the top of the stairs I call back softly.*) Good-by, Mama.

MY MOTHER (*Exasperated*): Oh Ruth! (*She catches sight of Punk in the parlor.*) Oh, *Punk!* You can't be trusted for one *single solitary* second! I'll just have to shut you up in here. (*She comes out of the parlor carrying Punk, who is lazily munching a spray of Boston fern.*) What on earth makes you enjoy eating *Boston fern?* (*She thrusts Punk into the kitchen. As she turns back into the dining room the screen door slams and My Father comes in.*) Clinton!

... Where have you *been?* Why, I even called up the factory! Ruth's just gone up to get dressed!

MY FATHER (*Grimly*): Well, tell her to heave to!

MY MOTHER: *What?*

MY FATHER: Tell her to never mind.

MY MOTHER: Clinton, what are you talking about?

MY FATHER: Tell her to never *mind* gettin' dressed!

MY MOTHER: She's *got* to get dressed to go to New York City, hasn't she?

MY FATHER: No, she don't!

MY MOTHER: Well, will you please tell me *why* she doesn't?

MY FATHER: Because she's not goin' to go.

MY MOTHER (*Making an effort to be reasonable*): Clinton, please! Don't pick *today* to be exasperating!

MY FATHER: I *didn't* pick it; it picked *me!*

MY MOTHER: If you were a drinking man, I'd swear you'd been to a saloon and taken a drink!

MY FATHER: Well, you'd be wrong. I didn't. I didn't take nothin' but a *position.*

MY MOTHER (*Relieved*): Well, *that's* good! You tell me about it when we've got Ruth on the train.

MY FATHER: She ain't goin' on the train and she better hyper down to the railroad station to turn in that parlor-car ticket.

MY MOTHER: *Clinton!*

MY FATHER: Or it ain't goin' to be any good.

MY MOTHER: What on earth do you mean, Clinton, Ruth *isn't* going?

MY FATHER: I can't afford to send no one off to be an actress because right this minute *I* ain't got a job!

MY MOTHER (*Despairingly*): Oh, how could this happen to us!

MY FATHER: It happened to us because

Mr. Dollaber had me come into his office and asked me did I think Charley Folsom was entitled to his bonus and I launched out and told him what I thought of his bonuses!

My Mother: Oh, but Clinton, you decided not to talk to him about it.

My Father: How could I help it when he went and talked to me first?

My Mother: Oh, Clinton! Oh dear!! *Oh dear!!!*

My Father: He didn't like it none, and he says to me very snippy, "Well, how would you propose to remedy that?" And I let him have it right out. "Pay me what's due me," I says, "and don't give me no lallygaggin' favors! Pay me like what the bonus would amount to if it was a weekly pay increase. Instead of you handin' me a hundred simoleons at the end of the fiscal year, split it up into a weekly raise of two dollars. Then I *got* it and I *know* I got it and there ain't no *worryin' palaver.*"

My Mother (*Almost in tears*): Oh, Clinton, to pick *today* of *all* days to speak up to Mr. Dollaber!

My Father (*Stubbornly*): I don't regret it, worked up as I was.

My Mother: And you mean he went and fired you just because you asked for something you were entitled to?

My Father: I didn't *wait* for him to fire me; I went and fired *myself!* He said, "You mean you don't care to continue on, the way you been goin' for the last twenty-four years?" And I says, "No," I says. I was kind of surprised *myself.*

My Mother: Oh, Clinton . . . Couldn't you have tried to be just a little more tactful?

My Father: Let *him* be tactful part of the time! For once I had to speak out. So he says they'd hate to lose me but it don't do for a man to try an' run the whole shop, so he'd have to let the matter rest till he

thought about it some. "It ain't the two dollars a week I'm begrudgin'," he says, "but the *principle* seems highhanded!" "Well," I says, "think it over, Mr. Dollaber. You can find me at Fourteen Elmwood Avenue, Wollaston!" I'm glad it happened. I'm only askin' for what's mine.

My Mother: But Ruth's *fifty* you were going to give her, Clinton, to go to New York City—

My Father: I can't spare it. She'll have to go some other time. I got sixty-two dollars in the Five Cent Savin's Bank and shellin' out fifty of it'd leave us sailin' too close to the wind.

My Mother: But, Clinton, she's got her heart set on going *today!*

My Father: Well, she can't! (*From upstairs there is a sudden burst of joyful singing.*)

My Voice: "Get out and get under . . . He *had* to get under . . . To fix up his little *machine!*"

My Mother (*Imploringly*): Clinton!

My Father: I can't *help* it! I can't stretch money further than it'll *go*, can I? She don't have to be an actress just tomorrow; she can wait to see where I'm *at!*

My Mother (*Distractedly trying to assemble an idea*): Well, look, Clinton— what about getting money some *other* way, then? What about . . . er . . . what about collecting on the insurance? . . . That insurance you got on *me*. . . . You aren't ever going to need that, because if anything happened to me, by *then* Ruth'd be supporting herself, and you'd go on working. . . . Why couldn't you give Ruth her fifty dollars and let her take the train like she planned to, then we can borrow on that?

My Father: I ain't goin' to do no borrowin'!

My Mother: But, Clinton, it would only be borrowing our own!

My Father: No, Ruth can *wait!* The

stage isn't going to fold up without her.

MY MOTHER (*Her brain going a mile a minute*): Well, would you let me do this, Clinton? . . . Would you let me borrow some money on my engagement ring?

MY FATHER: *No!* This is a family and Ruth's part of it; she can share the bad with the good! It ain't pleasant to be flung on the anxious seat, but I can weather it and so can *she!*

(*Down the stairs I come, done up to the nines in my going-away outfit that my mother and I had connived over ever since it was decided that I might go on the stage. It is a suit—peacock blue corded silk, made from a fifty-cent pattern in Bon Ton. The skirt is narrow and slit up a decent way. At the waist there is a double ruffle peplum of two gored frills. The jacket is a sort of long bolero, caught at the back with a black moire belt and at the front by a butterfly bow of the same black moire. It has bright steel buttons and a stand-up mildly Elizabethan lace ruff around the neck. My hat is a black tulle halo caught over one ear with a large white gardenia and a double loop of the black moire that has helped out my suit. My shoes are high-heeled, pointed-toed, black patent-leather pumps with cut-steel buckles. I am every inch an actress, so far as 14 Elmwood Avenue can concoct me out of bargain sales, birthday and graduation contributions, and odds and ends of eked-out household money. I come down the stairs, perfectly radiant, carrying my new straw suitcase in one hand and in the other a jaunty black moire purse, with a long tassel on it, and a pair of white kid gloves.*)

ME (*Deliriously happy at seeing My Father*): Papa! . . . Mama! why didn't you tell me he was here! Oh, Papa, look at me —I'm almost an actress already!

MY MOTHER (*With a little moan*): Oh, child.

ME (*Joyous*): Mama, don't be sad. Be proud!

MY MOTHER: Oh, Clinton, would you let me go out and sew for people? I could make *more* than fifty dollars.

ME: Why, what is it? Papa, what's the matter?

MY FATHER: You can't go. So get them duds off and stow away your gear.

ME (*Still holding my suitcase and wearing the stupidest smile*): Can't go!

MY FATHER: No, you can't. Not today.

ME (*Almost fiercely, suddenly scenting danger*): Why can't I?

MY FATHER: Because I ain't got the do-re-mi to give you.

ME (*Half indignation, and half boiling over with tears*): But, Papa, you said you could! You said you *could* give it to me!

MY FATHER (*Cutting in grimly*): Well, now I say I *can't,* so get them duds off and hyper down to the railroad station and turn back your parlor-car ticket or it ain't goin' to be no *good!* (*For a minute I just stand there—for one whole awful minute. I feel the way I did when the water closed over my head once at Nantasket Beach. Then, just as at Nantasket, I suddenly jerk my head up through the breakers and see some watery light.*)

ME: I will *not!* I will not take my ticket back! I will *so* go! You *said* I could be an actress and I *am* goin'!

MY FATHER: You *can't.* You haven't got the money; you can't go far without that.

ME: I can *so* go! I won't need any money. You paid my room at the Three Arts Club for two weeks in advance and I'll go like *I* said I was goin' to. You gave me your *word!*

MY MOTHER (*Despairingly*): Ruth, Papa had it out with Mr. Dollaber, and he lost his position.

ME (*Crying and not even knowing I*

am): Oh, Papa! Oh, *Papa!* How could that *be?*

MY FATHER: Because I couldn't kowtow no longer for what by rights is mine. I done what I could for you, but I can't bend the knee no lower.

MY MOTHER: Oh, Ruth, child, Papa wants to do for you, but now he just *can't.*

ME (*Hardly able to keep back the tears*): Oh, *Papa.*

MY MOTHER: I don't know where my handkerchief is. Give me a doily. (*Silently I get one from the sideboard and hand it to her.*) Fanny Mae Jackson embroidered me this doily. I never like to use it.

ME: Use it, Mama. It's nothin' to the ones I'll buy you. (*Turning to My Father*) Don't you care about the fifty dollars, Papa. I don't need it. I got two dollars and forty cents of my own money and my railroad ticket, so I'll just get a job sooner so's I can look after you and Mama.

MY MOTHER (*Beseechingly*): Oh, Clinton, she can't go be an actress on two dollars and forty cents.

ME: I can so! Where's my box of lunch, Mama? You'll hear from me day after tomorrow!

MY MOTHER: Oh, Clinton, let me give her my engagement ring. *Do* let me, Clinton, *please!*

MY FATHER: I gave you that to *keep.*

MY MOTHER (*Pleading*): She could get some money for it.

ME: Mama! You mean go in a *pawnshop? I'd rather be dead!*

MY FATHER: If you're goin' to be an actress, you'll be in and out of a pawnshop all the rest of your life!

ME: I'll go see every single manager in New York City tomorrow. I'll go see 'em beginning at six o'clock in the mornin'.

MY FATHER: Well, one thing, you've got spirit!

ME: I got anythin' I *want* to have; but I'll never have anythin' *at all* if trouble makes me go an' give *up!* I'm *never* goin' to let trouble stop me! Why, to actresses it's even a *help!* I don't know if it's any use to private people, but actresses have to *have* troubles, so's they can *act!* Why, I bet I can even learn to *welcome* trouble! I bet I can actually *enjoy* it. I bet—

MY FATHER: Hold on a minute! Hold on! No call to render a solo on the beauties of bein' in the soup. On the other hand, if what it takes to be an actress is *gumption,* you at least got that! I know what's goin' on inside you, Snuggy. Your mother says you take after me, and, better or worse, I guess you do. Of course I don't suppose you know what you're tacklin', but I'm willin' to give you a chance to find out. I always staked you up to now, and I'm willin' to continue on the same. Mama, go look on the parlor mantelpiece and get me down my spyglass.

MY MOTHER (*Startled*): Clinton! What're you going to do?

MY FATHER: I'm goin' to wrap it up in a newspaper if you got a decent one. Give me the Boston *Globe.* When you get to New York City, Ruth, take it down to Cap'n Alec Forbes, Twenty-two South Street, and he'll give you one hundred dollars for it. (*My Mother rushes into the parlor and returns with the spyglass.*)

ME (*Dazed*): Papa!

MY FATHER: And if Forbes is away on a voyage, take her to any ship chandler along the street; there ain't one wouldn't give you a hundred, spot cash.

ME: Papa! I *can't* take it. I *wouldn't.* It's your *spyglass!*

MY FATHER: Money's for those who need it. A spyglass ain't no further use to me.

ME: But, Papa—I *know* I can get along!

MY FATHER: Don't be bousin' your jib. You may love your Hazel Dawns and your

Doris Olssons, but money's a real lovin' friend, too. (*My Mother rushes back with the Boston* Globe.)

ME (*Anxiously*): But what about you and Mama, if just maybe I *didn't* get a job right off?

MY FATHER (*Starting to wrap up the spyglass*): Rest easy! I been on a pay roll since I was eight, and I been cast overboard before. It ain't like I was lookin' for a job as vice-president; there's always plenty of room at the bottom.

ME: Oh, Papa, I won't only just merely look after you and Mama, but we'll *have* things! And every time we feel like it, we'll throw *away* fifty dollars!

MY FATHER: Cap'n Alec Forbes, Twenty-two South Street, New York City—write it down for her, Mama. And when you're down in that vicinity, drop over to Fulton Market. Great sight, the way they handle fish. T Wharf and even Gloucester ain't nothin' alongside it! Here you are, all shipshape.

MY MOTHER: All right, Clinton, it's time to go—Ruth, have you got your handkerchief and your railroad and parlor-car ticket? Papa'll carry your suitcase for you. You take it, Clinton, and I'll take her lunch.

ME (*Rapturously*): Oh, Mama, tomorrow mornin' in New York City I'll be eatin' bread you made me and peanut butter from old Backus's grocery store.

MY FATHER (*Indignantly*): Backus! Why didn't it come from S. S. Pierce?

MY MOTHER: Clinton! Ruth, you take Papa's spyglass and Fred Whitmarsh's carnations.

MY FATHER: Well, come on, heave anchor—

MY MOTHER: What about taking your umbrella, Ruth? It might be raining when you get to New York City. (*She hurries into the hall and gets my umbrella from the stand. My Father stands and regards me for a minute.*)

MY FATHER: Snuggy, I ain't talked to you a whole lot, and I ain't goin' to start spoutin' out now. If I didn't think you could shift for yourself, I wouldn't let you go. But from my own personal experience of knockin' round the world, there's more temptation when you're rovin' than you're likely to run up against at home. However, I ain't goin' to impose a whole lot of rules on you, nor chart no exact course, but I want you to promise me *one thing*, Snuggy; no matter what you do, nor where you go, don't never act in no place where they serve hard liquor!

ME: Oh, Papa, no matter if it kills me, I'll make this up to you and Mama. I'll make good, Papa. You see if I don't.

MY MOTHER: It's a wonderful thing, Ruth, to have a father that believes in you a hundred dollars' worth!

ME: I'll make it up to you *somehow*, Papa!

MY FATHER: No, you don't have to doff your tops'l and feel beholden. What you're gettin' is what a person's got a right to. You're only gettin' your chance. And on your side of the ledger you can remember your mother and I pleasantly, and that'll make it come out square.

(*The moment has come. I throw my arms around My Father and My Mother, hugging them both. The spyglass, the straw suitcase, the umbrella, and Fred's carnations all unite in one last loving embrace, and then I walk slowly out of our dining-sitting room, out the door, across the porch. My Mother and My Father watch me for a moment. Then they follow. My Father locks the front door after him. We can be heard crunching down the gravel walk and our house seems very still.*)

CURTAIN

[Adapted]

The woman who wrote this play

RUTH GORDON   1896–

Years Ago was written by Ruth Gordon with the help of her husband, Garson Kanin. The play tells of her early life and her great desire to become an actress. As in the play, her father was an independent, land-bound sailor. Her mother helped her as much as she could, and young Ruth Gordon thought only in terms of the movies and the stage.

With her father's aid, she went to New York City to be an actress, but becoming an actress was difficult. To earn enough money to eat, she took bit parts with a silent movie company that was located in Fort Lee, New Jersey. She visited the casting offices, and she says that whether she walked from her apartment or took the subway depended on whether someone in her apartment house was lucky enough to have a spare nickel.

Gradually she got more and more important roles. She is now an experienced and famous actress, and she has had great successes on both the Broadway and London stages. In between her stage roles, she acts in the motion pictures or writes plays and stories.

Years Ago appeared on Broadway as a popular play, and it was later made into a movie called *The Actress* with Spencer Tracy and Pier Angeli in the major roles.

Let's consider . . .

1. Many young people, even after graduation from college, flounder about, not knowing what sort of career to pursue. Was Ruth unusually lucky in knowing exactly what career she wished to follow? How can you account for her being so sure of herself? Can you think of disadvantages in choosing your life's work at an early age?

2. Do you know anyone who has always been certain of his goal in life? How did he make his choice? What was Ruth's goal? Do you think she made a wise choice? Explain your answer.

3. In real life Ruth Gordon is a successful actress. Do you think she would have been equally successful if she had continued to call herself Ruth *Jones?* Many actors and actresses change their names, as do members of other professions. What is your opinion of this custom? Can you think of any famous people with "plain" names?

4. When Father lost his job he said, "This is a family and Ruth's part of it; she can share the bad with the good!" Do you agree with Father, or do you think parents should shield children from family misfortunes? Give several reasons to support your answer.

5. Look again at Father's final words in the play. How do you know that they had a lasting effect on Ruth?

6. Divide your class into groups. Cast members of each group in the different roles of *Years Ago.* Let each group present its favorite part of the play for the rest of the class.

The writer's craft . . .

A **play** is simply a story written so that it can be acted on a stage. When you see a play being performed, you not only see what the actors do; you also hear what they say. It is by means of the **action,** what the actors do, and the **dialogue,** what the actors say, that the story is told. However, the dialogue and action do more than just tell the story. They also bring the characters to life. For example, you came to know Father by listening to him talk and watching what he did. You learned that he had stubborn pride when he quit his job after telling his boss how he felt about taking a bonus. You learned, too, that he was a kind parent when he sacrificed his beloved telescope so that Ruth could get to New York.

Select your favorite character in "Years Ago." Then list all the qualities he possessed. Illustrate each quality with a specific reference to the dialogue or action of the play.

Knowing words . . .

You probably found that the stage directions added to your enjoyment of the play. Ruth Gordon helped you *hear* and *see* the characters by describing the tone in which they spoke and the manner in which they acted.

A. Read the following lines aloud in the tone indicated by the stage directions. If you are not sure of the meaning, refer to your glossary.

1. MY FATHER (*Ruminatively*): That feller lashed them ropes to the halliards like he'd took lessons from Corticelli's cat! How people handle rope and string is oftentimes characteristic.

2. ME (*Plaintively*): The Brighams live way up on Prospect!

3. MY FATHER (*Vehemently*): Yes, I can too! I even know what color it is; it's a rotten, dark brown. And it's everywhere I am, every day of the year in every kind of weather.

4. ME (*Adamant*): Then I'll say I'm sick. I'll say I have a headache.

5. MY FATHER (*In a hearty roar*): Reverend Skinner don't have to take a back seat to no *son!* He was the best sky pilot *around.*

6. MY MOTHER (*Ingratiatingly to Miss Glavin*): When he was a sailor, Mr. Jones got some picturesque expressions.

7. MY MOTHER (*Bridling*): Why, don't be so *silly!* I've put up with everything *else.* I've even talked Papa into letting you be just *Ruth Gordon* and give up the Jones. Papa's agreed to it, though he kicked like a steer. But if you aren't satisfied with that, then you can just not go on the stage.

B. Show the class how the following actions were performed.

1. (*My Father returns to his McClure's and I surreptitiously take a large magazine out from under some tablecloths in the sideboard drawer and start upstairs.*)

2. (*My father's eyes drift back despondently to the bill.*)

3. KATHERINE (*Placidly, turning the pages of her Latin book.*)

4. FRED (*After a mild nervous reaction, points to the kitchen*): Cocoa or water or *anything?*

5. (*Fred gives a wan smile and fades out.*)

NOW THINK BACK

THINK FOR YOURSELF

Have you been to the movies lately? Have you been reading a comic book, listening to a radio serial, or watching television? You've probably found yourself thinking, "This really isn't true to life; people just don't act that way." Yet there is a great demand for entertainment which paints a rosy picture of life. When people are unhappy over their own lives, they like to daydream about the achievements of imaginary people. They may even try to excuse their own failures by saying:

"She must have been born under a lucky star."

"It isn't *what* you know, but *whom* you know that brings success in life."

"Wishing will make it true."

"Getting started in life was a lot easier years ago."

"He was born with a silver spoon in his mouth."

Have you ever been guilty of saying these things yourself? Is there any truth in them? Do any of the characters in this Part either prove or *dis*prove these statements? How?

SHARE YOUR IDEAS

You have seen that facing life involves many different kinds of experiences. For some people, it means finding the right career. For others, it means gaining self-confidence. But for everyone, it means growing into a more mature person. As you share your ideas on the following questions, be sure to draw upon selections from FACING LIFE to illustrate your answers.

1. You have seen movies in which the hero or heroine achieved great success through little more than a series of lucky breaks. You may have thought that his or her success was not very true to life. How necessary is luck in achieving success? What is more important than luck?

2. What does *success* mean to you? Which people in FACING LIFE were successful? Which ones were unsuccessful?

3. Which person had the most difficult choice to make? Which person had the easiest choice? In each case explain your reasons for naming that person.

4. How large a part should parents play in the choice of their children's vocation? Which parents in this part helped their children find a career? How did these parents help? Did any parents hinder more than they helped?

5. Compare Polonius' advice to his son with the advice Ruth's father gave her when she was about to leave home. Which parent gave the sounder advice? Why?

6. How can reading widen your knowledge of vocations? What practical hints did FACING LIFE give you for being successful in your chosen work?

7. What are the advantages in deciding now what vocation you will follow? What are the disadvantages?

8. How does education help prepare you for life? Are you completely satisfied with the education you are getting? Why? If you think that your schooling could be improved, what changes would you recommend? Are there limits to what schools can do to prepare you for life? If so, what are these limits?

9. Which person that you read about was least prepared to face life? In what ways could that person have been better prepared?

10. Which person was best prepared to face life? List the ways in which that person was well prepared.

WIDEN YOUR EXPERIENCE

Things to do . . .

1. Interview the "breadwinners" in your family and among your neighbors. Ask them to tell you (a) how they happened to go into their field of work, (b) what satisfactions they get from their work, and (c) what they may have learned from their experiences in choosing and following their vocation.

2. Read one of the books recommended in *More to read.* In your book report, point out the difficulties which had to be faced and tell how these difficulties were solved.

3. Present an individual or committee oral report on one of the following topics:
People Who Succeeded in Spite of Their Handicaps
This Way to Success in Life
My Idea of a Perfect Career
Unusual Occupations in Our Land
Employment Opportunities in Our Community
Guidance Services in Our School (or Community)
How . . . Became a Successful Author
What You Must Do to Be a Successful . . .

4. If your school has a vocational or educational guidance counselor, you are very fortunate. This service is available to you at no cost, and the counselor has a special interest in you that outsiders might not have. Write a letter to such a counselor inviting him to address the group on how to plan a school career to best advantage. Allow time for a question-answer period at the end of his talk.

5. Try your skill at writing a short paper on one of the following topics:
My Experiences as a Baby Sitter
Behind the Counter
Business on a Bicycle
My Hobby Pays Dividends
The First Dollar I Ever Earned
The Customer Is Always Right (or Wrong)

More to read . . .

Vocations for Girls and *Vocations for Boys* by MARY R. LINGENFELTER and HARRY D. KITSON. Here you will find facts about hundreds of jobs in business, the professions, and the arts. Harcourt, Brace and Company, Inc., 1951, 1942.

Young Men and Machines by RAYMOND F. YATES. Anyone planning to work with machinery in industry will find this career guide a great help. Dodd, Mead & Company, Inc., 1944.

I Work on a Newspaper by HENRY B. LENT. This is the inside story of an average day in a newspaper plant, from the time the news is made until the paper is ready to read. The Macmillan Company, Inc., 1948.

Farm Boy by DOUGLAS GORSLINE. When rebellious Johnny goes to work on his uncle's farm, he faces the fact that before he can be really independent, he must learn self-discipline. The Viking Press, 1950.

Fifth Chinese Daughter by JADE SNOW WONG. A young girl in San Francisco's Chinese community has to choose between independence and the traditional-minded family she loves. Eventually she finds a way to bring them together. Harper & Brothers, 1950.

Skygirl by MARY F. MURRAY. If your ambition is to become an airline stewardess, you will find this a valuable handbook. Duell, Sloan and Pearce, Inc., 1951.

The Organdy Cupcakes by MARY STOLZ. Three student nurses face the decision on what to do when they have finished their training. The three young men in the picture complicate the problem. Harper & Brothers, 1951.

In the Big Time by KATHERINE BAKELESS. Here are the career stories of famous people of the theater and concert hall, including Bing Crosby, James Stewart, Marian Anderson, and Fred Astaire. J. B. Lippincott Company, 1953.

The Wright Brothers by FRED C. KELLY. The curiosity and persistence of these pioneer fliers brought them success, even when most people were laughing at their experiments. Farrar, Strauss and Young, Inc., 1950.

Lou Gehrig, a Quiet Hero by FRANK GRAHAM. This biography of the great Yankee ballplayer describes his rise to fame and his courage in facing the disease which eventually caused his death. G. P. Putnam's Sons, 1942.

Song of the Lark by WILLA CATHER. Thea Kronborg works long and hard to become a successful singer. Her story will fascinate and inspire anyone with musical ambitions. Houghton Mifflin Company, 1915.

The Right Job for Judith by ENID JOHNSON. Judith realizes that finding the work for which she is truly fitted is more important than trying to fulfill a dream of glamor. Julian Messner, Inc., 1951.

Circus Doctor by J. Y. HENDERSON and RICHARD TAPLINGER. A veterinarian who became doctor for Ringling Brothers and Barnum and Bailey circus tells of his experiences. Little, Brown and Company, 1951.

Student Dancer by REGINA L. WOODY. A girl's hard work preparing for a dancing career is the basis for a story that is filled with suspense as well as information. Houghton Mifflin Company, 1951.

My Friend Flicka by MARY O'HARA. Young Ken's devotion to his horse helps to win his father's respect for his judgment. J. B. Lippincott Company, 1941.

THE FAMILY

Many mothers and dads are not only good parents; they are good friends as well. Here you will meet the Williamses, the Maloneys, and other families who have learned to find happiness and friendship together. Here you may discover ideas for good times with your own family. You may even find ways of solving difficult family problems. Visiting in the homes of these story families will surely give you a fresh slant on your own family life.

LEF

PART FIVE

THE FAMILY

The Pheasant Hunter

WILLIAM SAROYAN

Mayo was a problem. He was self-confident, critical, and rude. His father thought he should "get off his high horse" and act like everybody else.

Mayo Maloney at eleven was a little runt of a fellow who was not rude so much as he was rudeness itself, for he couldn't even step inside a church, for instance, without giving everybody who happened to see him an uncomfortable feeling that he, Mayo, despised the place and its purpose.

It was much the same everywhere else that Mayo went: school, library, theater, home. Only his mother felt that Mayo was not a rude boy, but his father frequently asked Mayo to get down off his high horse and act like everybody else. By this, Michael Maloney meant that Mayo ought to take things easy and stop finding so much fault with everything.

Mayo was the most self-confident boy in the world, and he found fault with everything, or so at least it seemed. He found fault with his mother's church activities. He found fault with his father's interest in Shakespeare and Mozart. He found fault with the public school system, the Government, the United Nations, the entire population of the world. And he did all this faultfinding without so much as going into detail about anything. He did it by being alive, by being on hand at all. He did it by being nervous, irritable, swift, wise, and bored. In short, he was a perfectly normal boy. He had contempt for everything and everybody, and he couldn't help it. His contempt was unspoken but unmistakable. He was slight of body, dark of face and hair, and he went at everything in a hurry because everything was slow and stupid and weak.

The only thing that didn't bore him was the idea of hunting, but his father wouldn't buy him a gun, not even a .22-caliber single-shot rifle. Michael Maloney told Mayo that as soon as he was sure that Mayo had calmed down a little, he would think about buying him a gun. Mayo tried to calm down a little, so he could have his gun, but he gave it up after a day and a half.

"O.K.," his father said, "if you don't want your gun, you don't have to try to earn it."

"I did try to earn it," Mayo said.

"When?"

"Yesterday and today."

"I had in mind," his father said, "a trial covering a period of at least a month."

"A month?" Mayo said. "How do you expect a fellow to stay calm all through October with pheasant to shoot in the country?"

"I don't know how," Mike Maloney said.

"But if you want a gun, you've got to calm down enough so I can believe you won't shoot the neighbors with it. Do you think my father so much as let me sit down to my dinner if I hadn't done something to earn it? He didn't invite me to earn any gun to shoot pheasants with. He told me to earn my food, and he didn't wait until I was eleven, either. I started earning it when I was no more than eight. The whole trouble with you is you're too pent-up from not doing any kind of work at all for your food or shelter or clothing to be decently tired and ordinary like everybody else. You're not human, almost. Nobody's human who doesn't know how hard it is to earn his food and the other basic things. It's the fault of your mother and father that you're such a sarcastic and faultfinding man instead of a calm, handsome one. Everybody in this whole town is talking about how your mother and father have turned you into an arrogant ignoramus of a man by not making you earn your right to judge things."

Mr. Maloney spoke as much to the boy's mother as to the boy himself, and he spoke as well to the boy's younger brother and younger sister, for he had left the office at half past four, as he did once a week, to sit down with the whole family for early supper, and it was his intention to make these mid-week gatherings at the table memorable for everyone, including himself.

"Now, Mike," Mrs. Maloney said. "Mayo's not as bad as all that. He just wants a gun to hunt pheasant with."

Mike Maloney laid down his fork that was loaded with macaroni baked with tomatoes and cheese, and he stared at his wife a long time, rejecting one by one two dozen angry remarks he knew would do no one present any good at all to hear, and only make the gathering *unpleasantly* memorable.

At last he said, "I suppose you think I ought to get him a gun, just like that?"

"Mayo isn't really rude or anything like that," the boy's mother said. "It's just that he's restless, the way every human being's got to be once in his lifetime for awhile."

Mayo didn't receive this defense of himself with anything like gratitude. If anything, it appeared as if he were sick and tired of having so much made of a simple little matter like furnishing him with an inexpensive .22-caliber single-shot rifle.

"Now don't you go to work and try to speak up for him," Mike Maloney said to his wife, "because, as you can see for yourself, he doesn't like it. He doesn't enjoy being spoken up for, not even by his mother, poor woman, and you can see how much he thinks of what his father's saying this minute."

"What did I say?" Mayo asked.

"You didn't say anything," his father said. "You didn't need to." He turned to Mrs. Maloney. "Is it a gun I must buy for him now?" he said.

Mrs. Maloney didn't quite know how to say that it was. She remained silent and tried not to look at either her husband or her son.

"O.K.," Mike Maloney said to both his wife and his son. "I have to go back to the office a minute, so if you'll come along with me I'll drop into Archie Cannon's and buy you a gun."

He got up from the table and turned to Mrs. Maloney.

"Provided of course," he said, "that that meets with your approval."

"Aren't you going to finish your food?" Mrs. Maloney said.

"No, I'm not," Mike Maloney said. "And I'll tell you why, too. I don't want him to be denied anything he wants or anything his mother wants him to have, without earning it, for one unnecessary moment, and as you can see, his cap's on his head, he's at the door, and every moment I stand here explaining is unnecessary."

"Couldn't you both finish your food first?" Mrs. Maloney said.

"Who wants to waste time eating," Mike Maloney said, "when it's time to buy a gun?"

"Well," Mrs. Maloney said, "perhaps you'll have something after you buy the gun."

"We should have been poor," Mike Maloney said. "Being poor would have helped us with this problem."

Mike Maloney went to the door where his nervous son was standing waiting for him to shut up and get going.

He turned to his wife and said, "I won't be able to account for him after I turn the gun over to him, but I'll be gone no more than an hour. If we'd been poor and couldn't afford it, he'd know the sinfulness of provoking me into this sort of bitter kindness."

When he stepped out of the house onto the front porch, he saw that his son was at the corner, trying his best not to run. He moved quickly and caught up with him, and he moved along as swiftly as his son did.

At last he said, "Now, I'm willing to walk the half mile to Archie Cannon's, but I'm not going to run, so if you've got to run, go ahead, and I'll meet you outside the place as soon as I get there."

He saw the boy break loose and disappear far down the street. When he got to Archie Cannon's, the boy was waiting for him. They went in and Mike Maloney asked Archie to show him the guns.

"What kind of a gun do you want, Mike?" Archie said. "I didn't know you were interested in hunting."

"It's not for myself," Mike Maloney said.

"It's for Mayo here, and it ought to be suitable for pheasant shooting."

"That would be a shotgun," Archie said.

"Would that be what it would be?" Mike Maloney asked his son, and although the boy hadn't expected anything so precisely suitable for pheasant shooting, he said that a shotgun would be what it would be.

"O.K., Archie," Mike Maloney said. "A shotgun."

"Well, Mike," Archie said, "I wouldn't like to think a shotgun would be the proper gun to turn over to a boy."

"Careful," Mike Maloney said. "He's right here with us, you know. Let's not take unnecessary liberties. I believe he indicated the gun ought to be a shotgun."

"Well, anyway," Archie said, "it's going to have a powerful kick."

"A powerful kick," Mike Maloney repeated, addressing the three words to his son, who received them with disdain.

"That's no matter to him," Mike Maloney said to Archie Cannon. "Well, then," Archie Cannon said. "This here's a fine double-barrel twelve-gauge shotgun and it's just about the best bargain in the store."

"You shouldn't have said that, Archie," Mike Maloney said. "This man's not interested in bargains. What he wants is the best shotgun you've got that's suitable for pheasant shooting."

"That would be this twelve-gauge repeater," Archie Cannon said, "that sells for ninety-eight fifty, plus tax of course. It's the best gun of its kind."

"Anybody can see it's a better gun," Mike Maloney said. "No need to waste time with inferior firearms."

He handed the gun to Mayo Maloney, who held it barrel down, resting over his right arm, precisely as a gun, loaded or not, ought to be held.

"I'll show you how it works," Archie Cannon made the mistake of saying to Mayo Maloney. The boy glanced at Archie in a way that encouraged him to say quickly, "Anything else, then? Fishing tackle, hooks, boxing gloves, rowing machines, tennis rackets?"

"Anything else?" Mike Maloney said to his son, who said nothing, but with such irritation that Mike quickly said to Archie Cannon, "Shells, of course. What good is a shotgun without shells?"

Archie Cannon jumped to get three boxes of his best shotgun shells, and as he turned them over to Mike Maloney, who turned them over to Mayo, Archie said, "A hunting coat in which to carry the shells? A red hunting cap?"

Mayo Maloney was gone, however.

"He didn't want those things," Mike Maloney said.

"Some hunters go to a lot of trouble about costume," Archie Cannon said.

"He doesn't," Mike Maloney said. "What do I owe you?"

"One hundred and five dollars and sixty-nine cents, including tax," Archie said. "Has he got a license?"

"To hunt?" Mike Maloney said. "He hasn't got a license to eat, but darned if I don't halfway admire him sometimes. He must know something to be so sure of himself and so contemptuous of everybody else."

"To tell you the truth," Archie Cannon said, "I thought you were kidding, Mike. I thought you were kidding the way you sometimes do in court when you're helping a small man to fight a big company. I didn't expect you to actually buy a gun and turn it over to an eleven-year-old boy. Are you sure it's all right?"

"Of course it's all right," Mike Maloney said. "You saw for yourself the way he held the gun."

He began to write a check. "Now, what did you say it came to?"

"A hundred and five sixty-nine," Archie Cannon said. "I hope you know there's no pheasant to speak of anywhere near here. The Sacramento Valley is where the pheasant shooting is."

"Where you going to be around ten o'clock tonight?" Mike Maloney said.

"Home most likely," Archie Cannon said. "Why?"

"Will you be up?"

"Oh, yes," Archie said. "I never go to bed before midnight. Why?"

"Would you like to drop over to my house around ten?" Mike said.

"I'd like that very much," Archie said. "Why?"

"Well," Mike said, "The way I figure it is this: It's a quarter after five now. It'll take him about three minutes to hitch a ride with somebody going out to Riverdale, which is about twenty-five miles from here. That would take an average driver forty or forty-five minutes to make, but he'll get the driver, whoever he is, or she is, for that matter, to make it in about half an hour or under. He'll do it by being excited, not by saying anything. He'll get the driver to go out of his or her way to let him off where the hunting is, too, so he'll start hunting right away, or a little before six. He'll hunt until after dark, walking a lot in the meantime. He won't get lost or anything like that, but he'll have to walk back to a road with a little traffic. He'll hitch a ride back, and he'll be home a little before or a little after ten."

"How do you know?" Archie said. "How do you even know he's going hunting at all tonight? He just got the gun, and he may not even know how to work it."

"You saw him take off, didn't you?" Mike Maloney said. "He took off to go hunting. And you can be sure he either knows how to work the gun or will find out by himself in a few minutes."

"Well," Archie said, "I certainly would like to drop by, Mike, if you're serious."

"Of course, I'm serious," Mike said.

"I suppose you want to have somebody to share your amusement with when he gets back with nothing shot and his body all sore from the powerful kick of the gun," Archie said.

"Yes," Mike said. "I want to have somebody to share my amusement with but not for those reasons. He may be a little sore from the powerful kick of the gun, but I think he'll come back with something."

"I've never heard of anybody shooting any pheasant around Riverdale," Archie said. "There's a little duck shooting out there in season, and jack rabbits of course."

"He said pheasants," Mike Maloney said.

"Here's my check. Better make it a little before ten, just in case."

"I thought you were only kidding about the gun," Archie said. "Are you sure you did the right thing? I mean, considering he's only eleven years old, hasn't got a hunting license, and the pheasant-shooting season doesn't open for almost a month?"

"That's one of the reasons I want you to come by," Mike said.

"I don't get it," Archie said.

"You're game warden of this area, aren't you?"

"I am."

"O.K.," Mike said. "If it turns out that he's broken the law, I want you to know it."

"Well," Archie said, "I wouldn't want to bother about a small boy shooting a few days out of season or without a license."

"I'll pay his fine," Mike Maloney said.

"I don't think he'll get anything," Archie said, "so of course there won't be any fine to be paid."

"I'll see you a little before ten, then," Mike Maloney said.

He spent a half hour at his office, then walked home slowly, to find the house quiet and peaceful, the kids in bed, and his wife doing the dishes. He took the dish towel and began to dry and put the clean dishes into the cupboard.

"I bought him the best shotgun Archie Cannon had for pheasant shooting," he said.

"I hope he didn't make you too angry," Mrs. Maloney said.

"He did for awhile," Mike said, "but all of a sudden he didn't, if you know what I mean."

"I don't know what you mean," Mrs. Maloney said.

"I mean," Mike said, "it's all right not being poor."

"What's being poor got to do with it?" Mrs. Maloney said.

"I mean it's all right, that's all," Mike said.

"Well, that's fine," Mrs. Maloney said. "But where is he?"

"Hunting, of course," Mike said. "You don't think he wanted a gun to look at."

"I don't know what I think now," Mrs. Maloney said. "You've had so much trouble with him all along, and now all of a sudden you buy him an expensive gun and believe it's perfectly all right for him to go off hunting in the middle of the night on the third day of October. Why?"

"Well," Mike Maloney said, "it's because while I was preaching to him at the table something began to happen. It was as if my own father were preaching to me thirty years ago when I was Mayo's age. Oh, I did earn my food, as I said, and I wanted a gun, too, just as he's been wanting one. Well, my father preached to me, and I didn't get the gun. I mean, I didn't get it until almost five years later, when it didn't mean very much to me any more. Well, while I was preaching to him this afternoon I remembered that when my father preached to me I was sure he was mistaken to belittle me so, and I even believed that somehow—somehow or other, perhaps because we were so poor, if that makes sense —he would suddenly stop preaching and take me along without any fuss of any kind and buy me a gun. But of course he didn't. And I *remembered* that he didn't and I decided that perhaps I'd do for my son what my father had not done for me, if you know what I mean."

"Do you mean you and Mayo are alike?" Mrs. Maloney said.

"I do," Mike said. "I do indeed."

"Very much alike?"

"Almost precisely," Mike said. "Oh, he'll not be the great man he is now for long, and I don't want to be the one to cheat him out of a single moment of his greatness."

"You must be joking," Mrs. Maloney said.

"I couldn't be more serious," Mike said. "Archie Cannon thought I was joking, too, but why would I be joking? I bought him the gun and shells, and off he went to hunt, didn't he?"

"Well, I hope he doesn't hurt himself," Mrs. Maloney said.

"We'll never know if he does," Mike said. "I've asked Archie to come by around ten because I figure he'll be back by then."

"Is Mrs. Cannon coming with Archie?"

"I don't think so," Mike said.

"Then I suppose you don't want me to sit up with you," Mrs. Maloney said.

"I don't know why not, if you want to," Mike said.

But Mrs. Maloney knew it wouldn't do to sit up, so she said, "No, I'll be getting to bed long before ten."

Mike Maloney went out on the front porch with his wife, and they sat and talked about their son Mayo and other kids until a little after nine, and then Mrs. Maloney went inside to see what there was in the icebox and put some stuff out on the kitchen table. Then she went to bed.

Around a quarter to ten Archie Cannon came walking up the street and sat down in the rocker on the front porch.

"I've been thinking about what you did," he said, "and I still don't know if you did right."

"I did right all right," Mike Maloney said. "Let's go inside. He'll be along pretty soon."

They went inside and sat down at the kitchen table. There was a plate loaded with cold roast beef, ham, Bologna, and sliced store cheese, and another plate with rye bread on it, already buttered.

When it was almost twelve and Mayo Maloney hadn't come home, Archie Cannon wondered if he shouldn't offer to get up and go home or maybe even offer to get his car and go looking for the boy, but he decided he'd better not. Mike Maloney seemed excited and angry at himself for having done such a foolish thing, and he might not like Archie to rub it in. They had stopped talking about Mayo Maloney around eleven, and Archie knew Mike wanted the situation to remain that way indefinitely.

A little before one in the morning, after they had finished all the food Mrs. Maloney had set out for them, and talked about everything in the world excepting Mayo Maloney, they heard footsteps on the back porch, and after a moment he came into the kitchen.

He was a tired man. His face was dirty and flushed, and his clothes were dusty and covered with prickly burrs of several kinds. His hands were scratched and almost black with dirt. His gun was slung over his right arm, and nested in his left arm were two beautiful pheasants.

He set the birds on the kitchen table, and then broke his gun up for cleaning. He wrapped a dry dish towel around the pieces and put the bundle in the drawer in which he kept his junk. He then brought six unused shells out of his pockets and placed them in the drawer, too, locked the drawer with his key and put the key back into his pocket. Then he went to the kitchen sink and rolled up his sleeves and washed his hands and arms and face and neck, and after he'd dried himself, he looked into the refrigerator and brought out some Bologna wrapped in butcher paper, and began to eat it without bread while he fetched bread and butter and a chair. He sat down and began to put three slices of Bologna between two slices of buttered bread. Mike Maloney had never seen him eat so heartily. He didn't look restless and mean any more, either.

Mike Maloney got up with Archie Cannon, and they left the house by the back door in order not to disturb Mrs. Maloney and the sleeping kids.

When they were in the back yard, Archie Cannon said, "Well, aren't you going to ask him where he got them?"

"He's not ready to talk about it just yet," Mike said. "What's the fine?"

"Well," Archie said, "there won't be any fine because there's not supposed to be any pheasants in the whole area of which I'm game warden. I didn't believe he'd get anything, let alone pheasants, and both of them cocks, too. Darned if I don't admire him a little myself."

"I'll walk you home," Mike said.

In the kitchen, the boy finished his sandwich, drank a glass of milk, and rubbed his shoulder.

The whole evening and night had been unbelievable. Suddenly at the table, when his father had been preaching to him, he'd begun to understand his father a little better, and himself, too, but he'd known he couldn't immediately stop being the way he had been for so long, the way that was making everybody uncomfortable. He'd known he'd have to go on for awhile longer and see the thing through. He'd have to go along with his father. He'd known all this very clearly, because his father had suddenly stopped being a certain way— the way everybody believed a father ought to be—and Mayo had known it was going to be necessary for him to stop being a certain way, too—the way he had believed he had to be. But he'd known he couldn't stop until he had seen the thing through.

In the kitchen, almost asleep from weariness, he decided he'd tell his father exactly what he'd done, but he'd wait awhile first, maybe ten years.

He'd had a time finding out how the gun worked, and he hadn't been able to hitch

a ride at all, so he'd walked and run six miles to the countryside around Clovis, and there he'd loaded the gun and aimed it at a blackbird in a tree leaning over Clovis Creek, and pressed the trigger.

The kick had knocked him down and he had missed the bird by a mile. He'd had to walk a long way through tall dry grass and shrubs for something else to shoot at, but all it was was another blackbird, and again the kick had knocked him down and he'd missed it by a mile.

It was getting dark fast by then and there didn't seem to be anything alive around at all, so he began to shoot the gun just to get used to it. Pretty soon he could shoot it and not get knocked down. He kept shooting and walking, and finally it was dark and it seemed he was lost. He stumbled over a big rock and fell and shot the gun by accident and got a lot of dirt in his eyes. He got up and almost cried, but he managed not to, and then he found a road, but he had no idea where it went

to or which direction to take. He was scratched and sore all over, and not very happy about the way he'd shot the gun by accident. That should never have happened. He was scared, too, and he said a prayer a minute and meant every word of what he said. And he understood for the first time in his life why people liked to go to church.

"Please don't let me make a fool of myself," he prayed. "Please let me start walking in the right direction on this road."

He started down the road, hoping he was getting nearer home, or at least to a house with a light in it, or a store or something that would be open. He felt a lot of alive things in the dark that he knew must be imaginary, and he said, "Please don't let me get scared." And pretty soon he felt so tired and small and lost and hopeless and foolish that he could barely keep from crying, and he said, "Please don't let me cry."

He walked a long time, and then far

down the road he saw a small light, and he began to walk faster. It was a country store with a gasoline pump out front and a new pickup truck beside the pump. Inside the store was the driver of the truck and the storekeeper, and he saw that it was twenty minutes to twelve. The storekeeper was an old man with a thick white mustache who was sitting on a box and talking to the driver of the truck, who was about as old as the boy's father.

He saw the younger man wink at the older one, and he thanked God for both of them, and for the wink, because he didn't think people who could wink could be unfriendly.

He told them exactly what he had done, and why, and the men looked at him and at each other until he was all through talking. They both examined the brand-new gun, too. Then the storekeeper handed the gun back to the boy and said to the younger man, "I'll be much obliged to you, Ed, if you'll get this man home in your truck."

They were father and son, too, apparently, and good friends, besides. Mayo Maloney admired them very much, and on account of them, he began to like people in general, too.

"Not at all," the younger man said.

"And I'd like to think we might rustle up a couple of pheasant for him to take home, too."

"That might not be easy to do this hour of the night," the younger man said, "but we could try."

"Isn't there an all-night Chinese restaurant in town that serves pheasant in and out of season?" the old man said. "Commercial pheasant, that is?"

"I don't know," the younger man said, "but we could phone and find out."

"No," the older man said. "No use phoning. They wouldn't be apt to under-

stand what we were talking about. Better just drive up to it and go in and find out. It's on Kern Street between F and G, but I forget the name. Anyhow, it's open all night, and I've heard you can get pheasant there any time you like."

"It certainly is worth looking into," the younger man said.

The younger man got up, and Mayo Maloney, speechless with amazement, got up, too. He tried to say something courteous to the older man, but nothing seemed to want to come out of his dry mouth. He picked up his gun and went out to the truck and got in beside the younger man, and they went off. He saw the older man standing in the doorway of the store, watching them.

The younger man drove all the way to town in silence and when the boy saw familiar places, he thought in prayer again, saying, *I certainly don't deserve this, and I'm never going to forget it.*

The truck crossed the Southern Pacific tracks to Chinatown, and the driver parked in front of Willie Fong's, which was, in fact, open, although nobody was inside eating. The driver stepped out of the truck and went into the restaurant, and the boy saw him talking to a waiter. The waiter disappeared and soon came back with a man in a business suit. This man and the driver of the truck talked a few minutes, and then they both disappeared into the back of the restaurant, and after a few minutes the driver of the truck came back, and he was holding something that was wrapped in newspaper. He came out of the restaurant and got back into the truck, and they drove off again.

"How's your father?" the man said suddenly.

"He's fine," Mayo managed to say.

"I mean," the man said, "you *are* Mike Maloney's boy, aren't you?"

"Yes, I am," Mayo Maloney answered.

"I thought you were," the man said. "You look alike and have a lot in common. You don't have to tell me where you live. I know where it is. And I know you want to know who I am, but don't you think it would be better if I didn't tell you? I've had dealings with your father, and he lent me some money when I needed it badly and we both weren't sure I'd ever be able to pay him back. So it's all right. I mean, nobody's going to know anything about this from me."

"Did they have any pheasants?" the boy said.

"Oh, yes," the man said. "I'm sorry I forgot to tell you. They're in that newspaper. Just throw the paper out the window."

The boy removed the paper from around the birds and looked at them. They were just about the most wonderful-looking things in the whole world.

"Do they have any shot in them?" he asked. "Because they ought to."

"No, I'm afraid they don't," the driver said, "but we'll drive out here a little where it's quiet and we won't disturb too many sleeping farmers, and between the two of us we'll get some shot into them. You can do the shooting, if you like."

"I might spoil them," the boy said.

"I'll be glad to attend to it, then," the driver said.

They drove along in silence a few minutes, and then the truck turned into a lonely road and stopped. The driver got out and placed the two birds on some grass by the side of the road in the light of the truck's lights about twenty yards off. Then he took the gun, examined it, aimed, fired once, unloaded the gun, fetched the birds, got back into the truck and they drove off again.

"They're just right now," he said.

"Thanks," the boy said.

When the truck got into his neighborhood Mayo said, "Could I get off a couple of blocks from my house, so nobody will see this truck accidentally?"

"Yes, that's a good idea," the driver said.

The truck stopped. The boy carefully nested the two birds in his left arm, then got out, and the driver helped him get the gun slung over his right arm.

"I never expected anything like this to happen," the boy said.

"No, I suppose not," the man said. "I never expected to find a man like your father when I needed him, either, but I guess things like that happen just the same. Well, good night."

"Good night," the boy said.

The man got into the truck and drove off, and the boy hurried home and into the house.

When Mike Maloney got back from walking Archie Cannon home, he found the boy asleep on his folded arms on the kitchen table.

He shook the boy gently, and Mayo Maloney sat up with a start, his eyes bloodshot and his ears red.

"You better get to bed," Mike said.

"I didn't want to go," the boy said, "until you got back, so I could thank you for the gun."

"That wasn't necessary," the man said. "That wasn't necessary at all."

The boy got up and barely managed to drag himself out of the room without falling.

Alone in the kitchen, the father picked up the birds and examined them, smiling because he knew whatever was behind their presence in the house, it was certainly something as handsome as the birds themselves.

The man who wrote this story

WILLIAM SAROYAN 1908–

Saroyan was born in Fresno, California, the son of Armenian immigrants. His father, a former minister, had just started a grape farm when he died. William and his brothers and sisters were placed in an orphanage for five years until Mrs. Saroyan was able to earn enough for the family to live together. Saroyan quit school after he completed the eighth grade, but he read every volume in the Fresno library. For a while he moved from one job to another, working in offices, on farms, and on newspapers. He changed jobs so rapidly that employment agencies refused to recommend him.

Saroyan had started writing when he was thirteen, but his first short story was not published until he was twenty-five. This story, "Daring Young Man on the Flying Trapeze," was such an instant success that Saroyan was launched as a writer. Six years later he suddenly became a playwright, and his plays have been even more successful than his stories.

Although he is now famous, Saroyan hasn't changed as a person. He does not pretend to have social graces, nor does he want them. He prefers the company of rough and uncultured men who do not notice his battered hat or too-large overcoat.

Let's consider . . .

1. In the first part of the story Mayo was a rude and discontented boy. What did he find fault with? Why do you think he was so discontented?

2. William Saroyan wrote, "The only thing that didn't bore him was the idea of hunting, but his father wouldn't buy him a gun." What were Mr. Maloney's reasons? What made him change his mind? Maybe he was right in buying the gun, and maybe he was wrong. What do you think?

3. How had Mayo's attitude changed by the end of the story? How do you think he will behave in the future?

4. The strangers treated Mayo with a kindness he hadn't expected. How might this meeting have helped to change his attitude? What other events in the story might also have helped?

5. Mayo didn't tell his father about his pheasant-hunting adventures. What would you have done?

6. Think of something you have always wanted, but which your parents thought you shouldn't have. Write a brief paragraph explaining why you felt you should have had it. Then write another paragraph explaining the reasons your parents must have had for not getting it for you. Read both paragraphs to the members of your class and ask for their opinions on the matter.

The writer's craft . . .

At the beginning of "The Pheasant Hunter," the author helped you to see Mayo as his family and other people saw him. You probably decided he was a rude, faultfinding boy. In the middle of the story, you began to change your opinion because the author helped you to understand how Mayo felt and thought.

1. When you came to know Mayo better, did your feelings about him change?

2. Find the paragraph where the author shifted his attention from what others thought of Mayo to what Mayo thought about himself and his situation.

3. For the fun of it, imagine how your father sees you when you and he are disagreeing about something. Write a description of yourself as you think he sees you.

Knowing words . . .

Each of the italicized words below was used to describe Mayo's attitude toward people and things. Knowing what these words mean will give you a sharper picture of Mayo. After you are sure of the meaning of each italicized word, use it in a sentence of your own.

1. "A powerful kick," Mike Maloney repeated, addressing the three words to his son, who received them with *disdain*.

2. It's the fault of your mother and father that you're such a *sarcastic* and faultfinding man.

3. Everybody in this whole town is talking about how your mother and father have turned you into an *arrogant* ignoramus of a man by not making you earn your right to judge things.

Crabbèd Age and Youth

Crabbèd Age and Youth
Cannot live together:
Youth is full of pleasance,
Age is full of care;
Youth like summer morn,
Age like winter weather;
Youth like summer brave,
Age like winter bare.
Youth is full of sport,
Age's breath is short;

Youth is nimble, Age is lame;
Youth is hot and bold,
Age is weak and cold;
Youth is wild, and Age is tame.
Age, I do abhor thee;
Youth, I do adore thee;
O, my love, my love is young!
Age, I do defy thee:
O, sweet shepherd, hie thee!
For methinks thou stay'st too long.
                    William Shakespeare

My Mother and My Father

ERNIE PYLE

Ernie Pyle was the best-known war correspondent during World War II. He was a quiet, gentle man who won the love and respect of the boys overseas. As he tells you about his mother and father, you will catch a glimpse of his warmth and understanding. You will see, too, that Ernie Pyle doesn't deserve *all* the credit.

My mother would rather drive a team of horses in the field than cook a dinner. But in her lifetime she has done very little of the first and too much of the latter. She has had only three real interests—my father, myself, and her farm work. Nothing else makes much difference to her. And yet, when I left home in my late teens, to be gone forever except for brief visits, she was content for me to go, because she knew I was not happy on the farm.

My mother is living proof that happiness is within yourself; for a whole lifetime she has done nothing but work too hard, and yet I'm sure she has been happy. She loves the farm there outside Dana, Indiana. She wouldn't think of moving to town, as the other "retired" farmers do. She would rather stay home now and milk the cows than go to the state fair. She is the best chicken raiser and cake baker in the neighborhood. She loves to raise chickens and hates to bake cakes.

After she and my father had been married thirty years, they took a trip east and saw Niagara Falls. She didn't want to go and was glad to get back home, but did admit she enjoyed the trip. The highlight of the journey, which included Washington and New York, was a night in a tourist cabin near Wheeling, West Virginia. It was fixed so nice inside, she said, just like home. She talks about it yet.

My mother probably knows as little about world affairs as any woman in our neighborhood. Yet she is the broadest-minded and most liberal of the lot. I don't remember her ever telling me I couldn't do something. She always told me what she thought was right, and what was wrong, and then it was up to me. When I was about sixteen I forgot and left my corncob pipe lying on the window sill one day when I went to school. When I got home that night, she handed me the pipe and said, "I see you're smoking now." I said, "Yes." And that was all there was to that. She thinks it's awful for women to smoke, but I imagine if she had a daughter who smoked she'd think it was all right.

She is a devout Methodist and a prohibitionist. Yet she and my father voted for Al Smith in 1928, because they thought he was a better man than Hoover. Some of their neighbors wouldn't speak to them for months because they voted for a Catholic and a wet, but they didn't care. They are always doing things they think are right.

My mother has quite a temper. I remember once when the liniment man came, and said we hadn't paid him for a bottle of liniment. My mother said we had. The man said we hadn't. So my mother went and got the money, opened the screen door, and threw it in his face. He never came back.

She always tells people just what she thinks. A good many of our neighbors have deservedly felt the whip of her tongue, and they pout over it a while, but whenever they're in trouble they always thaw out and come asking for help. And of course they get it. My mother is the one the neighbors always call on when somebody gets sick, or dies, or needs help of any kind. She has practically raised a couple of kids besides myself. She has always been the confidante of the young people around there.

I started driving a team of horses in the fields when I was nine. I remember that first day perfectly. My mother had gone to a club meeting, but she came home in the middle of the afternoon and brought me a lunch of bread and butter and sugar out to the field. And also, I suppose, she wanted to make sure I hadn't been dragged to death under the harrow.

She played the violin when she was younger, but she gave it up after I took one term of lessons. I gave it up, too. You should have heard me.

My mother doesn't realize it, but her life has been the life of a real prairie pioneer. You could use her in a book, or paint her picture, as one of the sturdy stock of the ages who have always done the carrying-on when the going was tough.

She isn't so well any more, but she seems to work harder than ever. We try to get her to rest, but she says, "Oh, the work has to be done." We say, "Yes, but you don't have to do it. Supposing you were gone; the work would still be here, but you wouldn't have to do it." But she doesn't understand what we mean.

Perhaps you have heard of my father. He is the man who put oil on his brakes when they got to squeaking, then drove to Dana and ran over the curb and through a plate-glass window and right into a dry-goods store.

My father is also the man who ran with Roosevelt in 1932. He ran for township trustee, was the only Democrat in the county who lost, and was probably the happiest man who listened to election returns that night. He couldn't think of anything worse than being township trustee. The reason he lost was that all the people figured that if he was trustee he wouldn't have time to put roofs on their houses and paint their barns and paper their dining rooms and fix their chimneys, and do a thousand and one things for them. I guess when my father is gone that whole neighborhood will just sort of fall down.

He used to work as a hired hand way over on the other side of the Wabash River. When he was courting my mother, every Sunday he would drive a horse six miles to the river, row a boat across, and then ride a bicycle ten miles to my mother's house. At midnight he started to reverse the process. Mother figured he either loved her or else was foolish and needed somebody to look after him, so she married him.

My father has never lived anywhere except on a farm, and yet I don't think he ever did like the farm very well. He has been happiest, I think, since he started renting out the farm. Ever since then he has been carpentering and handy-manning all about the neighborhood. He is a wizard with tools, where other people are clumsy. He is a carpenter at heart.

Once when he was a young man, my father did start out to see the world. He went to Iowa to cut broom corn, but broke a leg and had to come home. He never went anywhere again till he was fifty-five, when he went to California to see his brother. He sat up all the way in a day coach. Later he went to New York, so he has seen both oceans.

When he was in Washington he kept butting his head against those big glass cases that hold exhibits in the Smithsonian Institute. The glass was polished so clean he couldn't see it. We all thought it was awfully funny. He got a splitting head-ache from it.

We got our first automobile in 1914. We kept it up in the north end of the wagon shed, right behind the wagon. At the south end of the wagon shed there was a big gravel pit. One day we came home from town, my mother and I got out at the house, and father went to put the car away. We saw him make the circle in the barn lot, and then drive into the north end of the shed. The next instant the south end of the shed simply burst open, a wagon came leaping out, and with one great bound was over the cliff and down in the gravel pit. My father said he never did know exactly what happened.

He is a very quiet man. He has never said a great deal to me all his life, and yet I feel that we have been very good friends. He never gave me much advice, or told me to do this or that, or not to. He bought

me a Ford roadster when I was about sixteen, and when I wrecked it a couple of weeks later he never said a word. But he didn't spare me either; I worked like a horse from the time I was nine.

He never shows much emotion, and he has never seen a big-league ball game. Yet my mother came home one afternoon during a World Series, and caught him sitting in front of the radio, all by himself, clapping and yelling for all he was worth.

My father is now getting a little deaf. Mother says he can always hear what he isn't supposed to hear. If my father doesn't like people, he never says anything about it. If he does like people, he never says much about that, either. He is very even-tempered. If he has an enemy in this whole country, I have yet to hear about it.

He doesn't swear or drink or smoke. He is honest, in letter and spirit. He is a good man without being at all annoying about it. He used to smoke cigars, but he quit the

Fourth of July that Johnson fought Jeffries in Reno—I think it was 1908. The event didn't have anything to do with it. His holiday cigar simply made him sicker than usual that day, so he quit.

The man who wrote this selection

ERNIE PYLE   1900–1945

Ernie Pyle was born on an Indiana farm, and in a few years he developed a definite dislike of horses. Later, at the state university, he decided to take the course in journalism because that would enable him to escape from the farm and the hated horses. He never stayed to finish the requirements for a degree because he was soon working for a newspaper. Although he was once a managing editor and held about every possible position in a newspaper office, he made his name as a roving reporter and a columnist.

He loved to travel and to drive. He visited every state three times; he traveled to many countries, by plane, car, train, boat, mule, and even by piggy-back. He collected information for his column as he went along, and he said, "I traveled for other people and wrote their letters home. I'm really a letter writer." People liked his "letters," and they began to appear in over sixty newspapers.

During the Second World War, Ernie Pyle was right with the troops. He reported on the campaigns in Africa, Sicily, and Italy, and ran ashore on D-Day. He earned the love of the common soldiers as well as the officers by writing about the soldiers as people. He had a big grin, a ready memory for names, and as he slogged along with the "G.I.'s" they felt an almost paternal love for the tiny man.

A few days before the end of the war, Ernie Pyle was killed by machine-gun fire on a small island near Okinawa.

Let's consider . . .

1. Ernie Pyle believed that "happiness is in yourself," and he was sure that his mother was a living proof of that statement. What things made her happy? Which of these things were in herself?

2. What would she have thought of the old saying, "Woman's place is in the home"? What do *you* think about it?

3. How did Ernie's father and mother differ in their methods of training him? Which method do you prefer? Why?

4. Ernie's mother and father had different qualities. Select one quality in each of them that you think is important in a good parent. Explain why you think these qualities are important.

5. Choose the passage you think is funniest and read it aloud to the class. Does it remind you of any parents you know? Is it disrespectful to find parents funny at times? Why might some parents object?

The writer's craft . . .

In this selection Ernie Pyle described his mother and father as he knew them. They were real people, and as Mr. Pyle told you about them—the things they did and said —they became real to you also.

Sometimes an author creates a character with the particular traits that people everywhere accept as belonging to him. For example, if he is creating a policeman, he will make him a big, red-faced Irishman. Or, if he is creating an old-maid aunt, he will make her prim and fussy. Such characters are seldom interesting or believable because they are not true to life. They are **stereotypes**—characters whose looks, thoughts, and actions conform to rigid and widely accepted patterns. Most comic book characters are stereotypes.

1. What did Ernie Pyle tell you in the first sentence that indicated his mother was not a stereotype?

2. In what ways was his mother an individual and not a stereotype?

3. List the ways in which your mother differs from a stereotype.

Song of a Little House

I'm glad our house is a little house,
    Not too tall or too wide;
I'm glad the hovering butterflies
    Feel free to come inside.

Our little home is a friendly house,
    It is not sour or vain;
It gossips with the talking trees,
    And makes friends with the rain.

And quick leaves cast a shimmer of green
    Against our whited walls,
And in the phlox, the courteous bees
    Are paying duty calls.

Christopher Morley

My Father Loved the Jumping-off Places

ROBERT P. TRISTRAM COFFIN

My father was a pioneer,
A very handsome man,
When he laid his herring in,
He laid in for a clan.

He salted herring by the ton.
He thought in hogsheads, tierces,
He turned his host of boys and girls
Out in the weather's mercies.

He wanted them to be good friends
With twelve winds and weather.
The house he ran up had hard time
Keeping all together.

He built it on the jumping-off
Island far at sea,
He had to chain it down each night
To know where it would be.

And when the wind changed, he would have
To rise in his night-tails
And shift the ox-chains over it
To suit the midnight gales.

The beets had to be anchored down,
And our white Leghorns tethered.
We grew up a handsome lot,
Beautifully weathered.

The cow we had—I guess for me—
Went to the landward shore
And lowed her soul towards the main
And cows she knew of yore.

The days went by lonely as loons,
I learned to creep on ledges.
I went to sleep by lighthouses
On the world's blue edges.

I rowed a boat before I walked,
I caught rock-cod before
I knew the alphabet, the whole
Atlantic filled my door.

Sometimes I think that windblown place
Made me what I am,
Sometimes I think my father was
Noah or Abraham.

The man who wrote this poem

ROBERT P. TRISTRAM COFFIN
1892–1955

Robert Coffin came from a long line of whalers and fishermen, farmers and hunters. His family had been in New England for over three hundred years. He was raised on a Maine saltwater farm, accustomed to fog and the sound of buoys at night. He received his first formal education in a rural, red-brick schoolhouse. Later he owned that little school and planned to make it "a monument to his boyhood and the boyhood of America."

He was a professor of English at Bowdoin College, where he lived "only a stone's throw from the house where he was born."

Coffin had very definite ideas about poetry—about what it meant, and what it should have meant. He often said, "Poetry is the art of making people feel well about life; poetry is saying the best one can about life; poetry is the art of putting different kinds of good things together . . . like boys and whistles. . . ."

Coffin was an extremely vigorous and active man. Besides lecturing, teaching, and writing (he had more than twenty published books), he was the busy father of a large family and an enthusiastic fisherman.

The poet's art . . .

1. Robert P. Tristram Coffin gave you several clues to his father's character. List the things you learned about him.

2. Would you have liked Mr. Coffin's father as a parent? Why, or why not?

3. Who were Noah and Abraham? In what ways was the boy's father like either of these two Biblical characters?

4. The poet loved growing up on a remote, windblown island. Do you think you would enjoy living in such a place? What would you like about that rugged life? What would you dislike?

5. Coffin wrote:

"Sometimes I think that windblown place
Made me what I am."

Everyone is affected somewhat by his childhood surroundings. How has your own environment helped shape *your* feelings and ideas?

6. Probably both your parents and your environment helped to make you the kind of person you are. Which do you think was more important? Illustrate your answer with an incident from your own life.

7. Coffin wrote that to keep the beets from blowing away they had to be anchored down. With this exaggerated statement he gave a dramatic picture of the force of the wind. Find other lines where exaggeration helped to emphasize an idea.

8. Write your own exaggerated account of something that happened to you. Think about your experiences with homework, getting up in the morning, or taking a trip with the family. Select some experience you would enjoy exaggerating. Then write it in such a way that the class will enjoy hearing you read it aloud.

Split Cherry Tree

JESSE STUART

When Dave got home from school two hours late, he expected to be whipped. He didn't expect his father to go looking for the teacher with a gun.

"I don't mind staying after school," I says to Professor Herbert, "but I'd rather you'd whip me with a switch and let me go home early. Pa will whip me anyway for getting home two hours late."

"You are too big to whip," says Professor Herbert, "and I have to punish you for climbing up in that cherry tree. You boys knew better than that! The other five boys have paid their dollar each. You have been the only one who has not helped pay for the tree. Can't you borrow a dollar?"

"I can't," I says. "I'll have to take the punishment. I wish it would be quicker punishment. I wouldn't mind."

Professor Herbert stood and looked at me. He was a big man. He wore a gray suit of clothes. The suit matched his gray hair.

"You don't know my father," I says to Professor Herbert. "He might be called a little old-fashioned. He makes us mind him until we're twenty-one years old. He believes: 'If you spare the rod you spoil the child.' I'll never be able to make him understand about the cherry tree. I'm the first of my people to go to high school."

"You must take the punishment," says Professor Herbert. "You must stay two hours after school today and two hours after school tomorrow. I am allowing you twenty-five cents an hour. That is good money for a high-school student. You can sweep the schoolhouse floor, wash the blackboards, and clean windows. I'll pay the dollar for you."

I couldn't ask Professor Herbert to loan me a dollar. He never offered to loan it to me. I had to stay and help the janitor and work out my fine at a quarter an hour.

I thought as I swept the floor, "What will Pa do to me? What lie can I tell him when I go home? Why did we ever climb that cherry tree and break it down for anyway? Why did we run crazy over the hills away from the crowd? Why did we do all of this? Six of us climbed up in a little cherry tree after one little lizard! Why did the tree split and fall with us? It should have been a stronger tree! Why did Eif Crabtree just happen to be below us plowing and catch us in his cherry tree? Why wasn't he a better man than to charge us six dollars for the tree?"

It was six o'clock when I left the schoolhouse. I had six miles to walk home. It would be after seven when I got home. I had all my work to do when I got home. It took Pa and me both to do the work. Seven cows to milk. Nineteen head of cattle to feed, four mules, twenty-five hogs, firewood and stovewood to cut, and water to draw from the well. He would be doing it when I got home. He would be mad and wondering what was keeping me!

I hurried home. I would run under the dark, leafless trees. I would walk fast uphill. I would run down the hill. The ground was freezing. I had to hurry. I had to run. I reached the long ridge that led to our cow pasture. I ran along this ridge. The wind dried the sweat on my face. I ran across the pasture to the house.

I threw down my books in the chipyard. I ran to the barn to spread fodder on the ground for the cattle. I didn't take time to change my clean school clothes for my old work clothes. I ran out to the barn. I saw Pa spreading fodder on the ground to the cattle. That was my job. I ran up to the fence. I says, "Leave that for me, Pa. I'll do it. I'm just a little late."

"I see you are," says Pa. He turned and looked at me. His eyes danced fire. "What in th' world has kept you so? Why ain't you been here to help me with this work? Make a gentleman out'n one boy in th' family and this is what you get! Send you to high school and you get too onery fer th' buzzards to smell!"

I never said anything. I didn't want to tell why I was late from school. Pa stopped scattering the bundles of fodder. He looked at me. He says, "Why are you gettin' in here this time o' night? You tell me or I'll take a hickory withe to you right here on th' spot!"

I says, "I had to stay after school." I couldn't lie to Pa. He'd go to school and find out why I had to stay. If I lied to him it would be too bad for me.

"Why did you haf to stay after school?" says Pa.

I says, "Our biology class went on a field trip today. Six of us boys broke down a cherry tree. We had to give a dollar apiece to pay for the tree. I didn't have the dollar. Professor Herbert is making me work out my dollar. He gives me twenty-five cents an hour. I had to stay in this afternoon. I'll have to stay in tomorrow afternoon!"

"Are you telling me th' truth?" says Pa.

"I'm telling you the truth," I says. "Go and see for yourself."

"That's just what I'll do in the mornin'," says Pa. "Just whose cherry tree did you break down?"

"Eif Crabtree's cherry tree!"

"What was you doin' clear out in Eif Crabtree's place?" says Pa. "He lives four miles from th' county high school. Don't they teach you no books at that high school? Do they just let you get out and gad over th' hillsides? If that's all they do I'll keep you at home, Dave. I've got work here fer you to do!"

"Pa," I says, "spring is just getting here. We take a subject in school where we have to have bugs, snakes, flowers, lizards, frogs, and plants. It is biology. It was a pretty day today. We went out to find a few of these. Six of us boys saw a lizard at the same time sunning on a cherry tree. We all went up the tree to get it. We broke the tree down. It split at the forks. Eif Crabtree was plowing down below us. He ran up the hill and got our names. The other boys gave their dollar apiece. I didn't have mine. Professor Herbert put mine in for me. I have to work it out at school."

"Poor man's son, huh," says Pa. "I'll attend to that myself in th' mornin'. I'll take keer o' 'im. He ain't from this county nohow. I'll go down there in th' mornin' and see 'im. Letting you leave your books and galavant all over th' hills. What kind of a school is it nohow! Didn't do that, my son, when I's a little shaver in school. All fared alike too."

"Pa, please don't go down there," I says, "just let me have fifty cents and pay the rest of my fine! I don't want you to go down there! I don't want you to start anything with Professor Herbert!"

"Ashamed of your old Pap are you, Dave," says Pa, "atter th' way I've worked to raise you! Tryin' to send you to school so you can make a better livin' than I've made.

"I'll straighten this thing out myself! I'll take keer o' Professor Herbert myself! He ain't got no right to keep you in and let the other boys off jist because they've got the money! I'm a poor man. A bullet will go in a professor same as it will any man. It will go in a rich man same as it will a poor man. Now you get into this work before I take one o' these withes and cut the shirt off'n your back!"

I thought once I'd run through the woods above the barn just as hard as I could go. I thought I'd leave high school and home forever! Pa could not catch me! I'd get away! I couldn't go back to school with him. He'd have a gun and maybe he'd shoot Professor Herbert. It was hard to tell what he would do. I could tell Pa that school had changed in the hills from the way it was when he was a boy, but he wouldn't understand. I could tell him we studied frogs, birds, snakes, lizards, flowers, insects. But Pa wouldn't understand. If I did run away from home it wouldn't matter to Pa. He would see Professor Herbert anyway. He would think that high school and Professor Herbert had run me away from home. There was no need to run away. I'd just have to stay, finish foddering the cattle, and go to school with Pa the next morning.

I would take a bundle of fodder, remove the hickory witheband from around it, and scatter it on rocks, clumps of green briers, and brush so the cattle wouldn't tramp it under their feet. I would lean it up against the oak trees and the rocks in the pasture just above our pigpen on the hill. The fodder was cold and frosty where it had set out in the stacks. I would carry bundles of the fodder from the stack until I had spread out a bundle for each steer. Pa went to the barn to feed the mules and throw corn in the pen to the hogs.

The moon shone bright in the cold March sky. I finished my work by moonlight. Professor Herbert really didn't know how much work I had to do at home. If he had known he would not have kept me after school. He would have loaned me a dollar to have paid my part on the cherry tree. He had never lived in the hills. He didn't know the way the hill boys had to work so that they could go to school. Now he was teaching in a county high school where all the boys who attended were from hill farms.

After I'd finished doing my work, I went to the house and ate my supper. Pa and Mom had eaten. My supper was getting cold. I heard Pa and Mom talking in the front room. Pa was telling Mom about me staying in after school.

"I had to do all th' milkin' tonight, chop th' wood myself. It's too hard on me atter I've turned ground all day. I'm goin' to take a day off tomorrow and see if I can't remedy things a little. I'll go down to that high school tomorrow. I won't be a very good scholar fer Professor Herbert nohow. He won't keep me in atter school. I'll take a different kind of lesson down there and make 'im acquainted with it."

"Now, Luster," says Mom, "you jist stay away from there. Don't cause a lot o' trouble. You can be jailed fer a trick like that. You'll get the Law atter you. You'll jist go down there and show off and plague your own boy Dave to death in front o' all th' scholars!"

"Plague or no plague," says Pa, "he don't take into consideration what all I haf to do here, does he? I'll show 'im it ain't right to keep one boy in and let the rest go scot-free. My boy is as good is th' rest, ain't he? A bullet will make a hole in a school-teacher same as it will anybody else. He can't do me that way and get by with it. I'll plug 'im first. I aim to go down there bright and early in the mornin' and get all this straight! I aim to see about bug larnin' and this runnin' all over God's creation huntin' snakes, lizards, and frogs. Ransackin' the country and goin' through cherry orchards and breakin' th' trees down atter lizards! Old Eif Crabtree ought to a-poured th' hot lead to 'em instead o' chargin' six dollars fer th' tree! He ought to a-got old Herbert th' first one!"

I ate my supper. I slipped upstairs and lit the lamp. I tried to forget the whole thing. I studied plane geometry. Then I studied my biology lesson. I could hardly study for thinking about Pa. "He'll go to school with me in the morning. He'll take a gun for Professor Herbert! What will Professor Herbert think of me! I'll tell him when Pa leaves that I couldn't help it. But Pa might shoot him. I hate to go with Pa. Maybe he'll cool off about it tonight and not go in the morning."

Pa got up at four o'clock. He built a fire in the stove. Then he built a fire in the fireplace. He got Mom up to get breakfast. Then he got me up to help feed and milk. By the time we had our work done at the barn, Mom had breakfast ready for us. We ate our breakfast. Daylight came and we could see the bare oak trees covered white with frost. The hills were white with frost. A cold wind was blowing. The sky was clear. The sun would soon come

out and melt the frost. The afternoon would be warm with sunshine and the frozen ground would thaw. There would be mud on the hills again. Muddy water would then run down the little ditches on the hills.

"Now, Dave," says Pa, "let's get ready for school. I aim to go with you this mornin' and look into bug larnin', frog larnin', lizard and snake larnin', and breakin' down cherry trees! I don't like no sicha foolish way o' larnin' myself!"

Pa hadn't forgot. I'd have to take him to school with me. He would take me to school with him. We were going early. I was glad we were going early. If Pa pulled a gun on Professor Herbert there wouldn't be so many of my classmates there to see him.

I knew that Pa wouldn't be at home in the high school. He wore overalls, big boots, a blue shirt and a sheepskin coat and a slouched black hat gone to seed at the top. He put his gun in its holster. We started trudging toward the high school across the hill.

It was early when we got to the county high school. Professor Herbert had just got there. I just thought as we walked up the steps into the schoolhouse, "Maybe Pa will find out Professor Herbert is a good man. He just doesn't know him. Just like I felt toward the Lambert boys across the hill. I didn't like them until I'd seen them and talked to them. After I went to school with them and talked to them, I liked them and we were friends. It's a lot in knowing the other fellow."

"You're th' Professor here, ain't you?" says Pa.

"Yes," says Professor Herbert, "and you are Dave's father."

"Yes," says Pa, pulling out his gun and laying it on the seat in Professor Herbert's office. Professor Herbert's eyes got big be-

hind his black-rimmed glasses when he saw Pa's gun. Color came into his pale cheeks.

"Jist a few things about this school I want to know," says Pa. "I'm tryin' to make a scholar out'n Dave. He's the only one out'n eleven youngins I've sent to high school. Here he comes in late and leaves me all th' work to do! He said you's all out bug huntin' yesterday and broke a cherry tree down. He had to stay two hours atter school yesterday and work out money to pay on that cherry tree! Is that right?"

"Wwwwy," says Professor Herbert, "I guess it is."

He looked at Pa's gun.

"Well," says Pa, "this ain't no high school. It's a bug school, a lizard school, a snake school! It ain't no school nohow!"

"Why did you bring that gun?" says Professor Herbert to Pa.

"You see that little hole," says Pa as he picked up the long blue forty-four and put his finger on the end of the barrel, "a bullet can come out'n that hole that will kill a schoolteacher same as it will any other man. It will kill a rich man same as a poor man. It will kill a man. But atter I come in and saw you I know'd I wouldn't need it. This maul o' mine could do you up in a few minutes."

Pa stood there, big, hard, brown-skinned, and mighty beside of Professor Herbert. I didn't know Pa was so much bigger and harder. I'd never seen Pa in a schoolhouse before. I'd seen Professor Herbert. He'd always looked big before to me. He didn't look big standing beside of Pa.

"I was only doing my duty," says Professor Herbert, "Mr. Sexton, and following the course of study the state provided us with."

"Course o' study," says Pa, "what study, bug study? Varmint study? Takin' youngins to th' woods and their poor old Ma's and Pa's at home a-slavin' to keep 'em in school and give 'em a education! You know that's dangerous, too, puttin' a lot o' boys and girls out together like that!"

Students were coming into the schoolhouse now.

Professor Herbert says, "Close the door, Dave, so others won't hear."

I walked over and closed the door. I was shaking like a leaf in the wind. I thought Pa was going to hit Professor Herbert every minute. He was doing all the talking. His face was getting red. The red color was coming through the brown, weather-beaten skin on Pa's face.

"I was right with these students," says Professor Herbert. "I know what they got into and what they didn't. I didn't send one of the other teachers with them on this field trip. I went myself. Yes, I took the boys and girls together. Why not?"

"It jist don't look good to me," says Pa, "a-takin' all this swarm of youngins out to pillage th' whole deestrict. Breakin' down cherry trees. Keepin' boys in atter school."

"What else could I have done with Dave, Mr. Sexton?" says Professor Herbert. "The boys didn't have any business all climbing that cherry tree after one lizard. One boy could have gone up in the tree and got it. The farmer charged us six dollars. It was a little steep, I think, but we had to pay. Must I make five boys pay and let your boy off? He said he didn't have the dollar and couldn't get it. So I put it in for him. I'm letting him work it out. He's not working for me. He's working for the school."

"I jist don't know what you could a-done with 'im," says Pa, "only a-larruped 'im with a withe! That's what he needed!"

"He's too big to whip," says Professor Herbert, pointing to me. "He's a man in size."

"He's not too big fer me to whip," says Pa. "They ain't too big until they're over twenty-one! It jist didn't look fair to me! Work one and let th' rest out because they got th' money. I don't see what bugs has got to do with a high school! It didn't look good to me nohow!"

He picked up his gun and put it back in its holster. The red color left Professor Herbert's face. He talked more to Pa. Pa softened a little. It looked funny to see Pa in the high-school building. It was the first time he'd ever been there.

"We're not only hunting snakes, toads, flowers, butterflies, lizards," says Professor Herbert, "but, Mr. Sexton, I was hunting dry timothy grass to put in an incubator and raise some protozoa."

"I don't know what that is," says Pa. "Th' incubator is th' new-fangled way o' cheatin' th' hens and raisin' chickens. I ain't so sure about th' breed o' chickens you mentioned."

"You've heard of germs, Mr. Sexton, haven't you?" says Professor Herbert.

"Jist call me Luster, if you don't mind," says Pa, very casual like.

"All right, Luster, you've heard of germs, haven't you?"

"Yes," says Pa, "but I don't believe in germs. I'm sixty-five years old and I ain't seen one yet."

"You can't see them with your naked eye," says Professor Herbert. "Just keep that gun in the holster and stay with me in the high school today. I have a few things I want to show you. That scum on your teeth has germs in it."

"What," says Pa, "you mean to tell me I've got germs on my teeth!"

"Yes," says Professor Herbert. "The same kind as we might be able to find in a living black snake if we dissect it!"

"I don't mean to dispute your word," says Pa, "but I don't believe it. I don't believe I have germs on my teeth!"

"Stay with me today and I'll show you. I want to take you through the school anyway! School has changed a lot in the hills since you went to school. I don't guess we had high schools in the country when you went to school!"

"No," says Pa, "jist readin', writin', and cipherin'. We didn't have all this bug larnin', frog larnin', and findin' germs on your teeth and in the middle o' black snakes! Th' world's changin'."

"It is," says Professor Herbert, "and we hope all for the better. Boys like your own there are going to help change it. He's your boy. He knows all of what I've told you. You stay with me today."

"I'll shore stay with you," says Pa. "I want to see th' germs off'n my teeth. I jist want to see a germ. I've never seen one in my life. 'Seein' is believin',' Pap allus told me."

Pa walks out of the office with Professor Herbert. I just hoped Professor Herbert didn't have Pa arrested for pulling his gun. Pa's gun has always been a friend to him when he goes to settle disputes.

The bell rang. School took up. I saw the students when they marched in the schoolhouse look at Pa. They would grin and punch each other. Pa just stood and watched them pass in at the schoolhouse door. Two long lines marched in the house. The boys and girls were clean and well dressed. Pa stood over in the school-yard under a leafless elm, in his sheepskin coat, his big boots laced in front with buckskin, and his heavy socks stuck above his boot tops. Pa's overalls legs were baggy and wrinkled between his coat and boot tops. His blue work shirt showed at the collar. His big black hat showed his gray-streaked black hair. His face was hard and weathertanned to the color of a ripe fodder blade. His hands were big and gnarled like the roots of the elm tree he stood beside.

When I went to my first class I saw Pa and Professor Herbert going around over the schoolhouse. I was in my geometry class when Pa and Professor Herbert came in the room. We were explaining our propositions on the blackboard. Professor Herbert and Pa just quietly came in and sat down for awhile. I heard Fred Wurts whisper to Glenn Armstrong, "Who is that old man? Lord, he's a rough-looking scamp." Glenn whispered back, "I think he's Dave's Pap." The students in geometry looked at Pa. They must have wondered what he was doing in school. Before the class was over, Pa and Professor Herbert got up and went out. I saw them together down on the playground. Professor Herbert was explaining to Pa. I could see the prints of Pa's gun under his coat when he'd walk around.

At noon in the high-school cafeteria Pa and Professor Herbert sat together at the little table where Professor Herbert always ate by himself. They ate together. The students watched the way Pa ate. He ate with his knife instead of his fork. A lot of the students felt sorry for me after they found out he was my father. They didn't have to feel sorry for me. I wasn't ashamed of Pa after I found out he wasn't going to shoot Professor Herbert. I was glad they had made friends. I wasn't ashamed of Pa. I wouldn't be as long as he behaved. He would find out about the high school as I had found out about the Lambert boys across the hill.

In the afternoon when we went to biology Pa was in the class. He was sitting on one of the high stools beside the microscope. We went ahead with our work just as if Pa wasn't in the class. I saw Pa take his knife and scrape tartar from one of his teeth. Professor Herbert put it on the lens and adjusted the microscope for Pa. He adjusted it and worked awhile. Then he says: "Now Luster, look! Put your eye right down to the light. Squint the other eye."

Pa put his head down and did as Professor Herbert said. "I see 'im," says Pa. "Who'd a ever thought that? Right on a body's teeth! Right in a body's mouth. You're right certain they ain't no fake to this, Professor Herbert?"

"No, Luster," says Professor Herbert. "It's there. That's the germ. Germs live in a world we cannot see with the naked eye. We must use a microscope. There are millions of them in our bodies. Some are harmful. Others are helpful."

Pa holds his face down and looks through the microscope. We stop and watch Pa. He sits upon the tall stool. His knees are against the table. His legs are long. His coat slips up behind when he bends over. The handle of his gun shows. Professor Herbert pulls his coat down quickly.

"Oh, yes," says Pa. He gets up and pulls his coat down. Pa's face gets a little red. He knows about his gun and he knows he doesn't have any use for it in high school.

"We have a big black snake over here we caught yesterday," says Professor Herbert. "We'll chloroform him and dissect him and show you he has germs in his body, too."

"Don't do it," says Pa. "I believe you. I jist don't want to see you kill the black snake. I never kill one. They are good mousers and a lot o' help to us on the farm. I like black snakes. I jist hate to see people kill 'em. I don't allow 'em killed on my place."

The students look at Pa. They seem to like him better after he said that. Pa with a gun in his pocket but a tender heart beneath his ribs for snakes, but not for man! Pa won't whip a mule at home. He won't whip his cattle.

"Man can defend hisself," says Pa, "but cattle and mules can't. We have the drop on 'em. Ain't nothin' to a man that'll beat a good pullin' mule. He ain't got th' right kind o' heart!"

Professor Herbert took Pa through the laboratory. He showed him the different kinds of work we were doing. He showed him our equipment. They stood and talked while we worked. Then they walked out together. They talked louder when they got out in the hall.

When our biology class was over I walked out of the room. It was our last class for the day. I would have to take my broom and sweep two hours to finish paying for the split cherry tree. I just wondered if Pa would want me to stay. He was standing in the hallway watching the students march out. He looked lost among us. He looked like a leaf turned brown on the tree among the treetop filled with growing leaves.

I got my broom and started to sweep. Professor Herbert walked up and says, "I'm going to let you do that some other time. You can go home with your father. He is waiting out there."

I laid my broom down, got my books, and went down the steps.

Pa says, "Ain't you got two hours o' sweepin' yet to do?"

I says, "Professor Herbert said I could do it some other time. He said for me to go home with you."

"No," says Pa. "You are goin' to do as he says. He's a good man. School has changed from my day and time. I'm a dead leaf, Dave. I'm behind. I don't belong here. If he'll let me I'll get a broom and we'll both sweep one hour. That pays your debt. I'll hep you pay it. I'll ast 'im and see if he won't let me hep you."

"I'm going to cancel the debt," says Professor Herbert. "I just wanted you to understand, Luster."

"I understand," says Pa, "and since I understand, he must pay his debt for th' tree and I'm goin' to hep 'im."

"Don't do that," says Professor Herbert. "It's all on me."

"We don't do things like that," says Pa, "we're just and honest people. We don't want somethin' fer nothin'. Professor Herbert, you're wrong now and I'm right. You'll haf to listen to me. I've larned a lot from you. My boy must go on. Th' world has left me. It changed while I've raised my family and plowed th' hills. I'm a just and honest man. I don't skip debts. I ain't larned 'em to do that. I ain't got much larnin' myself but I do know right from wrong atter I see through a thing."

Professor Herbert went home. Pa and I stayed and swept one hour. It looked funny to see Pa use a broom. He never used one at home. Mom used the broom. Pa used the plow. Pa did hard work. Pa says, "I can't sweep. Durned if I can. Look at th' streaks o' dirt I leave on th' floor! Seems like no work a-tall for me. Brooms is too light 'r somethin'. I'll jist do th' best I can, Dave. I've been wrong about th' school."

I says, "Did you know Professor Herbert can get a warrant out for you for bringing your pistol to school and showing it in his office! They can railroad you for that!"

"That's all made right," says Pa. "I've made that right. Professor Herbert ain't goin' to take it to court. He likes me. I like 'im. We jist had to get together. He had the remedies. He showed me. You must go on to school. I am as strong a man as ever come out'n the hills fer my years and th' hard work I've done. But I'm behind, Dave. I'm a little man. Your hands will be softer than mine. Your clothes will be better. You'll allus look cleaner than your old Pap. Jist remember, Dave, to pay your debts and be honest. Jist be kind to animals and don't bother th' snakes. That's all I got agin th' school. Puttin' black snakes to sleep and cuttin' 'em open."

It was late when we got home. Stars were in the sky. The moon was up. The ground was frozen. Pa took his time going home. I couldn't run like I did the night before. It was ten o'clock before we got the work finished, our suppers eaten. Pa sat before the fire and told Mom he was going to take her and show her a germ sometime. Mom hadn't seen one either. Pa told her about the high school and the fine man Professor Herbert was. He told Mom about the strange school across the hill and how different it was from the school in their day and time.

Let's consider . . .

1. What was Professor Herbert's reason for keeping Dave after school? Why was staying after school a worse punishment for Dave than a whipping would have been?

2. Why was Dave's father so angry when he learned that Dave had been kept after school? Was he right in being angry? Give several reasons to support your answer.

3. Mr. Sexton called himself "a just and honest man." Recall everything you learned about him. Do you agree with his description of himself? List several incidents from the story that helped you understand him.

4. Explain why Dave's father changed his opinion of the school. Why did he refuse to let Professor Herbert cancel the debt?

5. Why was Professor Herbert a good teacher?

6. What kind of parent do you think he would have made? What qualities do you expect to find in all good parents and teachers?

7. Ask your parents to point out ways in which your school is different from the one

they attended. What are the advantages of yours? What were the advantages of theirs?

8. One of the ways in which school problems can be solved is through the Parent-Teacher Association. Is there such an organization in your school? What is its purpose? In what ways could it be even more helpful to the school? How would a PTA have helped in Dave's school?

9. What is your opinion of physical punishment for teenagers? For young children? If you disapprove of such punishment, in what ways do you think young people should be disciplined (a) at home, and (b) at school?

Knowing words . . .

Dave was a country boy. As you read about him, did you notice the words that Jesse Stuart used to describe Dave's life on the farm? You will find a few of these words italicized in the sentences below. When you are sure of the meaning of each italicized word, use it in a sentence of your own.

1. I reached the long *ridge* that led to our cow pasture.

2. I threw down my books in the *chip-yard*.

3. I ran to the barn to spread *fodder* on the ground for the cattle.

Hills

I never loved your plains;—
Your gentle valleys,
Your drowsy country lanes
And pleached alleys.

I want my hills!—the trail
That scorns the hollow.
Up, up the ragged shale
Where few will follow.

Up, over wooded crest
And mossy boulder
With strong thigh, heaving chest,
And swinging shoulder.

So let me hold my way,
By nothing halted,
Until at close of day,
I stand, exalted,

High on my hills of dream—
Dear hills that know me!
And then, how fair will seem
The lands below me.

How pure, at vesper-time,
The far bells chiming!
God, give me hills to climb,
And strength for climbing!
Arthur Guiterman

Mama and Her Bank Account

KATHRYN FORBES

When a story is successful four times—as a book, a play, a movie, and a television series—there must be a reason. Mama, a humble Norwegian immigrant, made Broadway audiences weep. She successfully competed with Hollywood's glamour queens. Kathryn Forbes knows her secret and generously shares it with you.

For as long as I could remember, the small cottage on Castro Street had been home. The familiar background was there; Mama, Papa, my only brother, Nels. There was my sister Christine, closest to me in age, yet ever secret and withdrawn —and the littlest sister, Dagmar.

There, too, came the Aunts, Mama's four sisters. Aunt Jenny, who was the oldest and the bossiest; Aunt Sigrid; Aunt Marta; and our maiden Aunt, Trina.

The Aunts' old bachelor uncle, my Great-uncle Chris—the "black Norwegian" —came with his great impatience, his shouting and stamping. And brought mystery and excitement to our humdrum days.

But the first awareness was of Mama.

I remember that every Saturday night Mama would sit down by the scrubbed kitchen table and with much wrinkling of usually placid brows count out the money Papa had brought home in the little envelope.

There would be various stacks.

"For the landlord," Mama would say, piling up the big silver pieces.

"For the grocer." Another group of coins.

"For Katrin's shoes to be half-soled." And Mama would count out the little silver.

"Teacher says this week I'll need a notebook." That would be Christine or Nels or I.

Mama would solemnly detach a nickel or a dime and set it aside.

We would watch the diminishing pile with breathless interest.

At last, Papa would ask, "Is all?"

And when Mama nodded, we could relax a little and reach for schoolbooks and homework. For Mama would look up then and smile. "Is good," she'd murmur. "We do not have to go to the Bank."

It was a wonderful thing, that Bank Account of Mama's. We were all so proud of it. It gave us such a warm, secure feeling. No one else we knew had money in a big bank downtown.

I remember when the Jensens down the street were put out because they couldn't pay their rent. We children watched the big strange men carry out the furniture, took furtive notice of poor Mrs. Jensen's shamed tears, and I was choked with sudden fear. This, then, happened to people who did not have the stack of coins marked "Landlord." Might this, could this, violence happen to us?

I clutched Christine's hands. *"We* have a Bank Account," she reassured me calmly, and suddenly I could breathe again.

When Nels graduated from grammar school he wanted to go to high. "Is good," Mama said, and Papa nodded approvingly.

"It will cost a little money," Nels said.

Eagerly we brought up chairs and gathered around the table. I took down the gaily painted box that Aunt Sigrid had sent us from Norway one Christmas and laid it carefully in front of Mama.

This was the "Little Bank." Not to be confused, you understand, with the big

Bank downtown. The "Little Bank" was used for sudden emergencies, such as the time Christine broke her arm and had to be taken to a doctor, or when Dagmar got croup and Papa had to go to the drugstore for medicine to put into the steam kettle.

Nels had it all written out neatly. So much for carfare, for clothes, for notebooks and supplies. Mama looked at the figures for a long time. Then she counted out the money in the Little Bank. There was not enough.

She pursed her lips. "We do not," she reminded us gently, "want to have to go to the Bank."

We all shook our heads.

"I will work in Dillon's grocery after school," Nels volunteered.

Mama gave him a bright smile and laboriously wrote down a sum and added and subtracted. Papa did it in his head. He was very quick in arithmetic. "Is not enough," he said. Then he took his pipe out of his mouth and looked at it for a long time. "I give up tobacco," he said suddenly.

Mama reached across the table and touched Papa's sleeve, but she didn't say anything. Just wrote down another figure.

"I will mind the Elvington children every Friday night," I said. "Christine can help me."

We all felt very good. We had passed another milestone without having to go downtown and draw money out of Mama's Bank Account. The Little Bank was sufficient for the present.

So many things, I remember, came out of the Little Bank that year. Christine's costume for the school play, Dagmar's tonsil operation, my Girl Scout uniform. And always, in the background, was the comforting knowledge that should our efforts fail, we still had the Bank to depend upon.

Even when the Strike came, Mama would not let us worry unduly. We all worked together so that the momentous trip downtown could be postponed. It was almost like a game.

During that time Mama "helped out" at Kruper's bakery for a big sack of only slightly stale bread and coffeecake. And as Mama said, fresh bread was not too good for a person and if you put the coffeecake into the hot oven it was nearly as nice as when first baked.

Papa washed bottles at the Castro Creamery every night and they gave him three quarts of fresh milk and all the sour milk he could carry away. Mama made fine cheese.

The day the Strike was over and Papa went back to work, I saw Mama stand a little straighter, as if to get a kink out of her back.

She looked around at us proudly. "Is good," she smiled. "See? We did not have to go down to the Bank."

That was twenty years ago.

Last year I sold my first story. When the check came I hurried over to Mama's and put the long green slip of paper in her lap. "For you," I said, "to put in your Bank Account."

And I noticed for the first time how old Mama and Papa looked. Papa seemed shorter, now, and Mama's wheaten braids were sheened with silver.

Mama fingered the check and looked at Papa.

"Is good," she said, and her eyes were proud.

"Tomorrow," I told her, "you must take it down to the Bank."

"You will go with me, Katrin?"

"That won't be necessary, Mama. See? I've endorsed the check to you. Just hand it to the teller, he'll deposit it to your account."

Mama looked at me. "Is no account," she said. "In all my life, I never been inside a Bank."

And when I didn't—couldn't—answer, Mama said earnestly: "Is not good for little ones to be afraid—to not feel secure."

The woman who wrote this selection

KATHRYN FORBES 1907–

Kathryn Forbes was greatly impressed by her grandmother's kindly spirit. Her grandmother was a Norwegian immigrant who made the transition from Norwegian to American citizen with calmness, humor, and courage.

After Miss Forbes was graduated from a San Francisco high school, she began to write stories for popular magazines like *Collier's* and *The Ladies Home Journal.* When a story about her grandmother ap-

peared in the *Reader's Digest,* it brought thousands of letters from people who wanted to read more about that warm character. In response to their wishes, Miss Forbes wrote her first book, *Mama's Bank Account.*

It was an instant success, and John van Druten adapted it to make a hit play, *I Remember Mama.* Later the book was made into a movie and appeared as a television series.

When Miss Forbes was asked how her family felt about the book, she replied that an aunt had written her to say that the book was very nice, but anyone in the family could have written it.

Let's consider . . .

1. What was Mama's reason for letting her children think that she had a bank account? Why do you think she was wise in doing so? If you think she was unwise, explain why.

2. There are other ways in which people need to feel secure besides just having enough money. How did Mama provide these securities for her children?

3. When the family needed money to send Nels to high school, each member found a way to help. How did each of them contribute? Why did they volunteer to help one another?

4. Do you think high-school students should get an allowance, or should they work for their spending money? Explain.

5. How much money should teenagers have to spend? How far should this sum be expected to "stretch"? To what extent should parents supervise the way the allowance is spent?

The Happiest Heart

Who drives the horses of the sun
Shall lord it but a day;
Better the lowly deed were done,
And kept the humble way.

The rust will find the sword of fame,
The dust will hide the crown;
Ay, none shall nail so high his name
Time will not tear it down.

The happiest heart that ever beat
Was in some quiet breast
That found the common daylight sweet,
And left to Heaven the rest.

John Vance Cheney

The Death of the Hired Man

ROBERT FROST

Mary sat musing on the lamp-flame at the table
Waiting for Warren. When she heard his step,
She ran on tip-toe down the darkened passage
To meet him in the doorway with the news
And put him on his guard. 'Silas is back.'
She pushed him outward with her through the door
And shut it after her. 'Be kind,' she said.
She took the market things from Warren's arms
And set them on the porch, then drew him down
To sit beside her on the wooden steps.

'When was I ever anything but kind to him?
But I'll not have the fellow back,' he said.
'I told him so last haying, didn't I?
If he left then, I said, that ended it.
What good is he? Who else will harbor him
At his age for the little he can do?
What help he is there's no depending on.
Off he goes always when I need him most.
He thinks he ought to earn a little pay,
Enough at least to buy tobacco with,
So he won't have to beg and be beholden.
"All right," I say, "I can't afford to pay
Any fixed wages, though I wish I could."
"Someone else can." "Then someone else will have to."
I shouldn't mind his bettering himself
If that was what it was. You can be certain,
When he begins like that, there's someone at him
Trying to coax him off with pocket-money,—
In haying time, when any help is scarce.
In winter he comes back to us. I'm done.'

345

'Sh! not so loud: he'll hear you,' Mary said.

'I want him to: he'll have to soon or late.'

'He's worn out. He's asleep beside the stove.
When I came up from Rowe's I found him here,
Huddled against the barn-door fast asleep,
A miserable sight, and frightening, too—
You needn't smile—I didn't recognize him—
I wasn't looking for him—and he's changed.
Wait till you see.'

              'Where did you say he'd been?'

'He didn't say. I dragged him to the house,
And gave him tea and tried to make him smoke.
I tried to make him talk about his travels.
Nothing would do: he just kept nodding off.'

'What did he say? Did he say anything?'

'But little.'

          'Anything? Mary, confess
He said he'd come to ditch the meadow for me.'

'Warren!'

        'But did he? I just want to know.'

'Of course he did. What would you have him say?
Surely you wouldn't grudge the poor old man
Some humble way to save his self-respect.
He added, if you really care to know,
He meant to clear the upper pasture, too.
That sounds like something you have heard before?
Warren, I wish you could have heard the way
He jumbled everything. I stopped to look
Two or three times—he made me feel so queer—
To see if he was talking in his sleep.
He ran on Harold Wilson—you remember—
The boy you had in haying four years since.
He's finished school, and teaching in his college.
Silas declares you'll have to get him back.

He says they two will make a team for work:
Between them they will lay this farm as smooth!
The way he mixed that in with other things.
He thinks young Wilson a likely lad, though daft
On education—you know how they fought
All through July under the blazing sun,
Silas up on the cart to build the load,
Harold along beside to pitch it on.'

'Yes, I took care to keep well out of earshot.'

'Well, those days trouble Silas like a dream.
You wouldn't think they would. How some things linger!
Harold's young college boy's assurance piqued him.
After so many years he still keeps finding
Good arguments he sees he might have used.
I sympathize. I know just how it feels
To think of the right thing to say too late.
Harold's associated in his mind with Latin.
He asked me what I thought of Harold's saying
He studied Latin like the violin
Because he liked it—that an argument!
He said he couldn't make the boy believe
He could find water with a hazel prong—
Which showed how much good school had ever done him.
He wanted to go over that. But most of all
He thinks if he could have another chance
To teach him how to build a load of hay—'

'I know, that's Silas' one accomplishment.
He bundles every forkful in its place,
And tags and numbers it for future reference,
So he can find and easily dislodge it
In the unloading. Silas does that well.
He takes it out in bunches like big birds' nests.
You never see him standing on the hay
He's trying to lift, straining to lift himself.'

'He thinks if he could teach him that, he'd be
Some good perhaps to someone in the world.
He hates to see a boy the fool of books.
Poor Silas, so concerned for other folk,
And nothing to look backward to with pride,
And nothing to look forward to with hope,
So now and never any different.'

Part of a moon was falling down the west,
Dragging the whole sky with it to the hills.
Its light poured softly in her lap. She saw it
And spread her apron to it. She put out her hand
Among the harp-like morning-glory strings,
Taut with the dew from garden bed to eaves,
As if she played unheard some tenderness
That wrought on him beside her in the night.
'Warren,' she said, 'he has come home to die:
You needn't be afraid he'll leave you this time.'

'Home,' he mocked gently.

                    'Yes, what else but home?
It all depends on what you mean by home.
Of course he's nothing to us, any more
Than was the hound that came a stranger to us
Out of the woods, worn out upon the trail.'

'Home is the place where, when you have to go there,
They have to take you in.'

                    'I should have called it
Something you somehow haven't to deserve.'

Warren leaned out and took a step or two,
Picked up a little stick, and brought it back
And broke it in his hand and tossed it by.
'Silas has better claim on us you think
Than on his brother? Thirteen little miles
As the road winds would bring him to his door.
Silas has walked that far no doubt today.
Why doesn't he go there? His brother's rich,
A somebody—director in the bank.'

'He never told us that.'

       'We know it though.'

'I think his brother ought to help, of course.
I'll see to that if there is need. He ought of right
To take him in, and might be willing to—
He may be better than appearances.
But have some pity on Silas. Do you think
If he had any pride in claiming kin
Or anything he looked for from his brother,
He'd keep so still about him all this time?'

'I wonder what's between them.'

         'I can tell you.
Silas is what he is—we wouldn't mind him—
But just the kind that kinsfolk can't abide.
He never did a thing so very bad.
He don't know why he isn't quite as good
As anybody. Worthless though he is,
He won't be made ashamed to please his brother.'

'I can't think Si ever hurt anyone.'

'No, but he hurt my heart the way he lay
And rolled his old head on that sharp-edged chair-back.
He wouldn't let me put him on the lounge.
You must go in and see what you can do.
I made the bed up for him there tonight.
You'll be surprised at him—how much he's broken.
His working days are done; I'm sure of it.'

'I'd not be in a hurry to say that.'

'I haven't been. Go, look, see for yourself.
But, Warren, please remember how it is:
He's come to help you ditch the meadow.
He has a plan. You mustn't laugh at him.
He may not speak of it, and then he may.
I'll sit and see if that small sailing cloud
Will hit or miss the moon.'

                                It hit the moon.
Then there were three there, making a dim row,
The moon, the little silver cloud, and she.

Warren returned—too soon, it seemed to her,
Slipped to her side, caught up her hand and waited.

'Warren?' she questioned.

                        'Dead,' was all he answered.

The poet's art . . .

1. Silas was not actually a member of Mary and Warren's family. Yet he felt that he belonged with them. Can you explain why?

2. How do the following lines help you understand why Silas returned to Mary and Warren:

"Home is the place where, when you have to go there,
They have to take you in."

3. When Warren first learned that Silas had returned, he said, "I'll not have the fellow back." What were Warren's reasons?

4. But Mary said, "Be kind." She knew that Silas needed them. How was Mary affected by seeing Silas again? In what ways did she try to help him?

5. Silas had a successful brother who lived only a few miles away. Why didn't Silas go to him for help? In what other ways did Silas try to keep his self-respect?

6. Who was Harold Wilson? What were some of the things that he and Silas used to argue about? By including Harold Wilson in the poem, Robert Frost was able to point up values that Silas held. What were these values?

7. "The Death of the Hired Man" was written in an easy, conversational way. Read the poem aloud, and as you read, be sure to keep a natural, conversational tone to your voice.

The Lonesome Bear

HARRISON KINNEY

Henry was a useless bear. All he wanted to do was ride in automobiles and eat marshmallows.

Until he was twelve my brother George was the unofficial leader of a gang of boys about his own age in Fairfield. Being four years younger than George, I was never included in the activities of this group, but one day I was sitting on a lower limb of an apple tree in our back yard when my brother George came up to the tree with his hands in his pockets.

"Let's start a store," he said. "You put up the counter and I'll try to get the stuff."

"All right," I said, climbing down from the tree.

After George had gone I erected a counter with two boxes and a board, facing our driveway. When he got back, he pulled out a two-pound box of chocolates, a half dozen all-day suckers, a box of marshmallows, and eight chocolate bars. He arranged these on the counter.

"I'll go tell the gang to come and buy this candy from us," my brother George said.

"All right," I said.

George went away again and I was sitting on the ground, eating one of the chocolate bars, when a brown bear lum-

bered down through the apple orchard and came up to the candy counter, sniffing at the articles on the board.

"You'd better go away," I told the bear. "My brother George will get mad if you eat his candy."

The bear sat down and stared at the candy. After a while George and his gang came up the driveway. They stopped quite a distance from the counter when they saw the bear.

"You get away from that bear," one of the boys yelled to me. "He'll kill you with one swing of his paw."

"No, he won't," I said, patting the bear on the head.

"Give him some candy to eat and maybe he'll go away," another boy shouted.

So I took the wrappers off two candy bars, opened the box of marshmallows, and placed them on the ground in front of the bear. The animal just sniffed at the candy, but when he found the marshmallows he slid into a crouch and began chewing them, looking at me occasionally, his head bobbing, as he ate.

"I guess he just likes marshmallows."

351

said my brother George. "We'll get him some more for you to feed him and maybe he'll go away."

"The state will pay you a twenty-five-dollar bounty for a bear," another boy said to my brother George. "They kill sheep. Why don't you keep him and get the money?"

"I guess we could keep him in the icehouse," said George.

"How are you going to get him in the icehouse?" somebody asked.

"I think he'll follow my brother in," George replied. "You lead him in the icehouse," George said to me.

"All right," I answered.

So after the bear finished eating the marshmallows he followed me into the icehouse. My brother George locked the door after us and I climbed out the small trap door in the wall.

George told me not to tell anybody about the bear, for fear he would not get the money for himself. I promised I wouldn't.

My brother George promised to keep me in candy if I fed the bear. The diet was a rather irregular one, consisting largely of raw potatoes from a sack in our cellar, and meat bones I got from the butcher's store. The sawdust in the icehouse had dried into a comfortable bed for the bear. My family had had no use for the building after my father bought an electric refrigerator for our house.

After a few days the bear refused to eat anything. He would sit and make hoarse, whimpering noises in his throat.

"I think he wants some marshmallows," I told my brother George, who was standing outside the icehouse at the time.

"I'll get some," George said.

He went away and came back with a box of marshmallows, which he passed to me through the trap door. I opened the box and the bear rooted into them, getting marshmallow on his nose and whiskers and

chomping them noisily, looking at me as he ate them. When he had finished them he ate the raw potatoes and meat bones. I told George the bear was eating everything.

"We'll just give him some marshmallows once in a while," George said. "I guess he'll be all right."

The night the bear got out of the icehouse, one of my mother's aunts was visiting us. She was given my room, while a couch was set up in my parents' room for me as a temporary arrangement. During the warmer nights of midsummer we always left the doors open, inside the house, for purposes of circulation; all except my brother George's room in the attic. George walked in his sleep occasionally, so my father always locked him in at night and let him out in the morning. The trap door of the icehouse could only be secured from the inside, so George and I had propped a piece of two-by-four against it from the outside. It was always a matter of speculation as to how the bear was able to dislodge it. Everybody was asleep the night that the bear came into my father's room and tried to crowd under my couch to go to sleep. The couch had two folding sides, and the grunting animal lifted the couch at one end in his attempt to get his bulky body under it. In this manner the couch was pushed across the floor until it banged against the opposite wall. The bear snorted loudly in the darkness and lay down.

My father was a light sleeper. "Where are you, George?" he asked, sitting up in bed and thinking it was my brother George walking in his sleep.

"George isn't here," I said.

"Good Lord, son!" said my father. "Are you making all that noise?"

"No, sir," I said. "I think it's the bear."

"All right," said my father, lying down again. "Just don't wake your mother."

"No, sir," I replied.

After a few minutes my father sat up in bed again. "What did you say that noise was, son?" he asked quietly.

"I think the bear is sleeping under my bed," I said.

My father sat in the darkness for a time, thinking this over. Finally he turned on the table lamp beside his bed. This awakened my mother.

"What is it?" my mother asked with alarm. "Is it George again?"

My father got out of bed in his nightshirt without saying anything. He came over to the couch, got down on his hands and knees and looked at the bear under the couch.

"He eats marshmallows," I said.

Father got up and solemnly walked over to my mother's side of the bed. "We must all remain calm," he said. "Your aunt mustn't be upset. I don't think anybody is in immediate danger. There's a bear in our room."

My mother began weeping softly. "We'll all be torn limb from limb," she said.

"He won't hurt," I told her.

My father asked me where the bear came from and I told him. My mother went into the next room to sleep with her aunt, and my father and I pulled the couch off the bear. The bear sat up and yawned.

"I never saw a bear like this that liked to be around people," said my father, crossing his bare feet in contemplation, and leaning against the bedpost in his nightshirt.

"I think he follows me because I feed him marshmallows," I said.

"We must always be kind to animals, son—wild or domestic," my father told me.

"Yes, sir," I said.

"His coat isn't shaggy like a wild bear's at all," said my father, looking at the bear. "I think he's tame."

"Can we keep him?" I asked.

My father didn't answer me. He wandered slowly downstairs and came back with his ukulele. He sat down in a rocking chair in his nightshirt and absently strummed some basic cords. The bear sat and listened to the music, staring at my father.

"This is a very friendly bear, son," said my father after a while. "Maybe we can keep him until his owner shows up."

"Yes, sir," I said.

The next day my father and I went across the street to the courthouse, with the bear plodding behind us.

"We'd like to get a license for a bear," my father told Miss Barnes, the clerk in the outer office.

Miss Barnes took off her glasses and looked at my father for a moment. Then she stood up quickly and looked at the bear, sitting on the floor beside me.

"What kind of a license do you want?" Miss Barnes asked slowly, still looking at the bear.

"We want him for a household pet," my father said.

"He eats marshmallows," I told Miss Barnes, patting the bear on the head.

"He does?" said Miss Barnes stupidly. "Just a moment." She got up and went into the inside office, looking cautiously at the bear over her shoulder. After a while the door of the inner office opened a crack and Mr. Gordon, the town clerk, peeked out. He finally pushed the door wide open. Three or four other people stood behind him and stared at the bear, which was sitting beside me, looking out the courthouse window.

"Do you really mean to keep this animal in your home as a pet for a seven-year-old child?" Mr. Gordon asked my father.

"He's a civilized bear," said my father, a little annoyed. "He's lots more trustworthy than some dogs in town that I know of. You can get a dog licensed. Why can't you license a bear?"

"You're setting a dangerous precedent," said Mr. Gordon. "Next, people will be wanting to license wildcats and wolves."

"He eats marshmallows," I said.

"We should not be afraid of setting precedents," said my father in the tone of voice that he used on customers at his store. "The motto for the state of Maine is 'Dirigo': 'I direct.'"

"Oratorical rhetoric will get you nowhere," said Mr. Gordon, wiping his glasses and peering at the bear. "There are no regulations in the community, or Oswego County, governing this situation. There may be a state law which applies. I'll have to write to Augusta. In the meantime you will be solely responsible for the bear's behavior or he will have to be shot as being hazardous to the public welfare."

My father seemed annoyed as we left the courthouse. He sat down on the bottom step and the bear and I sat beside him.

"Son, a man could come up right now, as things stand, murder this bear and the state would pay him money," said my father. "By George, if Theodore Roosevelt were still in office I bet you could get a bear license."

My mother didn't care for the bear. She would never permit me to bring the bear as far as the back porch. My brother George soon lost interest in the animal, but my father usually brought marshmallows home from his general store. Sometimes my father would sit on the back-porch steps, play his ukulele and sing, while the bear sat in front of him and listened. Nothing could distract the bear's attention while my father was singing.

During the day, while my father was at work in his store and my brother George and I were at school, the bear was tethered to one of the apple trees by a long rope attached to the leather collar my father bought for him.

"We'll tie him close enough to the house so he won't get lonesome," my father told me.

The brown bear slept much of the time on the lower branches of the apple trees, or tumbled about on the ground, or ate the apples he could shake to the ground by hugging the tree trunks with his forepaws. On Mondays I would lock the bear in the icehouse, because he would ordinarily sit and watch the hired girl hang the week's laundry on the clothesline in the back yard, something which seemed to disturb her so much that she kept dropping parts of the wash on the ground.

The town's sheriff, Shirley Jones, who lived next door to us, knocked on our door one morning while we were eating breakfast. He was breathing heavily.

"Look, Stephen," he said to my father, "you've got to get rid of that bear. You don't have a license for him and I've got to insist. Do you know where that animal is right now?"

"In the icehouse," said my father, looking worried.

"He's sitting in the back seat of my car," said the sheriff. "He won't get out. He must have opened the door himself."

My father and I followed the sheriff next door. The bear had his head and forepaws protruding from a side window of the car, opposite the opened door.

"Go get the marshmallows, son," said my father quietly.

"Yes, sir," I said.

When the bear saw the marshmallows he climbed out of the sheriff's car and sniffed at the box in my hand.

"I have enough to worry about without a bear loose in town, scaring people and maybe taking a swipe at children," said the sheriff.

"He's a good bear," said my father.

"Just let him pull one funny move and I'll have him shot," said Sheriff Jones. "You'll have to get rid of him, anyway. You've heard about the bank robberies that have taken place north of here. We're expecting them to take a crack at the Farmers' Trust here in Fairfield any day now, and if I have to do any chasing of bank robbers I don't want a bear in my back seat breathing down my neck."

"We'll take him back to the woods this Saturday and lose him," said my father a little sadly.

"He'll be happier there," said my mother when we told her. She seemed cheerful about it. "It isn't really right to keep the poor animal in captivity, anyway."

When Saturday came my father hired an extra clerk for his store and got fishing rods out of the attic while I dug worms in the back yard. The brown bear made happy woofing sounds in his throat when we opened the rear door of our Essex for him.

"He likes to ride in cars, I guess," said my father, looking thoughtfully at the bear.

"He'll never be able to ride in cars if we leave him in the woods," I said.

"He won't mind," said my father. "He'll forget."

A few miles outside of town, tourists in a car with New York license plates blew their horn and started to pass us. The sound attracted the attention of the bear, who thrust his head out the left rear window just as the New York car was abreast of us. I heard a woman scream and the other car swerved off the road and shot up a grassy embankment, where it came to a stop. My father stopped the Essex and we walked back.

"Are you all right?" my father asked with some concern.

"Only a little shaken up," said the driver, a man in a white linen suit. "That animal frightened me. For a minute I thought he was driving."

"He's a tame bear," said my father. "I hope you aren't hurt."

"He eats marshmallows," I said. "We're taking him fishing."

"I see," said the man, looking from me to my father.

They waved at us as they passed us a few minutes later. My father waved back. He always made a point of being nice to out-of-state people so that they would think well of Maine. We kept the rear windows rolled up after that.

"Next they'll be saying this poor bear is a traffic hazard," my father explained.

We left the car on a farm road and walked several miles into the forest, the bear traipsing silently behind us. He gave no obvious acknowledgment of any change in environment. We fished for trout all that day in a clear water stream while the bear sat and watched us. At noon we ate the lunch the hired girl had put up for us and fed the bear some meat bones.

"A wild bear would crouch on the bank of that stream and knock trout out of it with his paw," said my father. "This is the most helpless animal I ever saw."

"Maybe he doesn't like fish," I said. "Maybe all he can eat now will be meat bones, potatoes, and marshmallows. Maybe he'll starve out here."

"No, he won't," said my father, eating a deviled-ham sandwich and looking at the bear. "He can eat berries and nuts like other bears. Maybe he'll find a mate and learn from her."

"He likes music," I said. "He likes to hear you sing."

"The woods are full of birds that sing," said my father.

"They can't play the ukulele," I said.

"There are times when I wish you wouldn't talk to me," my father said. "I think you take after your mother at times. Please be quiet."

"Yes, sir," I said.

We fished for a while longer in the afternoon and the bear became tired of watching and wandered away into the woods.

"You mustn't feel badly about the bear, son," my father said, as we carried the fish baskets and rods back through the trees. He blew his nose in a large linen handkerchief.

"We didn't say good-by to him," I said.

"It's probably better that way," said my father. He was a theatrical man.

It was dusk when we reached the car and started for home. Neither of us spoke for a while. When we were on the state highway the lights of a car behind us threw a silhouette of a bear's head on the inside of our windshield.

"Is the bear in the back seat, son?" my father asked quietly.

I turned and looked at the bear in the

back seat. He sat with his back to us, looking out the rear window.

"I think it's the bear," I said.

My mother locked herself in her room all the next day.

"I don't know why our home has to be turned into a zoo," she told my father tearfully.

"The circus will be passing through here in a few days," my father reassured her. "They'll be glad to have a tame bear."

The bear and I waited on the back steps that evening for my father to come out and sing, but he never did.

In late June the circus was playing Millinocket on its way north and my father wired the manager that he might have the bear if he called for it. One afternoon, a few days later, a man drove up in front of our house in a coupé with a large wire cage protruding from the half-opened trunk. I brought the bear around from the icehouse. The man looked at the bear.

"I knew it was Henry," he said, nodding his head thoughtfully.

"Is that the bear's name?" I asked.

"We lost him last summer up this way," the man explained. "He must have hibernated in the woods all winter."

"He eats marshmallows," I said.

"It used to be jelly beans," the man said. "He's the most temperamental animal I ever saw. He wouldn't eat anything unless we gave him jelly beans once in a while. He has quite a sweet tooth. I wish we hadn't found him. He's such a nuisance."

He raised the gate of the cage and sprinkled a few jelly beans from his pocket on the floor of the cage.

"Let's go, Henry," he said to the bear.

The bear ambled inside the cage and began chewing the jelly beans. The man closed the gate after him.

"He likes to ride in cars," I said, looking at the bear through the wire.

"I know," the man answered. "That's all we could get him to do, ride in the back of an old jalopy that two clowns drove around the ring. He's the most useless bear I ever saw. He wouldn't learn to ride bicycles, or roller-skate, and he ran away when we tried to teach him to dance. We were all glad."

The man sighed and got into the car.

"Thank your folks for taking care of him, kid," the man said sadly.

"Yes, sir," I said.

He drove away with the brown bear sitting in the wire cage chewing jelly beans.

It was the first year my family didn't go to see the circus when it played Presque Isle. My brother George threatened to run away from home, but my mother said she couldn't stand to look at another animal, and my father said he supposed it would make the bear unhappy if he saw us in the crowd.

"He rides in the back of an old car that two clowns drive," I told my father.

"He's probably very happy, then," said my father, patting me on the head. It was several weeks before he played his ukulele and sang on the steps of the back porch.

One morning my father was awakened by somebody throwing pebbles at his bedroom window. He got out of bed and went to the window. It was the hired girl. She told my father she didn't dare to come into the house because a bear was sitting on the front porch in front of the door. I followed my father downstairs and we looked at the bear through the curtains of the living-room windows.

"Look at the dust on his fur," said my father. "He must have walked twenty miles."

"Maybe he's mad at us for giving him to the circus," I said.

"No," my father replied. "He just got homesick for us."

I led the bear around to the icehouse and locked him in. When I got back my father was strumming on his ukulele.

"Son, Judge Holt told me he heard from Augusta that there's no legal protection for bears as pets," my father said. "I don't know what we'll do with him. We certainly can't keep him. Sheriff Jones and your mother just wouldn't stand for it."

My father went to work without telling my mother the bear was back, and it was about ten o'clock that morning when I discovered the bear had got out of the icehouse. I searched back of the orchard and finally started downtown to the store to tell my father the bear was loose in Fairfield. A block from the Farmers' Trust Building I saw the bear trudge out of an alley and climb into the front seat of a long black Pierce Arrow that was standing in front of the bank, its motor idling and the front door open. From the front seat the bear pushed himself over into the back and sat on the floor. I was looking at him through the car window when two men carrying guns and cloth sacks came running out of the bank and leaped into the car.

"The bear's in there," I told them, pointing.

The men didn't hear me, apparently. They slouched in the front seat and the car roared away just as the burglar alarm went off outside the bank. In a few minutes I saw Sheriff Jones's Reo and two cars filled with deputies race down Main Street in the direction the Pierce Arrow had taken.

My father was in the office of his store, sitting at his roller-top desk.

"The bear got in a car and the people drove away and didn't see him," I told him.

My father buried his face in his hands.

"Son," he said after a while, "this is the end. Those poor innocent people will find a bear in their car, not know he is a tame bear, go off the road and kill themselves. The bear will be shot, if he gets out alive, and I'll be put in jail."

"Sheriff Jones is chasing the bear," I said.

"You and George will have to go with your mother to live with her family," said my father absently. "You must always be good to her, son."

"Yes, sir," I said.

We drove slowly home in the Essex. He asked me not to talk to him for a while and I promised I wouldn't. A group of people were standing on the lawn in front of our house when we drove up.

"The bear is sitting in Sheriff Jones's car," I said.

"Those bank robbers didn't even get out of town," the sheriff told my father happily when we joined him. "The driver spotted that bear of yours in the rearview mirror, sitting on the back seat. They went over the edge of the culvert at the bottom of Mill Hill. Took them both without firing a shot. They're in the prison hospital."

My father sat down on the front steps to think.

"The bear likes to ride in cars," I said.

"He didn't get hurt a bit," said the sheriff. "We're going to give him part of the reward."

Several children gathered around the sheriff's car to look at the bear that had helped capture the bank robbers. The bear yawned and went to sleep on the back seat.

"He came back from the circus," I said, "but we can't keep him."

"I saw Judge Holt at the prison hospital," Sheriff Jones continued, sitting on the steps beside my father. "The judge doesn't see why the town can't give this bear a special license."

"By George!" said my father. "That's good of the judge. He's a good bear. We won't let him get loose again."

I shook the bear awake and led him back to the icehouse.

My mother was in a pleasant mood at supper that evening.

"With the two thousand dollars the sheriff is giving the bear," she said, "I think it would be a nice thing to build a comfortable enclosure for the animal in back of the orchard, with a little house for a shelter."

"We can buy him lots of marshmallows," I said.

"We might screen in the back porch too," my mother added. "I've always wanted that done."

"That might be arranged," my father said.

After supper the bear and I sat down on the steps of the back porch. After a while my father came out, carrying his ukulele. He patted the bear on the head.

"Son, tomorrow we'll get the bear a new collar with a shiny metal license tag," my father said.

"What will we do with him when winter comes?" I asked.

"He can sleep in the icehouse," said my father. "It will be dark and quiet in there. Fairfield is very proud of this bear and we must take good care of him."

"Yes, sir," I said.

Then my father began singing "Oh, Dear, Are You Lonesome Tonight?" while the bear and I sat and listened to him. My father had a pleasant voice to listen to, and I always knew he was happy when he sang.

The man who wrote this story

HARRISON KINNEY 1921–

Born in a small town in the potato-raising section of Maine, Harrison Kinney moved south to earn his degree in journalism at Washington and Lee University. His education was interrupted by three and a half years in the army medical department during the last world war. When his service was finished, he hurried back to school.

After taking his master's degree in English at Columbia, he began his writing career with *The New Yorker* magazine. Since then he has had many short stories published.

Let's consider . . .

1. Henry certainly was an unusual bear. In what ways was he different from most bears?

2. Which of Henry's antics did you enjoy the most? Read the description of it to the class.

3. Why did the family decide to take the bear to the woods? What happened when they tried to leave him there?

4. The circus man wasn't very happy about re-claiming Henry. Why did he call him a useless bear?

5. What were Father's feelings about Henry? Select incidents from the story that helped you understand how Father felt.

6. What were Mother's feelings toward the bear? What caused her to change?

7. Describe the way Henry helped to catch the bank robbers.

8. Name the members of the family who benefited in some way from Henry's reward.

9. Almost everyone enjoys hearing about other people's pets. Write a description of a pet you have owned. Be sure to include the things that made your pet different from most animals.

Knowing words . . .

A. The prefix *dis-* often means "away" or "apart." Harrison Kinney wondered how the bear was able to *dislodge* the two-by-four he had propped against the icehouse door. *Dislodge* means to "move away from the position occupied."

1. Use *dislodge* in a sentence of your own.

2. Explain the meaning of these words:

displace   dispatch
disorganize   disjoint
            dismiss

B. The prefix *dis-* may also signify "not" or "the reverse of something." Such words as *dislike, disability,* and *discontent* are examples of this meaning of the prefix *dis-*. List several other words which use the prefix *dis-* to imply a negative meaning.

A Bird Came Down the Walk

A bird came down the walk:
He did not know I saw;
He bit an angle-worm in halves
And ate the fellow, raw.

And then he drank a dew
From a convenient grass,
And then hopped sidewise to the wall
To let a beetle pass.

He glanced with rapid eyes
That hurried all abroad,—
They looked like frightened beads, I thought
He stirred his velvet head

Like one in danger; cautious,
I offered him a crumb,
And he unrolled his feathers
And rowed him softer home

Than oars divide the ocean,
Too silver for a seam,
Or butterflies, off banks of noon,
Leap, plashless, as they swim.

Emily Dickinson

How We Kept Mother's Day

STEPHEN LEACOCK

Stephen Leacock and his family wanted to show Mother that they really loved her. The proof wasn't to be in empty words or fleeting gifts but in a genuine celebration of Mother's Day. Watch how they did it.

Of all the different ideas that have been started lately, I think that the very best is the notion of celebrating once a year "Mother's Day." I don't wonder that May the eleventh is becoming such a popular date all over America and I am sure the idea will spread to England too.

It is especially in a big family like ours that such an idea takes hold. So we decided to have a special celebration of Mother's Day. We thought it a fine idea. It made us realize how much Mother had done for us for years, and all the efforts and sacrifice that she had made for our sake.

So we decided that we'd make it a great day, a holiday for all the family, and do everything we could to make Mother happy. Father decided to take a holiday from his office, so as to help in celebrating the day, and my sister Anne and I stayed home from college classes, and Mary and my brother Will stayed home from High School.

It was our plan to make it a day just like Xmas or any big holiday, and so we decided to decorate the house with flowers and with mottoes over the mantelpieces, and all that kind of thing. We got Mother to make mottoes and arrange the decorations, because she always does it at Xmas.

The two girls thought it would be a nice thing to dress in our very best for such a big occasion, and so they both got new hats. Mother trimmed both the hats, and they looked fine, and Father had bought four-in-hand silk ties for himself and us boys as a souvenir of the day to remember Mother by. We were going to get Mother a new hat too, but it turned out that she seemed to really like her old grey bonnet better than a new one, and both the girls said that it was awfully becoming to her.

Well, after breakfast we had it arranged as a surprise for Mother that we would hire a motor car and take her for a beautiful drive away into the country. Mother is hardly ever able to have a treat like that, because we can only afford to keep one maid, and so Mother is busy in the house nearly all the time. And of course the country is so lovely now that it would be just grand for her to have a lovely morning, driving for miles and miles.

But on the very morning of the day we changed the plan a little bit, because it occurred to Father that a thing it would be better to do even than to take Mother for a motor drive would be to take her fishing. Father said that as the car was hired and paid for, we might just as well use it for a drive up into the hills where the streams are. As Father said, if you just go out driving without any object, you have a sense of aimlessness, but if you are going to fish, there is a definite purpose in front of you to heighten the enjoyment.

So we all felt that it would be nicer for Mother to have a definite purpose; and anyway, it turned out that Father had just got a new rod the day before, which made the idea of fishing all the more appropriate, and he said that Mother could use it if she wanted to; in fact, he said it was practically for her, only Mother said she would much rather watch him fish and not try to fish herself.

So we got everything arranged for the trip, and we got Mother to cut up some sandwiches and make up a sort of lunch in case we got hungry, though of course we were to come back again to a big dinner in the middle of the day, just like Xmas or New Year's Day. Mother packed it all up in a basket for us ready to go in the motor.

Well, when the car came to the door, it turned out that there hardly seemed as much room in it as we had supposed, because we hadn't reckoned on Father's fishing basket and the rods and the lunch, and it was plain enough that we couldn't all get in.

Father said not to mind him, he said that he could just as well stay home, and that he was sure that he could put in the time working in the garden; he said that there

was a lot of rough dirty work that he could do, like digging a trench for the garbage, that would save hiring a man, and so he said that he'd stay home; he said that we were not to let the fact of his not having had a real holiday for three years stand in our way; he wanted us to go right ahead and be happy and have a big day, and not to mind him. He said that he could plug away all day, and in fact he said he'd been a fool to think there'd be any holiday for him.

But of course we all felt that it would never do to let Father stay home, especially as we knew he would make trouble if he did. The two girls, Anne and Mary, would gladly have stayed and helped the maid get dinner, only it seemed such a pity to, on a lovely day like this, having their new hats. But they both said that Mother had only to say the word, and they'd gladly stay home and work. Will and I would have dropped out, but unfortunately we wouldn't have been any use in getting the dinner.

So in the end it was decided that Mother would stay home and just have a lovely restful day around the house, and get the dinner. It turned out anyway that Mother doesn't care for fishing, and also it was just a little bit cold and fresh out of doors, though it was lovely and sunny, and Father was rather afraid that Mother might take cold if she came.

He said he would never forgive himself if he dragged Mother round the country and let her take a severe cold at a time when she might be having a beautiful rest. He said it was our duty to try and let Mother get all the rest and quiet that she could, after all that she had done for all of us, and he said that that was principally why he had fallen in with this idea of a fishing trip, so as to give Mother a little quiet. He said that young people seldom realize how much quiet means to people

landed them anyway, if she had been fishing for them, and Will and I fished too, though we didn't get so many as Father, and the two girls met quite a lot of people that they knew as we drove along, and there were some young men friends of theirs that they met along the stream and talked to, and so we all had a splendid time.

It was quite late when we got back, nearly seven o'clock in the evening, but Mother had guessed that we would be late, so she had kept back the dinner so as to have it just nicely ready and hot for us. Only first she had to get towels and soap for Father and clean things for him to put on, because he always gets so messed up with fishing, and that kept Mother busy for a little while, that and helping the girls get ready.

But at last everything was ready, and we sat down to the grandest kind of dinner— roast turkey and all sorts of things like on Xmas Day. Mother had to get up and down a good bit during the meal fetching things back and forward, but at the end Father noticed it and said she simply mustn't do it, that he wanted her to spare herself, and he got up and fetched the walnuts over from the sideboard himself.

The dinner lasted a long while, and was great fun, and when it was over all of us wanted to help clear the things up and wash the dishes, only Mother said that she would really much rather do it, and so we let her, because we wanted just for once to humor her.

It was quite late when it was all over, and when we all kissed Mother before going to bed, she said it had been the most wonderful day in her life, and I think there were tears in her eyes. So we all felt awfully repaid for all that we had done.

who are getting old. As to himself he could still stand the racket, but he was glad to shelter Mother from it.

So we all drove away with three cheers for Mother, and Mother stood and watched us from the verandah for as long as she could see us, and Father waved his hand back to her every few minutes till he hit his hand on the back edge of the car, and then said that he didn't think that Mother could see us any longer.

Well, we had the loveliest day up among the hills that you could possibly imagine, and Father caught such big specimens that he felt sure that Mother couldn't have

The man who wrote this essay

STEPHEN LEACOCK   1869–

When Leacock was seven, his parents moved from England to Canada, and, as Leacock says, he "decided to go with them." He was educated in Toronto and, at college, specialized in languages "living, dead, and half-dead." For most of his life he has been a teacher.

His writing career began with a textbook. He has now written over forty books, both humorous and serious. His popular reputation is based, of course, on his humorous books. In fact, he has been called one of the most popular humorists since Mark Twain. He says, "Personally I would rather have written *Alice in Wonderland* than the whole *Encyclopaedia Britannica.*"

Let's consider . . .

1. Stephen Leacock and his family certainly had an unusual way of celebrating Mother's Day. Describe the way that each member kept this day.

2. Now describe the way Mother spent the day.

3. How did you feel about the family's celebration of Mother's Day? List several words that describe their attitude toward Mother.

4. What is your opinion of the custom of setting aside "days" or "weeks" to honor special groups or products?

The writer's craft . . .

A. Have you ever started to school extra early so that you would be sure to arrive on time, only to have the bus come late? You probably felt that you just couldn't win. Everyone has found himself in such ironical situations. The word *ironical* is used to describe any situation in which the outcome is the opposite of what was intended. For example, to celebrate Mother's Day the girls both got new hats. Mother was supposed to get one too, but didn't. Everyone in the family had a holiday on Mother's Day—except Mother. Why was this an ironical way to celebrate Mother's Day?

Find three other ironical situations in "How We Kept Mother's Day." In each case, tell what was intended and then explain what actually happened.

B. Leacock is noted for his skill in writing the **informal essay:** a fairly short piece of writing which presents an idea and the author's feelings about it. In this essay, he used characters and incidents to illustrate his idea, but his purpose was to make you think about one aspect of human behavior.

Although Leacock wanted you to see the humor in this ironical celebration of Mother's Day, what serious meaning lay underneath the humor?

The Welsh Are Like That

EMMANUEL WINTERS

Your family probably has something in which all of you take pride. It may be a family heirloom, or a sense of family loyalty, or even a family pet. The Williams family were proud of their singing. In fact, Father was so proud of his voice that at times the family could barely live with him.

For eleven months of the year my father was just as meek and mild a miner as anyone could wish for in this beautiful and unbelievable world. For those eleven months he was also an ideal husband and a perfect father. But on the twelfth month of every year my father went completely mad. He became so enthralled with music to the exclusion of everything else that his gentleness turned sour, his tongue rattled boastfully, and his meekness became pride raving like a tiger.

My father had the sweetest tenor voice in or out of any mine in the state of Pennsylvania. That was the wonderful part.

He had been winning the local eisteddfod [1] prize for ten years straight without anyone to compete with him. That was the boastful part. The possibility that he *might* lose his crown was the pride-raving-like-a-tiger part. The combination for a month each year was something to behold.

My mother was a remarkable woman of great courage, determination, and mysterious religious depths. There were things about her that nobody knew, not even my father. Although she was generally gentle and merry, whenever her family welfare was involved she could be as ruthless, and even as cruel as a she-bear. She understood *everything* about my father. She realized that a Welshman with a sweet tenor voice found it hard, if not impossible, to act any other way whenever the eisteddfod came around.

Consequently, for ten years she suffered in silence.

But one year my mother decided that the time had come to change all this. As might be expected, it all had to do with me.

"I'm thinking," my mother remarked that lovely year as she was clearing the supper table, "that it's time for Davy to study voice, like every good Welsh lad of nine."

"What?" my father said.

"Davy's voice," my mother said. "It's time to train it."

My father pushed his chair away from

---

[1] *eisteddfod,* yearly meeting of Welsh musicians, singers, and poets to compete for prizes

the table. "Let me get this straight. You mean with a singing teacher?"

"Naturally."

"One you pay?"

"Well, of course."

My father made a horrible face. "I'll not have it," he shouted.

"Why, Emlyn, what are you shouting for?" my mother said.

"I'm not shouting," he shouted. "But no son of mine will disgrace the Welsh by carrying coals to Newcastle." [2]

My mother sank into a chair and stared at my father with recognition. "So the eisteddfod's only a month away," she said sadly.

"What has the eisteddfod to do with it?" my father said.

"It might have everything to do with it," my mother said. "You know how unreasonable you get one whole blessed month before the eisteddfod."

My father started pacing the kitchen.

"Well, reasonable or unreasonable," he said, "the matter is closed and finished."

"Now wait just a minute," my mother said with a strange, stubborn light in her eyes. "The boy has a voice, hasn't he?"

"Isn't he my son?" my father demanded.

"It's a Welsh voice, isn't it?"

"Of course, it's a Welsh voice."

"Then, by all the saints, it shall be trained."

My father came over and pounded the table. "A Welsh voice don't *need* training," he said. "A Welsh voice don't need anything except an eisteddfod now and then to bring forth its finer points. That's *all* it needs."

"And I say it needs training," my mother said.

"Now see here," my father said. He

tapped my mother's shoulder. "Haven't I won every eisteddfod in ten years?"

"You don't need to be telling me stale news," my mother said.

My father drew himself up triumphantly.

"Did you ever see me taking lessons for *my* voice?"

"I never did, unfortunately," my mother said.

"Well, then, let people who know nothing about music say no more on the subject," he said. "Let foolish talk cease. Let there be no further words on anti-Welsh questions."

My mother was grim. "Emlyn," she said.

"What?"

"The time has come to call a halt to boasting, devilishness, and pride."

"Do be telling me," my father scoffed.

"I do be telling you," she said. "For ten years we've suffered in silence your eisteddfod madness. But now the boy's future is at stake. I'm a Welsh mother and I shall call a halt."

My father set his jaw. "And how, my lovely, would you be calling a halt?"

"Only one way," my mother said. "The time has come at last for you to be losing the eisteddfod."

A terrible silence fell over the house.

"Me lose the eisteddfod?" my father said. "You mean it?"

"I mean nothing more."

"I'll be a stick of dynamite!" my father said.

"What's more," my mother went on, "I'm the one who'll see to it that you do."

"I'll be a double stick," my father said. "I suppose you'll find some great canary in this region to outsing me?"

"I shall."

"You would be willing to make a little wager, of course."

---

[2] *carrying coals to Newcastle,* since Newcastle is a center of the English coal industry, this expression has come to mean doing something that is completely useless

"I would."

My father gloated. "I'm listening, lovely."

My mother was as hard as a rock. "Then listen well, for if you lose the prize this year, Davy gets his teacher, and you'll never sing in an eisteddfod for the rest of your life."

"The Lord preserve us!" my father said. "You're a strange and terrible woman, Sara."

"I'm waiting for my answer," my mother said.

"Well, by heaven, you've got it!" my father shouted. "I'll take that wager and show you, once and for all, who's master in this house."

"That," my mother said, "is just what you will show."

Well, at that moment I was madly in love with my fourth-grade teacher and, regardless of what my mother and father felt about singing, the chief problem of *my* mind was how I could make her realize my superiority to every other pupil in the public-school system. Of course, being Welsh, I knew that I could outsing anyone, anytime, with or without training. But that was beside the point. I was wondering whether I ought to prove my manhood by getting a job in the breaker [3] *right away,* or wait a decent time until after the eighth grade.

However, when in the course of a day or two I mentioned that upon the outcome of a wager I might soon be taking voice lessons, my teacher solved the problem. She herself started paying special attention to me and never stopped. *Her* name was Miss Myfawnwy Jones. *She* sang contralto. She said, "You realize, of course, the rarity and historical importance of a trained Welsh voice."

"Yes, ma'am," I said.

"You also realize, of course, that there are *no* limits to the number of duets a natural-born contralto and a trained boy soprano can sing."

"No, ma'am."

"As soon as you've taken a few lessons, we'll start right in."

"You and me, ma'am?" I said.

"You and I, Davy. You and I."

"Yes, ma'am, that's what I said, ma'am," I said. "You and me, you and me."

This was a wholly unexpected turn of events. It caused me to take a profound interest in my parents' wager, after all, although, by this time, taking an interest wasn't hard, even without the matter of Miss Jones. For three weeks my mother left the house every afternoon, disappearing for hours at a time. Every evening she returned, looking tired, but grim and unextinguishable.

My father had never expected her search for a singer to be so thorough. "Why don't you give up this foolishness?" he said. "You'll *never* find anyone to beat me."

"Indeed?" my mother said. That was practically all she said for three weeks. . . .

When the day of the competition finally arrived, my father, my mother and myself found ourselves in the great hall together with hundreds of other contestants and spectators. My father and I were as close to nervous wrecks as any two Welshmen have a right to be. My mother had still not told us *if* she'd found anyone.

We listened carefully to every contestant; and by the time the adjudicator [4] came to my father's name on the list, no one's singing had even come close to what he could do.

"Emlyn Williams, champion of ten eisteddfods," the adjudicator announced. "Kindly come forward and sing."

My father walked down the aisle,

---

[3] *breaker,* machine for breaking up coal

[4] *adjudicator,* person who awards or judges

climbed up on the stage, and sang. It was "Open the Gates of the Temple." You could hear them opening. Ladies wept, and men listened with bowed heads.

"I'm afraid that there singing will be mighty hard to beat, Ma," I said.

"Just wait till the real competition starts, Davy," she said.

When he'd finished singing, my father came back and sat down. He grinned triumphantly at my mother.

"Well, where is your high and mighty canary?" he asked. My mother didn't pay attention. She was watching the adjudicator.

"E. Amardyce," the adjudicator announced. "Next on the program is E. Amardyce, who will sing the same song."

My mother stood up.

"What in the name of time are you doing, Sara?" my father protested.

"I'm going to sing," my mother said.

"Are you daft?" my father whispered. "*You've* never sung a note in your life."

"No, Emlyn lad?" my mother said.

"But they're calling an E. Amardyce," he protested.

My mother smiled grimly. "That, my lovely, is the name I *gave*."

She went up to the stage. She signaled the accompanist. She clasped her hands to her breast. She sang. Sweeter singing was never heard before or after on either side of the Atlantic Ocean. It was clearer than a bell and twice as lovely as a thrush and a canary put together.

"God in heaven!" my father said. He didn't stop saying it. He was still saying it when the judges awarded my mother the championship. *He* came in second.

At supper that night, my father was the meekest man alive. He didn't know which way to turn because my mother's smile was waiting for him everywhere. Around dessert he took himself in hand.

"Well, don't you think it's time to be explaining?" he said.

"Explain what?" my mother said innocently.

"Everything," my father said. "How did you learn to sing like Lily Pons in three weeks?"

"I was only rehearsing with my accompanist those three weeks," my mother said.

"Well how, where, and when did you learn?"

My mother smiled. "Did you ever hear of a man named Wencil Davies?" she said.

"The champion baritone of the national eisteddfod in Wales?"

"He was my great-grandfather," my mother said.

"Holy saints!" my father said.

"Did you ever hear of Dorothy Llewellyn?" my mother went on.

"The soprano champion?"

"She was my grandmother."

"What else?" my father said, in a small voice. "What other surprises do you have in store after fifteen years of married life?"

"Well, there was me, too," my mother said.

"What about you?"

"Before I came to America and married you, I was on the way to being the national soprano champion. Another year or two would have done it."

My father was as red as a beet. "You could have given me a hint," he said.

"There's a good reason, Emlyn lad. It was my father and brother."

"What about your father and brother?"

"They were trapped in the pits in the Great Disaster. My mother and I—*she* was contralto champion—went to church and got down on our knees. All night I prayed God to spare them. I vowed if they came out alive, I'd give up the thing most dear to me—my singing. I vowed it would be a forgotten thing with me. I'd never even boast about it."

"They *got* them out alive!" my father said.

"Yes, they got them out alive," my mother said.

My father thought for a long time. "But you did sing, finally," he said.

My mother came around the table and ruffled my father's hair. "I know," she said. Her smile was very merry. It was also very tender. "It was either that, or breaking up this family *and* your stubborn head—and God knows a good Welsh husband and the sanctity of the home are the one thing worth more than a vow, I'm thinking."

The man who wrote this story

EMMANUEL WINTERS 1910–

Born in Sweden, Emmanuel Winters was raised in Wilkes-Barre, in the heart of the Pennsylvania coal mining district. His class in high school contained many sons and daughters of Welsh miners, and from them he first got the idea for this story, "The Welsh Are Like That."

Mr. Winters had received his law degree from Cornell when the Second World War broke out. He served in the Pacific for four years, and he charged ashore at Oahu and Okinawa. He was stationed in Japan for a short time before returning to America to continue his education.

Since then he has earned a master of arts degree. He now directs a public relations firm while he works for his Ph.D.

Let's consider . . .

1. Everyone knew that Father had "the sweetest tenor voice in the state of Pennsylvania." Why then did he act like a tiger

whenever the *eisteddfod* came around?

2. For ten years the family suffered in silence at *eisteddfod* time. What made Mother finally decide it was time to "call a halt"?

3. Describe the wager between Mother and Father. What was the outcome?

4. Emmanuel Winters wrote that there were things about Mother which nobody knew, not even her husband. What were some of those things? Why did Mother keep them secret for so many years?

5. The Williams family took great pride in their singing. What particular talent or possession is your family proud of?

The writer's craft . . .

A good title is like a road sign. It tells you what to expect ahead. Writers choose their titles with great care. If the writing is of a serious nature, the writer doesn't mislead his readers with a humorous title. A good title not only puts the reader in the proper frame of mind, it also arouses his curiosity to read the story.

1. Look again at Emmanuel Winters' title. How did it arouse your curiosity?

2. How did the easy-going title "The Welsh Are Like That" put you in the proper mood for the story?

3. Think of two other titles that would be suitable for this story. Read your titles aloud to the class, and then select the one that the class likes the best.

Knowing words . . .

Father said, "Let there be no further words on *anti-Welsh* questions." *Anti-* is a prefix which means "against" or "opposed to." Often it is used with a hyphen and another word. *Anti-Welsh,* for example, means "against the Welsh."

1. List several words which have *anti-* as a prefix.

2. Explain the meaning of each of these words.

On Music

Many love music but for music's sake,
Many because her touches can awake
Thoughts that repose within the breast half-dead,
And rise to follow where she loves to lead.
What various feelings come from days gone by!
What tears from far-off sources dim the eye!
Few, when light fingers with sweet voices play
And melodies swell, pause, and melt away,
Mind how at every touch, at every tone,
A spark of life hath glistened and hath gone.

Walter Savage Landor

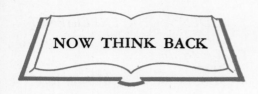

NOW THINK BACK

THINK FOR YOURSELF

Parents often judge you in one way or another. This is your chance to turn the tables.

Take your choice of any of the parents you have read about in THE FAMILY. Use the rating scale below. Before you start to fill in your ratings, discuss the standards with the members of your class. Be ready to defend your ratings with proofs from the selection you read.

Copy the rating scale into your notebook, or on a separate sheet of paper. (Please do not write in your book.)

MY RATING OF . . . . AS A PARENT

TITLE OF SELECTION . . . .

Directions: Read each question carefully. Give the person a score of

+2—if your answer is a positive YES
  0—if you are NOT SURE, or if the author did not tell you enough on which to base a rating
−2—if your answer is a loud NO

Enter your ratings in the proper columns. Add up your plus scores. Subtract the minus scores. You will then have your TOTAL RATING of this person as a parent.

STANDARDS	MY RATING		
	+2	0	−2
Does this parent			
a. Let the children have some say in the affairs of the family?			
b. Give each child a fair share of home duties and responsibilities?			
c. Train the children in the wise handling of money?			
d. Develop respect for the rights of others in the family?			
e. Set an example of love and devotion in the home?			
f. Use as good manners with his children as with adults?			
g. Respect the rights of children to make some decisions for themselves?			
h. Play no favorites with any of the children (if there is more than one in the family)?			
i. Give children a feeling of security in the home?			
j. Try to understand the child's point of view?			
TOTAL RATING	+	−	=

More for you to think about . . .

1. What, in your opinion, would be a fair "Passing Mark" for a parent? Why?

2. Discuss the rating that you or your committee gave to each of the parents.

3. Do you consider some of the standards in this rating scale more important than others? Which ones?

4. Which of the ten qualities suggested in the scale do you rank highest? Renumber them in order from "most important" to "least important."

5. Does this rating scale *omit* qualities that you consider important? What questions would you add? Why?

SHARE YOUR IDEAS

1. How much of a part should the father play in the raising of children? Or do you think that the real responsibility rests on the mother? Refer to the selections in this part when you discuss this question.

2. How can disagreements and other troubles between parents and children best be prevented? How were such problems solved by some of the families you read about?

3. What are some of the difficult responsibilities that most parents have? Which parents in THE FAMILY had the most serious problem to solve? How did they solve it? What other solution can you think of?

4. Should parents give greater freedom to their children when they reach their teens? If you were in their place, what privileges would you allow?

5. Sum up your discussion by listing

a. What boys and girls your age expect of their parents.

b. What parents have a right to expect of you.

WIDEN YOUR EXPERIENCE

Things to do . . .

1. Discuss the rating scale on page 371 with your parents. Get their suggestions and opinions. Ask them to tell you what questions *they* would use in rating children of teen age.

Let a committee collect these suggestions and draw up a rating scale for judging boys and girls your age.

Rate yourself on this scale. Ask your parents to rate you, too. Compare the two ratings. Do they agree? If not, why do they disagree?

2. Collect some of your family's favorite anecdotes. (Some examples of family anecdotes are in the sketch by Ernie Pyle.) Tell these anecdotes in class during a period which you might like to call "Family Secrets," or "Skeletons in Our Family Closet."

3. If you can get the cooperation of your parents, write a brief sketch telling how *they* got along with *their* parents.

4. Keep a personal diary for a period of two weeks, or longer, if you can. Pay special attention to the relationships you maintain between you and your own parents.

5. Appoint a committee to learn whether or not your school has a parents' association. If it has, the committee may want to interview officers of the association to learn about its activities. Perhaps one member of the parents' association would agree to visit your class at the time your committee makes its report.

6. Conduct a panel discussion on some of the issues raised in this part. Below are several ideas you may choose from. If it can be arranged, invite one or several parents to take part in your discussion.

Suggestions for panel discussion speakers:

My Ideal Family

Are Parents Fair?

Are We Fair to Our Parents?

When I Have a Teen-Age Daughter (or Son) of My Own—

7. Here are some topics on which you should be able to write with strong convictions:

Being the Youngest (or Oldest) in the Family

Problem Child

"Home Is Where You Hang Your Hat"

A Family Bull Session

Open Letter to Parents

Parents—Plagues or Pals?

A Successful Parent

Understanding Parents

More to read . . .

Little Women by LOUISA MAY ALCOTT. If you haven't already met Meg, Jo, Beth, and Amy March, now is the time. Their home life about a hundred years ago may be different from yours, but their thoughts and dreams are much the same. Little, Brown and Company, 1934. (First published 1868.)

The Yearling by MARJORIE KINNAN RAWLINGS. Jody Baxter lives in the Florida scrub pine country, where it is not easy to make enough to feed a family. His parents, a few neighbors, and the orphaned fawn he adopts—these are his world. Charles Scribner's Sons, 1938.

How Green Was My Valley by RICHARD LLEWELLYN. Boyhood in a family of coal-miners in the "green valley" of Wales makes a beautiful, sad, and funny story. The Macmillan Company, 1940.

Mama's Bank Account by KATHRYN FORBES. Wise and understanding Mama holds her Norwegian family together and keeps them happy through hard times. Harcourt, Brace and Company, Inc., 1943.

The Best of Clarence Day by CLARENCE DAY. In *Life with Mother* and *Life with Father,* one of the red-headed Day boys tells what it was like to grow up in the 1880's with his unpredictable parents. Alfred A. Knopf, Inc., 1948.

Cheaper by the Dozen by FRANK B. GILBRETH, JR., and ERNESTINE G. CAREY. Two of the Gilbreth children recall growing up in the midst of a family of fourteen, ruled on the assembly-line plan by their genius father. Grosset & Dunlap, Inc., 1948.

Family Circle by CORNELIA OTIS SKINNER. A famous actress tells how she grew up in the theater with her parents, both actors. Houghton Mifflin Company, 1948.

Swiss Family Robinson by JOHANN D. WYSS. Shipwrecked on a desert island, this family has one unusual adventure after another. E. P. Dutton & Co., 1951. (First published 1813.)

Silas Marner by GEORGE ELIOT. An old man takes an orphaned child into his lonely life and finds out that real happiness does not lie in gold coins. Dodd, Mead & Company, 1948. (First published 1861.)

Our Town by THORNTON WILDER. In this play you will find life from birth to death as it is lived in a typical American town. Samuel French, Inc., 1938.

My Name is Aram by WILLIAM SAROYAN. This is a collection of fanciful stories about the author and his relatives—Armenians living in California. Harcourt, Brace and Company, Inc., 1950.

The Family Nobody Wanted by HELEN
DOSS. A warm-hearted couple acquire
a large, oddly-assorted, and very happy
family by adopting children of mixed
racial background whom nobody else
would take. Little, Brown and Company, 1954.

As the Earth Turns by GLADYS HASTY CAR-
ROLL. A year in the life of a Maine
farm family is recorded here. The oldest daughter, Jen, is the center around
which the family life revolves. The
Macmillan Company, 1933.

*Theodore Roosevelt's Letters to His Chil-
dren* by JOSEPH B. BISHOP (ed.).
"Teddy" Roosevelt writes unusual and
informative letters, showing how he
followed his children's education and
daily activities with interest and affection. Charles Scribner's Sons, 1919.

Understood Betsy by DOROTHY CANFIELD.
Betsy, spoiled by her "understanding"
aunt, learns to think and act for herself when she goes to live on a Vermont farm with other relatives. Henry
Holt and Company, Inc., 1946.

SIDELIGHTS ON AMERICA

Really knowing your country is not a matter of being able to locate every great city on a map or name the capitals of all the states. Maps and names have a practical value, but they lack human warmth. The best way to discover the heart of America is to meet the people who call this country "home." Some of them were here long before the Pilgrims landed at Plymouth Rock. Some came to build a new nation, rich in opportunity and free from oppression. Others came when most of the building was done, and great cities stood where once had been forests or grassy plains. Because of what these people knew and loved about this country, each of them had his own answer to the question, "What is an American?"

PART SIX

SIDELIGHTS ON AMERICA

Ann Story, Yankee Pioneer

DOROTHY CANFIELD FISHER

You will probably remember Ann Story for a long time. She was a remarkable pioneer woman who not only raised her children in the wilds of
unsettled Vermont but also protected them from attacks by the Indians and
British. The author calls this story—which, by the way, is a true one—a
"footnote to history." After you have read it, you may decide it ought to be
called a "headline to history."

In 1774, when people left settled, civilized Connecticut to pioneer into the wild,
pathless woods of Vermont, they were
lucky if they had a sizeable river to travel
on, even part way. Mostly they had to
walk, leading a packhorse along the forest
trails. This four-legged baggage car carried
a couple of axes, wedges and levers; a bag
or two of seed for the first crop of wheat
and corn, a kettle or two (very precious),
a frying pan called "spider" because it had
legs; blankets, and a small ration of food to
fall back on in the days when fish couldn't
be fished nor game shot along the trail.

Often the father of the family went first.
If one of his sons was old enough he would
take him along. Otherwise he would team
up with a brother, a friend, or neighbor,
who also planned to settle in Vermont.
There weren't many people, even in those
sturdy days, who cared to make the rough,
long trip alone through the Indian hunting
territory and the wild woods.

Thus, in September, 1774, when Ann
Story's husband, Amos, arrived at the spot,

in the dense Vermont forest, which was to
become the town of Salisbury, Vermont,
their eldest son, Solomon, thirteen years
old, went with him. Together through
that long, cold, dark Vermont winter,
father and son felled trees, built a strong
log house out of the great tree-trunks,
and even constructed a chimney.

As spring came on, they said, "Well,
we've got our home-cabin done!" Then
they started clearing a field in the forest,
to plant wheat for the family bread next
winter. Their axes rang out—great trees
came down—they were creating a home—a
state. But disaster crashed down on them.
A huge sugar-maple, skilfully felled to drop
in a certain place, was caught by entan-
gling branches as it fell, twisted sidewise,
and roared down to the earth with Amos
Story's body pinned under its gigantic
weight.

He was instantly killed.

Solomon couldn't believe it. Snatching
up his axe, he began chopping in frantic
haste at the great cylinder of the granite-

hard tree, so that he could roll it away from the crushed body. Hardly of high-school age, he swung his axe with all the skill and sureness he had learned in the long winter's daily felling. When, dripping with sweat, yet cold with agonizing suspense, he had at last driven his axe-blade clear through the great tree trunk, he still could not stir it. He knelt down by his father again. This time he saw that he was dead.

Getting to his feet, he laid his hand again to the axe, chopping slowly now, but steadily delivering powerful, well-aimed blows. Once more through the thickness of the great tree, and Solomon could roll away the section which lay across his father.

The lad was now completely alone in the wilderness. The nearest human being was miles away along the threadlike trail through the unbroken woods. He followed the trail to a little clearing where the college town of Middlebury now stands, and brought back a man named Benjamin Smauley, and his two sons. These four pioneers carried Amos Story's body back over the trail. The grave they dug for Amos Story was beside the grave of the Smauleys' daughter who had lost her way in the forest and starved to death before she was found.

Of course the Smauleys offered to take in the fatherless boy, Solomon, now more than a hundred and fifty miles from where his mother with his four little brothers and sisters waited for news from the north. Families so sundered sometimes never succeeded in living together again. Lost boys and girls were gladly taken into pioneer families near where they were stranded. What else could lost children do?

The only way back was over the same Indian trail, through deep woods most of the way—no roads, no bridges, no shelters,

no mail, no wires, no means of communication; the same tough trip Solomon and his father had made so hopefully the year before.

Ann Story might have lived her years out without ever knowing what had happened to her husband or to her oldest son—a life of increasing hopeless mystery.

Solomon knew the terrible odds against the single traveler, but he took those odds. Alone, he started the long walk back to tell his mother the terrible news.

This is part of a treasured Vermont saga, so the records have been carefully kept. We know exactly what he *did;* no records tell what he felt. Nobody ever described that sad day when young Ann Story—she was only thirty-three—saw Solomon, sad-eyed, ragged, dusty, footsore, and alone, come trudging out of the woods, north of the house, the woods she had watched so eagerly, anxiously, and long for the return of her two men.

That is the last pathetic hour of this "footnote of history." The rest of it rings with vitality.

Ann Story had planned the new home in the northwoods with her husband. Instead of killing that plan, her sorrow over his death seemed to her a mighty motive for carrying it out. She sold her house and all her furniture in safe, comfortable Connecticut to buy a packhorse, and set out with her three sons—the other two were Ephraim and Samuel—and her two little girls, Hannah and Susanna, for the wilderness homestead her husband and Solomon had claimed and cleared. She and Solomon each carried a rifle to shoot the game they were to cook over their campfires. They slept in the open, round those fires, each keeping watch in turn. Held back by the short steps of the younger children, drawn forward by their future, they pushed on. About a year from the time

Amos and Solomon had reached the spot, Ann knelt at the hearth to light the first home-fire in the cabin they had built.

Now don't try to imagine this as if it were a movie. It would make an interesting movie. But it is a true story about real people. Try to imagine how it felt from real experiences you have had yourself. If you've ever gone for a hike, even a short one, with a bunch of younger children, you know how something is always happening to them. Remember the bumped heads, the squabbles, the skinned knees, maybe a cracked collarbone? Maybe one got lost and you had to run around and call and call for him. That is the way to think about those five little Storys camping for weeks along that Indian trail. Not a doctor who could set a bone, not a grocery store to buy something for supper, not a house where they could go in out of the rain, no man along to cut wood for their fires, or to pitch the fragment of canvas under which they slept, or to keep off wolves and catamounts.

Yet every one of those young ones stood safe and whole around their mother as she lighted that first fire on their Green Mountain hearth.

It was not long before the Story children were as much at home in these woods as the squirrels and chipmunks and bears. The boys soon handled their axes as competently as city boys now handle marbles. They all worked together to finish the clearing their father had begun. They planted their corn from precious seed they brought from Connecticut (there was no other way to have corn except to grow it). They chopped, split, and piled the firewood for the long winter. Hannah and Susanna helped with cooking and mending and making candles, and picking and drying the wild fruit. They made soap out of grease and wood-ashes to wash the family's clothes. They tried out the great slabs of fat from the bears their mother sometimes shot. Pioneers found bear-fat the best fat in the world for everything, from frying doughnuts to greasing boots.

On a diet of venison, fish, bear-fat, wild berries, cornmeal mush and maple syrup, pumpkins, squashes, and greens, the children grew tall, strong, hardy, and brave. Their mother, so the story runs, likewise grew even taller than she had been before. An old Vermonter thus described her: "A busting great woman who could cut off a two-foot log as quick as any man in the settlement." She had always been good-looking; now she took on a stately handsomeness. I don't think her children would have been human if they hadn't occasionally bragged about their mother.

But she was no narrow "homebody." She had political opinions. She did her own thinking, as well as her house and farm work. She educated her children. They all learned to read out of the Bible she'd brought up from Connecticut.

Ann Story's political thinking was unusually clear and strong. She wanted her children to be free, just as much as she wanted them to have plenty to eat. She felt in every fiber the independence of the pioneer.

Remember, the year Amos and Solomon Story had come up to Vermont was 1774. Did you realize how close that was to the Declaration of Independence? The Revolutionary War was already going on by the time Ann lit her Vermont hearth fire. Ann and most of her neighbors were on the revolutionary side in the big struggle.

But there was another struggle going on as well between the Vermont settlers who had got their land titles from New Hampshire, and people who wanted to move there with claims for the same land— claims which had been issued and sold them by the state of New York. Boundary lines were homemade things in those days, and first New Hampshire and then New York thought that the king had granted them the territory of Vermont. When New York started granting land it was already home for Vermonters who had earlier been given grants by New Hampshire.

Believe me, there was just as much rumpus between New York and New Hampshire as there was in the bigger revolution between England and her American colony.

In the big revolution a few Vermont settlers still held their original allegiance to the king and were Loyalists. But Loyalist or Revolutionist they were pretty solidly all on one side as regarded the claims of New York to their land.

Ann had only scorn for New Yorkers' legal claims as against the flesh-and-blood struggle of the settlers. Thin papers, however legal, seemed no match for thick walls, work, courage, and homemaking. The New Hampshire settlers had honestly paid once for their land. They were not going to let anybody, even a lawyer, take their homes away from them. Ann also felt the justice of the right to self-government of people who had made the beginnings of a nation in a new land. She hated the European system of tenant-farming for rich landowners, which the Dutch had brought into the neighboring Hudson River region. So she was heartily both on the Vermont side against New York, and the American side against the British.

She and the children had only begun carving out their farm from the woods, when news came that the British Army was enlisting Indians in war parties to raid the rebel settlers. Ann's neighbors knew what that meant and most of them fled their tiny farms. They sadly left their tiny clearings, sparsely sprinkled through the wilderness, and moved to the more settled part of Vermont, south of Rutland.

Not Ann. This family without a man stayed on; but not for their land and house alone. Ann wanted to help her side—the guerrilla fighters known as the Green Mountain Boys. In words exactly remembered in Vermont, she said to the local "Committee of Safety," who assigned the dangerous tasks to the revolutionists, "Give me a place among you, and see if I am the first to desert my post." The task they assigned her was to watch out for Loyalist and Indian raiding parties and report them to passing Green Mountain scouts.

Before long the Story children all learned how to be top-class sentinels. In every direction around their house some watchful youngster kept eyes alert and ears cocked, and ran silently as an Indian, hither and yon.

The real Indians came soon!

One day one of the Story children loped softly out of the woods to his mother and whispered to her that the abandoned cabin of a neighbor, about half a mile away, had been pillaged and was being burned by Indians. Theirs would be next!

The river was high with melted snow, had overflowed its banks and flooded low-lying parts of the forest. Working at top speed, Ann and her children loaded their canoe with the most vital household belongings—blankets, the precious iron "kittles" and "spider," the bags of seed soon to be planted, the wooden tub of maple sugar, the birch-bark pails of bear-grease. Then stepping in themselves, they paddled off swiftly on the flood-waters in among the dense trees, which hid them. But, though they could not be seen, they could see everything done by the Indians, who soon came whooping into the Story clearing. The Storys watched them ravage their carefully-kept home, and heard their relish-

ing shouts, as they set it on fire in a dozen places. When the cabin was entirely burned down, the Indians shouldered their booty and were off.

As soon as it was safe, Ann and her children returned to their ruined home. Did they give up and move away? You guess. Ann had one comfort (which was also common sense), to give the children. Maybe the Indians, having found so little to plunder, wouldn't bother to come again. "So," Ann told people afterwards, "we began cutting and laying up small trees, such as the children and I could handle, and it was not long before we had quite a comfortable cabin, made of poles instead of logs—where the former one had stood."

The new house continued to be what the old had been before the Indian raid, a switchboard for the Revolution.

To it came singly, or in small sauntering groups, men who looked like trappers or hunters. They dropped in casually for a chat with the widow Story over a dish of her excellent venison stew. But they left important messages to be passed on orally, to other buckskin-clad musket-carrying men who were to drop in some time later.

Sometimes, while the children kept watch, scattered in a wide circle in the woods all around the clearing, a canoe would come up the creek, loaded with kegs of gunpowder. These would be hastily rolled out and hidden, to be picked up by a party of the Green Rangers with the right password. Often men dropped in just to get what information Ann and her active children had picked up about the British and Indian movements and to tell what they knew. The children were everywhere, and Ann acquired a sort of F.B.I. ability to piece together odd items of information to make a clear whole. Sometimes visitors just came to get Ann Story's slant about what to think of some new move, political or military. For, of course, her judgment grew in value with what she saw and learned, as always happens to people who are active in important enterprises. So it was as patriot as well as homemaker that

Ann Story stayed on in that dangerous post at the front.

Now, for a while, the Storys slept where nobody could find them, in a real hide-out, which Tom Sawyer and Huck Finn would have loved. In the daytime, they stayed at the home place, growing food, keeping house, living as if they lived there, nights and all.

But at night? At night, or at any hint of danger, nobody ever saw a Story. Ann kept her own counsel, and the children were mum as partridges.

We know now where their hideout was. The banks of the Otter Creek, where their home stood, were high above the water. On the far side of the creek, down stream from their cabin, the Storys dug an underground passage deep into the bank and hollowed out a cave.

The mouth of the passage at water level they made just large enough to let a canoe float in with all its passengers lying flat in the bottom. Further in they hollowed out a place to sleep at one side, well above the level of the water. Prisoners digging escape tunnels have trouble hiding the fresh earth, but the Storys had only to drop their diggings into the swift-flowing stream. The roots of the trees acted as a natural arch to hold up the roof of what they built into a sizeable underground room.

Entered as it was from the water, no trodden leaf or broken stick could betray their cave to Indian or enemy. They kept the entrance thickly planted with over-hanging bushes so that nobody could see it from the river which served Indian, Revolutionary, and Loyalist alike, as a canoe highway to the north.

When they had finished this hideout, the Storys kept their canoe moored all day at the back of their cabin. This was natural. All settlers on lakes or rivers did. But after dark, they would file silently down the river, step into the canoe, push out without a sound, glide between the high, wooded banks around a bend in the Otter, and then with one deft, silent paddle stroke, they would swing the light craft through the hole in the bank into their cave. Look as one might, the Storys were gone, all six of them, as if they had evaporated.

One day, not long after the cave was finished, one of the boys came back from a far-ranging expedition, and reported that he had heard somebody crying in the woods. Going softly on his moccasined feet a little nearer, he'd seen through the branches a woman, sobbing.

Everybody knew that when Indians, under British instructions, burned the dwellings of the Revolutionist settlers, they carried off as many captives as they could, and sold them in Canada for servants. The Canadians who bought these captives were often able to sell them back to their American families, making a big profit by getting ransom money for them. Ann Story realized that this woman might have been such a prisoner, for those prisoners unable to keep up with the fast loping pace of the Indians, hurrying to get back over the Canadian line, often had to fall farther and farther behind until they were left to starve.

Yes, she could be one—a prisoner left to starve. But maybe not. She might be a decoy, pretending. She might be carrying out some plot against the Green Mountain Boys and their sympathizers.

Though Ann Story knew there was some danger in going to the rescue, she went. She went carefully. She listened. She waited for a while to make sure. Then, sure the girl was in real trouble, she stepped out before the despairing young creature. She appeared full of strength and friendliness, like a vision. The trouble was real enough. The poor girl had been unable to keep pace with her captors because she was expecting a baby.

You know beforehand what Ann Story would do! She took her home and helped her through the baby's birth, kept and fed and cared for them both, until they could safely leave.

So now there were two mothers, and five big boys and girls, and one baby to ride in that canoe each night and morning. The baby made it dangerous; how could the baby know he mustn't cry at such and such times?

It was just because of that baby that the enemy found the secret hideout. One night, just before dawn, the baby woke up. He let out a lusty yell. He often did, but this time there was somebody there to listen. That somebody just happened to be sneaking along the bank when the baby woke. He was an enemy. Though a Vermonter, he sided with the British, and was eager to help their cause.

His name was Ezekiel Jenny. He knew all about Ann Story. He knew what a big factor she was in the Revolutionary War in this region. He knew, too, that she and her family had never been found after dark by Loyalist or Indian. He knew they must have some mysterious hiding place. And now he knew where it was. This child's cry sounded right under the bank of the river where he stood! The mysterious hideout was right under his feet. This was a catch, indeed. Until dawn he gloatingly watched the spot to see that no one escaped. At dawn the canoe slipped silently out into the river.

"Now!" he thought, "I'll scare that pestiferous woman into telling what she's up to." He hurried along to the Story's house and, pointing his gun right at her breast,

confronted Ann as she stepped ashore. Then he began firing off questions to make her tell all the important secrets.

Years afterward Ann used to tell people about it. "I gave evasive and *dis-satisfactory* answers," she would explain. And though he kept on threatening her, she wouldn't be scared. Jenny was plotting to join the British and Indians in their raids on his fellow townsmen, and he had no time to lose. So, finally, though he gained no information, he gave up, and hurried along on the treacherous business which was very important to him. Now he knew that when they hid, he could send a band of Indians after Ann and her children. They wouldn't spy on the British again.

A whole band of these pro-Britishers, traveling singly in two's and three's, were (this very next night after the baby cried) hastening up to Canada to be enrolled in the British forces. Ezekiel was one of the leading local men. Having failed to pry any information out of Ann Story, he proceeded northward to a secret spot where the British had agreed to meet, little thinking how busy Ann was providing hindrances for his plans.

What she did first was to snatch the flyleaf out of her Bible (the only paper she had), and dash off a hasty note. Then she sent one of her flying, swift-footed boys along a shortcut trail, to the nearest Green Mountain Ranger. In no time Daniel Foote, Samuel Bently, and other Rangers had snatched their muskets from the pegs over the home-hearth and set off in pursuit of Ezekiel Jenny. I always hoped they took along that Story boy.

Silent as any wild inhabitant of the familiar forest, these American settlers, transformed into guerrilla fighters, followed the trail of the would-be English soldiers. When night came, the scattered pro-British band were far enough north to venture to make camp and lie down to sleep around a fire. Without a sound, the Green Mountain Rangers closed in on them; closer and closer they came, and then, on a signal, broke upon them with yells and musket-firing. But not to kill!

We Vermonters brag about the fact that in all the noisy quarreling on our soil for the right to own as free men the Vermont land our great-grandfathers had bought and paid for and cleared and tilled, not one human life was sacrificed in battle. Those Green Mountain Boys acted like the self-controlled, reasonable police force which we hope the armies of the future will be.

They marched their prisoners across country to Fort Ticonderoga (then in American hands) and gave them up to the proper authorities.

What do you think? Can we twentieth-century peoples, whose log cabins of nationalism have been set on fire so often by drunken old War—can we have the sense and courage Ann Story and her children had? Can we build up, out of "such materials as we can handle," such materials as friendliness, equality as neighbors, remembrance of our faults, and generosity about other people's? Can we build, like Ann Story, a homelike world?

The woman who wrote this story

DOROTHY CANFIELD FISHER 1879–

Dorothy Canfield was born in Kansas, where her father was a professor at the state university. When she was ten, her parents sent her to a school in France where she learned to speak French as fluently as English. She did her undergraduate work at Ohio State University and then studied at the Sorbonne in Paris. She received her Ph.D. in French at Columbia and was preparing to be a professor of languages when she was married to Mr. Fisher.

With her husband, Mrs. Fisher moved to one of the Canfield farms in Vermont. Her ancestors had been among the earliest Vermont pioneers, and her family owns land throughout the state. There she has done most of her writing.

When France was attacked during the First World War, the Fishers felt as if their own country were being invaded. They hurried to France to give that country all the help they could. Mr. Fisher joined the

ambulance corps, and Mrs. Fisher set up an organization for the printing of books and magazines for the blind. At the end of the war, Mrs. Fisher was running a convalescent home for sickly children in Southern France.

Today Mrs. Fisher is famous for her stories about New England. Though she has written more than thirty-five books, she is not a "career woman." She considers being a good wife, mother, and grandmother more important than writing.

Let's consider . . .

1. Travel was not easy during pioneer days. List the supplies which most pioneers carried with them. Explain why each of these supplies was an absolute necessity.

2. Amos and his son, Solomon, traveled into the Vermont forests to prepare a cabin-home for the family. Describe the accident that befell Amos.

3. After the accident, Solomon could easily have remained with the Smauleys. Instead, he chose to return to his mother.

Why were the odds against his getting home safely? What did his decision tell you about him as a person?

4. Some people say that the younger generation is getting soft—that you "can't take it" any more. Solomon was an extraordinary boy by any standards. Do you think there are no longer any boys like Solomon? Or do you think a modern boy could do as well in similar circumstances? Do you know of any teenagers who have shown heroism in the face of almost impossible odds?

5. Describe Ann's reaction to the news of her husband's death. What *might* she have done? Why didn't she do it? What advice do you suppose she would offer to other families faced with a similar tragedy?

6. Ann was an unusually courageous woman. Recall the different incidents in her life when she had to face danger. Select the incident which you think required the greatest amount of courage. Describe the situation and explain how Ann met it.

7. What is the usual picture of an "old-fashioned woman"? How did Ann Story differ from that picture? In what ways was she more advanced than some "modern" women you know?

8. You saw members of the Story family working together to help one another. Describe one way in which they cooperated. Why was cooperation necessary if they were to survive? Do you think the members of twentieth-century families work together as a unit? Give several reasons to support your answer.

9. Ann Story isn't the only heroic woman America has produced. Name some others.

10. The last paragraph of the story deserves real thought. Dorothy Canfield Fisher wrote, "Can we build, like Ann Story, a homelike world?" What steps are being taken in this direction? What can you do to help?

The writer's craft . . .

Dorothy Canfield Fisher wrote "Ann Story, Yankee Pioneer" in an easy, conversational style. She not only made her own remarks about the story but also asked what you thought about it. When she paused to comment about the story, didn't you feel as though she were sitting in your living room talking to you about this remarkable woman?

1. Find the places where Mrs. Fisher made personal comments in the story.

2. Usually writers do not inject personal comments into their stories. What did Mrs. Fisher's warm, friendly remarks add to the story?

3. Do you like to have a writer interrupt the action of his story to make comments? Why, or why not?

Knowing words . . .

A. In English many words may be combined with others to form interesting new compound words. For example, Mrs. Fisher used the word *buckskin,* which means "the skin of a buck." Find other compound words in the story and explain their meaning.

B. Sometimes two words are combined into one hyphenated word. Did you notice Mrs. Fisher's use of such words as *home-cabin, granite-hard,* and *well-aimed?*

1. Find other hyphenated words in the story.

2. Make up several of your own.

C. Explain why compound and hyphenated words are an economical use of language.

Song of the Settlers

JESSAMYN WEST

Freedom is a hard-bought thing—
A gift no man can give,
For some, a way of dying,
For most, a way to live.

Freedom is a hard-bought thing—
A rifle in the hand,
The horses hitched at sunup,
A harvest in the land.

Freedom is a hard-bought thing—
A massacre, a bloody rout,
The candles lit at nightfall,
And the night shut out.

Freedom is a hard-bought thing—
An arrow in the back,
The wind in the long corn rows,
And the hay in the rack.

Freedom is a way of living,
A song, a mighty cry.
Freedom is the bread we eat;
Let it be the way we die!

The woman who wrote this poem

JESSAMYN WEST

When the West family moved from Indiana to California, they felt as if they had left their native land behind. Jessamyn was a little girl, but she listened to her parents reminiscing about their life in the Middle West and the things their Quaker ancestors had done. From these conversations Jessamyn formed vivid pictures of early pioneer life and later used these pictures in her stories.

For a long time Miss West devoted herself to reading because she was convinced that she could not be a writer. When she began to write, however, she had little difficulty. Her first story was published soon after it was written, and she has been contributing stories to magazines like *The New Yorker* and *The Atlantic* ever since.

Occasionally Miss West teaches at writers' conferences. Her students are devoted to her because she brings the same enthusiasm to her teaching that she brings to her writing. *Cress Delahanty,* her fourth novel, was recently a Book-of-the-Month Club selection.

The poet's art . . .

1. In her "Song of the Settlers" Jessamyn West mentioned three essential things in the life of the pioneer:

> "A rifle in the hand,
>   The horses hitched at sunup,
>   A harvest in the land."

Describe the part that each of these things played in the settlers' life. What other things were equally important to the settlers?

2. Throughout the poem, Jessamyn West spoke of freedom in terms of a harvest, rows of corn, or bread. Why would having enough to eat provide a very important freedom for the settlers?

3. Jessamyn West repeated the line, "Freedom is a hard-bought thing." List the different obstacles to freedom which she mentioned in her poem. Are there still obstacles to freedom here in America? If so, what are they?

4. Jessamyn West wrote, "Freedom is a way of living." What freedoms do *you* enjoy in your daily living? How are these freedoms the same as the ones mentioned in the poem? How are they different?

What Is an American?

JEAN DE CRÈVECOEUR

Every boat returning to Europe from the American colonies brought exciting tales of a new kind of life. Jean de Crèvecoeur, a Frenchman, came to America to find out for himself how true these seemingly impossible stories were. Some of his discoveries are recorded in this stirring essay.

I wish I could be acquainted with the feelings and thoughts which must present themselves to the mind of an Englishman, when he first lands on this continent. He must greatly rejoice that he lived at a time to see this fair country discovered and settled, when he says to himself, this is the work of my countrymen, who took refuge here. They brought along with them their national genius, to which they principally owe what liberty they enjoy. Here he sees the industry of his native country displayed in a new manner. Here he beholds fair cities, substantial villages, extensive fields, and immense country filled with decent houses, good roads, orchards, meadows, and bridges, where an hundred years ago all was wild, woody, and un-cultivated! What a train of pleasing ideas this fair spectacle must suggest; it is a prospect which must inspire a good citizen with the most heartfelt pleasure.

The difficulty consists in the manner of viewing so extensive a scene. He is arrived on a new continent; a modern society offers itself to his contemplation, different from what he had hitherto seen. It is not composed, as in Europe, of great lords who possess everything, and of a herd of people who have nothing. The rich and the poor are not so far removed from each other as they are in Europe. Some few towns excepted, we are all tillers of the earth, from Nova Scotia to West Florida. We are a people of cultivators, scattered over an immense territory, communicating with each other by means of good roads and navigable rivers, united by the silken bands of mild government, all respecting the laws, without dreading their power, because they are equitable. We are all animated with the spirit of industry which is unrestrained, because each person works for himself.

If he travels through our rural districts he views not the hostile castle, and the haughty mansion, contrasted with the clay-built hut and miserable cabin, where cattle and men help to keep each other warm. The meanest [1] of our log-houses is a dry and comfortable habitation. Lawyer or merchant are the fairest titles our towns afford. On a Sunday, he sees a congregation of respectable farmers and their wives, all clad in neat homespun, well mounted, or riding in their own humble waggons. He sees a parson as simple as his flock, a farmer who does not riot on the labour of others. We have no princes, for whom we toil, starve, and bleed: we are the most perfect society now existing in the world. Here man is free as he ought to be. Many ages will not see the shores of our great lakes replenished with inland nations, nor the unknown bounds of North America entirely peopled. Who can tell how far it extends? Who can tell the millions of men whom it will feed and contain? for no European foot has as yet travelled half the extent of this mighty continent!

The next wish of this traveler will be to know whence came all these people? They are a mixture of English, Scotch, Irish, French, Dutch, Germans, and Swedes. From this breed, that race now called Americans have arisen.

In this great American asylum,[2] the poor

---

[1] *meanest,* poorest
[2] *asylum,* place of safety; retreat

of Europe have by some means met together; to what purpose should they ask
one another what countrymen they are?
Alas, two thirds of them had no country.
Can a wretch who wanders about, who
works and starves, whose life is a continual
scene of sore affliction; can that man call
England or any other kingdom his country?
A country that had no bread for him,
whose fields procured him no harvest, who
met with nothing but the frowns of the
rich, the severity of the laws, with jails
and punishments; who owned not a single
foot of this planet? No! urged by a variety
of motives, here they came. Everything
has tended to regenerate them; new laws,
a new mode of living, a new social system;
here they are become men: in Europe they
were as so many useless plants, wanting
vegetative mould, and refreshing showers;
they withered, and were mowed down by
want, hunger, and war; but now by the
power of transplantation, like all other
plants they have taken root and flourished!
Formerly they were not numbered in any
civil lists of their country, except in those
of the poor; here they rank as citizens.

What attachment can a poor European
emigrant have for a country where he had
nothing? The knowledge of the language,
the love of a few kindred as poor as himself, were the only cords that tied him:
his country is now that which gives him
land, bread, protection, and consequence.
Where bread is, there is a fatherland.

What then is the American, this new
man? He is neither an European, or the
descendant of an European, hence that
strange mixture of blood, which you will
find in no other country. I could point out
to you a family whose grandfather was an
Englishman, whose wife was Dutch, whose
son married a French woman, and whose
present four sons have now four wives of
different nations. *He* is an American, who,
leaving behind him all his ancient prejudices and manners, receives new ones from
the new mode of life he has embraced, the
new government he obeys, and the new
rank he holds.

Here individuals of all nations are
melted into a new race of men, whose
labours and posterity will one day cause
great changes in the world. The Americans were once scattered all over Europe;
here they are incorporated into one of the
finest systems of population which has ever
appeared. The American ought therefore
to love this country much better than that
wherein either he or his forefathers were
born. Here the rewards of his industry
follow with equal steps the progress of his
labour; his labour is founded on the basis
of nature, *self-interest*; can it want a stronger allurement? Wives and children, who
before in vain demanded of him a morsel
of bread, now, fat and frolicsome, gladly
help their father to clear those fields
whence crops are to arise to feed and to
clothe them all; without any part being
claimed, either by a despotic prince, a rich
abbot, or a mighty lord.

Here religion demands but little of him;
a small voluntary salary to the minister,
and gratitude to God; can he refuse these?

The American is a new man, who acts
upon new principles; he must therefore
entertain new ideas, and form new opinions. From involuntary idleness, depend-
ence, and useless labour, he has passed to
toils of a very different nature, rewarded
by ample subsistence.

—This is an American.

The man who wrote this essay

JEAN DE CRÈVECOEUR 1731–1813

De Crèvecoeur was born and educated in Normandy, France. There are no exact records of his journey to America, but he is supposed to have first landed in Canada. There he served under Montcalm during the French and Indian War. Before he settled in New York, he explored and surveyed what is now known as the Midwest.

As he worked on his small farm, he wrote a series of descriptive letters about life in the colonies. These letters were collected and published in England as a book entitled *Letters from an American Farmer*.

De Crèvecoeur was one of the first colonists to see America as the giant melting pot of the world. Here, differences in nationality disappeared as people were blended into a new and free nation.

Let's consider . . .

1. Jean de Crèvecoeur began this essay by wishing he could know the feelings and thoughts of an Englishman just arrived in America. What did De Crèvecoeur imagine those feelings would be?

2. What would an Englishman see that would arouse such feelings?

3. De Crèvecoeur compared life in America with life abroad. What differences did he find? Which of these seem most important to you? Explain why.

4. In America, De Crèvecoeur found that everyone was industrious. What reasons did he give for this spirit of hard work? Can you think of other reasons?

5. Why did the colonists respect the laws without dreading their power?

6. According to De Crèvecoeur, the motto of all emigrants is, "Where bread is, there is a fatherland." What does this motto mean? Explain why you agree or disagree with it.

7. Jean de Crèvecoeur believed that, in the future, Americans would bring about great changes in the world. What changes have Americans made in the world?

8. Almost two hundred years ago De Crèvecoeur wrote that Americans must "welcome new ideas and form new opinions." Would that statement apply to Americans today? Explain. What new ideas have Americans welcomed in recent years? Have these ideas met with much opposition? From whom? Why?

9. This essay, "What Is an American?" was taken from De Crèvecoeur's *Letters from an American Farmer,* printed in England in 1782. In your own words, sum up how he answered the question he had raised. Now write a composition giving your answer to the same question.

Knowing words . . .

Below are several sentences taken from the selection. Each of the sentences has one or two words written in italics. After you are sure of the meaning of the italicized word, use it in a sentence of your own.

1. Here he beholds fair cities, *substantial* villages, *extensive* fields, an *immense* country filled with decent houses, good roads, orchards, meadows, and bridges.

2. If he travels through our *rural* districts he views not the *hostile* castle, and the haughty mansion.

3. The meanest of our log-houses is a dry and comfortable *habitation*.

4. Here individuals of all nations are melted into a new race of men, whose labours and *posterity* will one day cause great changes in the world.

5. Everything has tended to *regenerate* them.

6. Can a wretch who wanders about, who works and starves, whose life is a continual scene of sore *affliction;* can that man call England or any other kingdom his country?

7. What a train of pleasing ideas this fair *spectacle* must suggest.

8. The difficulty consists in the manner of viewing so *extensive* a scene.

9. His labour is founded on the basis of nature, self-interest; can it want a stronger *allurement?*

The Builders

All are architects of Fate,
    Working in these walls of Time;
Some with massive deeds and great,
    Some with ornaments of rhyme.

Nothing useless is, or low;
    Each thing in its place is best;
And what seems but idle show
    Strengthens and supports the rest.

For the structure that we raise,
    Time is with materials filled;
Our todays and yesterdays
    Are the blocks with which we build.

Truly shape and fashion these;
    Leave no yawning gaps between;
Think not, because no man sees,
    Such things will remain unseen.

In the elder days of Art,
    Builders wrought with greatest care

Each minute and unseen part;
    For the gods see everywhere.

Let us do our work as well,
    Both the unseen and the seen;
Make the house, where gods may dwell,
    Beautiful, entire, and clean.

Else our lives are incomplete,
    Standing in these walls of Time,
Broken stairways, where the feet
    Stumble as they seek to climb.

Build today, then, strong and sure,
    With a firm and ample base;
And ascending and secure
    Shall tomorrow find its place.

Thus alone can we attain
    To those turrets, where the eye
Sees the world as one vast plain,
    And one boundless reach of sky.
        Henry Wadsworth Longfellow

We Are All One People

HIAMOVI

Will Rogers was a beloved American humorist back in the 1930's. Although the nation still remembers him with admiration and affection, not everyone knows that he had Cherokee Indian blood in his veins, blood of which he was justly proud. Tired of hearing people boast of their ancestors' part in the building of America, Will once said, "My ancestors didn't come over on the *Mayflower,* but we was there to meet the boat!" Bear this point in mind as you read what an Indian chief has to say about his country and yours.

To the Great Chief at Washington, and to the Great Chiefs of Peoples across the Great Water:

Long ago the Great Mystery caused this land to be, and made the Indians to live in this land. Well had the Indian fulfilled the intent of the Great Mystery for him. . . .

Once, only Indians lived in this land. Then came strangers from across the Great Water. No land had they; we gave them of our land. No food had they; we gave them of our corn. The strangers are become many and they fill all the country. They dig gold—from my mountains; they build houses—of the trees of my forests; they rear cities—of my stones and rocks; they make fine garments—from the hides and wool of animals that eat my grass. None of the things that make their riches did they bring with them from beyond the Great Water; all comes from my land, the land the Great Mystery gave unto the Indian.

And when I think upon this I know that it is right, even thus. In the heart of the

Great Mystery it was meant that stranger-visitors—my friends across the Great Water

393

—should come to my land; that I should bid them welcome; that all men should sit down with me and eat together of my corn. It was meant by the Great Mystery that the Indian should give to all peoples.

But the white man never has known the Indian. It is thus: there are two roads, the white man's road, and the Indian's road. Neither traveller knows the road of the other. Thus ever it has been, from the long ago, even unto today. . . .

I want all white men to read and learn how the Indians lived and thought in the olden time, and may it bring holy-good upon the younger Indians to know of their fathers. A little while, and the old Indians will no longer be, and the young will be even as white men. When I think, I know that it is the mind of the Great Mystery that white men and Indians who fought together should now be one people.

There are birds of many colors—red, blue, green, yellow—yet it is all one bird. There are horses of many colors—brown, black, yellow, white—yet it is all one horse. So cattle, so all living things—animals, flowers, trees. So men: in this land where once were only Indians are now men of every color—white, black, yellow, red—yet all one people. That this should come to pass was in the heart of the Great Mystery. It is right thus. And everywhere there shall be peace.

(signed)

HIGH CHIEF

Let's consider . . .

1. Hiamovi described the generous way in which the Indians had treated the strangers who came to their land. List the riches which the strangers received from the Indians.

2. Why did Hiamovi believe that the Indians were wise in sharing their land and resources?

3. According to Hiamovi, what will bring peace to men?

4. Hiamovi said that the white man had never known the Indian. What did he want the white man to learn about the Indians? What additional suggestions could you offer?

The writer's craft . . .

Hiamovi wrote that although birds are of many different colors, they are all birds. He made the same observation about horses. He then carried his comparison to men. "So men: in this land where once were only Indians are now men of every color—white, black, yellow, red—yet all one people." Hiamovi was using an analogy to illustrate the idea that even though men are of different races they are still all one people.

An **analogy** is an illustration which shows a likeness between two or more things which are basically different but have certain features in common. Writers often use analogies to explain unfamiliar or difficult ideas. By showing how a new idea is similar to one the reader already knows and understands, the writer can present this new idea easily and clearly.

Select a topic which you are studying in English or in one of your other classes. Imagine that you are explaining this topic to someone who knows nothing about it. Write a short paragraph using an analogy that will help him understand your explanation.

Indian

STEPHEN VINCENT BENÉT

I don't know who this Indian is,
A bow within his hand,
But he is hiding by a tree
And watching white men land.

They may be gods—they may be friends—
They certainly look rum.
He wonders who on earth they are
And why on earth they've come.

He knows his streams are full of fish,
His forests full of deer,
And his tribe is the mighty tribe
That all the others fear.

—And, when the French or English land,
The Spanish or the Dutch,
They'll tell him they're the mighty tribe
And no one else is much.

They'll kill his deer and net his fish
And clear away his wood,
And frequently remark to him
They do it for his good.

Then he will scalp and he will shoot
And he will burn and slay
And break the treaties he has made
—And, children, so will they.

We won't go into all of that
For it's too long a story,
And some is brave and some is sad
And nearly all is gory.

But, just remember this about
Our ancestors so dear:
They didn't find an empty land.
The Indians were *here*.

The man who wrote this poem

STEPHEN VINCENT BENÉT   1898–1943

The Benét family produced three famous writers in a single generation. There were Stephen Vincent and his sister and brother, Laura and William Rose Benét. Because their father was an American army officer, the children were brought up on various army posts from California to New York. Their father loved poetry, and in the evenings he would read aloud to his children.

Stephen Benét published his first book of poems when he was seventeen, and critics were amazed at the skill of such a young poet. By the time he finished college at Yale, he had written three books. Then he went to Paris to write and study. There he met his wife, Rosemary Carr, who was also a writer. To support himself and his family, he wrote novels and short stories. His best stories, like "Johnny Pye and the Fool Killer" and "The Devil and Daniel Webster," were based on material drawn from American history and folklore. Stephen Benét was an ardent patriot, and his love for democracy and America colored all his stories and poems.

From the time he was a small boy— reading American history until his eyes ached—Stephen Benét wanted to write a long poem on America. Finally a scholarship enabled him to write his most famous work, *John Brown's Body*. This long poem has frequently been called the "American epic," and it has established Stephen Benét as an important American poet.

The poet's art . . .

1. When the white men landed in America, they found fish in the streams and deer in the forests. Why did they take the fish and the deer and "clear away" the forests?

2. What do you think of the white men's explanation of their actions?

3. Why did both the Indians and the white men begin to "burn and slay"?

4. What would you say was Benét's attitude toward the Indians? What was his attitude toward the white men?

5. What is the condition of the American Indian today? How does he earn a living? What are his educational opportunities? How has his way of living changed?

6. Do you think the Indians benefited from the settling of America by Europeans? Explain your answer.

The Word-passer

JEROME BAHR

People sometimes forget that American Indians have a long history and rich tradition. For Volney, the story of his people belonged not only to the past but also to the future.

Until that Saturday after graduation, when he was to leave for good, Volney would never tell me why he had come to our town. Volney did not belong to our town; he had neither relatives nor family friends in Wisconsin. But every September, during his high-school years, he would arrive on the train from some place in Oklahoma and go to our public school. Then in the middle of June he would depart.

Among us boys Volney was a great mystery. The only definite thing we knew about him was that he was a descendant of the famous Indian chief, Black Hawk. And we learned about this only through an accident, when he took the double dive off the top of the river bridge.

It was the second year of Volney's stay in our town. He was a sophomore then— brown and tough as buckskin. We were all down at the river one hot September evening, swimming under the bridge. Pud Thompson, an older boy, dared Volney to take the dive. The bridge was high as a house top above the water, but Volney climbed to its most dangerous point and executed his double dive with perfection,

slipping into the water without the slightest semblance of a belly flop.

Then Pud Thompson had to follow suit. But when Pud went off, he hit a telephone wire and landed like a ton of bricks on the planks below. Three of his ribs were broken and his head was cut open. He was out of school for the rest of the term.

It was through Pud's misfortune that we learned about Volney's famous ancestor. While Pud's injuries were being attended to in the doctor's office, Jake O'Neil, the town busybody, said nobody but an Indian could dive successfully off that bridge. Then one of the schoolteachers came out and said he had known all the time that Volney was a descendant of old Chief Black Hawk.

When I asked Volney about it the next day, he wrinkled up his nose and admitted it. But that was all he would tell me. Not until that last Saturday after graduation, when he was returning to Oklahoma for good, did he tell me the whole story.

It was a hot, clear day—that last Saturday. We had arranged the night before to meet just after sunup at the bridge, and

397

when I saw Volney coming toward me there was a long faded feather sticking from his cap and he was carrying a strange-looking cane. Slowly he approached me, greeting me with scarcely a word.

Then I caught a good look at the cane. It was very old and carved with many figures. Volney saw me staring at it, but he offered no explanation.

"What sort of cane is that?" I asked at last.

"It's for a word-passer."

"What's a word-passer?"

"An Indian chosen because of his good memory to learn by heart the legends, history, traditions of the tribe and pass them down."

That was all Volney would say. When I asked permission to examine the cane, he ignored my question and told me to walk single file, which is Indian fashion. It was still early and there was no one on the street to see us. At the brewery he turned away from the town, and I followed him up the narrow road past an abandoned farmhouse. Then I knew we were on our way to Barn's Bluff.

"It's going to be a long climb," I said.

"Yes," replied Volney, as though he had not heard me.

Barn's Bluff is an old Indian landmark, rising fiercely above the low range of hills that skirts the town's western horizon. It cuts Main Street dead, and its aged sand face looms over the West Side like a huge barn. A clump of small trees grows out from its high overhanging peak, and below, boring into its base, are storage rooms for the brewery's beer vats.

By the time Volney and I reached the top of this bluff, the town had already come to life. Beneath us we could see people moving about in the lower basin, and in the older section of the village an automobile was going swiftly across the tableland. The day was clear, and in the smooth contour of the distant hills we saw the green valleys and the indented nooks where the farmers lived.

For a long time we lay there, on our bellies between the small trees. The rounded peak extended far out and the roof of the brewery beneath us was barely visible.

"It was different in the old days," said Volney, almost to himself. "The country was all brush and wild grass then, and the Winnebagoes used to burn it over every year so that they could hunt better. . . ."

With his cane Volney pointed scornfully down to the valley. "But those fellows down there don't know that. They don't know a thing about their past." Suddenly he turned to me, adding, "Did you know Black Hawk was captured right here in this town?"

His remark almost took my breath away. In school we had often listened to accounts of the Battle of Bad Axe, when Black Hawk made his last stand against the white people moving west. But no one had ever told us Black Hawk was captured in our own town. I lay there in silence, wondering how Volney happened to know so much.

Volney had bitten off a blade of grass and lay propped on his elbow, staring down into the awakening valley. The stores were opening, and all along the roads we could see the farmers driving their teams to market.

"Black Hawk was captured on the very spot where the town's livery barn now stands," Volney went on. "And Barn's Bluff, right where we're lying this second, was responsible for his capture. I have the true story because I am a descendant of Black Hawk. He was the brother of my great-great-grandmother, who married a white man. If there had not been a Barn's

Bluff, old Chief Black Hawk would never have been caught."

Volney lapsed into silence, biting again at his blade of grass. He seemed hesitant to go on, as though he didn't quite trust me. But at last he turned over on his side, and, facing me directly, began his story.

"The last time Black Hawk visited his sister, my great-great-grandmother, was in 1832. That was when he was running away with his tribe from General Dodge. Shortly afterward he moved his tribe to the mouth of the Bad Axe River, where his last big fight took place.

"Everyone knows how General Atkinson's soldiers slaughtered Black Hawk's tribe. They hated him because he was the only chief who had courage enough to keep on fighting against the whites who were taking land from the Indians. But Black Hawk escaped from the Battle of Bad Axe. He escaped with two of his braves. And that's how he happened to come to this part of the country. He knew if he stayed along the Mississippi he would be caught. The Winnebagoes were after him, too. So when he saw this little river pouring into the Mississippi, he decided to follow it inland and hide out until he recovered his strength.

"In those days this river was called Flooding River, because it always overflowed its banks in the spring. The whole country was covered with tangled brush, and if Black Hawk had kept moving he would have been all right. But Black Hawk and his two braves were hungry. The only meat they had eaten was the flesh of a couple of half-starved horses. And so, when they reached this part of the valley, they decided to set up camp and catch some game. They moved away from Flooding River and camped right where the livery barn now stands. . . ."

Volney paused, staring down into the valley. His face had grown pale and he seemed to be reliving the experience of those hunted men.

"What happened then?" I asked.

"See how the river curls through the valley," said Volney, rising to his feet. "See the many bends in it. You can't see two hundred yards ahead. Well, Black Hawk was being followed by four Winnebago braves, and he didn't know it. He had no idea that enemies were so close behind him. They had picked up his trail when he left the Mississippi and followed him all the way here. They followed him by his footprints."

"Did they swoop down on him, then?" I asked, trying to help Volney with his story.

"No," said Volney. "That's the strange part of it. The Winnebagoes lost the trail just before they reached here. It was terribly wild country, and they were going to give up the chase. They were going to turn back and go home. But one of the Winnebagoes was more determined than the others. He must have hated Black Hawk. When he saw Barn's Bluff, he said, 'Let's go up there and have a last look. Maybe we can see him from up there.'

"The other braves were lazy and didn't like the idea of climbing way up to this bluff. They had to go all the way around the hill, as we did just now. It was even worse in those days, for there was no pasture land to make the climb easier. But the Winnebagoes finally decided to climb the bluff and have a last look. They came up here, right to the very spot where we're now standing. They could see all over the valley just as we can now. They could see for miles—the river, the hills, the tableland, everything."

"And they saw him from up here?"

"Yes," said Volney. "They saw a thin smoke rising from Black Hawk's campfire. It was all they needed to go on, for they

knew there were no other people around here. They were sure it was Black Hawk. At last they had the great warrior trapped! At last they were about to get their hands on him!"

Volney paused to control himself. He was quivering with excitement, in spite of the calm way he was telling the story. "They didn't dare to fight him fairly," Volney said finally. "They knew his braves would have licked them. So they decided to wait until Black Hawk's camp went to sleep. In the dead of the night the Winnebagoes split up into two pairs and crept up on Black Hawk's camp from both sides. They didn't make a sound as they swooped down on the sleeping camp. They captured Black Hawk without a struggle.

"And that was the end of Black Hawk's freedom. He was turned over to the white men and later taken to the Jefferson Barracks in Missouri. He died in 1838, somewhere along the Des Moines River."

"Then it was this bluff, after all, which was responsible for his capture?"

"Yes, this bluff where we're standing right now. If it hadn't been for this bluff, Black Hawk would never have been caught. He was too great a warrior to be taken in a fair fight. I'll never forget this spot as long as I live. I have come up here many times."

"What happened to the two braves who were with Black Hawk?"

Abruptly Volney turned to me, as though I had hit upon the most important question of all.

"That is what I've never been able to find out," he said. "That's why I've kept coming back to your town for four years. I thought maybe one of the braves might have got away. I thought maybe one of his descendants might still be living here."

"And did you find any?"

"No," said Volney. "I know now there are none of my people living in this town."

Volney had begun to gather up his things. He straightened the feather in his cap and picked up his cane. For a long time he stood there, staring at the cane. In the mild morning sun the carved figures looked very strange and beautiful.

"I'm the last word-passer!" he suddenly cried out. "On this cane is carved the whole history of our family's leadership of the Sauk tribe. It was made by Black Hawk in the barracks in Missouri and given to my great-grandfather when he was a boy. Black Hawk spent two days making him memorize it. Since then we have all been word-passers. The cane has been handed down and the history memorized by all the sons in our family. But now my mother and father are dead, and my grandfather is eighty-two. In a few years I'll be the only descendant of Black Hawk left."

"If you should die," I said, "the secrets of your tribe would die with you, wouldn't they?"

"Yes," said Volney. "If I do not live long enough to have children of my own, I shall be the last word-passer. Then there will be no one to inherit the cane. . . ."

Volney's voice had died off sadly and he turned to go down the hill. I followed him silently, single file in Indian fashion. He was carrying his cane under his arm, clutching it as if it were the most important treasure in the world.

"Do you think a white boy could be trained to be a word-passer?" I offered hesitantly.

But Volney was going swiftly down the hill and seemed not to hear me. Perhaps he was too proud to hear me. When we reached the street he was the same as before—silent and impassive. I never saw him again.

The man who wrote this story

JEROME BAHR 1909–

When he was a boy, Jerome Bahr often heard his neighbors repeat a popular legend about how Black Hawk had been captured just outside their town of Arcadia, Wisconsin. Many years later, Mr. Bahr recalled these conversations, and "The Word-passer" was created.

He began his writing career when he was sixteen and later reported for papers in Minneapolis and St. Paul. In the 1930's, he moved to New York City to devote himself to writing short stories which soon began to appear in magazines like *The New Yorker, Mademoiselle,* and *American Mercury.* Two collections of his stories were published in book form.

At the outbreak of World War II, Mr. Bahr joined the Air Force as a specialist in intelligence and public information. He was a special agent in counterintelligence until the end of the recent Korean conflict. For a short time, he was even a private detective. Presently he is a civilian worker for the Army. He has the novel occupation of writing speeches for various generals.

Let's consider . . .

1. Although Volney lived in Oklahoma, he traveled all the way to Wisconsin to attend school. What did he hope to find?

2. What did "Barn's Bluff" mean to the people of the town? What did it mean to Volney?

3. Volney was concerned because he would soon be the only living descendant of his tribe. Why did this matter so much to him?

4. America has been built and developed by different groups of settlers and immigrants. Why is it important for all these groups to remember their heritage and keep

it alive? How can people of different nations become part of America and still preserve some of their own traditions?

5. What does America gain when these traditions are preserved?

6. Indian civilization has left its mark on America. What traces of the Indians are still in existence today?

7. Volney's friend was thrilled when he learned that Black Hawk had been captured right in the boy's own town. Why had he never learned this before?

8. The names of states, cities, and rivers are constant reminders that America once belonged to the Indian peoples. List all such names which you know—especially those in your own state.

9. Who are the word-passers today?

Knowing words . . .

At the beginning of the story Jerome Bahr wrote that among the boys Volney was a great mystery. However, as you read the story you began to get some insight into Volney's character.

A. Each of the sentences below contains a description of the boy's appearance or actions. When you are sure of the meaning of each italicized word, use it in a sentence of your own.

1. When I asked permission to examine the cane, he *ignored* my question and told me to walk single file, which is Indian fashion.

2. With his cane Volney pointed *scornfully* down to the valley.

3. Volney *lapsed* into silence, biting again at his blade of grass.

4. He seemed *hesitant* to go on, as though he didn't quite trust me.

5. When we reached the street he was the same as before—silent and *impassive*.

6. Volney paused to control himself. He was *quivering* with excitement.

B. Explain how the italicized words helped you to understand Volney.

Song of the Sky Loom

O our Mother the Earth. O our Father the Sky,
Your children are we, and with tired backs
We bring you the gifts you love.
Then weave for us a garment of brightness;
May the warp be the white light of morning,
May the weft be the red light of evening,
May the fringes be the falling rain,
May the border be the standing rainbow.
Thus weave for us a garment of brightness,
That we may walk fittingly where birds sing,
That we may walk fittingly where grass is green,
O our Mother the Earth, O our Father the Sky.
                              Tewa Indian Song

My Song Yankee Doodle

CARL GLICK

Jin-Wai couldn't explain to his father how much he dreaded the Pageant of All Nations. After all, his father didn't go to the American school. He wasn't laughed at and ridiculed.

"What is this, my son?" asked Fong, viewing with distrust the sealed envelope from the American school which Jin-Wai handed him.

"An invitation to a party," replied Jin-Wai unhappily.

Fong beamed. "Better—much better than a note from your teacher suggesting you go immediately to the doctor and have your tonsils removed, which is painful to you and expensive to me."

"I wrote the invitation myself," said Jin-Wai. "Teacher told me what to say."

"How nice," said Fong, breaking the seal of the letter. He handed it to Mrs. Fong. She couldn't read English, but she looked it over carefully, and echoing the sentiments of her husband, said, "How nice!"

"I shall translate it for you," said Fong. "It says that our honorable presence—yours and mine—is requested at a Pageant of All Nations to be held at two o'clock next Wednesday at the American school three blocks away where my unworthy son sits all day in classes trying to learn the American language, so when he becomes a man

he can do much big business with the Americans in their American way."

The letter didn't say exactly that, but Jin-Wai knew his father enjoyed his little joke. Mrs. Fong nodded her head happily. It was the first invitation to attend a party she had received since the Fong family had moved last summer from Chinatown to this "faraway foreign city called the Bronx." She had no intention of attending the party as she never left the house, thus displaying the proper Chinese modesty in a woman. But she had been invited. That was a social triumph. To her there was more pleasure in receiving an invitation than in attending.

"Party—party—party!" cried Hing, the four-year-old baby brother, his little face beaming with delight. But then he was very young, and had not yet learned to control his emotions. The invitation, however, neither pleased nor delighted Jin-Wai. The very thought of the party terrified him.

"Tell me more about it," suggested Fong. This was what Jin-Wai had been expecting and dreading. But his father had instructed him in the ways of truthfulness as explained by the philosophers, and he knew by heart "The Five Principles of Filial Duty." A disobedient son is a disgrace to a Chinese father. It makes him lose "face."

So with eyes downcast and hands folded in his lap, Jin-Wai spoke. "The idea is my teacher's," he said. That completely absolved him from any blame in thinking up such a thoroughly stupid and embarrassing thing. "Wednesday is a day of celebration for my teacher."

"A feast?" asked his mother.

"No, honorable mother. A celebration, but we don't eat."

"The Americans at their celebrations make very long speeches and eat very little," explained Fong. "Why this celebration?"

"Because my teacher says all winter long she's been having us sing songs and do dances, and now she celebrates that we've learned the songs and do the dances. So she says we invite our honorable parents to celebrate with her. She says she is proud of us, and we make our honorable parents proud, too. She says the school does this every year and now the time has come again."

"How nice," murmured Fong.

"She says there is more to it than even that also. She says this is a great big free country but it wasn't once, and now it is. And she says it's a free country because so many different people come here with many different ideas. Many foreigners from many foreign lands, but we all belong to one country now and are all alike, and so we put on costumes of our native country and sing American songs and show we are all one big happy family even though we come from different countries, and it's teacher's idea, but I think it's silly."

Fong scratched his chin and said nothing.

"Teacher says that I—" Jin-Wai paused. How he hated to tell this next. "Teacher says each child should come dressed in costume of his own country, but I don't think it's a good idea."

Fong frowned. "A man should never be ashamed of the proper dress of his own country."

Jin-Wai knew that perfectly. Yet how could he explain how he felt to his father? His father didn't have to go day after day to the American school. He wasn't laughed at and called names. It had been difficult from the very first day. He was the only Chinese boy in the classroom, and he wanted so much to make friends. He wanted to be like the American boys, play the games they did, and understand all the beautiful swear words they used so humorously.

So after school he stepped over to a group of boys, and said, "Howdy?"

The boys turned and looked him over critically. "Hi, Chink," said one.

"Likee flied licee?" said another.

Then, "Chink! Chink! Chink!" they all began to yell. Jin-Wai, without another word, turned and fled. It wasn't until he reached the corner, out of hearing distance from the taunts, that he stopped and wiped the tears of shame from his eyes.

After that he made no more attempts to be friendly, but kept to himself. And even though the boys still called him "Chink," he had learned to control his tears and keep his face perfectly expressionless, lest they see how much they were hurting him.

And now his father thought it would be nice to wear a Chinese costume at the "celebration." How could he? The boys would laugh at him more than ever, and yell a lot more, too.

Then to his dismay his father said, "I

think it very good if you took your younger brother, Jin-Hing, with you to the party. He has never been, and it will be a new experience for him."

"Party-party-party," cried Hing.

"He is *only* four years old."

"One is never too old to learn," responded Fong. "He will not disgrace you. When one is the father of two sons, one looks with humble but becoming pride upon their appearance in public correctly dressed in the costume of their native country."

Jin-Wai went to bed that night sad at heart.

Had Jin-Wai been an American boy he would have argued with his father, pleaded, made threats, stormed, and done everything possible to keep from being "dressed up." But being Chinese and trained in obedience, had his father told him to cut off his hand—he would probably have hesitated a moment, and then obeyed. Better to lose a hand than to cause your honorable parent to lose face.

His father had spoken, and also Hing was keenly anticipating the party. He would not disappoint either one of them. It was the first burden of manliness placed upon him. And while he tossed all night in restless slumber, he knew he would go through with it and never utter one word of complaint.

But the next day he suffered from self-pity. He was sorry he was Chinese. He wished he could be like the other boys, accepted as one of them, and not be looked upon as being different. Didn't he like to go roller skating, too? Didn't he like to play marbles? And didn't he know some fancy swear words he could use on the proper occasions? He could even show the boys some new games, if they'd only let him.

Wednesday came as usual. School was dismissed early after the morning session so the children could go home and dress. Jin-Wai's mother had gotten the clothes from a box where they had been packed away in sweet-smelling herbs. And his father stopped work in the laundry to assist and give instructions. Hing giggled and laughed as he was told how to wear the clothes: the white stockings, the black satin shoes, the silk trousers bound at the ankles, and the beautiful blue blouse.

Jin-Wai closed his eyes tightly as his father put on him the long gown that he said was the proper thing for a scholar to wear. And he squirmed as the round black cap with a button on the top was adjusted on his head.

"Very proud father," said Fong. "Very proud, although I am lacking in modesty to say so. You will do me great honor, my sons. Come home after the celebration is over, and we shall have a feast to celebrate my sons' first appearance in public as becomes Chinese gentlemen."

"Proud?" thought Jin-Wai. His father didn't have to walk through the streets wearing skirts like a girl. He didn't have to have everybody look at him and laugh. And when Hing knew what jibes and jeers were awaiting him he wouldn't be smiling so happily either.

Taking Hing by the hand, Jin-Wai trotted out onto the street. His father and mother stood in the doorway and waved their hands. Jin-Wai looked neither to the right nor to the left, but trudged manfully forward, pulling Hing along after him.

"Too fast! Too fast!" said Hing, who had short legs and had to give a little jump every now and then to keep up.

But Jin-Wai paid no attention. As he drew nearer the school it wasn't half as bad as he thought it would be. Other boys all dressed up were going to the school, and they were all too busy with their mothers standing about and fussing over details of their attire to pay any attention to him. He found his seat in the classroom and pulled Hing up beside him. As the other boys took their places Jin-Wai looked straight ahead and kept saying to himself, "I am obeying my father. I am obeying my father." The only consoling thought he had.

The exercises were to be held in the assembly hall. It wasn't until they were marching to join the children from the other classrooms that Jin-Wai's teacher saw him. She had been fluttering around trying to calm the excited mothers and keep the boys from mussing up their costumes.

"Why, Jin-Wai!" she said breathlessly. "I didn't know you were planning to come dressed up. How nice you look. And is this your brother? Isn't he cute. Dear, dear—we'll have to think up something for

you to do. I wish I'd known." And she dashed ahead to separate two boys who had started to fight.

So she hadn't expected him to come dressed up! In vain had been his suffering of the past few days. He could have stayed away, and he wouldn't have been missed. And now Miss Teacher suggested he do something. He wished the schoolhouse would burn down—right to the ground— this very minute—and everybody in it, too —including himself.

Seats were reserved down front for the children. The proud mothers sat in the back.

The program started with everyone singing "My Country 'Tis of Thee." Then the school orchestra hesitantly played what was called a medley of popular airs. And as each group went upon the stage to perform, the orchestra sounded forth with a few bars of the national anthem of their country.

Five little Scotch boys in kilts danced to the tune of "The Campbells Are Coming." Jin-Wai felt a little happier when he saw that they, too, were wearing skirts. Thank goodness his bare legs weren't being displayed to the public.

A group of Italian children sang several of their folk songs. Some Finnish boys did a drill. The Spanish boys and girls danced to clicking castanets. And so on until all the nationalities had performed. As each group finished they lined up on the stage. Only Jin-Wai and his brother remained in the auditorium.

He heard his teacher say, "But I didn't expect . . . I didn't rehearse anything."

Then the lady whom he knew to be Number One Teacher replied, "He will be so disappointed if he can't come up with the others. And he looks so sweet."

Jin-Wai shuddered. Disappointed? Not he. He was hoping he wouldn't be noticed.

But his teacher bent over him and whispered. "Wouldn't you like to go up on the platform with the others? Just walk around so everyone can see how nice you look. We don't know what melody to play. We haven't practiced the Chinese national anthem—if there is one."

The pride of centuries of a race of proud ancestors came to Jin-Wai's assistance at this crucial moment. Just because he was a despised Chinese didn't mean that he didn't know the proper thing to do. "Play 'Yankee Doodle,'" he said. "We'll take that tune."

A whispered consultation was held with the pianist, and as "Yankee Doodle" was pounded out upon the piano, Jin-Wai, holding Hing by the hand, marched upon the stage. There was a burst of applause. For Jin-Wai carried himself with such dignity, walked so proudly, and had such perfect self-possession that he won the hearts of all the mothers. He faced the audience.

"He's going to do something," whispered the teacher.

Jin-Wai bowed. And Hing, properly trained to do as his elder brother did in public, folded his hands in front of his round little tummy and bowed too. Suddenly Jin-Wai felt proud and happy. Proud he was wearing his Chinese dress. It was beautiful. Much more beautiful than the homemade costumes the other children were wearing. Silk, his was. Not cheesecloth nor cheap material. He wasn't afraid any longer.

He took one step forward and began to recite in Chinese. The audience listened amused but pleased. When he finished he bowed again. And Hing bowed too. Then Jin-Wai took Hing by the hand and led him to a place on the stage by the side of the other boys from his classroom. There was a loud burst of applause from the audience.

While the orchestra played another number, there was a hurried consultation among the teachers. Then Jin-Wai saw his teacher come upon the stage.

"The prize this afternoon for the best costume and the nicest performance by unanimous choice goes to Jin-Wai Fong, our Chinese neighbor. Come here, Jin-Wai."

Jin-Wai, still holding Hing by the hand, stepped forward. "What was it you said in Chinese?" asked the teacher.

"I said 'The Five Principles of Filial Duty' by Mr. Confucius. It means you should always obey your parents and do exactly as they tell you to do even though it does not seem to you to be the thing for you to do."

Cheers from the audience at these words so touchingly expressed. The suffering mothers present understood and applauded vigorously. Then the teacher handed Jin-Wai the prize—a nice book full of pictures of the presidents and their wives. Jin-Wai bowed low.

"Present?" asked Hing.

For a moment Jin-Wai paused. He had no right to accept this prize. He had not won it because of anything he had wanted to do. He had made no effort of his own. He was not entitled to it. And if he accepted the prize and ever in his own thought felt pride, he would to himself forever lose face.

So he turned to Hing and placed the prize in his hands. Let Hing have all the honor. Let him be the one tonight to boast to their honorable father. Then Jin-Wai smiled happily. He had done the proper thing—saved his face.

He took his place again with his classmates. The teacher pulled a rope, and the American flag concealed in the space above the stage unfurled and hovered over the children as they all began to sing "The Star-Spangled Banner."

"Hi, kid," said the boy next to Jin-Wai

under his breath, and smiled when he said it.

"Hi, yourself," replied Jin-Wai. His heart began to thump happily. The first friendly word he had had. Maybe his father did know what was best. Maybe he should always do things in the approved Chinese way—his way. Maybe that was the right way to understanding and friendliness.

The man who wrote this story

CARL GLICK 1890–

Carl Glick was born in a small Iowa town, where his father was a local manufacturer and his mother a former schoolteacher. His father wanted him to become a manufacturer also, but Mrs. Glick, who had once wanted to be a writer, passed her ambition on to her son. When he was a high-school student, Carl Glick's first play was published in the school paper. Later, while a student at Northwestern, he wrote scenarios for the movies and acted with a theatrical company.

When Mr. Glick returned to Iowa, he established the first community theatre in the state. In the following years he directed little theatre groups in many parts of the country, from Florida to Massachusetts. Between performances, he found time to teach drama at several universities.

During the depression, when theatre groups were less active, Mr. Glick found a job as the athletic director for the Church of All Nations in New York City. Though not an athlete, he was interested in his work. He had a great sense of humor, and his Chinese-American group liked him.

Gradually Mr. Glick became more and more interested in the Chinese and began to write articles and stories about them.

Shake Hands With the Dragon, one of his early books, was very popular and gained him a reputation as a spokesman for Chinese-Americans.

Let's consider . . .

1. Jin-Wai knew that a disobedient son made his father "lose face." What does the expression "lose face" mean? How did Jin-Wai keep his father from losing face? How did Jin-Wai save face himself?

2. Describe Jin-Wai's attitude toward his father. Is his attitude different from yours? What are the good points of his and your attitudes?

3. Why was Jin-Wai's request for the song "Yankee Doodle" a particularly happy choice for the school pageant? What other songs would also have been good choices?

4. Jin-Wai's mother obtained more pleasure from receiving the invitation than from actually attending the party. How can you explain this?

5. Look again at the last two sentences of the story. In your own words explain their meaning. How does this ending help you to understand how all peoples have contributed to America's greatness?

6. Why did the school have the Pageant of All Nations? Do you think celebrations of this kind are a good idea? Explain.

The First Day

GEORGE and HELEN PAPASHVILY

George Papashvily came to America without very clear ideas of what he could expect to find. He soon discovered that America is a place where anything can happen.

At five in the morning the engines stopped, and after thirty-seven days the boat was quiet.

We were in America.

I got up and stepped over the other men and looked out the porthole. Water and fog. We were anchoring off an island. I dressed and went on deck.

Now began my troubles. What to do? This was a Greek boat and I was steerage, so of course by the time we were half way out I had spent all my landing money for extra food.

Hassan, the Turk, one of the six who slept in the cabin with me, came up the ladder.

"I told you so," he said as soon as he saw me. "Now we are in America and you have no money to land. They send you home. No money, no going ashore. What a disgrace. In your position, frankly, I would kill myself."

Hassan had been satisfied to starve on black olives and salt cheese all the way from Gibraltar, and he begrudged every skewer of lamb I bribed away from the first-cabin steward.

We went down the gangplank into the big room. Passengers with pictures in their hands was rushing around to match them to a relative. Before their tables the inspectors was busy with long lines of people.

The visitors' door opened and fellow with big pile of caps, striped blue and white cotton caps with visors and a top button, came in. He went first to an old man with a karakul hat near the window, then to a Cossack in line. At last he came to me.

"Look," he said in Russian, "look at your hat. You want to be a greenhorn all your life? A karakul hat! Do you expect to see anybody in the U.S.A. still with a fur hat? The customs inspector, the doctor, the captain—are they wearing fur hats? Certainly not."

I didn't say anything.

"Look," he said. "I'm sorry for you. I was a greenhorn once myself. I wouldn't

409

want to see anybody make my mistakes.
Look, I have caps. See, from such rich
striped material. Like wears railroad engineers, and house painters, and coal miners."
He spun one around on his finger. "Don't
be afraid. It's a cap in real American style.
With this cap on your head, they couldn't
tell you from a citizen. I'm positively guar-
anteeing. And I'm trading you this cap
even for your old karakul hat. Trading
even. You don't have to give me one
penny."

Now it is true I bought my karakul
coudie [1] new for the trip. It was a fine
skin, a silver lamb, and in Georgia it would
have lasted me a lifetime. Still—

"I'll tell you," the cap man said. "So you
can remember all your life you made
money the first hour you were in America,
I give you a cap and a dollar besides.
Done?"

I took off my *coudie* and put on his cap.
It was small and sat well upon my head,
but then in America one dresses like an
American and it is a satisfaction always to
be in the best style. So I got my first dollar.

Ysaacs, a Syrian, sat on the bench and
smoked brown paper cigarettes and
watched all through the bargain. He was
from our cabin, too, and he knew I was
worried about the money to show the
examiners. But now, as soon as the cap
man went on to the next customer, Ysaacs
explained a way to get me by the examiners
—a good way.

Such a very good way, in fact, that when
the inspector looked over my passport and
entry permit I was ready.

"Do you have friends meeting you?" he
asked me. "Do you have money to support
yourself?"

I pulled out a round fat roll of green
American money—tens, twenties—a nice

[1] *coudie,* hat [*Georgian*]

thick pile with a rubber band around.
"O.K.," he said. "Go ahead." He
stamped my papers.

I got my baggage and took the money
roll back again to Ysaacs' friend, Arapoule-
opolus, the money lender, so he could rent
it over again to another man. One dollar
was all he charged to use it for each landing. Really a bargain.

On the outer platform I met Zurabeg, an
Ossetian, who had been down in steerage,
too. But Zurabeg was no greenhorn coming for the first time. Zurabeg was an
American citizen with papers to prove it,
and a friend of Gospadin Buffalo Bill besides. This Zurabeg came first to America
twenty years before as a trick show rider,
and later he was boss cook on the road with
Gospadin Buffalo Bill. Every few years,
Zurabeg, whenever he saved enough
money, went home to find a wife—but so
far with no luck.

"Can't land?" he asked me.

"No, I can land," I said, "but I have no
money to pay the little boat to carry me to
shore." A small boat went chuffing back
and forth taking off the discharged passengers. "I try to make up my mind to swim,
but if I swim how will I carry my baggage?
It would need two trips at least."

"Listen, donkey-head," Zurabeg said,
"this is America. The carrying boat is
free. It belongs to my government. They
take us for nothing. Come on."

So we got to the shore.

And there—the streets, the people, the
noise! The faces flashing by—and by
again. The screams and chatter and cries.
But most of all the motion, back and forth,
pressing deeper and deeper on my eyeballs.

We walked a few blocks through this
before I remembered my landing cards and
passport and visas. I took them out and
tore them into little pieces and threw them
all in an ash can. "They can't prove I'm

not a citizen, now," I said. "What we do next?"

"We get jobs," Zurabeg told me. "I show you."

We went to an employment agency. Conveniently, the man spoke Russian. He gave Zurabeg ticket right away to start in Russian restaurant as first cook.

"Now, your friend? What can he do?" he asked me.

"I," I said, "am a worker in decorative leathers particularly specializing in the ornamenting of crop handles according to the traditional designs."

"My God!" the man said. "This is the U. S. A. No horses. Automobiles. What else can you do?"

Fortunately my father was a man of great foresight and I have two trades. His idea was that in the days when a man starves with one, by the other he may eat.

"I am also," I said, "a swordmaker. Short blades or long; daggers with or without chasing; hunting knives, plain or ornamented; tempered, fitting, pointing—" I took my certificate of successful completion of apprenticeship out of my *chemidon*.[2]

"My God! A crop maker—a sword pointer. You better take him along for a dishwasher," he said to Zurabeg. "They can always use another dishwasher."

We went down into the earth and flew through tunnels in a train. It was like the caves under the Kazbeck where the giant bats sleep, and it smelled even worse.

The restaurant was on a side street and the lady-owner, the *hasaika*, spoke kindly. "I remember you from the tearoom," she said to Zurabeg. "I congratulate myself on getting you. You are excellent on the *piroshkis*,[3] isn't it?"

"On everything, madame," Zurabeg said grandly. "On everything. Buffalo Bill, an old friend of mine, has eaten thirty of my *piroshkis* at a meal. My friend—" he waved toward me— "will be a dishwasher."

I made a bow.

The kitchen was small and hot and fat— like inside of a pig's stomach. Zurabeg unpacked his knives, put on his cap, and, at home at once, started to dice celery.

"You can wash these," the *hasaika* said to me. "At four we have party."

It was a trayful of glasses. And such glasses—thin bubbles that would hardly hold a sip—set on stems. The first one snapped in my hand, the second dissolved, the third to tenth I got washed, the eleventh was already cracked, the twelfth rang once on the pan edge and was silent.

Perhaps I might be there yet, but just as I carried the first trayful to the service slot, the restaurant cat ran between my feet.

When I got all the glass swept up, I told Zurabeg, "Now, we have to eat. It's noon. I watch the customers eat. It makes me hungry. Prepare a *shashlik*[4] and some cucumbers, and we enjoy our first meal for good luck in the New World."

"This is a restaurant," Zurabeg said, "not a *duquani*[5] on the side of the Georgian road where the proprietor and the house eat with the guests together at one table. This is a restaurant with very strict organization. We get to eat when the customers go, and you get what the customers leave. Try again with the glasses and remember my reputation. Please."

I found a quart of sour cream and went into the back alley and ate that and some bread and a jar of caviar which was very salty—packed for export, no doubt.

---

[2] *chemidon,* suitcase or trunk [*Russian*]
[3] *piroshkis,* pie which may be filled with mushrooms, cabbage, onions, meat, or rice [*Georgian*]

[4] *shashlik,* small cubes of lamb cooked on a rod or stick [*Georgian*]
[5] *duquani,* small eating or drinking place [*Georgian*]

The *hasaika* found me. I stood up. "Please," she said, "please go on. Eat sour cream. But after, could you go away? Far away? With no hard feelings. The glasses —the caviar—it's expensive for me—and at the same time I don't want to make your friend mad. I need a good cook. If you could just go away? Quietly? Just disappear, so to speak? I give you five dollars."

"I didn't do anything," I said, "so you don't have to pay me. All in all, a restaurant probably isn't my fate. You can tell Zurabeg afterward."

She brought my cap and a paper bag. I went down through the alley and into the street. I walked. I walked until my feet took fire in my shoes and my neck ached from looking. I walked for hours. I couldn't even be sure it was the same day. I tried some English on a few men that passed. "What watch?" I said. But they pushed by me so I knew I had it wrong. I tried another man. "How many clock?"

He showed me on his wrist. Four-thirty.

A wonderful place. Rapidly, if one applies oneself, one speaks the English.

I came to a park and went in and found a place under a tree and took off my shoes and lay down. I looked in the bag the *hasaika* gave me. A sandwich from bologna and a nickel—to begin in America with.

What to do? While I decided, I slept.

A policeman was waking me up. He spoke. I shook my head I can't understand. Then with hands, with legs, rolling his eyes, turning his head, with motions, with gestures (really he was as good as marionettes I saw once in Tiflis), he showed me to lie on the grass is forbidden. But one is welcome to the seats instead. All free seats in this park. No charge for anybody. What a country.

But I was puzzled. There were iron arm rests every two feet along the benches. How could I distribute myself under them? I tried one leg. Then the other. But when

I was under, how could I turn around? Then, whatever way I got in, my chin was always caught by the hoop. While I thought this over, I walked and bought peanuts for my nickel and fed the squirrels.

Lights began to come on in the towers around the park. It was almost dark. I found a sandy patch under a rock on a little bluff above the drive. I cut a *shashlik* stick and built a fire of twigs and broiled my bologna over it and ate the bread. It lasted very short. Then I rolled up my coat for a pillow like the days during the war and went to sleep.

I was tired from America and I slept some hours. It must have been almost midnight when the light flashed in my face. I sat up. It was from the head lamp of a touring car choking along on the road below me. While I watched, the engine coughed and died. A man got out. For more than an hour he knocked with tools and opened the hood and closed it again.

Then I slid down the bank. In the war there were airplanes, and of course cars are much the same except, naturally, for the wings. I showed him with my hands and feet and head, like the policeman: "Give me the tools and let me try." He handed them over and sat down on the bench.

I checked the spark plugs and the distributor, the timer and the coils. I looked at the feed line, at the ignition, at the gas. In between, I cranked. I cranked until I cranked my heart out onto the ground. Still the car wouldn't move.

I got mad. I cursed it. I cursed it for the son of a mountain devi. I cursed it for the carriage of the diavels in the cave. I cursed it by the black-horned goat, and when I finished all I knew in Georgian I said it again in Russian to pick up the loose ends. Then I kicked the radiator as hard as I could. The car was old Model T, and it started with a snort that shook the chassis like an aspen.

The man came running up. He was laughing and he shook my hands and talked at me and asked questions. But the policeman's method didn't work. Signs weren't enough. I remembered my dictionary—English-Russian, Russian-English—it went both ways. I took it from my blouse pocket and showed the man. Holding it under the headlights, he thumbed through.

"Work?" he found in English.

I looked at the Russian word beside it and shook my head.

"Home?" he turned to that.

"No," again.

I took the dictionary. "Boat. Today."

"Come home—" he showed me the words—"with me—" he pointed to himself. "Eat. Sleep. Job." It took him quite a time between words. "Job. Tomorrow."

"Automobiles?" I said. We have the same word in Georgian.

"Automobiles!" He was pleased we found one word together.

We got in his car, and he took me through miles and miles of streets with houses on both sides of every one of them until we came to his own. We went in and we ate and we drank and ate and drank again. For that, fortunately, you need no words.

Then his wife showed me a room and I went to bed. As I fell asleep, I thought to myself: Well, now, I have lived one whole day in America and—just like they say—America is a country where anything, anything at all can happen.

And in twenty years—about this—I never changed my mind.

The people who wrote this selection

GEORGE and HELEN PAPASHVILY

When George Papashvily was a small boy in Georgia, a section of Southern Russia, he was proud of the fact that his mother was the only person in the village who could read and write. His family could not afford to send him to school, so he would sit on the steps outside the schoolhouse and try to hear what the teacher was saying. When the teacher noticed him, he slammed the school door. That ended George's formal education. Later, at the cost of a sack of grain for two private lessons, he learned to write his name.

Nothing has been able to upset George Papashvily's confidence and humor. His experiences as an immigrant in America—experiences that might have made another man bitter—became material for a book. After his marriage to an American girl, he told her his adventures. Since he did not read or write, his wife wrote them down. These adventures have been hilariously described in the best-seller, *Anything Can Happen.* Many of you may remember the movie which was made from this book.

The couple has now published several other books. They live happily on a farm in Pennsylvania where Mr. Papashvily experiments with raising vegetables and animals.

Let's consider . . .

1. George's first day in America was filled with surprises. Which of his experiences did you enjoy the most?

2. What things about America amazed George? Think of several other things he might have seen that would also have amazed him.

3. Describe George's experiences as a dishwasher. What did he learn about America from these experiences?

4. What trades had George been trained for? Why were these trades useless in America?

5. Why had his father prepared him for two trades? What is your opinion of this practice?

6. In what ways did people take advantage of George when he first arrived in the United States? How did this affect him?

7. How are today's immigrants protected from unscrupulous people?

8. At the end of his first day, George thought to himself: "America is a country where anything, anything at all can happen." Why did he feel this way? Explain why you agree or disagree with him.

9. Recall one of the important "firsts" in your life—your first trip alone, your first day in a new school, your first date. Write a description of one of these "firsts" which you think the class would enjoy hearing about.

The writer's craft . . .

You may have wondered how this selection came to have two authors. When George Papashvily told his American-born wife, Helen, about his hilarious experiences as a newcomer to America, she suggested that he share them with other people. The result of her suggestion was the book, *Anything Can Happen.* It was George's own story, but Helen did all of the writing. Since Helen's name was signed to the story along with her husband's, she is what is known as a *co-author.* If she had not signed her name, she would have been a *ghost writer.* Why is the term *ghost writer* a good description of the unknown person who does the writing for someone else?

I Am an American

ELIAS LIEBERMAN

I am an American.
My father belongs to the Sons of the Revolution;
My mother, to the Colonial Dames.
One of my ancestors pitched tea overboard in Boston Harbor;
Another stood his ground with Warren;
Another hungered with Washington at Valley Forge.
My forefathers were America in the making:
They spoke in her council halls;
They died on her battle-fields;
They commanded her ships;
They cleared her forests.
Dawns reddened and paled.
Stanch hearts of mine beat fast at each new star
In the nation's flag.
Keen eyes of mine foresaw her greater glory:
The sweep of her seas,
The plenty of her plains,
The man-hives in her billion-wired cities.
Every drop of blood in me holds a heritage of patriotism.
I am proud of my past.
I am an American.

I am an American.
My father was an atom of dust,
My mother a straw in the wind,
To his serene majesty.
One of my ancestors died in the mines of Siberia;
Another was crippled for life by twenty blows of the *knout.*[1]
Another was killed defending his home during the massacres.
The history of my ancestors is a trail of blood
To the palace-gate of the Great White Czar.
But then the dream came—
The dream of America.

---
[1] *knout,* a kind of whip once used in Russia to punish criminals

In the light of the Liberty torch
The atom of dust became a man
And the straw in the wind became a woman
For the first time.
"See," said my father, pointing to the flag that fluttered near,
"That flag of stars and stripes is yours;
It is the emblem of the promised land.
It means, my son, the hope of humanity.
Live for it—die for it!"
Under the open sky of my new country I swore to do so;
And every drop of blood in me will keep that vow.
I am proud of my future.
I am an American.

The man who wrote this poem

ELIAS LIEBERMAN   1883–

Born in Russia, Elias Lieberman was seven years old when he was brought to America by his parents. The Liebermans settled in New York City, and Elias received his schooling there. In 1911 he earned his Ph.D. from New York University, and since then he has been connected with the New York City public school system.

Mr. Lieberman started to write professionally soon after he was graduated from college. He has written two plays that appeared on Broadway, but most of his work has been poetry, and his poems have appeared in many collections. "I Am an American" is his best-known poem, and during the First World War it was widely reprinted and distributed to the American soldiers.

The poet's art . . .

1. "I Am an American" presented the points of view for two Americans. Each was proud of his country. The first speaker took pride in his American heritage. List the contributions that his ancestors made to America.

2. The second speaker was thankful that America had given him dignity as an individual. He said:

"My father was an atom of dust,
My mother a straw in the wind"

What made it possible for his parents to become more than just an "atom" and a "straw"?

3. The two Americans came from different backgrounds. The first was proud of his past; the second was proud of his future. Explain why both felt the same duty and obligation to America?

4. To what event in American history did the first speaker refer when he said, "One of my ancestors pitched tea overboard in Boston Harbor"?

5. Can you identify the country from which the second speaker's ancestors came? What clues helped you identify it?

6. "I Am an American" is a poem that does not rhyme. Try reading it aloud. You will quickly hear the forceful *rhythm* of the lines.

The Story of Saudin

As Told by SAUDIN to AGNES KEITH

Saudin, a native of Borneo, came to this country with Mr. and Mrs. Martin Johnson, the celebrated explorers and wild game hunters. It was Saudin's job to tend the animals on board ship during the voyage from Borneo. His reward was a three-month vacation in a land of wonder. Listen, as he tells you about his experiences in a strange new world.

When I came to Sandakan from Kampong Ambual, I thought that Sandakan was a big place. But when I went from Sandakan to Singapore, I thought *that* was a very big place, probably the biggest place there was. Of the great size of Singapore I was not surprised, because many Malays come to Borneo from there and tell much about it. Then we went from Singapore to Capetown, and that was even more mighty. So I asked men, was America as great as that? And men answered me that it was even greater. And now that I return to Borneo from America I think that Sandakan is only as big as the end of my little finger.

We left Singapore on a very big boat. White men did the work of natives on this boat, and spoke a language which was not English. We sailed to Colombo, a place I did not know of before, but a very fine place indeed, and I bought bananas and coconuts and ate them there. Then the boat sailed on again and we came to India. I did not see very much of India because the animals were sick and I was busy taking care of them. Sally, one of the orangutans, was very sick in her stomach and everything she ate came out like water, and she died. So I could not go into India, but I think it is only a small place, probably like Kudat, and that all the natives had come down to meet the boat.

After India we sailed on farther and farther, and the waves became very tall, and the captain said to tell men that a storm was coming. I saw black mountains ahead, and I said, "We are running into mountains!" But men said, "No, that is fog." And it was fog. In the fog we met a very cold climate, and taller and taller waves, and a stronger and stronger storm. The boat threw itself from side to side for many days. I was very sick, and the animals were very sick, and nine small monkeys died, and the orangutan from Kudat died, but I did not. But I was very glad when we arrived at Capetown, which is Africa.

In the distance I could see that Capetown was white and shining, and the only thing that I knew that was like that was the stone-water that white men use and call ice. So I said, "There is ice on everything there!" But men said, "No, that is the houses and the streets shining in the sun."

417

And so it was.

Mr. Johnson took me to land at Capetown, and there the man said I could not land because I was Chinese. I said I was not Chinese, I was Malay. Then I could land. But always it was like this and men would think that I was Chinese. I never told men that I was a man of the Muruts because it seems that nobody knows about Muruts, but all people know about Chinese. So I said I was Malay because some people know about Malays.

In Capetown it was a very cold climate, and both the animals and I shivered. I had a shirt and trousers and this is a great deal for a Murut to wear, but it was not enough. Mr. Johnson asked me if I had any more clothes. He bought me shirts and trousers, and short coats, and a very long black coat which hung down to my feet and had big shoulders and was very handsome, and a hat and nine neckties. He told me that I must close my shirt and tie up my necktie around my neck when I was in Capetown, as this is the custom there. All my new clothes cost nineteen pounds, nine shillings, and sixpence.

We left Capetown and the ship sailed on until we came to Dakar, which is also Africa, but is very hot. So I said to men, "Why is it so cold in one place and so hot in another place?" And men said, "Well,

because it just is that way." So I said, "Yes, probably that is just the way it is."

This time we were on the ship many days, and then we came to America. When we were going to land the Customs man said to me, "You are Chinese; you cannot land." So Mr. Johnson said, "No, he is Malay, and I will send him back to Borneo in three months." The Customs man said, "Can you speak English and read and write?" I said, "Yes, a little." He said, "Read this," and handed me my passport. I could not read it, but I remembered what was on it, because Mr. Johnson had told me, and so I said what was on it to the man. Then the man said, "O.K. Come into America!"

2.

So we entered into America and went to a very great village with a thousand thousand lights. It was night when we arrived, but when I looked up at the sky above this village it was very bright and red and sparkling and there was light everywhere. And I said, "Is this morning?" And they said, "No, this is New York."

I was so astonished by New York that I just wanted to look and look and look at it. I forgot all about feeding the animals and my work. Every night men had their names put in the sky with bright lights so

that they would not be forgotten, because
there are so many people in New York
that it would be easy to forget some of
them. All the time there was a great noise
made by motorcars and buses and trains.
There were trains above me on bridges,
there were trains below me, and there were
more trains that were below the trains that
were below. Always the trains were very
full of people. I think if the trains all
stopped and the people got off them there
would be no space in New York for all the
people. So the people would take turns
living in the trains. I used to walk and
walk because I was afraid to get on those
trains to ride as I did not know how to get
off or where I should be when I did, or if
I might have to live on one.

The streets were very clean. They
washed and polished them every morning.
I thought there could be no sickness there
with everything so clean.

The buildings were very tall. Sometimes
I had to go up and down in what men call
an elevator. This is a little room that you
get into, and very suddenly it goes up. And
when it stops your stomach does not stop.
But when it goes down you feel that everything has gone out of you. It is much
worse than an airplane. I was always afraid
in it, but said nothing, because I thought
men would say, "He is just a jungle man!"

In winter there is a very cold climate in New York. Often I shivered and was cold although I wore many clothes and my handsome black coat. All men wore heavy clothes and coats like mine which hung down to their knees. But truly I was astonished at the women! They did not wear many clothes except around their necks, where they wore the skins of animals. . . . Their stockings were just like nothing. Truly I was astonished that they did not feel cold.

In New York we put Mr. Johnson's animals in Central Park Zoo, and I went there every day to take care of them. At first Mr. Johnson went with me so that I would not be lost, and later I could go alone. But I was always afraid of the motorcars. I walked a great deal, up and down the same street and never far away, as I was afraid of being lost. At night I did not go away at all, because when lights were in the sky all things became different and I was confused.

One day he told me to go to a cinema. When I went in it was daylight, but when I came out it was dark. It was only five o'clock and in my country that is still daytime. But in New York in winter that is nighttime and the lights are on. When I looked up I could see nothing but very tall buildings and a red glow at the top of the buildings, and no sky. All men were hurrying from here to there, all trains made noises, all lights blinked, and I became confused. I walked and walked, but could not find the place where I lived. Mr. Johnson had written a letter for me telling who I was and where I lived in case I should be lost some day. And, as I was lost then, I looked in my coat, and was much astonished to find that the letter was lost also.

I went to a policeman and asked him how to go to Central Park Zoo, because if I could find that I could find my house,

which was near it. The policeman said it was twelve blocks away, so I said, "Thank you very much," and walked on some more. Then I asked another policeman and he said nine blocks farther, and I walked some more. But the next policeman I asked said, "Here is Central Park Zoo!" And there I was at the Zoo, but I did not recognize it with the lights on. So then I found my house, which I think was very good fortune, because I had indeed been lost.

One day newspaper men came to talk to me, and they said, "Do you like New York? What do you like the best?" And I said, "Yes, I like New York, and I like best the red electric light signs that run like streams of fire, and the lights that chase each other around like small animals."

One day I was out walking and I came to a large place with many horses in it. I said to a man with a uniform, "Can I enter?" And he said, "You must buy a ticket." I said, "Sure!" So I entered and I saw large and wonderful horses, and handsome men with beautiful colored uniforms. They played music and the horses danced to the music. I think the horses in New York are smarter than are the policemen in my country. So I struck my hands together the way other people did, with astonishment and joy. When the playing was finished all the people wanted to leave at once in a great hurry, and everybody pushed everybody and I fell down. A man picked me up, and I said, "Thank you very much," and went home.

I went also to see boxing and wrestling. Boxing is all right, but wrestling is too rough. In my country we do not act like that unless we wish to kill men.

One day a man fell down in the streets and lay there wounded. Everybody just looked at him and walked on. So I looked at him and walked on too, because I was afraid if I stayed near him people would think that I had wounded him. Afterwards I told Mr. Johnson and he said, "People get killed here every day!"

I was out walking one day and met a man who was drunk, the same as a man is in Borneo when he drinks too much rice beer. The man said, "You are a Filipino like me!" I said, "No, I am a Malay." He said, "No, you are a Filipino!" I said, "You are drunk. You had better go home. Don't you know that people get killed here every day?" But he didn't go home, and he wanted to fight me because I wasn't a Filipino. So I ran and stood by an important man in a uniform who stood at the door of a hotel. I stood very close to this important man, and as he wouldn't let the drunken Filipino come to the hotel he couldn't fight me.

Mr. Johnson took me to eat at a place where you put money in a hole and take out a plate of food. The different holes have names on them to tell you what foods are concealed within. We had vegetable and potato and meat all cooked together in a flour wrapping which they call a pie. I think this place was very cunning indeed, because the hole to receive a ten-cent piece was so small that you could not put in a five-cent piece, and the hole for a five-cent piece did not answer if you put in a one-cent piece.

One time a man gave me some wine to drink. I drank a little, and then I remembered about the many motorcars and trains outside, the great noise and confusion, and people who got killed there every day. And I was afraid I might be hit, lost, or killed if I drank any more, so I didn't drink any more.

Mr. Johnson took me to a club where they were going to talk to people about Borneo. When we arrived he told me that I must stand up and talk to them in Malay. I said that it was useless for me to do so because they did not understand Malay.

But he said that I must speak in Malay and then he would tell them in English what I said. I was afraid and ashamed because there were many people there and I am not practiced in speaking to many people. But, although I shivered as with cold, I talked, and I told them about my village with only thirty people in it, which was so small that I was astonished that they wished to hear about it. And when I finished they struck their hands together to show that they were pleased, and I sat down and Mr. Johnson talked. He showed them a roll of his film about the bird's-nest caves at Gomantong, and the proboscis monkeys, and the walking fish. Afterwards people came up to me and said, "We liked what you said tonight. What did you say? Was that Chinese you were speaking? Are you Chinese?" So I said, "No, I am Malay. Thank you very much."

3.

Mr. Jim, who used to drive the flying-ship in Borneo, was in New York too, but he did not live there. One day we flew from New York to his home in a very large flying-ship. I was not afraid because I was used to flying before, but it was very different from flying over Borneo. In my country I looked down on jungle trees and rivers of which I am not afraid, but here I looked down on buildings and trains which would be difficult to fall upon with comfort. In New York there were snow and ice on the wings of the flying-ship. It was very rough weather, the same as on our boat before coming to Capetown, and I was sick, but I did not vomit. We went many miles before coming to Mr. Jim's village, but I do not remember the name of this village. We went into his house and his people gave us food and drink. But I was ashamed to eat with them because I did not know how to eat the food cleverly as they did, because all my life in my country I was accustomed to eat with my fingers. It is difficult to carry the food with those small weapons to the mouth. I did not wish to be rude by not eating the food after their custom, so I pretended I was not very hungry, and I went to bed soon. The next day we returned to New York.

One day Mrs. Johnson came to the hotel to take me to talk to some women. I was following after her, but for one minute I looked away and when I looked back I couldn't see her. Then I saw her again and followed her until she turned upon me with anger. Then I saw it wasn't Mrs. Johnson, but a strange woman. So I feared I was lost again, but Mrs. Johnson ran after us and she said to me, "Why do you not follow me?" I said, "I thought I was following you, because this other woman looks just like you." And Mrs. Johnson looked at her and said, "Humph! I don't think so!"

For two weeks I was sick. They took me to the hospital, but I didn't stay there because I was afraid to, as people were dying there. So I got up from the bed and walked back to my house and was sick there. . . . The doctor came to see me many times and after two weeks I was well.

One day Mr. Johnson said to me that in two days he must put me on a ship to return to Borneo. I was very sad to hear this because he was very good to me, and America was so astonishing. I cried like a child and I couldn't eat anything. First I thought that I would stay in America and work, but the next day I thought, "Well, never mind; if he says I must go, I will go."

This was the day before the New Year, and he bought me a watch for a present. I went to Times Square that night to see the New York people make a holiday. There were so many people that I was frightened and wanted to return because

we were like fish caught in a fish trap. Men blew things in my ears that made the noise of goats. I said to them, "Don't do that!" And they said, "Don't you like that? Don't you do this in your country?" And I said, "No!" I wanted to go home to bed, but I couldn't go home all that night. I couldn't go home until one o'clock in the morning, because it was New Year in New York and you can't go home on New Year in New York.

That was the first day of the first month, and I was sad because I had to sail for Borneo that day. Mr. Johnson took my hand and said *"Selemat belayer"* in Malay, and I said "Good-bye" in English, which I think was polite. Mrs. Johnson took me to the Dutch ship *Kota Djandi,* and I felt so sad to leave them that I forgot to take my two blankets, two pillows, and my rubber shoes, but I remembered my nine neckties and my big hat and my black coat.

So I sailed for home, and when the ship arrived at Singapore I took a letter to a man there from Mr. Johnson. The man took the letter, and after he read it he said, "Don't you know that this man is already dead? He fell in a flying-ship many days ago, and he is already dead."

And I just looked at him and I could not talk at all because I felt so sad and terrified. I could not believe that it was so. But I asked many men, and all men answered me that it was true. Then I cried like a child for two days and could not eat or sleep. And now I know my heart will always be sad for this man.

Now I will go back to my village and see my people. I will buy more buffaloes and plant more rice. When the harvest season comes I will harvest my rice, and I will drink rice beer and take a wife. But although I will live as all men do here, never will I forget America.

[Abridged]

The woman who wrote this selection

AGNES NEWTON KEITH   1905–

Agnes Keith believes that "parents and home life determine the land in which children grow up more than geography." Therefore, although she was born in Oak Park, Illinois, she considers that she was brought up in a more tropical environment. Her father was an Englishman who became an American citizen just to marry her mother. The couple were exceptionally devoted to one another, and this devotion spread to their children and gave them a feeling of being raised in a warm and sunny climate.

When Mrs. Keith finished college, she started with the *San Francisco Examiner* as a reporter. Unlike most young reporters, however, her name was soon in the headlines—because she was nearly murdered by a crazed drug-addict. Her newspaper career ended abruptly, and she was forced to spend six years convalescing from her injuries.

After her marriage to Mr. Keith, she went to Borneo, where her husband was the Director of Agriculture. Her life there is described in a pleasant and amusing book, *Land Below the Wind*.

During the Second World War, the Keiths were captives of the Japanese. For four long years they managed to evade starvation by a combination of trading and trickery. From a secret diary which Mrs. Keith kept during those years, she wrote her second book, *Three Came Home*.

Let's consider . . .

1. When Saudin returns to his village, do you think he will be able to give his friends an accurate picture of America? In what ways will their idea of America be distorted?

2. Have you gone through any of the experiences which Saudin described? Which of his descriptions best expressed what you have felt yourself?

3. Which of Saudin's descriptions impressed you as particularly clever, especially in view of his limited vocabulary and experience?

4. How would you describe the personality of this "wild man of Borneo"? Why do you suppose the Johnsons brought him with them to America? Do you think he would have been happy if he had remained here permanently?

5. What New York customs, behavior, and styles did Saudin criticize? Do you think his criticisms make sense?

6. What kind of mental picture do *you* have of Borneo? Or, for that matter, of Chicago, Brooklyn, Hollywood, Paris, London, Cairo? How did you arrive at this picture? Is there anyone in your class who has lived in, or visited, any of these places? If so, check with him to see if your pictures are accurate. What other sources of information would help you to discover what these places are really like?

7. Because Saudin knew only the most simple English words, he had a real problem expressing himself. See if you can describe some familiar object, limiting yourself to a very simple and non-technical vocabulary. For example, pretend you are Saudin as you explain a typewriter, an automobile, a radio, or a television set.

8. Assume that you live in a small town, that you have never traveled, and that you have had very little education. You are in some ways a "native." Describe a visit to a neighboring town. What things would strike you as being totally different and new?

All Yankees Are Liars

ERIC KNIGHT

People abroad get some pretty strange ideas about America. When Mr. Smith tried to describe America to a group of Yorkshiremen, they thought he was either an awful liar or a fool. The only thing to do was to tell them what they wanted to hear.

You can always tell the Irish,
You can always tell the Dutch,
You can always tell a Yankee;
But you cannot tell him much.

Mr. Smith was pleased with The Spread Eagle. He was pleased with Polkingthorpe Brig. The village was off the beaten track —the truly rural sort of English village the American always wants to see.

The inn was low and rambling, with great sloping roofs. Over the door swung the sign—a darksome bird in a weather-beaten setting.

Everything justified his decision to take this bicycle trip up into the north—the mullioned windows, the roaring fire, the Yorkshire accents of the men who shuffled over the sanded stone floor of the low-ceilinged room as they played darts. Mr. Smith was almost beginning to understand what they were talking about. During his excellent high tea he had sorted out the four men playing darts. One was Saw Cooper, a farmer; a small old man was referred to as Sam; a young, bright-faced lad who played darts left-handed was Gollicker

Pearson; and the fourth, a huge man, was just called Ian.

Mr. Smith watched them play, listening to the endless thwock of the darts in the cork board as he finished his meal. The barmaid, plump, corn-haired, came toward him, her apron rustling stiffly.

"Would there be owt else?"

"No. It was a very good meal." Mr. Smith smiled. He wanted to make the girl talk some more. "Er—what do they do for fun in this place of an evening?"

"Foon?" she repeated. "Well, they sit here—or o' Sat'day neights lots o' fowk goa ovver to Wuxley to t' pictures." She waited. "They gate Boock D'arcy i' 'T' Singing Cowboy,'" she added suggestively.

Mr. Smith had already become acquainted with British cinemas in small towns. Also, he was a Southern Californian, and had that familiarity with movies that belongs to all Southern Californians. He had no inclination to go four miles to see a last year's Class B Western.

"No. I think I'll have another ale and sit here," he said.

424

"If tha'll sit ovver by t' fire, Ah'll bring it to thee theer. Then Ah can clean oop here."

Mr. Smith sat on the bench by the generous fire and nursed his ale. The dart game came to an end with Saw Cooper losing and paying for the round. The men brought their mugs to the fire. Mr. Smith shifted politely. The men, in the presence of a stranger, grew quiet. Mr. Smith decided to put them at ease.

"Pretty chilly for an October evening, isn't it?"

The men considered the remark, as if looking at both sides of it. Finally Saw Cooper spoke.

"Aye," he said.

The others nodded. There was silence, and the five regarded the fire. Then, suddenly, young Gollicker smiled.

"Tha shouldn't heed t' cowd, being a Yankee," he said.

"Ah, but I'm not a Yankee," Mr. Smith said.

They stared at him in disbelief.

"Yankees," explained Mr. Smith, "come from New England."

They looked from Mr. Smith to one another. The big man named Ian took a deep breath.

"Yankees," he said, "coom fro' t' United States."

"Well, yes. New England is a part of the United States," Mr. Smith said. "But it's thousands of miles away from where I live. In fact, believe it or not, I should think you're closer to the Yankees than I am. You see, the United States is a big country. In the part where the Yankees come from, it gets very cold in the winter. Where I am—in Southern California—it never snows. Why, I've never known it to snow there in all my life."

"No snow?" Gollicker breathed.

Mr. Smith smiled. For after all, he was a Southern Californian—and they were discussing climate. "No snow," he said. "In wintertime we have a bit of a rainy season, but after February it clears, and then it doesn't even rain for nine months—not a drop."

"Noa rain for a nine month—noan at all?" Saw Cooper asked.

"Not a drop. Day after day, the sun comes out, clear skies, never a drop of rain for nine months. Never!"

"Whet do ye graw theer, lad?" Saw asked, slyly.

"Lots of things. Truck, vegetables, oranges—all kinds of things."

There was a silence again. Big Ian took a breath.

"Oringis," he said, and then took another breath, "graw i' Spain."

He looked at Mr. Smith so emphatically that Mr. Smith nodded.

"Oh, yes," he said. "They grow in Spain, too, I understand."

"Oringis," Ian repeated, "graw i' Spain."

That seemed to settle the question. They all looked in the fire in silence. Saw Cooper sniffed.

"What else graws theer?"

"Well, I have a ranch there; we grow alfalfa."

"Whet's that off to be?"

"Alfalfa? We use it for hay. It's a desert plant originally, but it thrives in California. We get eight cuttings a year."

"Eight cuttings o' hay a year?"

"Eight cuttings a year."

The little man, Sam, spoke for the first time: "Mister, if it doan't rain for a nine month, how can ye get eight cuttings o' hay a year?"

"Oh, that's easy," Mr. Smith said. "We irrigate the land." He went into a short but conclusive description of irrigating.

"Heh," Saw Cooper said. "Wheer's this here watter coom fro'?"

"In the San Fernando Valley we buy it from the water company, just like you do in your homes."

"Wheer do they get it?"

"From reservoirs."

"If it doan't rain, where's t' reservoys get t' watter?"

"Oh, we pipe it down from five hundred miles north. It rains a lot up there."

"And ye sprinkle t' farming land out o' t' watter tap. How mony acres hesta?"

"It isn't like sprinkling from the tap, of course. I used that to illustrate. The pipes are large—we have fourteen-inch valves on our pipes. We flood the land—cover it right over with water."

Saw looked in the fire. "Does corn graw theer?"

"Well, generally our land is too valuable to put into corn. But it will grow corn fourteen feet high."

They made noises in their throats and shifted their feet.

"Fohteen foot," Saw breathed. "Eigh, ba gum!"

"Mister," Sam said, "once Ah were oop to see t' Firth o' Forth brig. Ah suppose they hev bigger brigs i' Yankeeland?"

Mr. Smith should have touched on the new Oakland bridge, but then, he was a *Southern* Californian.

"We have bridges, but they're building vehicular tunnels under the rivers now."

"Whet for?"

"Well, there's so much motor traffic."

"How mony moatorcars goa through 'em?"

Mr. Smith lit his pipe happily. They seemed quite interested in America.

"I couldn't say. The way they turn 'em out, I should say there's hundreds of thousands."

"How fast do they turn 'em out?" Gollicker asked.

"I don't know. I think they roll out finished at the rate of one every couple of minutes."

"And they goa i' tunnels, not i' brigs?" Sam commented.

"Oh, we have some bridges."

"Big uns, Ah suppose."

"Well," Mr. Smith said modestly, thinking of the Pulaski Skyway coming into New York, "we have some that go right over entire towns. You're practically on one bridge for miles."

Saw Cooper spat into the fire. "How mony fowk is there in all America?"

Mr. Smith didn't know but he felt expansive. And after all, there was South America too.

"A quarter of a billion, I should say," he hazarded.

"A quarter of a billion," they repeated. Then they stared at Mr. Smith and he became aware of their disbelief.

"Wait a moment," he said. "I think a billion is different in America from here. It's a thousand million in America and a million million here, isn't it?"

"A billion," said Ian slowly, "is a billion."

The others nodded, and then Ian stood. The others rose too.

"Oh—er—wait a minute. Won't you all have a drink with me?" Mr. Smith invited.

"Us is off to play darts for a round— us four," Ian said, meaningly.

The other three laughed.

"Ah knew them theer brigs o' thine'd hev to be big," Saw Cooper said as a parting shot as he swung over the bench. "That's so's they'd be able to goa ovver wheat what graws fohteen foot high when ye sprinkle it fro' t' watter tap."

He grinned at the others in victory.

"I didn't say wheat; I said corn," Mr. Smith protested.

"Same thing," Saw snapped.

"It isn't. Wheat grows in an ear. Corn grows on a cob; it has broad long leaves."

"Heh! That's maize," Saw said.

Big Ian stepped between Saw Cooper and Mr. Smith.

"Now, lad," he said flatly, "tha said corn, and Ah heeard thee. Thee and thy oringis, and farming out o' t' watter tap, and brigs ovver cities, and it nivver rains, and denying th' art a Yankee, and a billion is a billion and yet it ain't. Tha's tripped thysen oop a dozen times, it seems to me. Now, hesta owt to say?"

Mr. Smith looked at Big Ian, standing belligerently with legs widespread and his thumbs in the waistband of his corduroy trousers. He looked round and saw everyone in the inn waiting, silent.

Then a curious thing happened. In that minute the smell of soft-coal smoke and pig-twist tobacco and ale was gone, and instead Mr. Smith was smelling the mixed odor of sun-baked land and citrus blossom and jasmine and eucalyptus trees, just as you smell it in the cool darkness coming across the San Fernando Valley. And he was homesick. Suddenly it felt unreal that he should be so far from home, sitting in an English inn with these men about him. He looked up at the faces, forbidding in their expression of disapproval. And he began to laugh.

It was all so unreal that he laughed until he cried. Every time he looked up he saw the faces, now even more comical in their bewilderment than they had been in their disapproval. They stared at him, and then Big Ian began to laugh.

"Eigh, Ah'll be jiggered!" he roared. "Drat ma buttons if Ah won't!"

It was Mr. Smith's turn to be puzzled now.

Big Ian roared, and suddenly slapped Mr. Smith on the back so heartily that his chin flew up in the air and then banged back on his chest. The others looked on in amazement.

"Why, whet's oop, Ian?" Saw asked.

"Why, ye gowks!" Ian roared. "He's laughing at ye! He's been heving us on! Sitting theer for an hour, keeping his mug straight and telling us the tale! And us swallering it, thinking he was serious!"

"But," Mr. Smith said—"but you don't—"

"Nay, now no moar on it!" Ian roared. "Ye've codded us for fair, and done it champion! Lewk at owd Sam's face!"

The others regarded Ian and scratched their heads and grinned sheepishly, and finally looked at Mr. Smith in admiration.

"But—" Mr. Smith began again.

"Nay, now, ye copped us napping," Ian said, "and here's ma hand on it. Soa we'll hev noa moar—onless ye'd like to tell us whet Yankeeland's rightly like."

Mr. Smith drew a deep breath. "Well, what would you like to hear about?"

"About cowboys," young Gollicker breathed. "Werta ivver a cowboy?"

For a moment Mr. Smith stood on a brink, and then an imp pushed him over.

"Of course I've been a cowboy—naturally," Mr. Smith said. "What would you like to hear about it?"

"Wait a minute," Gollicker said. They all adjusted themselves on the bench. "Now," he went on, "tell us about a roundup—tha knows, 'Ah'm yeading for t' last roundup,' like Bing Crosby sings."

Mr. Smith held his mental breath and plunged.

"Ah," he said. "A roundup and the life of a cowboy. Up at the crack of dawn, mates, and down to the corral. There you rope your horse—"

"A mustang?" Gollicker asked.

"A mustang," Mr. Smith agreed.

"A wild one off'n the prairies, happen?"

"Indeed a wild one from off the prairies," Mr. Smith agreed. "I see you know America yourself."

Gollicker grinned modestly. "Doan't let me interrupt, measter," he apologized.

Mr. Smith drew another breath. He saw he was up against at least one expert, so he made it very good. Inwardly he thanked fate for what he had hitherto regarded as two entirely misspent weeks on a Nevada dude ranch. He gave them, in more senses than one, a moving picture of the cowboy's life.

When he was done, Gollicker sighed and Big Ian nodded.

"Now," Sam said, "how about them bloody buffalo?"

"Ah, the buffalo," Mr. Smith said. "The thundering herd! The bison! For a while there was danger—or thought to be—that the herds were dying out. But now, I am glad to say—and no doubt you are just as glad to hear—the herds are increasing, and ere long, again the crack of a rifle will bring down a bull in full gallop."

"But how about them bloody Indians?"

Saw put in. Mr. Smith considered the Indians at the station in Santa Fe. They didn't seem at all satisfactory. But he was inspired. He drew himself up.

"You will pardon me if I do not speak of that," he said. "We have not too much love for the paleface who stole our lands. I say 'we,' for my mother was Yellow Blanket, a princess of the Blackfoot tribe. Therefore, let us not speak of the white man and the red man."

He stared into the fire—majestically, he hoped.

"Now, see what tha's done?" Ian said to Saw. "Happen it'll learn thee to keep thy yapper shut once in a while. . . . Tha maun excuse him, measter. Tell us about gangsters instead. Didta ivver run into any gangsters?"

"Run into them? Why, how could you help it?" Mr. Smith asked.

Swiftly and graphically he painted for them an America in which here was the town where the bullets of the gangs cracked day and night. Here was the last street, and on it the last house, and beyond that was the trackless prairie where the buffalo thundered, the cowboy rode, and the Indian ever lurked.

As he finished, he looked up. Everyone in the inn was listening. Men had gathered behind him silently. At the bar, the maid leaned on her elbows, entranced.

"Ah, I talk too much," Mr. Smith said.

"Nay, goa on, lad," they said. "Goa on."

"Well, it's dry work. How about a drink?"

"Champion."

"Owd on," Big Ian said. "Us'll play darts for a round."

"Now, Ian, if the lad wants to buy—"

"Ah said," Ian repeated, "us'll play darts —onybody that wishes to be in on t' round. And t' loser will pay."

Mr. Smith paid anyhow, for the dart game was trickier than he had thought, and they all seemed to be experts.

He was getting very much better when the barmaid called: "Time, gentlemen, please."

Mr. Smith was sorry. It had been a good evening. They all said good night cheerfully. Big Ian shook him by the hand.

"Well soa long, lad. We had a champion time. But Ah just want to say, tha didn't fool me when tha were kidding us at first. Tha sees, for one thing, us goas to t' pictures and so us knaws whet America's really like. And then Ah'd allus heeard tell that all Yankees were liars."

"Yes," Mr. Smith said, regarding his conscience, "I did tell some lies."

"Aye, but Ah suppose it's a way ye Yankees hev," Ian said. "But it's all right as long as tha told us t' trewth finally."

The man who wrote this story

ERIC KNIGHT   1897–1943

Because he was the third son of a poor English family, Eric Knight did not get to America until he was fifteen. His mother was the first of the family to come to America, and the children were sent to her, one by one. By the time Eric arrived, he had already worked in English factories for three years. His first job in the United States was as a copy boy for the Philadelphia *Press*. Soon he was writing feature articles in his spare time. Then he started to catch up on his education. He was interested in art and attended four different art schools before the First World War began. After the war started, Knight enlisted in the Canadian army. When he finally returned to the United States to become an artist, he learned that he was almost totally color-blind. He tried to be a cartoonist but soon returned to newspaper work and writing.

At the outbreak of World War II, Knight again enlisted, this time as a major in the American army. He was killed in an airplane crash while en route to Africa.

Let's consider . . .

1. The Yorkshiremen had some rather strange ideas about America. Where did they get these ideas? How could this kind of misinformation about America be corrected?

2. List the imaginary characteristics of American life which Mr. Smith finally described to the Yorkshiremen.

3. Which items in Mr. Smith's true ac-

count of the United States did the York-shiremen think were untrue? Why didn't they believe him?

4. The Yorkshiremen thought that all Americans were Yankees. How did Mr. Smith try to correct them? What does your community mean by the term, *Yankee?* What other meanings are there?

5. What is a "white lie"? Find one that is told in this story. Have you ever told one? Are white lies justifiable? Why, or why not?

6. Think of movies you have seen. In what ways have these films given a false picture of life in the United States? In what ways have they truthfully portrayed American life?

b. Did Knight imply that *all* York-shiremen are like the ones in this story?

The English characters in this story spoke a Yorkshire dialect—that kind of English used by people living in Yorkshire, England. You probably noticed differences between their way of speaking English and yours. For example, the waitress asked, "Would there be owt else?" An American waitress would say, "Will there be anything else?" Find as many illustrations of the Yorkshire dialect as you can. Divide your paper into two columns. In the first column, write the expressions as they appeared in the story. In the second column, write these expressions as you would say them here in the United States.

The writer's craft . . .

You recall that a **stereotype** is a character who conforms to certain widely accepted ideas of how he should think, act, and even look. When an author creates such characters, he is stereotyping them. A person doesn't have to be an author to stereotype people. Any one can stereotype another person by simply believing that because he belongs to a certain group he will look or act in a particular way.

1. Explain why the Yorkshireman was stereotyping Americans when he said: "All Yankees are liars"?

2. Did Eric Knight stereotype the York-shiremen in this story? Before answering consider these questions:

    a. Were the Yorkshiremen exactly alike, or did Knight give them individual personalities?

Knowing words . . .

Below are several sentences taken from the selection. Read these sentences to find the meaning of the words printed in italics. After you are sure of the meaning of the italicized words, use each of them in a sentence of your own.

1. "Oh, that's easy," Mr. Smith said. "We *irrigate* the land."

2. He went into a short but *conclusive* description of irrigating.

3. "In the San Fernando Valley we buy it from the water company, just like you do in your homes."

"Wheer do they get it?"

"From *reservoirs.*"

4. Swiftly and *graphically* he painted for them an America in which here was the town where the bullets of the gangs cracked day and night.

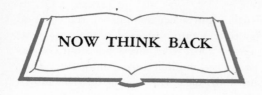

NOW THINK BACK

THINK FOR YOURSELF

When Mr. Smith visited an English inn, he found that his companions had very definite ideas about "Yankees" and the United States. Though the Yorkshiremen had never seen America and probably knew very few Americans, nothing Mr. Smith said could shake their firmly rooted beliefs. The Yorkshiremen had stereotyped Mr. Smith as a typical American.

It is all too easy to think that whole groups of people have certain characteristics. It is convenient to make stereotypes of the individual members of a group. You have probably heard remarks to the effect that Americans are ambitious or that Irishmen have quick tempers. Undoubtedly you've wanted to challenge such statements, for you know that *all* Americans are not ambitious, and that *all* Irishmen are not quick-tempered. You know, too, that each individual, even though he is part of a group, has a right to be judged on his own merits.

In SIDELIGHTS ON AMERICA you read about several different "groups" of people. Choose a group from a selection you have read either in this Part or in an earlier Part of the book. Below is a partial list which you can choose from or add to if you wish.

Foreigners	Yankees
Immigrants	Englishmen
Indians	Russians
Chinese	

1. Which group did you choose?

2. In which selection did you find a person who belonged to this group?

3. What characteristics are you apt to assign to people when you know they are part of this group?

4. Was there any person in this selection who you think was a stereotype of this group? In what ways was this person a stereotype?

5. Was there anything in the selection that proved that the character was an individual in his own right and not a stereotype? Point out such passages to the members of your committee or class.

6. Very few people are free of stereotyped thinking in one form or another. What characteristics do you think of when someone mentions policemen, detectives, doctors, or teachers?

7. How do you think specific characteristics come to be associated with different groups of people?

8. What suggestions do you have for ridding yourself of the habit of thinking of people as stereotypes?

9. In your opinion, does reading help to break down prejudices that people cling to? How? Did you learn anything new from your reading in this part? What stereotypes did you discover in your own thinking?

SHARE YOUR IDEAS

What do you think is meant by the term *100 per cent American?* Is there any such person? Here are some suggestions to help you arrive at the answers to these questions.

1. If you were going to award someone a prize for being a good American, what *three* qualities would you look for first? Was there any character—or author—in this part to whom you would give this

award? Explain why you selected this person.

2. Where do people in other lands get their false ideas about America? (Remember Mr. Smith's experience in Yorkshire.) What can be done to keep others from getting these ideas?

3. Immigrants to America have been faced with three ways of adjusting to life in this country:

   a. They could keep up their Old World customs and language, living apart with people who have the same national background.

   b. They could completely drop their old customs and language.

   c. They could become "Americanized" in customs and language, but at the same time keep what is valuable from the past and add it to the sum total of American life.

Which way do you think is best for the immigrants themselves? Which is best for the nation as a whole? How did the selections in SIDELIGHTS ON AMERICA help you answer this question?

WIDEN YOUR EXPERIENCE

Things to do . . .

1. Run a contest. Complete this sentence in twenty-five words or less: *I'm glad I live in America because—* Accept entries from individuals in your class, or plan this as a committee competition. Pick your judges, and set a deadline for submitting entries. Offer some kind of prize to the winner, if you can.

2. Conduct an experiment "in the field." First of all, divide yourselves into committees. Let each committee choose as its topic one of the groups dealt with in SIDELIGHTS ON AMERICA. You might even go further and select some racial, religious, or political group *not* represented in these stories. Once you have made your choice, let each committee take a miniature "Gallup Poll" of at least ten assorted members of the community. Strive for variety among the people you interview. Question doctors, teachers, grocers, artists, druggists, clergymen, plumbers; in short, people who are engaged in every kind of activity you can find in your neighborhood. It's a good idea to let some of them be complete strangers to you. Ask each one to give you *his* definition of the group your committee has chosen to investigate. Pool your results. How much do the opinions differ? Does the profession or trade of the person interviewed seem to influence his opinion? To what extent? How do you account for the similarities and differences? How guilty is your community of thinking of people as stereotypes?

3. Keep a class scrapbook of newspaper clippings, cartoons, and overheard remarks, which illustrate stereotyped thinking. Watch yourself. If you are an offender, be honest enough to include your own errors in judgment.

4. Set up a "Hall of Fame" bulletin board in your classroom. Put on display pictures and newspaper clippings of foreign-born Americans who have distinguished themselves in some way.

5. Organize committees to draw up lists of books on different aspects of American life. Decide what subjects your class would be most interested in. Include subjects like *The Indians of America* and *Great Americans Who Were Immigrants*.

6. Plan a class or assembly program based on the theme of this part. If your school observes Brotherhood Week or I Am an American Day, arrange to have your program presented at a school assembly. Committees may dramatize scenes from the

selections. Try to include some of the short quotations, and excerpts from the longer selections in your presentation. Assign these to individual pupils to read or recite.

7. Here are some suggestions for composition topics. Let what you write grow out of the class discussions, but be sure that you keep it very close to *you*.

World Peace Begins on Our Street
America—Hollywood Version
Meet My Neighbor
My Family's American History
Mr. Stranger, Meet America

More to read . . .

Book of Americans by ROSEMARY and STEPHEN VINCENT BENÉT. Ballads are fun to read, especially if they are about famous Americans, from Pocahontas to Woodrow Wilson. Rinehart & Co., Inc., 1933.

Cowboy Songs and Other Frontier Ballads by JOHN and ALLEN LOMAX (eds.). If you like to sing, play music, or read the history of America in its folk songs, look at this book and two others by the same authors: *American Ballads and Folk Songs* and *Folk Songs: U.S.A.* The Macmillan Company, 1938, 1934; Duell, Sloan & Pearce, Inc., 1948.

Yankee Doodle's Cousins by ANNE BURNETT MALCOLMSON (ed.). Here are more tales about Pecos Bill, John Henry, Paul Bunyan and many other legendary American heroes. Houghton Mifflin Company, 1941.

On Our Way by ROBERT PATTERSON. In each of these stories a different young American tells how he was "on his way." Here you meet people like Bob Feller, Burl Ives, and Mark Twain. Holiday House, Inc., 1952.

Leif Eriksson, First Voyager to America by KATHERINE B. SHIPPEN. The boyhood of Leif Eriksson in Iceland, Greenland, and Norway is beautifully described and illustrated in this book. Harper & Brothers, 1951.

Drums by JAMES BOYD. James Fraser's father sent him to England to keep him out of the Revolutionary War. But Jim meets John Paul Jones and sees active service. Charles Scribner's Sons, 1928.

Young 'Un by HERBERT BEST. A family of young children, without mother or father, make a home for themselves. This is an interesting story of frontier life along Lake Champlain soon after the Revolutionary War. The Macmillan Company, 1944.

Geronimo: The Last Apache War Chief by EDGAR WYATT. The last Indian to hold out against the white man was a fierce warrior. This is the exciting story of his life. McGraw-Hill Book Company, Inc., 1952.

America's Robert E. Lee by HENRY S. COMMAGER. This biography tells you more about the Civil War than you could learn from fiction. Houghton Mifflin Company, 1951.

Brave Men by ERNIE PYLE. The news dispatches which Ernie Pyle sent home during World War II from the American fronts in France and Sicily were widely read. No one knew the American soldier better than this writer who was the favorite voice of the "G.I." Henry Holt and Company, Inc., 1944.

Our Foreign Born Citizens by ANNIE E. S. BEARD (ed.). True stories can be as interesting as fiction. These deal with the lives of people from many countries who made important contributions to American life. The Thomas Y. Crowell Company, 1946.

Johnny Tremain by ESTHER FORBES. Johnny, an apprentice silversmith, burns his hand badly but finds a chance to conquer his handicap. He becomes a messenger during the Revolutionary War and even helps to send Paul Revere on his famous ride. Houghton Mifflin Company, 1943.

Glamorous Dolly Madison by ALICE CURTIS DESMOND. This is a full-length biography of the Quaker girl who became the wife of a president and the friend of many of the most important men of the Revolution. Dodd, Mead & Company, 1946.

Daniel Boone by JAMES HENRY DAUGHERTY. Daniel Boone, one of the most famous frontiersmen, is described with all the high spirit and manly laughter of his time. The Viking Press, 1939.

The Pony Express by SAMUEL H. ADAMS. Here is a vivid picture of the men who carried the mails through Indian country, across deserts, and over mountains. Random House, Inc., 1951.

Anything Can Happen by GEORGE and HELEN PAPASHVILY. You will laugh with George Papashvily as he tells of his adventures as an American immigrant. For more good fun, try his book on animals, *Thanks to Noah*. Harper & Brothers, 1945, 1951.

The Luck of Roaring Camp, and Other Stories by BRET HARTE. These short stories, by a great American author, describe the life of the Western mining towns when the gold rush was only a few years past. Houghton Mifflin Company, 1942.

My Antonia by WILLA CATHER. Dark-eyed, attractive Tony and her Bohemian family struggle for existence as pioneers in Nebraska. Houghton Mifflin Company, 1918.

The Other Side of the Fence by JOHN R. TUNIS. A young man hitchhikes across the country and learns that the grass just *seems* greener on the other side of the fence. William Morrow & Company, Inc., 1953.

PEOPLE WHO DARED

Some people go in search of challenges. No one forced Admiral Byrd to spend six months alone in the coldest region of the world. He *chose* to test himself against the cold and loneliness of the South Pole.

Other people have challenges thrust upon them. You may have heard of Helen Keller, a deaf and blind girl, who struggled against a world of silent darkness. Her courage brought her a rich, full life. And did you know that Supreme Court Justice William O. Douglas fought a crippling paralysis and learned to walk again?

There are no limits for people who dare. Even now, adventurous men and women are preparing to explore the unknown regions of space.

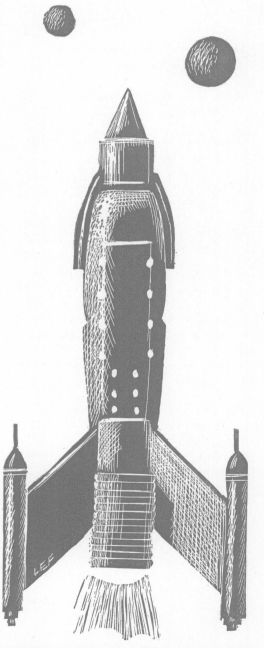

PART SEVEN

PEOPLE WHO DARED

The Victory

WILLIAM O. DOUGLAS

Bill's friends thought he was a fool. Why should a person go climbing all over the mountainside when there were plenty of amusements in town and a lot more comfort? Bill had his reasons, though. Do they make sense to *you?*

There was a driving force that took me first to the foothills and then to the mountains, though I myself did not recognize it for what it was until years later. From the time I was about twelve years old I took every occasion to slip out of town for hikes into the foothills. The occasions were not frequent, for each day after school I delivered newspapers and on Saturdays I worked in stores, creameries, and cold storage plants. In the summer months I worked in the packing houses and orchards at all the jobs that were available—thinning of fruit, spraying, irrigating, picking, making boxes, packing fruit, icing and loading refrigerator cars. There was a regular sequence of fruit during the summer—cherries, apricots, peaches, pears, and apples. But there were gaps between the crops. And in the fall, winter, and spring, there were Sunday afternoons, holidays, and occasional evenings when a few hours would be free. On these occasions I explored the foothills.

I would leave the town and head toward Selah Gap, the point of the foothills nearest my home on North Fifth Avenue. There I could test my legs and lungs against the hillside. It was hard work: two

miles at the fast pace of perhaps five or six miles an hour; the climb of a hillside 500 feet or more in elevation; then a return to home and bed, dead tired, every muscle of my legs aching. Time and again I followed this routine, turning my back on more pleasant diversions that Yakima offered.

A friend who preferred the shade of the locust trees in the city, the movies, and the reading room of the Y.M.C.A. would taunt me about these trips. He conceded that it took something special to climb the monotonous foothills over and again. But he added, "Being a fool don't hurt any either."

It was, however, infantile paralysis that drove me to the outdoors.

I had had it when I was a small child. I ran a high fever for several weeks. All but the country doctor despaired of my life, and he had only a slightly more optimistic view. He finally confided in Mother and gave her his candid opinion: There was a good chance that I would lose the use of my legs; even if I did not, I would not live long—probably not beyond forty. He had no remedy for the short life. He did, however, have a prescription for the legs—a prescription that the medical profession forty years later had hardly improved upon. His prescription was frequent massage in salt water, a fifteen-minute massage every two hours every day for weeks.

Mother kept a vigil. She soaked my legs in warm salt water and rubbed it into my pores, massaging each leg muscle every two hours, day after day, night after night. She did not go to bed for six weeks. The fever passed; but the massages continued for weeks thereafter.

I vaguely recall the ordeal. I lay in bed too weak to move. My legs felt like pipe-stems; they seemed almost detached, the property of someone else. They were so small and thin that Mother's hands could go clear around them. She would knead them like bread; she would push her hands up them and then down, up and down, up and down, until my skin was red and raw. But she would not stop because of that. She said she wanted me to be strong, to be able to run. She told me that when she was a girl she could run like the wind; no one could catch her. She wondered if I would ever be able to do so. And then she'd laugh and rub my legs—rub and rub and rub—and two hours later, rub some more.

One day the doctor came and I sat on the edge of the bed. I could not stand alone. I reached for Mother's hand, pulled myself up, and stood there weak and un-steady. I tried to walk but could not. I saw tears in Mother's eyes, and she and the doctor went away to have a whispered con-versation.

The massages continued. I lay in bed most of the time. Each day I tried to walk a bit. The weakness in my legs gradually disappeared. My feet would flop a bit; the muscles of my knees would twitch; curious numb sensations would come and go. But before many months I relearned to walk, and the frailty which the disease had

caused seemed to pass. Someone said that the salt water and massages had effected wonders. Mother was silent awhile and then said, "So did my prayers."

But the ordeal had left its scars. Mother believed the doctor implicitly, and was con-vinced that the sand would fast run out of my glass. So she set about to guard my health, to protect me against physical strains, to do all sorts of favors designed to save my energy. I was waited on, hand and foot. Worse than that, I began to hear what Mother was saying to others: "He's not as strong as other boys; he has to be careful what he does—you know, his legs were almost paralyzed."

This solicitousness set up a severe reac-tion. It seemed to me I was being publicly recognized as a puny person—a weakling. Thus there began to grow in me a great rebellion. I protested against Mother's descriptions of me. But I believe my re-bellion was not so much against her as it was against the kind of person I thought I was coming to be.

The crisis in my attitude was reached when I was around thirteen years old. I wore knee breeches, knickerbocker style. Black cotton stockings covered my legs. I was spindly. Concentrated exercise, like sprinting or wrestling, made me feel faint; and sometimes I'd be sick at my stomach or get a severe headache. I was deeply sensitive about my condition and used many a stratagem to conceal my physical weakness.

One day I was walking to school, carry-ing a pile of books under one arm. I heard a group of boys coming behind. They were older boys in the same public school, but strangers to me. As they caught up, one said, "Look at that kid's skinny legs. Aren't they something? Did you ever see anything as funny?"

The others laughed; then another one

ashamed of my appearance. I became self-conscious and shy. I was irritable and sensitive to criticism.

I imagined I saw in the appraising eyes of everyone who looked at me the thought, "Yes, he's a weakling." The idea festered. As I look back on those early years, I think I became a rebel with a cause. My cause was the disproof of the charge of inferiority that had been leveled by the jury of my contemporaries. There was no one in whom I could confide; no one to whom I could express my inner turmoil and tension. So the revolt grew and grew in my heart.

My first resolve, I think, was to prove my superiority by achievement in a field that was open even to a boy with weak and puny legs. That field was the schoolroom. "I can get good grades, if I work," I said. "I can get better grades than any strong-legged boy in school. I can get 100 in every course."

No one could get higher grades than that. I'd prove I was not a weakling. So I threw myself into that endeavor. I poured every ounce of energy I could muster into my studies and came close to making the scholastic record I had set for myself.

But my scholastic achievements did not solve my difficulties. There was the haunting thought that infantile paralysis had left me a weakling, that I was indeed a cripple, unable to compete with other boys in the physical world. And the physical world loomed large in my mind. I read what happened to cripples in the wild. They were the weak strain that nature did not protect. They were cast aside, discarded for hardier types. The coyote got the deer or fawn that was too weak to keep up with the others. The crippled bird did not have much chance to survive the cats and hawks and other enemies that roamed the country-

said, "Sure would cover them up if they were mine."

The words were a lash across my face. The laughter burned like an iron on my neck. I was humiliated and ashamed. I wanted to retort. But I trembled and my throat became dry so I could not answer. Then, as quickly as a flash flood, came tears.

I could not face up to the boys because of the tears. I had to turn away. It seemed that by crying I had not only confirmed but had proved the charge twice over. I stood condemned in the public eye—a weakling.

A great depression swept over me and lingered for months. I didn't want to go to school, I wanted to hide. I wanted long trousers—an idea that Mother pooh-poohed. I wanted to stay indoors. I felt side. Man was the same, I thought. Only strong men can do the work of the world —operating trains, felling trees, digging ditches, managing farms. Only robust men can be heroes of a war.

During my school studies I had read of the Spartans of ancient Greece. They were rugged and hardy people, the kind that I aspired to be. So I searched out the literature that described their habits and capacities to see if I could get some clue to their toughness. My research brought to light various staggering bits of information. I found in Plato's *Republic* a passage that shattered my morale. Plato talked of the dangers to the race through propagation of the "inferior" type of person. By the "inferior" he meant those who were physical weaklings. There was no doubt about it, because he described what should be done with children of that character.

The proper officers will take the off-spring of the good parents to the pen or fold, and there they will deposit them with certain nurses who dwell in a separate quarter, but the offspring of the inferior, or of the better when they chance to be deformed, will be put away in some mysterious, unknown place, as they should be.

These were ideas that I struggled against. It was oppressive to think that I would have been destroyed by the Spartans to make room for some hardier boy. By boyhood standards I was a failure. If I were to have happiness and success, I must get strong. And so I searched for ways and means to do it.

One day I met another boy, whom I had known at Sunday school, coming in on a fast walk from the country. He was a husky, long-legged chap, to me a perfect physical specimen. I asked him where he'd been, and he replied that he had been climbing the foothills north of town. I asked him why he did it. He told me that his doctor had advised it; that he was trying to correct certain difficulties following an illness. He was climbing the foothills every day to develop his lungs and legs.

An overwhelming light swept me. My resolution was instantaneous. I would do the same. I would make my legs strong on the foothills. Thus I started my treks, and used the foothills as one uses weights or bars in a gymnasium. First I tried to go up the hills without stopping. When I conquered that, I tried to go up without change of pace. When that was achieved, I practiced going up not only without a change of pace but whistling as I went.

That fall and winter the foothills began to work a transformation in me. By the time the next spring arrived, I had found new confidence in myself. My legs were filling out. They were getting stronger. I could go the two miles to Selah Gap at a fast pace and often reach the top of the ridge without losing a step or reducing my speed. Following these hikes the muscles of my knees would twitch and make it difficult for me to sleep at night. But I felt an increasing flow of health in my legs, and a growing sense of contentment in my heart.

The man who wrote this selection

WILLIAM O. DOUGLAS 1898–

William Douglas is the son of a poor traveling preacher from Minnesota. The life of a traveling preacher was harsh, and the elder Douglas died when William was a child. The family was left with little money, and the mother and children wandered over most of the West before they finally settled in Washington. William

Douglas had to work to help support his family. He would never have been able to go to college if he had not won a scholarship, but with the scholarship and part-time jobs, he was able to graduate and send money to his family as well.

He came to New York with twelve cents in his pocket, determined to earn a degree in law. He borrowed enough money from a fraternity brother to pay his enrollment fee at law school. He was an excellent student, and in six months he found profitable jobs that he could do and still keep up his studies.

After graduation, he taught at several law schools. He was such a good teacher that he was once offered an enormous salary to teach at the University of Chicago. His reputation spread, and in 1939 he was appointed a justice of the U. S. Supreme Court. He is the youngest appointee in over a century.

In his spare time, Justice Douglas is an ardent mountain climber and traveler. He has written a book about his mountain climbing experiences, *Of Men and Mountains*. A description of some of his travels is included in *Strange Lands and Friendly People*.

Let's consider . . .

1. Infantile paralysis left Bill so weak that he could not walk. Yet each day he *tried* to walk a little. Why was his trying such an important part of his recovery?

2. When Bill's mother began telling people that he was not as strong as other boys, how did Bill react?

3. A group of boys ridiculed Bill's thin legs. Why were their comments unjust? Thoughtless remarks often hurt people— even though such remarks are usually made unintentionally. Have you ever been the victim of this kind of remark? How did it make you feel? Have you ever been guilty of making such remarks yourself? What were the results of your thoughtlessness? What is the best way to avoid this kind of unpleasantness?

4. When Bill felt that everyone considered him a weakling, he became self-conscious, shy, and irritable. He felt compelled to show that he was as strong as other boys. How did he use the classroom to prove that he was not weak?

5. Describe Bill's work-outs on the foothills.

6. Which took the greater courage, victory in the classroom or victory on the foothills? How did the first victory help him to achieve the second?

7. Even if Bill's physical weakness had not improved, how could he still have been strong, happy, and successful?

8. Describe Mrs. Douglas' role in her son's recovery. How may parents and other members of the family help an invalid to get back to everyday living? What can friends contribute? What can strangers do?

9. Do you know anyone who has overcome a serious physical handicap or learned to live with it? How did he meet the challenge?

The writer's craft . . .

In his story William O. Douglas told you how he won a victory over a physical handicap. Now try your hand at writing a story about an obstacle which you have overcome. You might describe the way you overcame your fear of high places, or the way you mastered a new skill. Think of all the obstacles you have overcome and select one which you think your classmates would enjoy hearing about. Be sure to give your story human interest appeal.

Knowing words . . .

Below are several sentences taken from the selection. Each of the sentences has one word written in italics. After you are sure of the meaning of the italicized word, use it in a sentence of your own.

1. There was a regular *sequence* of fruit during the summer—cherries, apricots, peaches, pears, and apples.

2. He finally confided in Mother and gave her his *candid* opinion.

3. Mother kept a *vigil*.

4. Mother believed the doctor *implicitly*.

5. But before many months I relearned to walk, and the *frailty* which the disease had caused seemed to pass.

6. I imagined I saw in the *appraising* eyes of everyone who looked at me the thought, "Yes, he's a weakling."

Stone

By my own acts, the trumpet or the chain
May blare or bind, I stand by what I said.
I wear no cross, I bear no nation's pain,
By my own acts I stumble or fall dead.

Then on my stone may these few words be read:
"He saw a cloud and followed it all day.
His feet tripped often for his lifted head;
His cloud was vapor, and it blew away."

"I saw a cloud, I saw a cloud!" he said.
He saw a cloud, there is no more to say.
                                    Donald Drummond

David and Goliath

OLD TESTAMENT

The Bible is rich in stories which people never tire of reading. You may have already heard or read this tale of the plucky little shepherd who challenged to single combat the most ferocious soldier of the enemy troops.

Now the Philistines [1] mustered their armed forces for war, and they were gathered together at Socoh, which belongs to Judah; and they encamped between Socoh and Azekah. And Saul and the men of Israel were gathered together and encamped in the valley of Elah; and they drew up in line of battle facing the Philistines. And the Philistines stood on a mountain on one side, and Israel stood on a mountain on the other side: and there was a valley between them.

And there came out a champion from the camp of the Philistines, named Goliath of Gath, whose height was about ten feet. And he had a helmet of bronze upon his head, and he was armed with a coat of mail [2] which weighed some two hundred pounds. And he had guards of bronze upon his legs, and a round shield of bronze between his shoulders. And the shaft of his spear was like a weaver's beam, [3] and the head of his iron spear weighed twenty-four pounds, and his shield-bearer went before him.

And he stood and shouted to the armies of Israel, and said to them, "Why have you come out to draw up the line of battle? Am I not a Philistine and you the servants of Saul? Choose for yourselves a man and let him come down to me. If he is able to fight with me and can kill me, then we will be your servants; but if I overcome him and kill him, then you shall be our servants and serve *us*."

And the Philistine said, "I defy the armies of Israel today; give me a man that we may fight together." When Saul and all Israel heard these words of the Philistine, they were dismayed and greatly afraid.

Now David was the son of an Ephrathite of Bethlehem in Judah, whose name was Jesse. Jesse had eight sons, and in the days of Saul he was an old man. His three eldest sons followed Saul to battle, and their names were Eliab the firstborn, and the second Abinadab, and the third Shammah. But David was the youngest, so the three eldest having followed Saul, David went with them, but returned from Saul to feed his father's flock at Bethlehem.

And Goliath, the Philistine, drew near morning and evening and repeated his challenge to the armies of Israel for forty days.

---

[1] *Philistines*, members of an ancient warlike tribe that once lived along the coast of Palestine
[2] *mail*, a type of armor made of small metal rings
[3] *weaver's beam*, large rod that is part of the loom used in weaving

Jesse said to David his son, "Take now your brothers a bushel of this parched grain and those ten loaves, and take them quickly to the camp to your brothers. And carry these ten cheeses to the captain of their thousand. And see how your brothers fare, and give them my blessing."

So David rose up early in the morning and left the flock with a keeper and took, and went, as Jesse had commanded him. And he came to the encampment just as the army was going forth to the battle-lines facing each other. And David left his supplies in the care of the keeper of the baggage and ran to the battle-line and came and greeted his brothers. And while he was talking to them, the champion, the Philistine of Gath, Goliath by name, was seen coming up from the Philistine's lines, and he spoke the same words as before; and David heard them. And all the men of Israel, when they saw the man, fled from him and were panic-stricken. And the men of Israel said, "Have you seen this man who comes up? Surely to defy Israel he comes. And it shall be that the man who slays him, the king will enrich with great riches, and will give him his daughter, and make his father's house free in Israel."

Then David spoke to the men who stood by him, saying, "What did you say shall be done for the man who overcomes this Philistine and takes away the reproach from Israel? For who is this heathen Philistine that he should defy the armies of the living God?"

And the people replied to him repeating the above words, saying, "Thus it shall be done for the man who overcomes him."

Now Eliab his eldest brother heard when he spoke to the men, and Eliab's anger was aroused against David, and he said, "Why have you come down? And with whom have you left those few sheep in the wilderness? I know your pride and the wickedness in your heart: you have come down to see the battle."

And David said, "What have I done now? Is there not cause enough for some one to speak out?" And turning away from his brother, he spoke to others around him as he had been speaking. And they answered him as at first. And when the words that David spoke were widely heard, they were reported to Saul, and the king sent for him.

Then David said to Saul, "Let not my lord's courage fail him; your servant will go and fight with this Philistine."

And Saul said to David, "You are not able to go against this Philistine to fight with him, for you are but a youth, and he has been a warrior from his youth."

But David said to Saul, "Your servant has been a shepherd with his father's flock, and when a lion or a bear would come and take a sheep out of the flock, I would go out after him and attack him and deliver it from his mouth. And if he rose up against me, I would seize him by his beard and wound him and kill him.

"Your servant has killed both lion and bear, and this heathen Philistine shall be as one of them, since he has defied the armies of the living God. The Lord who delivered me from the paw of the lion and the paw of the bear, will deliver me from the hand of this Philistine."

Thereupon Saul said to David, "Go, and may the Lord be with you."

And Saul clothed David with his garments, and put a helmet of bronze on his head, and armed him with a coat of mail. And David girded his sword upon his armor, then tried to walk, but could not, for he was not used to them.

And David said to Saul, "I cannot go with these for I am not used to them." And David took all the armor off. And he took his staff in his hand, and chose five smooth

stones out of a brook and put them in a shepherd's bag which he had. And with his sling in his hand he advanced toward the Philistine.

And the Philistine came on and drew near to David, and the man that bore his shield went before him. And when the Philistine looked closely at David, he scorned him for he was but a youth and ruddy and of a fair countenance.

And the Philistine said to David, "Am I a dog that you come out to me with sticks?" And the Philistine cursed David by his gods, and said to David, "Come to me and I will give your flesh to the birds of the heavens and the beasts of the field."

Then David said to Goliath, "You come to me with a sword and with a spear and with a shield; but I come to you in the name of the Lord of hosts, the God of the armies of Israel whom you have defied. Today the Lord will deliver you into my hands, and I will slay you, and take your head from you, and give the carcasses of the host of the Philistines today unto the fowls of the air and to the wild beasts of the earth, that all the earth may know that there is a God in Israel. And all this multitude shall know that not with the sword and spear does the Lord deliver, for the battle is the Lord's and he will give you into our hands."

And when the Philistine arose and drew near to meet David, David also hastened and ran to meet the Philistine. And David put his hand in his bag and took from it a stone and slung it and struck the Philistine on the forehead; and the stone sank into the forehead so that he fell on his face to the earth.

So David prevailed over the Philistine with a sling and with a stone, and smote [4] the Philistine and slew him; but there was no sword in the hand of David. And David ran and stood over the Philistine, and took his sword and drew it out of its sheath, and cut off his head with it. And when the Philistines saw that their champion was dead, they fled.

[Adapted from the first book of Samuel]

---

[4] *smote,* hit

Let's consider . . .

1. David seemed a poor match for Goliath. Compare the physical qualifications of the two men. Although Goliath had great physical strength, how was David superior?

2. Why did David win against such overwhelming odds? What important lesson can you learn from his story?

3. How do reports in today's newspapers prove there are still some Davids in the world? Bring a newspaper clipping to class that tells of the triumph of the "small" over the "mighty."

4. Why has the triumph of the little man been such a popular subject throughout the ages? Can you think of other examples of these triumphs which you have met in your reading?

The writer's craft . . .

"David and Goliath" was certainly dramatic. Did you notice how the drama of the story was intensified by words which described physical actions? Look again at the many action words in the story and see how they heightened the dramatic effect.

1. Select a paragraph from the story and list all the words representing different kinds of action.

2. Demonstrate how important these words were to the dramatic quality by trying to rewrite the paragraph without using them.

3. Now describe a dramatic incident which you have seen or heard about. Make the incident "come to life" by using as many action words as you can.

"O God! Our Help in Ages Past"

O God! our help in ages past,
　Our hope for years to come,
Our shelter from the stormy blast,
　And our eternal home!

Under the shadow of Thy Throne
　Thy saints have dwelt secure;
Sufficient is Thine arm alone,
　And our defense is sure.

Before the hills in order stood,
　Or earth received her fame,
From everlasting Thou art God,
　To endless years the same.

A thousand ages in Thy sight
　Are like an evening gone;
Short as the watch that ends the night
　Before the rising sun.

Time, like an ever-rolling stream,
　Bears all its sons away;
They fly, forgotten, as a dream
　Dies at the opening day.

O God! our help in ages past,
　Our hope for years to come,
Be Thou our guide when troubles last,
　And our eternal home!

Isaac Watts

Kon-Tiki

THOR HEYERDAHL

Thor Heyerdahl and five companions risked their lives to prove a scientific theory. They believed that the South Sea Islands were peopled by Indians from ancient Peru who had crossed the ocean on crude log rafts. Few scientists supported this theory. How could a raft stay afloat in the rough waters of the Pacific Ocean? To prove that such a voyage was possible, Heyerdahl and his companions constructed a raft just like a prehistoric Indian vessel and started across the Pacific. You will read about their first few days at sea.

There was a bustle in Callao Harbor the day the *Kon-Tiki* was to be towed out to sea. The minister of marine had ordered the naval tug *Guardian Rios* to tow us out of the bay and cast us off clear of the coastal traffic, out where in times gone by the Indians used to lie fishing from their rafts. The papers had published the news under both red and black headlines, and there was a crowd of people down on the quays from early in the morning of April 28.

We six who were to assemble on board all had little things to do at the eleventh hour, and, when I came down to the quay, only Herman was there keeping guard over the raft. I intentionally stopped the car a long way off and walked the whole length of the mole to stretch my legs thoroughly for the last time for no one knew how long. I jumped on board the raft, which looked an utter chaos of banana clusters, fruit baskets, and sacks which had been hurled on board at the very last moment and were to be stowed and made fast. In the middle of the heap Herman sat resignedly holding on to a cage with a green parrot in it, a farewell present from a friendly soul in Lima.

"Look after the parrot a minute," said Herman. "I must go ashore. The tug won't be here for hours."

He had hardly disappeared among the swarm on the quay when people began to point and wave. And round the point at full speed came the tug *Guardian Rios*. She dropped anchor on the farther side of a waving forest of masts which blocked the way in to the *Kon-Tiki* and sent a large motorboat to tow us out between the sailing craft. She was packed full of seamen, officers, and movie photographers, and, while orders rang out and cameras clicked, a stout towrope was made fast to the raft's bow.

"*Un momento,*"[1] I shouted in despair from where I sat with the parrot. "It's too early; we must wait for the others—*los expedicionarios,*"[2] I explained and pointed toward the city.

But nobody understood. The officers only smiled politely, and the knot at our bow was made fast in more than exemplary manner. I cast off the rope and flung it overboard with all manner of signs and gesticulations. The parrot utilized the opportunity afforded by all the confusion to stick its beak out of the cage and turn the knob of the door, and when I turned round it was strutting cheerfully about the bamboo deck. I tried to catch it, but it shrieked rudely in Spanish and fluttered away over the banana clusters. With one eye on the sailors who were trying to cast a rope over the bow I started a wild chase after the parrot. It fled shrieking into the bamboo cabin, where I got it into a corner and caught it by one leg as it tried to flutter over me. When I came out again and stuffed my flapping trophy into its cage, the sailors on land had cast off the raft's moorings, and we were dancing helplessly in and out with the backwash of the long swell that came rolling in over the mole. In despair I seized a paddle and vainly tried to parry a violent bump as the raft was flung against the wooden piles of the quay. Then the motorboat started, and with a jerk the *Kon-Tiki* began her long voyage.

My only companion was a Spanish-speaking parrot which sat glaring sulkily in a cage. People on shore cheered and waved, and the swarthy movie photographers in the motorboat almost jumped into the sea in their eagerness to catch every detail of the expedition's dramatic start from Peru. Despairing and alone I stood on the raft looking out for my lost companions, but none appeared. So we came out to the *Guardian Rios,* which was lying with steam up ready to lift anchor and start. I was up the rope ladder in a twinkling and made so much row on board that the start was postponed and a boat sent back to the quay. It was away a good while, and then it came back full of pretty *señoritas* but without a single one of the *Kon-Tiki's* missing men. This was all very well but it did not solve my problems, and, while the raft swarmed with charming *señoritas,* the boat went back on a fresh search for *los expedicionarios noruegos.*[3]

Meanwhile Erik and Bengt came sauntering down to the quay with their arms full of reading matter and odds and ends. They met the whole stream of people on its way home and were finally stopped at a police barrier by a kindly official who told them there was nothing more to see. Bengt told the officer, with an airy gesture of his cigar, that they had not come to see anything; they themselves were going with the raft.

"It's no use," the officer said indulgently. "The *Kon-Tiki* sailed an hour ago."

"Impossible," said Erik, producing a parcel. "Here's the lantern!"

"And there's the navigator," said Bengt, "and I'm the steward."

They forced their way past, but the raft had gone. They trotted desperately to and fro along the mole where they met the rest of the party, who also were searching eagerly for the vanished raft. Then they caught sight of the boat coming in, and so

---

[1] *un momento,* one moment [*Spanish*]
[2] *los expedicionarios,* the members of the expedition [*Spanish*]

[3] *los expedicionarios noruegos,* the Norwegian members of the expedition [*Spanish*]

we were all six finally united and the water was foaming round the raft as the *Guardian Rios* towed us out to sea.

It had been late in the afternoon when at last we started, and the *Guardian Rios* would not cast us off till we were clear of the coastal traffic next morning. Directly we were clear of the mole we met a bit of a head sea, and all the small boats which were accompanying us turned back one by one. Only a few big yachts came with us out to the entrance to the bay to see how things would go out there.

The *Kon-Tiki* followed the tug like an angry billy goat on a rope, and she butted her bow into the head sea so that the water rushed on board. This did not look very promising, for this was a calm sea compared with what we had to expect. In the middle of the bay the towrope broke, and our end of it sank peacefully to the bottom while the tug steamed ahead. We flung ourselves down along the side of the raft to fish for the end of the rope, while the yachts went on and tried to stop the tug. Stinging jellyfish as thick as washtubs splashed up and down with the seas alongside the raft and covered all the ropes with a slippery, stinging coating of jelly. When the raft rolled one way, we hung flat over the side waving our arms down toward the surface of the water, until our fingers just touched the slimy towrope. Then the raft rolled back again, and we all stuck our heads deep down into the sea, while salt water and giant jellyfish poured over our backs. We spat and cursed and pulled jellyfish fibers out of our hair, but when the tug came back the rope end was up and ready for splicing.

When we were about to throw it on board the tug, we suddenly drifted in under the vessel's overhanging stern and were in danger of being crushed against her by the pressure of the water. We dropped everything we had and tried to push ourselves clear with bamboo sticks and paddles before it was too late. But we never got a proper position, for when we were in the trough of the sea we could not reach the iron roof above us, and when the water rose again the *Guardian Rios* dropped her whole stern down into the water and would have crushed us flat if the suction had carried us underneath. Up on the tug's deck people were running about and shouting; at last the propeller began to turn alongside us, and it helped us clear of the backwash under the *Guardian Rios* in the last second. The bow of the raft had had a few hard knocks and had become a little crooked in the lashings, but this fault rectified itself by degrees.

"When a thing starts so damnably, it's bound to end well," said Herman. "If only this towing could stop; it'll shake the raft to bits."

The towing went on all night at a slow speed and with only one or two small hitches. The yachts had bidden us farewell long ago, and the last coast light had disappeared astern. Only a few ships' lights passed us in the darkness. We divided the night into watches to keep an eye on the towrope, and we all had a good snatch of sleep. When it grew light next morning, a thick mist lay over the coast of Peru, while we had a brilliant blue sky ahead of us to westward. The sea was running in a long quiet swell covered with little white crests, and clothes and logs and everything we took hold of were soaking wet with dew. It was chilly, and the green water round us was astonishingly cold for 12° south.

We were in the Humboldt Current, which carries its cold masses of water up from the Antarctic and sweeps them north all along the coast of Peru till they swing west and out across the sea just below the

Equator. It was out here that Pizarro, Zárate, and the other early Spaniards saw for the first time the Inca Indians' big sailing rafts, which used to go out for 50 to 60 sea miles to catch tunnies and dolphins in the same Humboldt Current. All day long there was an offshore wind out here, but in the evening the onshore wind reached as far out as this and helped the rafts home if they needed it.

In the early light we saw our tug lying close by, and we took care that the raft lay far enough away from her bow while we launched our little inflated rubber dinghy. It floated on the waves like a football and danced away with Erik, Bengt, and myself till we caught hold of the *Guardian Rios*' rope ladder and clambered on board. With Bengt as interpreter we had our exact position shown us on our chart. We were 50 sea miles from land in a northwesterly direction from Callao, and we were to carry lights the first few nights so as not to be sunk by coasting ships. Farther out we would not meet a single ship, for no shipping route ran through that part of the Pacific.

We took a ceremonious farewell of all on board, and many strange looks followed us as we climbed down into the dinghy and went tumbling back over the waves to the *Kon-Tiki*. Then the towrope was cast off and the raft was alone again. Thirty-five men on board the *Guardian Rios* stood at the rail waving for as long as we could distinguish outlines. And six men sat on the boxes on board the *Kon-Tiki* and followed the tug with their eyes as long as they could see her. Not till the black column of smoke had dissolved and vanished over the horizon did we shake our heads and look at one another.

"Good-by, good-by," said Torstein. "Now we'll have to start the engine, boys!"

We laughed and felt the wind. There was a rather light breeze, which had veered from south to southeast. We hoisted the bamboo yard with the big square sail. It only hung down slack, giving Kon-Tiki's face a wrinkled, discontented appearance.

"The old man doesn't like it," said Erik. "There were fresher breezes when he was young."

"It looks as if we were losing ground," said Herman, and he threw a piece of balsa wood overboard at the bow.

"One-two-three . . . thirty-nine, forty, forty-one."

The piece of balsa wood still lay quietly in the water alongside the raft; it had not yet moved halfway along our side.

"We'll have to go over with it," said Torstein optimistically.

"Hope we don't drift astern with the evening breeze," said Bengt. "It was great fun saying good-by at Callao, but I'd just as soon miss our welcome back again!"

Now the piece of wood had reached the end of the raft. We shouted hurrah and began to stow and make fast all the things that had been flung on board at the last moment. Bengt set up a primus stove at the bottom of an empty box, and soon after we were regaling ourselves on hot cocoa and biscuits and making a hole in a fresh coconut. The bananas were not quite ripe yet.

"We're well off now in one way," Erik chuckled. He was rolling about in wide sheepskin trousers under a huge Indian hat, with the parrot on his shoulder. "There's only one thing I don't like," he added, "and that's all the little-known crosscurrents which can fling us right up on the rocks along the coast if we go on lying here like this."

We considered the possibility of paddling but agreed to wait for a wind.

And the wind came. It blew up from the southeast quietly and steadily. Soon the sail filled and bent forward like a swelling breast, with Kon-Tiki's head bursting with pugnacity. And the *Kon-Tiki* began to move. We shouted westward ho! and hauled on sheets and ropes. The steering oar was put into the water, and the watch roster began to operate. We threw balls of paper and chips of wood overboard at the bow and stood aft with our watches.

"One, two, three . . . eighteen, nineteen —now!"

Paper and chips passed the steering oar and soon lay like pearls on a thread, dipping up and down in the trough of the waves astern. We went forward yard by yard. The *Kon-Tiki* did not plow through the sea like a sharp-prowed racing craft. Blunt and broad, heavy and solid, she splashed sedately forward over the waves. She did not hurry, but when she had once got going she pushed ahead with unshakable energy.

At the moment the steering arrangements were our greatest problem. The raft was built exactly as the Spaniards described it, but there was no one living in our time who could give us a practical advance course in sailing an Indian raft. The problem had been thoroughly discussed among the experts on shore but with meager results. They knew just as little about it as we did. As the southeasterly wind increased in strength, it was necessary to keep the raft on such a course that the sail was filled from astern. If the raft turned her side too much to the wind, the sail suddenly swung round and banged against cargo and men and bamboo cabin, while the whole raft turned round and continued on the same course stern first. It was a hard struggle, three men fighting with the sail and three others rowing with the long steering oar to get the nose of the wooden raft round and away from the wind. And, as soon as we got her round, the steersman

had to take good care that the same thing did not happen again the next minute.

The steering oar, nineteen feet long, rested loose between two tholepins [4] on a large block astern. It was the same steering oar our native friends had used when we floated the timber down the Palenque in Ecuador. The long mangrove-wood pole was as tough as steel but so heavy that it would sink if it fell overboard. At the end of the pole was a large oar blade of fir wood lashed on with ropes. It took all our strength to hold this long steering oar steady when the seas drove against it, and our fingers were tired out by the convulsive grip which was necessary to turn the pole so that the oar blade stood straight up in the water. This last problem was finally solved by our lashing a crosspiece to the handle of the steering oar so that we had a sort of lever to turn. And meanwhile the wind increased.

By the late afternoon the trade wind was already blowing at full strength. It quickly stirred up the ocean into roaring seas which swept against us from astern. For the first time we fully realized that here was the sea itself come to meet us; it was bitter earnest now—our communications were cut. Whether things went well now would depend entirely on the balsa raft's good qualities in the open sea. We knew that, from now onward, we should never get another onshore wind or chance of turning back. We were in the path of the real trade wind, and every day would carry us farther and farther out to sea. The only thing to do was to go ahead under full sail; if we tried to turn homeward, we should only drift farther out to sea stern first. There was only one possible course, to sail before the wind with our bow toward the sunset. And, after all, that was the object

---

[4] *tholepins*, wooden pegs set into the gunwale or deck to hold an oar in position

of our voyage—to follow the sun in its
path as we thought Kon-Tiki and the old
sun-worshipers must have done when they
were driven out to sea from Peru.

We noted with triumph and relief how
the wooden raft rose up over the first
threatening wave crests that came foaming
toward us. But it was impossible for the
steersman to hold the oar steady when the
roaring seas rolled toward him and lifted
the oar out of the tholepins, or swept it to
one side so that the steersman was swung
round like a helpless acrobat. Not even
two men at once could hold the oar steady
when the seas rose against us and poured
down over the steersmen aft. We hit on
the idea of running ropes from the oar
blade to each side of the raft; and with
other ropes holding the oar in place in the
tholepins it obtained a limited freedom of
movement and could defy the worst seas if
only we ourselves could hold on.

As the troughs of the sea gradually grew
deeper, it became clear that we had moved
into the swiftest part of the Humboldt
Current. This sea was obviously caused by
a current and not simply raised by the
wind. The water was green and cold and
everywhere about us; the jagged mountains
of Peru had vanished into the dense cloud
banks astern. When darkness crept over
the waters, our first duel with the elements
began. We were still not sure of the sea;
we were still uncertain whether it would
show itself a friend or an enemy in the intimate proximity we ourselves had sought.
When, swallowed up by the darkness, we
heard the general noise from the sea around
us suddenly deafened by the hiss of a roller
close by and saw a white crest come grop-
ing toward us on a level with the cabin
roof, we held on tight and waited uneasily
to feel the masses of water smash down
over us and the raft.

But every time there was the same sur-

prise and relief. The *Kon-Tiki* calmly
swung up her stern and rose skyward unperturbed, while the masses of water rolled
along her sides. Then we sank down again
into the trough of the waves and waited
for the next big sea. The biggest seas often
came two or three in succession, with a
long series of smaller seas in between. It
was when two big seas followed each other
too closely that the second broke on board
aft, because the first was still holding our
bow in the air. It became, therefore, an
unbreakable law that the steering watch
must have ropes round their waists, the
other ends of which were made fast to the
raft, for there were no bulwarks. Their
task was to keep the sail filled by holding
stern to sea and wind.

We had made an old boat's compass fast
to a box aft so that Erik could check our
course and calculate our position and speed.
For the time being it was uncertain where
we were, for the sky was overclouded and
the horizon one single chaos of rollers.
Two men at a time took turns as steering
watch and, side by side, they had to put all
their strength into the fight with the leaping oar, while the rest of us tried to snatch
a little sleep inside the open bamboo cabin.

When a really big sea came, the men at
the helm left the steering to the ropes and,
jumping up, hung on to a bamboo pole
from the cabin roof, while the masses of
water thundered in over them from astern
and disappeared between the logs or over
the side of the raft. Then they had to
fling themselves at the oar again before the
raft could turn round and the sail thrash
about. For, if the raft took the seas at an
angle, the waves could easily pour right
into the bamboo cabin. When they came
from astern, they disappeared between the
projecting logs at once and seldom came
so far forward as the cabin wall. The
round logs astern let the water pass as if

through the prongs of a fork. The advantage of a raft was obviously this: the more leaks the better. Through the gaps in our floor the water ran out but never in.

About midnight a ship's light passed in a northerly direction. At three another passed on the same course. We waved our little paraffin lamp and hailed them with flashes from an electric torch, but they did not see us and the lights passed slowly northward into the darkness and disappeared. Little did those on board realize that a real Inca raft lay close to them, tumbling among the waves. And just as little did we on board the raft realize that this was our last ship and the last trace of men we should see till we had reached the other side of the ocean.

We clung like flies, two and two, to the steering oar in the darkness and felt the fresh sea water pouring off our hair while the oar hit us till we were tender both behind and before and our hands grew stiff with the exertion of hanging on. We had a good schooling those first days and nights; it turned landlubbers into seamen. For the first twenty-four hours every

man, in unbroken succession, had two hours at the helm and three hours' rest. We arranged that every hour a fresh man should relieve one of the two steersmen who had been at the helm for two hours.

Every single muscle in the body was strained to the uttermost throughout the watch to cope with the steering. When we were tired out with pushing the oar, we went over to the other side and pulled, and when arms and chest were sore with pressing, we turned our backs while the oar kneaded us green and blue in front and behind. When at last the relief came, we crept half-dazed into the bamboo cabin, tied a rope round our legs, and fell asleep with our salty clothes on before we could get into our sleeping bags. Almost at the same moment there came a brutal tug at the rope; three hours had passed, and one had to go out again and relieve one of the two men at the steering oar.

The next night was still worse; the seas grew higher instead of going down. Two hours on end of struggling with the steering oar was too long; a man was not much

use in the second half of his watch, and the seas got the better of us and hurled us round and sideways, while the water poured on board. Then we changed over to one hour at the helm and an hour and a half's rest. So the first sixty hours passed, in one continuous struggle against a chaos of waves that rushed upon us, one after another, without cessation. High waves and low waves, pointed waves and round waves, slanting waves and waves on top of other waves.

The one of us who suffered worst was Knut. He was let off steering watch, but to compensate for this he had to sacrifice to Neptune and suffered silent agonies in a corner of the cabin. The parrot sat sulkily in its cage, hanging on with its beak and flapping its wings every time the raft gave an unexpected pitch and the sea splashed against the wall from astern. The Kon-Tiki did not roll excessively. She took the seas more steadily than any boat of the same dimensions, but it was impossible to predict which way the deck would lean each time, and we never learned the art of moving about the raft easily, for she pitched as much as she rolled.

On the third night the sea went down a bit, although it was still blowing hard. About four o'clock an unexpected deluge came foaming through the darkness and knocked the raft right round before the steersmen realized what was happening. The sail thrashed against the bamboo cabin and threatened to tear both the cabin and itself to pieces. All hands had to go on deck to secure the cargo and haul on sheets and stays in the hope of getting the raft on her right course again, so that the sail might fill and curve forward peacefully. But the raft would not right herself. She would go stern foremost, and that was all. The only result of all our hauling and pushing and rowing was that two men nearly went overboard in a sea when the sail caught them in the dark.

The sea had clearly become calmer. Stiff and sore, with skinned palms and sleepy eyes, we were not worth a row of beans. Better to save our strength in case the weather should call us out to a worse passage of arms. One could never know. So we furled the sail and rolled it round the bamboo yard. The Kon-Tiki lay sideways on to the seas and took them like a cork. Everything on board was lashed fast, and all six of us crawled into the little bamboo cabin, huddled together, and slept like mummies in a sardine tin.

We little guessed that we had struggled through the hardest steering of the voyage. Not till we were far out on the ocean did we discover the Incas' simple and ingenious way of steering a raft.

We did not wake till well on in the day, when the parrot began to whistle and halloo and dance to and fro on its perch. Outside the sea was still running high but in long, even ridges and not so wild and confused as the day before. The first thing we saw was that the sun was beating down on the yellow bamboo deck and giving the sea all round us a bright and friendly aspect. What did it matter if the seas foamed and rose high so long as they only left us in peace on the raft? What did it matter if they rose straight up in front of our noses when we knew that in a second the raft would go over the top and flatten out the foaming ridge like a steam roller, while the heavy threatening mountain of water only lifted us up in the air and rolled groaning and gurgling under the floor? The old masters from Peru knew what they were doing when they avoided a hollow hull which could fill with water, or a vessel so long that it would not take the waves one by one. A cork steam roller—that was what the balsa raft amounted to.

When the sea was not too rough, we were often out in the little rubber dinghy taking photographs. I shall not forget the first time the sea was so calm that two men felt like putting the balloon-like little thing into the water and going for a row. They had hardly got clear of the raft when they dropped the little oars and sat roaring with laughter. And, as the swell lifted them away and they disappeared and reappeared among the seas, they laughed so loud every time they caught a glimpse of us that their voices rang out over the desolate Pacific. We looked around us with mixed feelings and saw nothing comic but our own hirsute faces; but as the two in the dinghy should be accustomed to those by now, we began to have a lurking suspicion that they had suddenly gone mad. Sunstroke, perhaps. The two fellows could hardly scramble back on board the *Kon-Tiki* for sheer laughter and, gasping, with tears in their eyes they begged us just to go and see for ourselves.

Two of us jumped down into the dancing rubber dinghy and were caught by a sea which lifted us clear. Immediately we sat down with a bump and roared with laughter. We had to scramble back on the raft as quickly as possible and calm the last two who had not been out yet, for they thought we had all gone stark staring mad.

It was ourselves and our proud vessel which made such a completely hopeless, lunatic impression on us the first time we saw the whole thing at a distance. We had never before had an outside view of ourselves in the open sea. The logs of timber disappeared behind the smallest waves, and, when we saw anything at all, it was the low cabin with the wide doorway and the bristly roof of leaves that bobbed up from among the seas. The raft looked exactly like an old Norwegian hayloft lying helpless, drifting about in the open sea—a warped hayloft full of sunburned bearded ruffians. If anyone had come paddling after us at sea in a bathtub, we should have felt the same spontaneous urge to laughter. Even an ordinary swell rolled halfway up the cabin wall and looked as if it would pour in unhindered through the wide open door in which the bearded fellows lay gaping. But then the crazy craft came up to the surface again, and the vagabonds lay there as dry, shaggy, and intact as before. If a higher sea came racing by, cabin and sail and the whole mast might disappear behind the mountain of water, but just as certainly the cabin with its vagabonds would be there again next moment. The situation looked bad, and we could not realize that things had gone so well on board the zany craft.

Next time we rowed out to have a good laugh at ourselves we nearly had a disaster. The wind and sea were higher than we supposed, and the *Kon-Tiki* was cleaving a path for herself over the swell much more quickly than we realized. We in the dinghy had to row for our lives out in the open sea in an attempt to regain the unmanageable raft, which could not stop and wait and could not possibly turn around and come back. Even when the boys on board the *Kon-Tiki* got the sail down, the wind got such a grip on the bamboo cabin that the raft drifted away to westward as fast as we could splash after her in the dancing rubber dinghy with its tiny toy oars. There was only one thought in the head of every man—we must not be separated. Those were horrible minutes we spent out on the sea before we got hold of the runaway raft and crawled on board to the others, home again.

From that day it was strictly forbidden to go out in the rubber dinghy without having a long line made fast to the bow, so that those who remained on board could haul the dinghy in if necessary. We never went far away from the raft, thereafter, except when the wind was light and the Pacific curving itself in a gentle swell. But we had these conditions when the raft was halfway to Polynesia and the ocean, all dominating, arched itself round the globe toward every point of the compass. Then we could safely leave the *Kon-Tiki* and row away into the blue space between sky and sea.

When we saw the silhouette of our craft grow smaller and smaller in the distance, and the big sail at last shrunken to a vague black square on the horizon, a sensation of loneliness sometimes crept over us. The sea curved away under us as blue upon blue as the sky above, and where they met all the blue flowed together and became one. It almost seemed as if we were suspended in space. All our world was empty and blue; there was no fixed point in it but the tropical sun, golden and warm, which burned our necks. Then the distant sail of the lonely raft drew us to it like a magnetic point on the horizon. We rowed back and crept on board with a feeling that we had come home again to our own world—on board and yet on firm, safe ground. And inside the bamboo cabin we found shade and the scent of bamboos and withered palm leaves. The sunny blue purity outside was now served to us in a suitably large dose through the open cabin wall. So we were accustomed to it and so it was good for a time, till the great clear blue tempted us out again.

It was most remarkable what a psychological effect the shaky bamboo cabin had on our minds. It measured eight by fourteen feet, and to diminish the pressure of the wind and sea it was built low so that we could not stand upright under the ridge of the roof. Walls and roof were made of strong bamboo canes, lashed together and

guyed, and covered with a tough wickerwork of split bamboos. The green and yellow bars, with fringes of foliage hanging down from the roof, were restful to the eye as a white cabin wall never could have been, and, despite the fact that the bamboo wall on the starboard side was open for one third of its length and roof and walls let in sun and moon, this primitive lair gave us a greater feeling of security than whitepainted bulkheads and closed portholes would have given in the same circumstances.

We tried to find an explanation for this curious fact and came to the following conclusion. Our consciousness was totally unaccustomed to associating a palm-covered bamboo dwelling with sea travel. There was no natural harmony between the great rolling ocean and the drafty palm hut which was floating about among the seas. Therefore, either the hut would seem entirely out of place in among the waves, or the waves would seem entirely out of place round the hut wall. So long as we kept on board, the bamboo hut and its jungle scent were plain reality, and the tossing seas seemed rather visionary. But from the rubber boat, waves and hut exchanged roles.

The fact that the balsa logs always rode the seas like a gull, and let the water right through aft if a wave broke on board, gave us an unshakable confidence in the dry part in the middle of the raft where the cabin was. The longer the voyage lasted, the safer we felt in our cozy lair, and we looked at the white-crested waves that danced past outside our doorway as if they were an impressive movie, conveying no menace to us at all. Even though the gaping wall was only five feet from the unprotected edge of the raft and only a foot and a half above the water line, yet we felt as if we had traveled many miles away from the sea and occupied a jungle dwel-

ling remote from the sea's perils once we had crawled inside the door. There we could lie on our backs and look up at the curious roof which twisted about like boughs in the wind, enjoying the jungle smell of raw wood, bamboos, and withered palm leaves.

Sometimes, too, we went out in the rubber boat to look at ourselves by night. Coal-black seas towered up on all sides, and a glittering myriad of tropical stars drew a faint reflection from plankton in the water. The world was simple—stars in the darkness. Whether it was 1947 B.C. or A.D. suddenly became of no significance. We lived, and that we felt with alert intensity. We realized that life had been full for men before the technical age also—in fact, fuller and richer in many ways than the life of modern man. Time and evolution somehow ceased to exist; all that was real and that mattered were the same today as they had always been and would always be. We were swallowed up in the absolute common measure of history—endless unbroken darkness under a swarm of stars.

The man who wrote this selection

THOR HEYERDAHL   1914–

Thor Heyerdahl, a Norwegian, began early to love the life of both the scholar and the outdoorsman. When he was not studying zoology, he was mountain climbing or making long trips by dog sled. Occasionally, he wrote articles about outdoor life for the Norwegian newspapers.

Shortly after he was married, he and his young wife decided to go to the Marquesas Islands in French Oceania with a romantic notion of "escaping" from civilization and "getting back to nature." At the same time, he would carry on field work in zoology. His discoveries on the island soon led him from zoology to the study of the origin and distribution of human races. He believed that much of the art and tradition of the Islanders was remarkably similar to that of the ancient Peruvians. He thought the Islanders were probably descendants of the Peruvians. When he returned to Norway to carry out further study on his theory, the Second World War interrupted.

During the war, Heyerdahl served with the Free Norwegian Army and Air Force. As soon as the Germans surrendered, he returned to his study. He determined that the Peruvians must have traveled on rafts to the Islands. In an effort to prove to doubting navigators and scientists that this was possible, Thor and five other young Scandinavians built a replica of the ancient Peruvian raft. On it they drifted for 101 days until they landed on Tuamotu Island. Their adventures were soon written down and appeared as a very popular book, *Kon-Tiki*.

Let's consider . . .

1. Describe the confusion at the start of the voyage.

2. Why did the men have difficulty sailing the raft?

3. Why did Heyerdahl write that the old sailing masters from Peru knew what they were doing in designing their rafts?

4. The first time the men rowed away from the raft, they burst into hysterical laughter. Explain why.

5. You may have been in a shelter that was not very strong but, nevertheless, gave you a feeling of being safe. The men had the same feeling when they were in the shaky, bamboo cabin. Explain why it gave them this sense of security.

6. How did being in the little rubber boat at night give the men a feeling of belonging to all history? Think of a time when you have been near the water at night or alone in the woods. What feelings and thoughts did *you* have? In what ways were your feelings similar to those of the men on the *Kon-Tiki*?

7. Thor Heyerdahl wrote that before the modern technical age men had led full lives. What things do you think provided this fullness of living in the past?

8. Thor Heyerdahl and his companions risked their lives to prove a scientific theory. What other men have risked their lives for scientific causes? Why do people take risks for such causes as science, democracy, or religion?

The writer's craft . . .

Men who have undergone exciting adventures often record their experiences so that others may share them. *Kon-Tiki* is such a record. Since this adventure actually happened, the book is **non-fiction**. Other adventure stories you have read, such as "I Turn Pearl Diver" and "The Reluctant Tiger," were created out of the writers' imaginations. These stories are **fiction**.

Of course, adventure stories are not the only kind of non-fiction writing. Autobiographies, biographies, essays, travel books, cook books, and text books are also non-fiction.

1. Go to your library and list some of the different kinds of books that are classified as non-fiction.

2. Check the kinds of non-fiction books you have read. For example, if you have read an autobiography, place a check after

the word *autobiography* on your list.

3. For your next reading assignment, select a type of non-fiction book you have never read before. By reading many different kinds of books you will develop an interest in new activities and thus enrich your life.

Knowing words . . .

As you read about the sailing adventures of the men on *Kon-Tiki,* you came across many nautical expressions. Each of the sentences below contains an italicized word or words, which in some way are associated with the sea. Explain the meaning of each word. Then use it in a sentence of your own.

1. The papers had published the news under both red and black headlines, and there was a crowd of people down on the *quays* from early in the morning of April 28.

2. We spat and cursed and pulled jellyfish fibers out of our hair, but when the tug came back the rope end was up and ready for *splicing*.

3. The yachts had bidden us farewell long ago, and the last coast light had disappeared *astern*.

4. In the early light we saw our tug lying close by, and we took care that the raft lay far enough away from her bow while we *launched* our little inflated rubber *dinghy*.

5. Walls and roof were made of strong bamboo canes, *lashed* together and *guyed*, and covered with a tough wickerwork of split bamboos.

A Wet Sheet and a Flowing Sea

A wet sheet and a flowing sea,
  A wind that follows fast,
And fills the white and rustling sail,
  And bends the gallant mast;
And bends the gallant mast, my boys,
  While, like the eagle free,
Away the good ship flies, and leaves
  Old England on the lee.

O for a soft and gentle wind!
  I heard a fair one cry;
But give to me the snoring breeze,
  And white waves heaving high;
And white waves heaving high, my boys,
  The good ship tight and free—
The world of waters is our home,
  And merry men are we.

There's tempest in yon hornèd moon,
  And lightning in yon cloud;
And hark the music, mariners!
  The wind is piping loud;
The wind is piping loud, my boys,
  The lightning flashing free—
While the hollow oak our palace is,
  Our heritage the sea.

Allan Cunningham

Learning to Speak

HELEN KELLER

Helen Keller became deaf and blind when she was a very young child. Until she learned to speak, she felt lost in a dark sea, without compass or sounding line. With *words* came light.

The most important day I remember in all my life is the one on which my teacher, Anne Mansfield Sullivan, came to me. I am filled with wonder when I consider the immeasurable contrasts between the two lives which it connects. It was the third of March, 1887, three months before I was seven years old.

On the afternoon of that eventful day, I stood on the porch, dumb, expectant. I guessed vaguely from my mother's signs and from the hurrying to and fro in the house that something unusual was about to happen, so I went to the door and waited on the steps. The afternoon sun penetrated the mass of honeysuckle that covered the porch, and fell on my upturned face. My fingers lingered almost unconsciously on the familiar leaves and blossoms which had just come forth to greet the sweet southern spring. I did not know what the future held of marvel or surprise for me. Anger and bitterness had preyed upon me continually for weeks, and a deep languor had succeeded this passionate struggle.

Have you ever been at sea in a dense fog, when it seemed as if a tangible white dark-ness shut you in, and the great ship, tense and anxious, groped her way toward the shore with plummet and sounding line, and you waited with beating heart for something to happen? I was like that ship before my education began, only I was without compass or sounding line, and had no way of knowing how near the harbor was. "Light! give me light!" was the wordless cry of my soul, and the light of love shone on me in that very hour.

I felt approaching footsteps. I stretched out my hand, as I supposed, to my mother. Someone took it, and I was caught up and held close in the arms of her who had come to reveal all things to me and, more than all else, to love me.

The morning after my teacher came, she led me into her room and gave me a doll. The little blind children at the Perkins Institution had sent it and Laura Bridgman had dressed it; but I did not know this until afterward. When I had played with it a little while, Miss Sullivan slowly spelled into my hand the word "d-o-l-l." I was at once interested in this finger play and tried to imitate it. When I finally succeeded in making the letters correctly, I was flushed with childish pleasure and pride. Running downstairs to my mother, I held up my hand and made the letters for doll. I did not know that I was spelling a word or even that words existed; I was simply making my fingers go in monkeylike imitation. In the days that followed I learned to spell in this uncomprehending way a great many words, among them *pin, hat, cup,* and a few verbs like *sit, stand,* and *walk.* But my teacher had been with me several weeks before I understood that everything has a name.

One day, while I was playing with my new doll, Miss Sullivan put my big rag doll into my lap also, spelled "d-o-l-l" and tried to make me understand that "d-o-l-l" applied to both. Earlier in the day we had had a tussle over the words "m-u-g" and "w-a-t-e-r." Miss Sullivan had tried to impress it upon me that "m-u-g" is *mug* and "w-a-t-e-r" is *water,* but I persisted in confounding the two. In despair she dropped the subject for the time, only to renew it

at the first opportunity. I became impatient at her repeated attempts and, seizing the new doll, I dashed it upon the floor. I was keenly delighted when I felt the fragments of the broken doll at my feet. Neither sorrow nor regret followed my passionate outburst. I had not loved the doll. In the still, dark world in which I lived, there was no strong sentiment or tenderness. I felt my teacher sweep the fragments to one side of the hearth, and I had a sense of satisfaction that the cause of my discomfort was removed. She brought me my hat, and I knew I was going out into the warm sunshine. This thought, if a wordless sensation may be called a thought, made me hop and skip with pleasure.

We walked down the path to the wellhouse, attracted by the fragrance of the honeysuckle with which it was covered. Someone was drawing water, and my teacher placed my hand under the spout. As the cool stream gushed over one hand, she spelled into the other the word *water,* first slowly then rapidly. I stood still, my

LEONARD EVERETT FISHER

whole attention fixed upon the motions of her fingers. Suddenly I felt a misty consciousness as of something forgotten—a thrill of returning thought; and somehow the mystery of language was revealed to me. I knew then that "w-a-t-e-r" meant the wonderful cool something that was flowing over my hand. That living word awakened my soul, gave it light, hope, joy, set it free! There were barriers still, it is true, but barriers that could in time be swept away.

I left the well-house eager to learn. Everything had a name, and each name gave birth to a new thought. As we returned to the house, every object which I touched seemed to quiver with life. That was because I saw everything with the strange, new sight that had come to me. On entering the door I remembered the doll I had broken. I felt my way to the hearth and picked up the pieces. I tried vainly to put them together. Then my eyes filled with tears; for I realized what I had done, and for the first time I felt repentance and sorrow.

I learned a great many new words that day, I do not remember what they all were; but I do know that *mother, father, sister, teacher* were among them—words that were to make the world blossom for me, "like Aaron's rod,[1] with flowers." It would have been difficult to find a happier child than I was as I lay in my crib at the close of that eventful day and lived over the joys it had brought me, and for the first time longed for a new day to come.

I had now the key to all language, and I was eager to learn to use it. Children who hear acquire language without any particular effort; the words that fall from others' lips they catch on the wing, as it were, delightedly, while the little deaf child must trap them by a slow and often painful process. But whatever the process, the result is wonderful. Gradually from naming an object we advance step by step until we have traversed the vast distance between our first stammered syllable and the sweep of thought in a line of Shakespeare.

At first, when my teacher told me about a new thing I asked very few questions. My ideas were vague, and my vocabulary was inadequate; but as my knowledge of things grew, and I learned more and more words, my field of inquiry broadened, and I would return again and again to the same subject, eager for further information. Sometimes a new word revived an image that some earlier experience had engraved on my brain.

I remember the morning that I first asked the meaning of the word "love." This was before I knew many words. I had found a few early violets in the garden and brought them to my teacher. She tried to kiss me; but at that time I did not like to have anyone kiss me except my mother. Miss Sullivan put her arm gently around me and spelled into my hand, "I love Helen."

"What is love?" I asked.

She drew me closer to her and said, "It is here," pointing to my heart, whose beats I was conscious of for the first time. Her words puzzled me very much because I did not then understand anything unless I touched it.

I smelt the violets in her hand and asked, half in words, half in signs, a question which meant, "Is love the sweetness of flowers?"

"No," said my teacher.

Again I thought. The warm sun was shining on us.

---

[1] *Aaron's rod,* a sacred rod which is supposed to have burst into bloom during the exodus of the Jews from Egypt

"Is this not love?" I asked, pointing in the direction from which the heat came, "Is this not love?"

It seemed to me that there could be nothing more beautiful than the sun, whose warmth makes all things grow. But Miss Sullivan shook her head, and I was greatly puzzled and disappointed. I thought it strange that my teacher could not show me love.

A day or two afterward I was stringing beads of different sizes in symmetrical groups—two large beads, three small ones, and so on. I had made many mistakes, and Miss Sullivan had pointed them out again and again with gentle patience. Finally I noticed a very obvious error in the sequence, and for an instant I concentrated my attention on the lesson and tried to think how I should have arranged the beads. Miss Sullivan touched my forehead and spelled with decided emphasis, "Think."

In a flash I knew that the word was the name of the process that was going on in my head. This was my first conscious perception of an abstract idea.

For a long time I was still—I was not thinking of the beads in my lap, but trying to find a meaning for "love" in the light of this new idea. The sun had been under a cloud all day, and there had been brief showers; but suddenly the sun broke forth in all its southern splendour.

Again I asked my teacher, "Is this not love?"

"Love is something like the clouds that were in the sky before the sun came out," she replied. Then in simpler words than these, which at that time I could not have understood, she explained: "You cannot touch the clouds, you know; but you feel the rain and know how glad the flowers and the thirsty earth are to have it after a hot day. You cannot touch love, either; but you feel the sweetness that it pours into everything. Without love you would not be happy or want to play."

The beautiful truth burst upon my mind —I felt that there were invisible lines stretched between my spirit and the spirits of others.

From the beginning of my education Miss Sullivan made it a practice to speak to me as she would speak to any hearing child; the only difference was that she spelled the sentences into my hand instead of speaking them. If I did not know the words and idioms necessary to express my thoughts, she supplied them, even suggesting conversation when I was unable to keep up my end of the dialogue.

This process was continued for several years; for the deaf child does not learn in a month, or even in two or three years, the numberless idioms and expressions used in the simplest daily intercourse. The little hearing child learns these from constant repetition and imitation. The conversation he hears in his home stimulates his mind and suggests topics and calls forth the spontaneous expression of his own thoughts. This natural exchange of ideas is denied to the deaf child. My teacher, realizing this, determined to supply the kinds of stimulus I lacked. This she did by repeating to me as far as possible, verbatim, what she heard, and by showing me how I could take part in the conversation. But it was a long time before I ventured to take the initiative, and still longer before I could find something appropriate to say at the right time.

The deaf and the blind find it very difficult to acquire the amenities of conversation. How much more this difficulty must be augmented in the case of those who are both deaf and blind! They cannot distinguish the tone of the voice or, without assistance, go up and down the gamut of tones that give significance to words; nor can they watch the expression of the speaker's face, and a look is often the very soul of what one says.

It was in the spring of 1890 that I learned to speak. The impulse to utter audible sounds had always been strong within me. I used to make noises, keeping one hand on my throat while the other hand felt the movements of my lips. I was pleased with anything that made a noise and liked to feel the cat purr and the dog bark. I also liked to keep my hand on a singer's throat, or on a piano when it was being played. Before I lost my sight and hearing, I was fast learning to talk, but after my illness it was found that I had ceased to speak because I could not hear. I used to sit in my mother's lap all day long and keep my hands on her face because it amused me to feel the motions of her lips; and I moved my lips, too, although I had forgotten what talking was. My friends say that I laughed and cried naturally, and for a while I made many sounds and word-elements, not because they were a means of communication, but because the need of exercising my vocal organs was imperative. There was, however, one word the meaning of which I still remembered, *water*. I pronounced it *"wa-wa."* Even this became less and less intelligible until the time Miss Sullivan began to teach me. I stopped using it only after I had learned to spell the word on my fingers.

I had known for a long time that the people about me used a method of communication different from mine; and even before I knew that a deaf child could be taught to speak, I was conscious of dissatisfaction with the means of communication I already possessed. One who is entirely dependent upon the manual alphabet has al-

ways a sense of restraint, of narrowness. This feeling began to agitate me with a vexing, forward-reaching sense of a lack that should be filled. My thoughts would often rise and beat up like birds against the wind; and I persisted in using my lips and voice. Friends tried to discourage this tendency, fearing lest it would lead to disappointment. But I persisted and an accident soon occurred which resulted in the breaking down of this great barrier—I heard the story of Ragnhild Kaata.

In 1890 Mrs. Lamson, who had been one of Laura Bridgman's teachers, and who had just returned from a visit to Norway and Sweden, came to see me, and told me of Ragnhild Kaata, a deaf and blind girl in Norway who had actually been taught to speak. Mrs. Lamson had scarcely finished telling me about this girl's success before I was on fire with eagerness. I resolved that I, too, would learn to speak. I would not rest satisfied until my teacher took me, for advice and assistance, to Miss Sarah Fuller, principal of the Horace Mann School. This lovely, sweet-natured lady offered to teach me herself, and we began the twenty-sixth of March, 1890.

Miss Fuller's method was this: she passed my hand lightly over her face, and let me feel the position of her tongue and lips when she made a sound. I was eager to imitate every motion and in an hour had learned six elements of speech: M, P, A, S, T, I. Miss Fuller gave me eleven lessons in all. I shall never forget the surprise and delight I felt when I uttered my first connected sentence, "It is warm." True, they were broken and stammering syllables; but they were human speech. My soul, conscious of new strength, came out of bondage, and was reaching through those broken symbols of speech to all knowledge and all faith.

No deaf child who has earnestly tried to

speak the words which he has never heard
—to come out of the prison of silence,
where no tone of love, no song of bird, no
strain of music ever pierces the stillness—
can forget the thrill of surprise, the joy of
discovery which came over him when he
uttered his first word. Only such a one can
appreciate the eagerness with which I
talked to my toys, to stones, trees, birds,
and dumb animals, or the delight I felt
when at my call Mildred ran to me or my
dogs obeyed my commands. It is an unspeakable boon to me to be able to speak in
winged words that need no interpretation.
As I talked, happy thoughts fluttered up
out of my words that might perhaps have
struggled in vain to escape my fingers.

But it must not be supposed that I could
really talk in this short time. I had learned
only the elements of speech. Miss Fuller
and Miss Sullivan could understand me,
but most people would not have understood
one word in a hundred. Nor is it true that,
after I had learned these elements, I did
the rest of the work myself. But for Miss
Sullivan's genius, untiring perseverance,
and devotion, I could not have progressed
as far as I have toward natural speech. In
the first place, I laboured night and day before I could be understood even by my
most intimate friends; in the second place,
I needed Miss Sullivan's assistance constantly in my efforts to articulate each
sound clearly and to combine all sounds in
a thousand ways. Even now she calls my
attention every day to mispronounced
words.

All teachers of the deaf know what this
means, and only they can at all appreciate
the peculiar difficulties with which I had to
contend. In reading my teacher's lips I was
wholly dependent on my fingers: I had to
use the sense of touch in catching the
vibrations of the throat, the movements of
the mouth, and the expression of the face;

and often this sense was at fault. In such
cases I was forced to repeat the words or
sentences, sometimes for hours, until I felt
the proper ring in my own voice. My work
was practice, practice, practice. Discourage-
ment and weariness cast me down frequently; but the next moment the thought
that I should soon be at home and show my
loved ones what I had accomplished,
spurred me on, and I eagerly looked forward to their pleasure in my achievement.

"My little sister will understand me
now," was a thought stronger than all obstacles. I used to repeat ecstatically, "I am
not dumb now." I could not be despondent
while I anticipated the delight of talking
to my mother and reading her responses
from her lips. It astonished me to find how
much easier it is to talk than to spell with
the fingers, and I discarded the manual
alphabet as a medium of communication
on my part; but Miss Sullivan and a few
friends still use it in speaking to me, for
it is more convenient and more rapid than
lip reading.

Just here, I had better explain our use
of the manual alphabet, which seems to
puzzle people who do not know us. One
who reads or talks to me spells with his
hand, using the single-hand manual alphabet generally employed by the deaf. I
place my hand on the hand of the speaker
so lightly as not to impede its movements.
The position of the hand is as easy to feel
as it is to see. I do not feel each letter any
more than you see each letter separately
when you read. Constant practice makes
the fingers very flexible, and some of my
friends spell rapidly—about as fast as an
expert writes on a typewriter. The mere
spelling is, of course, no more a conscious
act than it is in writing.

When I had made speech my own, I
could not wait to go home. At last the happiest of happy moments arrived. I had

made my homeward journey talking constantly to Miss Sullivan, not for the sake of talking, but determined to improve to the last minute. Almost before I knew it, the train stopped at the Tuscumbia station, and there on the platform stood the whole family. My eyes fill with tears now as I think how my mother pressed me close to her, speechless and trembling with delight,

taking in every syllable that I spoke, while little Mildred seized my free hand and kissed it and danced, and my father expressed his pride and affection in a big silence. It was as if Isaiah's prophecy had been fulfilled in me, "The mountains and the hills shall break forth before you into singing, and all the trees of the field shall clap their hands!"

The woman who wrote this autobiography

HELEN KELLER   1880–

Miss Keller was less than two years old when an illness left her deaf and blind. Her life since then has been a magnificent battle to overcome these handicaps and to help and give courage to other people like her.

In three years of constant, personal instruction, Miss Keller learned the Braille and manual alphabets and began to read. Later she took speech lessons but, though she has practiced for many years, her speaking voice is still hard for strangers to understand. However, with her intense desire to learn, she attended college and was graduated high in her class.

Then Miss Keller was faced with the problem of earning a living because she had to support her devoted teacher, a secretary, and herself. She lectured, did literary work, and even acted in a motion picture based on her life. A few wealthy men, impressed by her moral force and courage, solved her financial problems by granting her a permanent income.

Never afraid and always interested in the life around her, Miss Keller has become the friend of many famous people who admire and respect her. By her own efforts,

she has led some thirty states to set up organizations for the care of the blind and deaf.

Let's consider . . .

1. Helen Keller stated that the most important day in her life was the one on which her teacher, Anne Mansfield Sullivan, came to her. Explain why Miss Sullivan played such an important role in Miss Keller's life.

2. Both Helen Keller and Miss Sullivan were courageous women. Describe how each was courageous in her own way.

3. The discovery of words opened the way for Helen Keller to become a complete person. Describe how Miss Sullivan first taught Helen that everything has a name. What was Helen's reaction to this discovery?

4. Helen had difficulty understanding the word *love*. At first she thought of love as being the sweetness of flowers, then as the warmth of sunshine. How did Miss Sullivan finally explain *love?* How would you explain it?

5. Helen Keller spoke of the dependency of thought upon language. Explain how her development shows that language is an invaluable aid to thought and understanding.

6. How does Helen Keller's love of life serve as an inspiration to everyone who hears about her?

The writer's craft . . .

In a **biography,** the author reports the events and happenings in another person's life. In an **autobiography,** the author is reporting the events and happenings in his own life, and he therefore can describe the exact feelings which he experienced. In the selection from Helen Keller's autobiography which you have just read, Miss Keller expressed her great thrill when the world of sound and language was opened up to her.

1. Why couldn't a biographer have described this experience as completely as Miss Keller did?

2. Find several incidents in Miss Keller's long struggle to learn to speak which only she could have described.

Knowing words . . .

Each of the sentences below has one word missing. From the list, select the appropriate word. On a separate sheet of paper, copy the completed sentences. Do not write in this book.

abstract perseverance
uncomprehending impede
idioms perception

1. You must find a way to overcome the obstacles that . . . your progress.

2. The idea was too . . . for the child to understand.

3. He was a brilliant boy but he lacked the . . . to be a really good student.

4. Her immediate . . . of the problem helped to save the situation.

5. Just knowing words cannot help you to really understand a language. You must also be familiar with the . . . .

6. He looked at the puzzle in an . . . way and decided that he could never solve it.

A Little Song of Life

Glad that I live am I;
That the sky is blue;
Glad for the country lanes,
And the fall of dew.

After the sun the rain;
After the rain the sun;
This is the way of life,
Till the work be done.

All that we need to do,
Be we low or high,
Is to see that we grow
Nearer the sky.

Lizette Woodworth Reese

The Blow

RICHARD E. BYRD

During the winter of 1934, Admiral Richard E. Byrd lived alone at an advance antarctic weather base. His mission was primarily scientific: to observe and record weather conditions in this remote spot. But he also wanted the experience of living alone in the "coldest cold on the face of the earth."

Out of the cold and out of the east came the wind. It came on gradually, as if the sheer weight of the cold were almost too much to be moved. On the night of the 21st the barometer started down. The night was black as a thunderhead when I made my first trip topside; and a tension in the wind, a bulking of shadows in the night indicated that a new storm center was forming. Next morning, glad of an excuse to stay underground, I worked a long time on the Escape Tunnel by the light of a red candle standing in a snow recess. That day I pushed the emergency exit to a distance of twenty-two feet, the farthest it was ever to go. My stint done, I sat down on a box, thinking how beautiful was the red of the candle, how white the rough-hewn snow. Soon I became aware of an increasing clatter of the anemometer cups.[1] Realizing that the wind was picking up, I went topside to make sure that everything was secured. It is a queer experience to watch a blizzard rise. First there is the wind, rising out of nowhere. Then the Barrier[2] unwrenches itself from quietude; and the surface, which just before had seemed as hard and polished as metal, begins to run like a making sea. Sometimes, if the wind strikes hard, the drift comes across the Barrier like a hurrying white cloud, tossed hundreds of feet in the air. Other times the growth is gradual. You become conscious of a general slithering movement on all sides. The air fills with tiny scraping and sliding and rustling sounds as the first loose crystals stir. In a little while they are moving as solidly as an incoming tide, which creams over the ankles, then surges to the waist, and finally is at the throat. I have walked in drift so thick as not to be able to see a foot ahead of me; yet, when I glanced up, I could see the stars shining through the thin layer just overhead.

Smoking tendrils were creeping up the

[1] *anemometer cups,* small cups attached to a device for measuring the velocity of the wind

[2] *Barrier,* a floating sheet of ice which is roughly the size of France and 500 to 1500 feet thick, located in Antarctica

anemometer pole when I finished my inspection. I hurriedly made the trapdoor fast, as a sailor might batten down a hatch; and knowing that my ship was well secured, I retired to the cabin to ride out the storm. It could not reach me, hidden deep in the Barrier crust; nevertheless the sounds came down. The gale sobbed in the ventilators, shook the stovepipe until I thought it would be jerked out by the roots, pounded the roof with sledge-hammer blows. I could actually feel the suction effect through the pervious snow. A breeze flickered in the room and the tunnels. The candles wavered and went out. My only light was the feeble storm lantern.

Even so, I didn't have any idea how really bad it was until I went aloft for an observation. As I pushed back the trapdoor, the drift met me like a moving wall. It was only a few steps from the ladder to the instrument shelter, but it seemed more like a mile. The air came at me in snowy rushes; I breasted it as I might a heavy surf. No night had ever seemed so dark. The beam from the flashlight was choked in its throat; I could not see my hand before my face.

My windproofs were caked with drift by the time I got below. I had a vague feeling that something had changed while I was gone, but what, I couldn't tell. Presently I noticed that the shack was appreciably colder. Raising the stove lid, I was surprised to find that the fire was out, though the tank was half full. I decided that I must have turned off the valve unconsciously before going aloft; but, when I put a match to the burner, the draught down the pipe blew out the flame. The wind, then, must have killed the fire. I got it going again, and watched it carefully.

The blizzard vaulted to gale force. Above the roar the deep, taut thrumming note of the radio antenna and the anemom-

eter guy wires reminded me of wind in a ship's rigging. The wind direction trace[3] turned scratchy on the sheet; no doubt drift had short-circuited the electric contacts, I decided. Realizing that it was hopeless to attempt to try to keep them clear, I let the instrument be. There were other ways of getting the wind direction. I tied a handkerchief to a bamboo pole and ran it through the outlet ventilator; with a flashlight I could tell which way the cloth was whipped. I did this at hourly intervals, noting any change of direction on the sheet. But by 2 o'clock in the morning I had had enough of this periscope sighting. If I expected to sleep and at the same time maintain the continuity of the records, I had no choice but to clean the contact points.

The wind was blowing hard then. The Barrier shook from the concussions overhead; and the noise was as if the entire physical world were tearing itself to pieces. I could scarcely heave the trapdoor open. The instant it came clear I was plunged into a blinding smother. I came out crawling, clinging to the handle of the door until I made sure of my bearings. Then I let the door fall shut, not wanting the tunnel filled with drift. To see was impossible. Millions of tiny pellets exploded in my eyes, stinging like BB shot. It was even hard to breathe, because snow instantly clogged the mouth and nostrils. I made my way toward the anemometer pole on hands and knees, scared that I might be bowled off my feet if I stood erect; one false step and I should be lost forever.

I found the pole all right; but not until my head collided with a cleat. I managed to climb it, too, though ten million ghosts were tearing at me, ramming their thumbs into my eyes. But the errand was useless.

---

[3] *wind direction trace,* device which records wind direction on paper

Drift as thick as this would mess up the contact points as quickly as they were cleared; besides, the wind cups were spinning so fast that I stood a good chance of losing a couple of fingers in the process. Coming down the pole, I had a sense of being whirled violently through the air, with no control over my movements. The trapdoor was completely buried when I found it again, after scraping around for some time with my mittens. I pulled at the handle, first with one hand, then with both. It did not give. It's a tight fit, anyway, I mumbled to myself. The drift has probably wedged the corners. Standing astride the hatch, I braced myself and heaved with all my strength. I might just as well have tried hoisting the Barrier.

Panic took me then, I must confess. Reason fled. I clawed at the three-foot square of timber like a madman. I beat on it with my fists, trying to shake the snow loose; and, when that did no good, I lay flat on my belly and pulled until my hands went weak from cold and weariness. Then I crooked my elbow, put my face down, and said over and over again, You fool, you fool. Here for weeks I had been defending myself against the danger of being penned inside the shack; instead, I was now locked out; and nothing could be worse, especially since I had only a wool parka and pants under my windproofs. Just two feet below was sanctuary—warmth, food, tools, all the means of survival. All these things were an arm's length away, but I was powerless to reach them.

There is something extravagantly insensate [4] about an antarctic blizzard at night. Its vindictiveness cannot be measured on an anemometer sheet. It is more than just wind: it is a solid wall of snow moving at gale force, pounding like surf. The whole malevolent [5] rush is concentrated upon you as upon a personal enemy. In the senseless explosion of sound you are

---

[4] *insensate,* inhuman
[5] *malevolent,* spiteful

reduced to a crawling thing on the margin of a disintegrating world; you can't see, you can't hear, you can hardly move. The lungs gasp after the air is sucked out of them, and the brain is shaken. Nothing in the world will so quickly isolate a man.

Half-frozen, I stabbed toward one of the ventilators, a few feet away. My mittens touched something round and cold. Cupping it in my hands, I pulled myself up. This was the outlet ventilator. Just why, I don't know—but instinct made me kneel and press my face against the opening. Nothing in the room was visible, but a dim patch of light illuminated the floor, and warmth rose up to my face. That steadied me.

Still kneeling, I turned my back to the blizzard and considered what might be done. I thought of breaking in the windows in the roof, but they lay two feet down in hard crust, and were reinforced with wire besides. If I only had something to dig with, I could break the crust and stamp the windows in with my feet. The pipe cupped between my hands supplied the first inspiration; maybe I could use that to dig with. It, too was wedged tight; I pulled until my arms ached, without budging it; I had lost all track of time, and the despairing thought came to me that I was lost in a task without an end. Then I remembered the shovel. A week before, after

leveling drift from the last light blow, I had stabbed a shovel handle up in the crust somewhere to leeward. That shovel would save me. But how to find it in the avalanche of the blizzard?

I lay down and stretched out full length. Still holding the pipe, I thrashed around with my feet, but pummeled only empty air. Then I worked back to the hatch. The hard edges at the opening provided another grip, and again I stretched out and kicked. Again no luck. I dared not let go until I had something else familiar to cling to. My foot came up against the other ventilator pipe. I edged back to that, and from the new anchorage repeated the maneuver. This time my ankle struck something hard. When I felt it and recognized the handle, I wanted to caress it.

Embracing this thrice-blessed tool, I inched back to the trapdoor. The handle of the shovel was just small enough to pass under the little wooden bridge which served as a grip. I got both hands on the shovel and tried to wrench the door up; my strength was not enough, however. So I lay down flat on my belly and worked my shoulders under the shovel. Then I heaved, the door sprang open, and I rolled down the shaft. When I tumbled into the light and warmth of the room, I kept thinking, How wonderful, how perfectly wonderful.

The man who wrote this selection

RICHARD EVELYN BYRD   1888–

Richard Byrd comes from an old and distinguished Virginia family. When he was twelve, he began his career as a famous explorer by making a trip around the world.

Byrd was educated in Virginia and Annapolis. His early naval career was short-lived because of a physical disability, but when America entered the First World War, he rejoined the Navy to serve with the air forces stationed in Canada. He got his first look at the Arctic Zone when he commanded the air forces with a naval polar expedition.

Since then he has made many expeditions to both the North and South Poles, and has recorded these experiences in articles and books. One of his visits to the South Pole is described in *Alone,* the book from which "The Blow" was taken.

Admiral Byrd holds many honors for his service to America as an explorer. He has received the Congressional Medal of Honor and more than twenty naval citations.

Let's consider . . .

1. Admiral Byrd fully understood the power and danger of an antarctic blizzard. Yet he risked his life to go aloft to repair equipment. What does this tell you about him as a scientist?

2. How did Byrd get locked out of his shack? Describe his efforts to get back to warmth and safety.

3. Byrd wrote that nothing in the world so quickly isolates a man as a blizzard. How did his experience in the blizzard prove the truth of this statement?

4. What other daring adventures have scientists taken part in so that man will know more about himself and the world?

The writer's craft . . .

Admiral Byrd gave you his first-hand impressions of what it feels like to be caught in an antarctic blizzard. He included many specific details which made his writing vivid and dramatic. He wrote of the snow exploding in his eyes like BB shot, and the beauty of candle-light against the white snow. Find other details which helped you to *see* and *feel* the experiences he described.

Recall a storm you have been in. Write your own description of it. Be sure to include those specific details which will describe what *you* felt, saw, and heard. Make the storm seem as *real* to your readers as Byrd made the blizzard seem to you.

Knowing words . . .

In order to fully appreciate Admiral Byrd's struggle against the antarctic blizzard, you must understand the words he used to describe his experience. Below are several sentences taken from the selection. Each of the sentences contains one word written in italics. After you are sure of the meaning of the italicized word, use it in a sentence of your own.

1. Millions of tiny *pellets* exploded in my eyes, stinging like BB shot.

2. There is something extravagantly *insensate* about an antarctic blizzard at night.

3. The whole *malevolent* rush is concentrated upon you as upon a personal enemy.

4. But how to find it in the *avalanche* of the blizzard?

5. Just two feet below was *sanctuary*—warmth, food, tools, all the means of survival.

Can We Survive in Space?

HEINZ HABER

Man has an astonishing ability to adjust himself to extreme conditions. He has learned to survive almost anywhere on the face of the earth. Now that he is beginning to explore space, can he solve these new problems of survival?

All day long, the frail little man attending the forum had listened to the engineers and scientists discuss the conquest of the heavens with huge rocket ships and space stations. Now he had a question.

"Mr. Chairman," he said, "you fellows seem to have worked out all the details. You know how your rocket ships should be designed, you even have plans on paper for machines to reach the moon and other planets. But as an ordinary layman who knows little about these matters, I would like to ask this one question:

"Who is going to design the crew?"

The questioner had put his finger on the greatest difficulty facing the engineers, scientists, and doctors in reaching space—man himself.

If the jet plane, guided missile, or rocket ship is not perfect, the engineer can redesign the machine over and over until all the kinks have been ironed out. He has a great variety of materials and devices at his disposal. He may eventually succeed in developing a flawless machine. The same cannot be said for man. He is the most important link, and yet the weakest one, in any attempt to conquer space. And he cannot be redesigned.

True, man can adapt himself to extraordinary conditions—he manages to survive anywhere on the face of this globe. But what will happen to him if he ventures into the alien environment known as space —the void beyond the atmosphere?

There is no oxygen for breathing.

The lack of atmospheric pressure can cause his blood to boil.

Dangerous radiation (ultraviolet rays) from the sun hits him with full force and can broil him within minutes.

Atomic bullets, called cosmic rays, plow through his body.

He will be weightless, floating helplessly about, with no up or down.

In short, man was not made to survive in the "hostile territory of space." It becomes the problem of the engineers, therefore, to create a highly mobile, self-contained, "packaged" environment for spacefaring man. In other words, he needs an air-tight shell to produce and preserve earthly conditions as nearly as possible.

Man is extremely hard to please in his

demands, but the engineers can lick the problem and supply the crew of a rocket ship or space station with all the necessities for survival. Neither rocket ship nor space station will have the snug comfort of Mother Earth, the flying through space will be a rough job that will call for healthy, tough, and physically well-trained individuals. But it can be done.

Some pessimists maintain that the crew members of a rocket ship wouldn't live to experience space, because they wouldn't even survive the tremendous stresses placed upon them during the ascent. The thrust of the operating rocket motors exerts strong forces upon the ship and its passengers. A motorist gets an inkling of one of these forces: if he steps on the accelerator, he is gently pressed against the back of the automobile seat. But this soft pressure in a car becomes a crushing force in a fast-rising rocket ship. As the space vehicle is whipped forward by the fiery jet of its escaping gases, the force increases in a slowly rising, irresistible surge. To the passenger, it will appear as though several men his own weight are standing on his chest. He will find it difficult to breathe. The acceleration will distend his features into a grotesque mask.

The stress of acceleration is not, of course, the only hazard man will encounter as he leaves the friendly atmosphere of the earth. A continuously flowing supply of breathing air is a necessity in the emptiness of space. Man can live without food or water for a considerable length of time. But without oxygen he can live only a few minutes. The crew of the space station must not be allowed to run low on oxygen at any time. Rocket ships will replenish the oxygen containers of the satellites at regular intervals.

Another problem, also tied up with the elementary fact that man cannot live without oxygen, is created by the existence of meteorites. They are the most important single danger to all space-travel projects.

Unfortunately, "empty" space beyond the atmosphere is by no means completely empty. In fact, you might call it a "no man's land" in which ultra-high speed cosmic "bullets" fly about at random. Hundreds of millions of these "bullets" of various sizes enter the earth's atmosphere every day and often can be seen as meteors or shooting stars. When a cosmic pebble the size of a pea strikes the upper atmosphere, the air resistance heats it until it burns away. This can be seen hundreds of miles distant as a bright streak or flare. Such a meteor hurtling through space at 25 miles a second would puncture more than an inch of armor plate. Very small meteors, the size of large grains of sand, could riddle the thin walls of the space station, permitting the air to escape.

However, engineering can do something even about the meteoric menace. One device, suggested by Dr. Fred L. Whipple of Harvard University's Department of Astronomy is called "meteor bumper" and consists of a thin secondary wall placed an inch or so outside the main wall of the space station or rocket ship. Incoming meteors would shatter on the outer wall, leaving the inner wall intact. If properly constructed of heavy enough materials, the meteor bumper could reduce the hazards very considerably, stopping 99 out of 100 meteors.

But even with these safety measures, there remains a probability that once every few years a relatively large meteor will smash through both walls of the space station. What would happen to the crew in that compartment?

The air would whistle out, and there would be a rapid drop in pressure. The crew would have exactly fifteen seconds left to restore their oxygen supply before losing consciousness. Without the oxygen they would die in a few minutes. In the early days of space exploration, it may be found safest to wear a pressure suit even in the pressurized cabin of the rocket ship. But because of the protective devices inside the space station, pressure suits might be worn there only in times of emergency.

Pressure suits for use by the crew outside the space station can be made of several layers of rubberized nylon topped by a sturdy metal helmet. The helmet's window would have to be made with a darkened piece of transparent material to ward off the sun's excessive ultraviolet rays. Of course the crew members will carry their own oxygen, and the suits will be equipped with a small air-conditioning unit for removing the exhaled stale gases.

In venturing into space, man abandons the powerful shield or filter of the atmosphere which protects him on earth from the hazards of the little-known effects of cosmic rays. These atomic bullets—which, like the meteors, crisscross space at enormous speeds—are one of the great mysteries of the region beyond our atmosphere. Scientists know they exist and have measured their biological effectiveness. They may be dangerous.

Cosmic rays are potentially dangerous because they are related to some of the types of rays produced in atomic explosions and in the manufacture of the A-bomb. Civil defense has made the public conscious of the term "radiation sickness." Will exposure in space cause radiation sickness?

We have no clear-cut answer to this question. Cosmic rays are so powerful that they cannot be reproduced artificially in the laboratory. But, although we do not know where they come from, we do know that they are extremely rare. We can con-

clude, therefore, that short trips through the thin rain of cosmic rays will almost certainly be harmless affairs. A round-the-moon trip can be made without getting radiation sickness.

Of course, long before man ventures into space, animals will be sent up in small rocket ships for the study of radiation effects over extended periods of time. A sheep, a rooster, and a duck were the first living beings to take to the air in a balloon, more than 150 years ago. And it seems that more such honors are in store for the animal kingdom. But, in the final analysis, the exploration of space must wait the arrival of man.

It will be, needless to say, a strange experience. And one of its strangest aspects will be the absence of gravity (except within the space station, which will provide its own "synthetic gravity" by spinning slowly to produce centrifugal force). The result of the lack of gravitational pull will be weightlessness—and there can be no doubt that the weightlessness will be the most unearthly and unforgettable experience shared by those who venture beyond the earth's atmosphere. Space and weightlessness will become synonymous, like desert and thirst, or arctic and cold.

While the machinery of the body will go on operating in an orderly fashion even if it is weightless, man will possibly encounter trouble when he attempts to go about his daily routine. Weightless man may well find himself in this position:

Imagine a muscular weight lifter taking a good grip on what he thinks is a solid 300-pound weight, but is actually a much lighter contraption made of wood. His anticipation is utterly deceived, and the ill-adjusted strength he applies, to his great surprise, throws the fake weight violently upward.

Space-faring man will consistently experience much the same thing: he will find that his co-ordination, based on a life-long experience with gravity, suddenly fails him in this new environment. A simple movement on earth, such as rising from his chair, will, in space, jerk him across the cabin toward the opposite wall. The co-ordination of the body, which is so automatic here on earth that we take it for granted, will have to be acquired all over again.

Since the customary effects of gravity are absent, there is no "up" or "down"—a factor certain to prove confusing. Normally, we rely to a great extent on gravity for orientation. But in a rocket ship, all orientation will depend on the eyes. It probably can be acquired, but until it has been learned, there exists the possibility of "space sickness," which will reduce efficiency even if it does not completely incapacitate the crew.

Not only the men will float around aim-lessly, in the weightlessness of a coasting rocket ship—objects will do the same, and this will cause trouble if careful thought is not given to the design beforehand.

In space, we must use other forces to substitute for gravity. Every metal object must be made of steel, or at least have a steel strip inlaid somewhere on it. Such tools can be kept in place with magnets, along the lines of the magnetic knife board in use in many of today's kitchens. Where magnetism cannot do the job, as with papers, friction will have to substitute for gravity —the clip-board is an everyday example of such a device.

As for eating utensils, the function of the knife and fork will remain the same. The knife still cuts and the fork utilizes friction to hold food after it has been speared. The spoon, however, is useless aboard a rocket ship (and so is the fork when used like a spoon), so the well-planned table in space will include some offspring of the

sugar tongs, something which will hold food by friction.

Liquids will be especially annoying; any liquid from milk to Burgundy is likely to imitate what any bottled sauce does on the ground. If you tilt a bottle in space nothing will come out, for, since the liquid does not weigh anything, there is no reason for it to pour. But when you shake the bottle, all the contents will come out in one splash. The solution to that particular problem is a very old invention: the drinking straw, which does not rely on gravity but on air pressure. Another method: plastic bottles, which, when squeezed, eject liquid.

Cooking aboard the space station will not be too difficult, because the satellite enjoys synthetic gravity. However, in rocket ships it will be quite different from the same process on the ground. Open pots or pans are useless, for boiling water will simply erupt from an open pot because of the steam bubbles which form at the bottom. Likewise, the first explosive sizzle of a steak's fat will send the meat floating across the cabin. Only closed cooking pots can be used and the ideal broiler is the so-called electronic range which cooks by short wave. (Naturally, if the crew members of the rocket ship are wearing pressure suits, they will have to open the visors of their helmets to eat.)

In long rocket-ship trips from the space station to other planets, seasoned space travelers may enjoy sleeping literally on an air cushion, just floating in air, possibly with a string tied to their wrists or ankles so that the reaction of their breathing will not "float" them away.

So far, we don't know whether the familiar pressure of a bed against the body is necessary for falling asleep. If it is, it can be "faked" during the weightless state by having a set of rubber straps force the body against a board or other flat surface. Beginners, however, will have to sleep in special bunks. These will look like six-foot lengths of pipe, upholstered inside and equipped with wire mesh covers at both ends. These wire mesh covers—the "wire" would probably be nylon string and the mesh widely spaced—would keep the sleeper inside his "bed." Without them, he might push himself out of it by unconscious movements or even be sucked over to the outlet end of the air-conditioning system.

For most of us, weightlessness will hardly be an agreeable and welcome feeling, and learning to live with it may prove a painful lesson. However, man has an astonishing ability to adjust to extreme conditions. A few individuals may even get to enjoy weightlessness, after a fashion. The crew members will probably be able to master its intricacies and go about their daily chores with ease.

We can be reasonably sure that man will be able to survive in space because we have sufficient knowledge of what will happen to the rocket ship or space station and to man himself. We can plan intelligently for his survival. Unlike the earth's early explorers, the pioneers of space know pretty well what they are headed for, and they know they will be equipped adequately.

The conquest of space hinges on man's survival in space. And the crews of rocket ships and space stations, while they can never be completely protected against hazards such as meteors, will probably be safer than pedestrians crossing a busy street at a rush hour.

The man who wrote this article

HEINZ HABER   1913–

Unlike the authors of most of the selections in this book, Heinz Haber is not a professional writer. He is a scientist whose special field is astrophysics, the combination of physics and astronomy.

Dr. Haber comes from a family of scientists. One of his brothers is a biochemist; the other is an aerodynamics engineer. In 1946, Dr. Haber came to the United States to teach for the Air Force School of Aviation Medicine in Texas. There he has been one of the pioneers in a new field of scientific study called "space medicine." With other prominent scientists, he is interested in discovering the effects of space travel on the human body.

Popular articles by Dr. Haber have appeared in *Collier's* and *Scientific American*. Most of his writings, of course, have been highly technical papers on optics or aviation and space medicine.

Let's consider . . .

1. Heinz Haber wrote that the greatest difficulty facing the scientists, engineers, and doctors who are working on the problems of survival in space is man himself. Explain why man is the weakest link in any attempt to conquer space. What are some of the problems involving man which must be solved before space can be safely explored?

2. Explain why man is also the most important link in the attempt to conquer space.

3. The problems of surviving in space are in many ways similar to the problems of surviving under water or in a high-flying plane. For example, deep-sea divers and high-altitude pilots must wear special oxygen containers. How are the problems of underwater and high-altitude survival similar to those of survival in space?

4. In what ways are the problems of survival in space completely different from survival under water or at a high altitude?

5. Balloons were sent into the air before men actually attempted to fly. Water bells were sent below before men actually explored the deeps in diving suits and submarines. How will space travel probably follow the same pattern?

6. The exploration of space will be a strange experience. One of the strangest aspects will be the absence of gravity. Describe living under conditions without gravity.

7. Heinz Haber wrote that man has an astonishing ability to adjust himself to extreme conditions. Can you think of any unusual conditions with which man has learned to cope?

8. What is Heinz Haber's answer to the question, "Can We Survive in Space?" Why do you agree or disagree with him?

Knowing words . . .

In discussing the problems of survival in space, Heinz Haber used many technical terms. You should understand the meaning of these terms if you wish to get the full implication of what he was saying. Below are several sentences taken from the selection. Each contains one or two italicized technical words. After you are sure of their meaning, use them in sentences of your own.

1. The lack of *atmospheric* pressure can cause his blood to boil.

2. And one of its strangest aspects will be the absence of *gravity* (except within the space station, which will provide its

own "synthetic gravity" by spinning slowly to produce *centrifugal* force).

3. Another problem, also tied up with the elementary fact that man cannot live without oxygen, is created by the existence of *meteorites*.

4. Some pessimists maintain that the crew members of a rocket ship wouldn't live to experience space, because they wouldn't even survive the tremendous *stresses* placed upon them during the *ascent*.

Post Early for Space

Once we were wayfarers, then seafarers, then airfarers;
We shall be spacefarers soon,
Not voyaging from city to city or from coast to coast,
But from planet to planet and from moon to moon.

This is no fanciful flight of imagination,
No strange, incredible, utterly different thing;
It will come by obstinate thought and calculation
And the old resolve to spread an expanding wing.

We shall see homes established on distant planets,
Friends departing to take up a post on Mars;
They will have perils to meet, but they will meet them,
As the early settlers did on American shores.

We shall buy tickets later, as now we buy them
For a foreign vacation, reserve our seat or berth,
Then spending a holiday month on a moon of Saturn,
Look tenderly back to our little shining Earth.

And those who decide they will not make the journey
Will remember a son up there or a favorite niece,
Eagerly awaiting news from the old home-planet,
And will scribble a line to catch the post for space.

Peter J. Henniker-Heaton

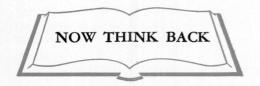

NOW THINK BACK

THINK FOR YOURSELF

You have read about people who did more than accept whatever came their way. They took their lives in their hands and created something richer and fuller than they had before.

1. List each of the challenges which the people in this part faced. Select the challenge you think required the greatest amount of courage. Explain why this particular challenge required so much courage. Write a brief description of the way this challenge was met. If you can, suggest other ways which might also have been successful.

2. Which selections were about people who created their own challenges? From this group, choose the person you found the most interesting. Then write a brief character sketch of him or her.

3. List the people who faced challenges which were forced upon them. Which of these people would you like to know personally? Prepare a one-minute talk explaining why.

4. What satisfactions did each of the main characters in PEOPLE WHO DARED receive as a result of his or her daring?

5. Some of the people you have read about worked alone. Others had the aid of parents or teachers. Select one of these parents or teachers and explain how he or she was challenged to act courageously. Explain how he or she met this challenge.

6. People who attempt difficult tasks often meet with failure. How can defeat serve as a test of courage?

SHARE YOUR IDEAS

1. Tell the class about a teacher you have known or read about who helped someone overcome a difficulty.

2. Write a description of someone you know who has met a challenge in a courageous way.

3. Describe someone you know who is foolhardy rather than courageous. What is the difference between courage and foolhardiness?

4. Are people born with courage or do they have to develop this quality?

5. What challenges do most teenagers face today? Which of these challenges can young people meet by themselves? Which are best met with the help of an older person?

6. What are the great challenges that all men face today? Select one of these and find out what is being done about it. Tell the class how men are using their courage and sense of daring to conquer this particular challenge.

WIDEN YOUR EXPERIENCE

Things to do . . .

1. Bring to class a newspaper clipping which tells about someone who dared to act courageously. Read your clipping aloud.

2. Make a PEOPLE WHO DARED bulletin board. Appoint a committee to keep the clippings for this board up to date.

3. Select several of the newspaper clippings which lend themselves to dramatization. Divide the class into committees. Have each group prepare a dramatization based on one of the clippings.

4. Conduct a round-table discussion on the question: What Makes a Courageous Person?

More to read . . .

Johnny Reb by MERRITT P. ALLEN. A poor boy from South Carolina fights bravely for the South with cavalry troops in the Civil War. Longmans, Green & Co., Inc., 1952.

Storm Canvas by ARMSTRONG SPERRY. A young American finds real adventure on the U. S. frigate *Thunderbolt* during the War of 1812. This exciting story, illustrated by the author, is a favorite among young people who like the sea. John C. Winston Company, 1944.

The Red Badge of Courage by STEPHEN CRANE. At first a coward, the hero of this book learns courage the hard way. Modern Library, Inc., 1942.

The Adventures of Odysseus and the Tale of Troy by PADRAIC COLUM. This is a vigorous and easy-to-read version of *The Iliad* and *The Odyssey,* Homer's great books of adventure. The Macmillan Company, 1918.

Coast Guard to the Rescue by KARL BAARSLAG. Here are some of the heroic and daring rescues performed by the Coast Guard—plus many official action photographs. Rinehart & Co., Inc., 1937.

The Story of Ernie Pyle by LEE G. MILLER. The little man who became the favorite of thousands of "G.I.'s" during World War II lives again in this biography. As a newspaperman, he shared dangers and hardships with the soldiers. Henry Holt and Company, Inc., 1950.

Young Patriots by HESTER O'NEILL. These are true stories of brave young people in fourteen countries during World War II. No sacrifice was too great if it would help bring peace and liberty back to the world. Thomas Nelson & Sons, 1948.

Man-Eaters of Kumaon by JAMES E. CORBETT. A professional hunter writes vividly of his experiences with man-eating tigers and leopards. Oxford Book Company, Inc., 1946.

Kon-Tiki by THOR HEYERDAHL. This recent book is already known as one of the great adventure stories of the sea. Six men make a voyage of over four thousand miles on a raft. Rand McNally & Company, 1950.

Arctic Venture by KENNETH GILBERT. Chuck Morgan's friendship for an Eskimo boy becomes stronger as they share the dangers of an ice-locked boat, a walrus hunt, and a mutiny. Henry Holt and Company, Inc., 1950.

Amelia Earhart, Heroine of the Skies by DORIS SHANNON GARST. The great courage, daring, and gentleness of this pioneer aviatrix are brought out clearly in her biography. Julian Messner, Inc., 1947.

Of Men and Mountains by WILLIAM O. DOUGLAS. As the author tells of his boyhood in the wilderness around Yakima, Washington, he shares with you his enthusiasm for mountaineering adventures. Harper & Brothers, 1950.

The Lure of Danger by MARGARET SCOGGIN (comp.) In this book Miss Scoggin has collected many true stories of danger and adventure throughout the world. Alfred A. Knopf, Inc., 1947.

Men Without Fear by JOHN J. FLOHERTY. Test pilots, sandhogs, and divers have extremely dangerous jobs, as you will discover when you read of the world's most dangerous occupations. J. P. Lippincott Company, 1940.

Man of Molokai by ANN ROOS. Father Damien worked devotedly to relieve suffering at a famous leper colony. J. B. Lippincott Company, 1943.

Captain Blood: His Odyssey by RAFAEL SABATINI. Peter Blood was a doctor, a slave, a soldier, a pirate, and finally the governor of Jamaica. This fast-moving story is packed with action and excitement. Houghton Mifflin Company, 1922.

Out on a Limb by LOUISE BAKER. Losing her leg in an accident did not keep this girl from living a happy and hearty life. Never sorry for herself, Miss Baker tells her story with humor and spirit. McGraw-Hill Book Company, Inc., 1946.

Half Mile Down by WILLIAM BEEBE. Down went the diving bell, until the only light came from living ocean creatures themselves. Dr. Beebe's trips into the ocean depths in his bathysphere were adventures into the unknown. Little, Brown and Company, 1951.

The Old Man and the Sea by ERNEST HEMINGWAY. An old man can fight many kinds of battles. This old man fights his age and the sharks that come to destroy his prize. Charles Scribner's Sons, 1952.

ON THE LIGHTER SIDE

You will look long and hard before you find a wise man who does not laugh. Perhaps it is his wisdom that helps him see the humorous side of life. In the most trying experiences he can find something to smile at—even if it is only his own over-anxious concern.

The Bible says, "A merry heart doeth good like a medicine." The wise man agrees. He knows that a sense of humor can save even the tense moments in one's life. He knows, too, that the man who can laugh at himself is likely to come out on top.

PART EIGHT

ON THE LIGHTER SIDE

The Ransom of Red Chief

O. HENRY

How talented a baby-sitter are you? Perhaps all the mothers in your neighborhood clamor for your services. Even so, you would probably have your hands full with the Dorset youngster. No wonder a pair of inexperienced kidnapers were baffled.

Sam, one of the kidnapers, tells the story. He has a way of using big words that should make you grin. You really don't need a dictionary at your side in order to enjoy the story. However, if you want to squeeze out every last bit of fun, go after Sam's big words. It's worth the trouble.

It looked like a good thing; but wait till I tell you. We were down south, in Alabama—Bill Driscoll and myself—when this kidnaping idea struck us. It was, as Bill afterwards expressed it, "during a moment of temporary mental apparition"; but we didn't find that out till later.

There was a town down there, as flat as a flannel cake, and called Summit, of course. It contained inhabitants of as undeleterious and self-satisfied a class of peasantry as ever clustered around a Maypole.

Bill and me had a joint capital of about six hundred dollars, and we needed just two thousand dollars more to pull off a fraudulent town-lot scheme in Western Illinois with. We talked it over on the front steps of the hotel. Philoprogenitiveness, says we, is strong in semirural communities; therefore, and for other reasons, a kidnaping project ought to be done better there than in the radius of newspapers that send reporters out in plain clothes to stir up talk about such things. We knew that Summit couldn't get after us with anything stronger than constables and, maybe, some lackadaisical bloodhounds and a diatribe or two in the *Weekly Farmer's Budget*. So it looked good.

We selected for our victim the only child of a prominent citizen named Ebenezer Dorset. The father was respectable and tight, a mortgage fancier and a stern, upright collection-plate passer and forecloser. The kid was a boy of ten, with bas-relief freckles, and hair the color of the cover of the magazine you buy at the newsstand when you want to catch a train. Bill and me figured that Ebenezer would melt down for a ransom of two thousand dollars to a cent. But wait till I tell you.

About two miles from Summit was a little mountain covered with a dense cedar brake. On the rear elevation of this mountain was a cave. There we stored provisions.

One evening after sundown, we drove in a buggy past old Dorset's house. The kid was in the street, throwing rocks at a kitten on the opposite fence.

"Hey, little boy!" says Bill, "would you like to have a bag of candy and a nice ride?"

The boy catches Bill neatly in the eye with a piece of brick.

"That will cost the old man an extra five hundred dollars," says Bill, climbing over the wheel.

That boy put up a fight like a welterweight cinnamon bear; but, at last, we got him down in the bottom of the buggy and drove away. We took him up to the cave, and I hitched the horse in the cedar brake. After dark, I drove the buggy to the little village, three miles away, where we had hired it, and walked back to the mountain.

Bill was pasting court plaster over the scratches and bruises on his features. There was a fire burning behind the big rock at the entrance of the cave, and the boy was watching a pot of boiling coffee, with two buzzard feathers stuck in his red hair. He points a stick at me when I come up, and says:

"Ha! cursed paleface, do you dare enter the camp of Red Chief, the terror of the plains?"

"He's all right now," says Bill, rolling up his trousers and examining some bruises on his shins. "We're playing Indian. We're making Buffalo Bill's show look like magic-lantern views of Palestine in the town hall. I'm old Hank, the Trapper, Red Chief's captive, and I'm to be scalped at daybreak. By Geronimo! that kid can kick hard."

Yes, sir, that boy seemed to be having the time of his life. The fun of camping out in a cave had made him forget he was a captive himself. He immediately christened me Snake Eye, the Spy, and announced that, when his braves returned from the warpath, I was to be broiled at the stake at the rising of the sun.

Then we had supper; and he filled his mouth full of bacon and bread and gravy, and began to talk. He made a during-dinner speech something like this:

"I like this fine. I never camped out before; but I had a pet 'possum once, and I was nine last birthday. I hate to go to school. Rats ate up sixteen of Jimmy Talbot's aunt's speckled hens' eggs. Are there any real Indians in these woods? I want some more gravy. Does the trees moving make the wind blow? We had five puppies. What makes your nose so red, Hank? My father has lots of money. Are the stars hot? I whipped Ed Walker twice, Saturday. I don't like girls. You dassent catch toads unless with a string. Do oxen make any noise? Why are oranges round? Have you got beds to sleep on in this cave? Amos Murray has got six toes. A parrot can talk, but a monkey or a fish can't. How many does it take to make twelve?"

Every few minutes he would remember that he was a pesky redskin, and pick up his stick rifle and tiptoe to the mouth of the cave to rubber for the scouts of the hated paleface. Now and then he would let out a war whoop that made Old Hank, the Trapper, shiver. That boy had Bill terrorized from the start.

"Red Chief," says I to the kid, "would you like to go home?"

"Aw, what for?" he says. "I don't have any fun at home. I hate to go to school. I like to camp out. You won't take me back home again, Snake Eye, will you?"

"Not right away," says I. "We'll stay here in the cave a while."

"All right," says he. "That'll be fine. I never had such fun in all my life."

We went to bed about eleven o'clock.

We spread down some wide blankets and quilts and put Red Chief between us. We weren't afraid he'd run away. He kept us awake for three hours, jumping up and reaching for his rifle and screeching: "Hist! pard!" in mine and Bill's ears, as the fancied crackle of a twig or the rustle of a leaf revealed to his young imagination the stealthy approach of the outlaw band. At last, I fell into a troubled sleep, and dreamed that I had been kidnaped and chained to a tree by a ferocious pirate with red hair.

Just at daybreak, I was awakened by a series of awful screams from Bill. They weren't yells, or howls, or shouts, or whoops, or yawps, such as you'd expect from a manly set of vocal organs—they were simply indecent, terrifying, humiliating screams, such as women emit when they see ghosts or caterpillars. It's an awful thing to hear a strong, desperate, fat man scream incontinently in a cave at daybreak.

I jumped up to see what the matter was. Red Chief was sitting on Bill's chest, with one hand twined in Bill's hair. In the other hand he had the sharp case knife we used for slicing bacon; and he was industriously and realistically trying to take Bill's scalp, according to the sentence that had been pronounced upon him the evening before.

I got the knife away from the kid and made him lie down again. But, from that moment, Bill's spirit was broken. He lay down on his side of the bed, but he never closed an eye again in sleep as long as that boy was with us. I dozed off for a while, but along toward sunup I remembered that Red Chief had said I was to be burned at the stake at the rising of the sun. I wasn't nervous or afraid; but I sat up and lit my pipe and leaned against a rock.

"What you getting up so soon for, Sam?" asked Bill.

"Me?" says I. "Oh, I got kind of a pain in my shoulder. I thought sitting up would rest it."

"You're a liar!" says Bill. "You're afraid. You was to be burned at sunrise, and you was afraid he'd do it. And he would, too, if he could find a match. Ain't it awful, Sam? Do you think anybody will pay out

money to get a little imp like that back home?"

"Sure," said I. "A rowdy kid like that is just the kind that parents dote on. Now, you and the Chief get up and cook breakfast, while I go up on the top of this mountain and reconnoiter."

I went up on the peak of the little mountain and ran my eye over the contiguous vicinity. Over toward Summit I expected to see the sturdy yeomanry of the village armed with scythes and pitchforks beating the countryside for the dastardly kidnapers. But what I saw was a peaceful landscape dotted with one man plowing with a dun mule. Nobody was dragging the creek, no couriers dashed hither and yon, bringing tidings of no news to the distracted parents. There was a sylvan attitude of somnolent sleepiness pervading that section of the external outward surface of Alabama that lay exposed to my view. "Perhaps," says I to myself, "it has not yet been discovered that the wolves have borne away the tender lambkin from the fold. Heaven help the wolves!" says I, and I went down the mountain to breakfast.

When I got to the cave I found Bill backed up against the side of it, breathing hard, and the boy threatening to smash him with a rock half as big as a coconut.

"He put a red-hot boiled potato down my back," explained Bill, "and then mashed it with his foot; and I boxed his ears. Have you got a gun about you, Sam?"

I took the rock away from the boy and kind of patched up the argument. "I'll fix you," says the kid to Bill. "No man ever yet struck the Red Chief but what he got paid for it. You better beware!"

After breakfast the kid takes a piece of leather with strings wrapped around it out of his pocket and goes outside the cave unwinding it.

"What's he up to now?" says Bill, anx-

iously. "You don't think he'll run away, do you, Sam?"

"No fear of it," says I. "He don't seem to be much of a homebody. But we've got to fix up some plan about the ransom. There don't seem to be much excitement around Summit on account of his disappearance; but maybe they haven't realized he's gone. His folks may think he's spending the night with Aunt Jane or one of the neighbors. Anyhow, he'll be missed today. Tonight we must get a message to his father demanding the two thousand dollars for his return."

Just then we heard a kind of war whoop, such as David might have emitted when he knocked out the champion Goliath. It was a sling that Red Chief had pulled out of his pocket, and he was whirling it around his head.

I dodged, and heard a heavy thud and a kind of sigh from Bill, like one a horse gives out when you take his saddle off. A rock the size of an egg had caught Bill just behind his left ear. He loosened himself all over and fell in the fire across the frying pan of hot water for washing the dishes. I dragged him out and poured cold water on his head for half an hour.

By and by, Bill sits up and feels behind his ear and says: "Sam, do you know who my favorite Biblical character is?"

"Take it easy," says I. "You'll come to your sense presently."

"King Herod," says he. "You won't go away and leave me here alone, will you Sam?"

I went out and caught that boy and shook him until his freckles rattled.

"If you don't behave," says I, "I'll take you straight home. Now, are you going to be good, or not?"

"I was only funning," says he sullenly. "I didn't mean to hurt Old Hank. But what did he hit me for? I'll behave, Snake

Eye, if you won't send me home, and if you'll let me play the Black Scout today."

"I don't know the game," says I. "That's for you and Mr. Bill to decide. He's your playmate for the day. I'm going away for a while, on business. Now, you come in and make friends with him and say you are sorry for hurting him, or home you go, at once."

I made him and Bill shake hands, and then I took Bill aside and told him I was going to Poplar Cove, a little village three miles from the cave, and find out what I could about how the kidnaping had been regarded in Summit. Also, I thought it best to send a peremptory letter to old man Dorset that day, demanding the ransom and dictating how it should be paid.

"You know, Sam," says Bill, "I've stood by you without batting an eye in earthquakes, fire, and flood—in poker games, dynamite outrages, police raids, train robberies, and cyclones. I never lost my nerve yet till we kidnaped that two-legged skyrocket of a kid. He's got me going. You won't leave me long with him, will you Sam?"

"I'll be back some time this afternoon," says I. "You must keep the boy amused and quiet till I return. And now we'll write the letter to old Dorset."

Bill and I got paper and pencil and worked on the letter while Red Chief, with a blanket wrapped around him, strutted up and down, guarding the mouth of the cave. Bill begged me tearfully to make the ransom fifteen hundred dollars instead of two thousand. "I ain't attempting," says he, "to decry the celebrated moral aspects of parental affection, but we're dealing with humans, and it ain't human for anybody to give up two thousand dollars for that forty-pound chunk of freckled wildcat. I'm willing to take a chance at fifteen hundred

dollars. You can charge the difference up to me."

So, to relieve Bill, I acceded, and we collaborated a letter that ran this way:

Ebenezer Dorset, Esq.:

We have your boy concealed in a place far from Summit. It is useless for you or the most skillful detectives to attempt to find him. Absolutely the only terms on which you can have him restored to you are these: We demand fifteen hundred dollars in large bills for his return; the money to be left at midnight tonight at the same spot and in the same box as your reply—as hereinafter described. If you agree to these terms, send your answer in writing by a solitary messenger tonight at half past eight o'clock. After crossing Owl Creek, on the road to Poplar Cove, there are three large trees about a hundred yards apart, close to the fence of the wheat field on the right-hand side. At the bottom of the fence post opposite the third tree will be found a small pasteboard box.

The messenger will place the answer in this box and return immediately to Summit.

If you attempt any treachery or fail to comply with our demand as stated, you will never see your boy again.

If you pay the money as demanded, he will be returned to you safe and well within three hours. These terms are final, and if you do not accede to them, no further communication will be attempted.

Two Desperate Men

I addressed this letter to Dorset, and put it in my pocket. As I was about to start, the kid came up to me and says:

"Aw, Snake Eye, you said I could play the Black Scout while you was gone."

"Play it, of course," says I. "Mr. Bill will play with you. What kind of a game is it?"

"I'm the Black Scout," says Red Chief, "and I have to ride to the stockade to warn the settlers that the Indians are coming. I'm tired of playing Indian myself. I want to be the Black Scout."

"All right," says I. "It sounds harmless to me. I guess Mr. Bill will help you foil the pesky savages."

"What am I to do?" asks Bill, looking at the kid suspiciously.

"You are the hoss," says Black Scout. "Get down on your hands and knees. How can I ride to the stockade without a hoss?"

"You'd better keep him interested," said I, "till we get the scheme going. Loosen up."

Bill gets down on his all fours, and a look comes in his eyes like a rabbit's when you catch it in a trap.

"How far is it to the stockade, kid?" he asks in a husky manner of voice.

"Ninety miles," says the Black Scout. "And you have to hump yourself to get there on time. Whoa, now!"

The Black Scout jumps on Bill's back and digs his heels in his side.

"For heaven's sake," says Bill, "hurry back, Sam, as soon as you can. I wish we hadn't made the ransom more than a thousand. Say, you quit kicking me, or I'll get up and warm you good."

I walked over to Poplar Cove and sat around the post office and store, talking with the chawbacons [1] that come in to trade. One whiskerando says that he hears Summit is all upset on account of Elder Ebenezer Dorset's boy having been lost or stolen. That was all I wanted to know. I bought some smoking tobacco, referred casually to the price of black-eyed peas, posted my letter surreptitiously and came away. The postmaster said the mail carrier would come by in an hour to take the mail on to Summit.

When I got back to the cave Bill and the boy were not to be found. I explored the vicinity of the cave, and risked a yodel or two, but there was no response.

[1] *chawbacons,* people who live in the country or small towns

So I lighted my pipe and sat down on a mossy bank to await developments.

In about half an hour I heard the bushes rustle, and Bill wabbled out into the glade in front of the cave. Behind him was the kid, stepping softly like a scout, with a broad grin on his face. Bill stopped, took off his hat and wiped his face with a red handkerchief. The kid stopped about eight feet behind him.

"Sam," says Bill, "I suppose you'll think I'm a renegade, but I couldn't help it. I'm a grown person with masculine proclivities and habits of self-defense, but there is a time when all systems of egotism and predominance fail. The boy is gone. I have sent him home. All is off. There was martyrs in old times," goes on Bill, "that suffered death rather than give up the particular graft they enjoyed. None of 'em ever was subjugated to such supernatural tortures as I have been. I tried to be faithful to our articles of depredation; but there came a limit."

"What's the trouble, Bill?" I asks him.

"I was rode," says Bill, "the ninety miles to the stockade, not barring an inch. Then when the settlers was rescued, I was given oats. Sand ain't a palatable substitute. And then, for an hour I had to try to explain why there was nothin' in holes, how a road can run both ways, and what makes the grass green. I tell you, Sam, a human can only stand so much. I takes him by the neck of his clothes and drags him down the mountain. On the way he kicks my legs black and blue from the knees down; and I've got to have two or three bites on my thumb and hand cauterized."

"But he's gone," continues Bill, "gone home. I showed him the road to Summit and kicked him about eight feet nearer there at one kick. I'm sorry we lose the ransom; but it was either that or Bill Driscoll to the madhouse."

Bill is puffing and blowing, but there is a look of ineffable peace and growing content on his rose-pink features.

"Bill," says I, "there isn't any heart disease in your family, is there?"

"No," says Bill, "nothing chronic except malaria and accidents. Why?"

"Then you might turn around," says I, "and have a look behind you."

Bill turns and sees the boy, and loses his complexion and sits down plump on the ground and begins to pluck aimlessly at grass and little sticks. For an hour I was afraid for his mind. And then I told him that my scheme was to put the whole job through immediately and that we would get the ransom and be off with it by midnight if old Dorset fell in with our proposition. So Bill braced up enough to give the kid a weak sort of smile and a promise to play the Russian in a Japanese war with him as soon as he felt a little better.

I had a scheme for collecting that ransom without danger of being caught by counterplots that ought to commend itself to professional kidnapers. The tree under which the answer was to be left—and the money later on—was close to the road fence with big, bare fields on all sides. If a gang of constables should be watching for anyone to come for the note they could see him a long way off crossing the fields, or in the road. But no, siree! At half past eight I was up in that tree as well hidden as a tree toad, waiting for the messenger to arrive.

Exactly on time, a half-grown boy rides up the road on a bicycle, locates the pasteboard box at the foot of the fence post, slips a folded piece of paper into it, and pedals away again back toward Summit.

I waited an hour and then concluded the thing was square. I slid down the tree, got the note, slipped along the fence till I struck the woods, and was back at the cave in another half an hour. I opened the note, got near the lantern, and read it to Bill. It was written with a pen in a crabbed hand, and the sum and substance of it was this:

Two Desperate Men:

Gentlemen: I received your letter today by post, in regard to the ransom you ask for the return of my son. I think you are a little high in your demands, and I hereby make you a counterproposition, which I am inclined to believe you will accept. You bring Johnny home and pay me two hundred and fifty dollars in cash, and I agree to take him off your hands. You had better come at night, for the neighbors believe he is lost, and I couldn't be responsible for what they would do to anybody they saw bringing him back.

Very respectfully,
Ebenezer Dorset

"Great pirates of Penzance!" says I, "of all the impudent—"

But I glanced at Bill, and hesitated. He had the most appealing look in his eyes I ever saw on the face of a dumb or a talking brute.

"Sam," says he, "what's two hundred and fifty dollars, after all? We've got the money. One more night of this kind will send me to a bed in Bedlam. Besides being a thorough gentleman, I think Mr. Dorset is a spendthrift for making us such a liberal offer. You ain't going to let the chance go, are you?"

"Tell you the truth, Bill," says I, "this little he ewe lamb has somewhat got on my nerves, too. We'll take him home, pay the ransom, and make our getaway."

We took him home that night. We got him to go by telling him that his father had bought a silver-mounted rifle and a pair of moccasins for him, and we were going to hunt bears the next day.

It was just twelve o'clock when we knocked at Ebenezer's front door. Just at the moment when I should have been abstracting the fifteen hundred dollars from the box under the tree, according to the original proposition, Bill was counting out two hundred and fifty dollars into Dorset's hand.

When the kid found out we were going to leave him at home he started up a howl like a calliope and fastened himself tight as a leech to Bill's leg. His father peeled him away gradually, like a porous plaster.

"How long can you hold him?" asks Bill.

"I'm not as strong as I used to be," says old Dorset, "but I think I can promise you ten minutes."

"Enough," says Bill. "In ten minutes I shall cross the Central, Southern, and Middle Western States, and be legging it trippingly for the Canadian border."

And, as dark as it was, and as fat as Bill was, and as good a runner as I am, he was a good mile and a half out of Summit before I could catch up with him.

The man who wrote this story

O. HENRY (WILLIAM SYDNEY PORTER)   1862–1910

William Porter was once a teller in a poorly run bank in Austin, Texas. A government inspector found the bank's records so inaccurate that he felt someone should be punished for embezzlement. Though there was no evidence that Porter had been connected with the loss of the money, he was ordered to report for trial. He fled. In Honduras he fell in with two famous outlaws, the Jenning brothers, and toured South America and Mexico with them. When the outlaws wanted Porter to join them in a robbery, he refused. He learned that his wife was very ill and returned to Texas. The authorities left him alone until after his wife's death. Then he was brought to trial and sentenced to five years imprisonment.

In prison Porter chose O. Henry as his pen name and wrote short stories in his spare time. He blended together his broad sense of humor and his experiences with the Jenning brothers. When he left prison three years later, he had become a professional writer. At the invitation of his editor, he traveled to New York.

O. Henry found New York City fascinating. At night he prowled the streets near his apartment and noted the strange individuals who haunted the bars and park benches. From these observations came his most famous collection of short stories, *The Four Million*. When O. Henry died, he had written over six hundred short stories. Many writers have since copied his use of the surprise ending—the sudden twist at the end of a story. Though O. Henry cannot be called the father of the American short story, he certainly helped to make the short story the popular form of writing that it is today.

Let's consider . . .

1. When you first saw Johnny, he was throwing rocks at a kitten. What did this action tell you about his character?

2. When Bill asked Johnny if he wanted a bag of candy, what did Johnny do? If Sam and Bill had really been smart, what would they have done at this point?

3. Johnny wasn't at all terrified of being kidnaped. In fact, he had the time of his life. Explain why he had so much fun.

4. How did Sam and Bill finally get rid of Red Chief?

5. Why did Johnny's father suggest that the kidnapers return the boy after dark?

6. Ordinarily, kidnaping is a serious offense. How did O. Henry manage to make it seem funny?

7. Did Red Chief's methods of wearing down adult resistance seem familiar to you? What baby-sitting experiences have you had that are similar? What tricks do you know for getting along with youngsters?

8. How much do you think western movies, comics, and television shows influence the lives of children?

9. For the curious: Why did Bill say that King Herod was his favorite Biblical character?

Knowing words . . .

Sam had his own individual way of telling a story. Often he used a big word to express a very simple meaning. Part of the humor of this story resulted from his scattering such words in sentences which weren't even grammatical.

What did Sam really mean by these big words which rolled so happily off his tongue? Look up each of the following italicized words in the dictionary. Then rewrite the sentences, replacing the big words with smaller ones to give a similar meaning.

1. *Philoprogenitiveness,* says we, is strong in semi-rural communities.

2. It contained inhabitants of as *undeleterious* and self-satisfied a class of peasantry as ever clustered around a Maypole.

3. So, to relieve Bill, I *acceded,* and we *collaborated* a letter that ran this way.

4. There was a *sylvan* attitude of *somnolent* sleepiness *pervading* that section of the external outward surface of Alabama that lay exposed to my view.

I'm in a Hurry

WILLIAM HAZLETT UPSON

Many things may stand in the way of young love. In the case of David
Crockett Suggs, the barrier was a disabled tractor.

Dry River Junction, Texas
October 1, 1924
To the Farmers Friend Tractor Company
Earthworm City, Illinois
DEAR SIR: I'm in a hurry I want a new main
drive gear for my tractor. This tractor was
formerly owned by Joe Banks of Llano,
Texas, and bought by me at the auction
after he died. The main drive gear in the
tractor has busted and I just been over and
asked the widow Banks where Joe used to
buy parts for his tractors and she said she
ain't sure but she thinks it was The Farmers Friend Tractor Company, Earthworm
City, Illinois. So please let me know if you
are the folks, and if so please send the gear
at once. As I am in a hurry. It is the main
drive gear. It is the big bull gear in the
back end of the transmission that goes
round and round and drives the tractor
excuse this paper as my regular business
letter paper has not come yet yours truly,

DAVID CROCKETT SUGGS

FARMERS' FRIEND TRACTOR COMPANY
MAKERS OF EARTHWORM TRACTORS
EARTHWORM CITY, ILL.
October 3, 1924
Mr. David Crockett Suggs
Dry River Junction, Tex.
DEAR SIR: This will acknowledge receipt of
your letter of October 1, in which we note
that you request us to send you a gear for
your tractor.

In this connection we are pleased to advise that an inspection of our files reveals
the fact that Mr. Joseph Banks of Llano,
Tex., was the owner of one of our old-style
Model 45 Earthworm Tractors. Mr. Banks
acquired this tractor on June 3, 1915. We
are changing our records to indicate that
this tractor has been purchased by yourself,
and we are most happy to assure you that
all the resources of the Farmers' Friend
Tractor Company are at your service and
that we can supply you promptly with
everything you may need in the way of
spare parts, service, and information.

We regret, however, that your description of the gear which you desire is not sufficient for us to identify same, as there are a number of gears in the transmission to which the description "main drive gear" might conceivably apply. Kindly look up this gear in the parts book and advise us the proper part number and name as given therein. When necessary information is received, immediate shipment will be made.

In the meantime, we wish to extend you a most cordial welcome into the happy family of Earthworm users, to congratulate you upon selecting an Earthworm Tractor —even though it be of such an old model —and to assure you of our constant interest and desire to coöperate with you to the fullest extent.

Very truly yours,
FREDERICK R. OVERTON
Parts Department

Dry River Junction, Texas
October 6, 1924
To the Farmers Friend Tractor Company
Earthworm City, Illinois
DEAR SIR: I got your letter I got no parts book. I asked the widow of Joe Banks, who is the man that owned the tractor before I bought it at the auction after he died, I asked her did they have a parts book for the tractor and she said they once had a parts book but it is lost. I would look up the gear in the parts book if I could, but you can understand that I can't look up the gear in the parts book if I got no parts book. What I want is the big bull gear way at the back. The great big cog wheel with 44 cogs on it that goes round and round and drives the tractor.

I'm in a hurry because the tractor is unfortunately broke down right while I'm doing a very important job for Mr. Rogers of this city. The tractor run fine until 3 P.M. October 1, when there came a loud and very funny noise in the back and the tractor would no longer pull. We took the cover off the transmission case, and this big cog wheel was busted. Six cogs was busted off it, and the tractor will not pull; only make a funny noise.

I am a young man 24 years of age just starting in business and expect to get married soon, so please send the gear at once as I'm in a hurry and oblige,

DAVID CROCKETT SUGGS

FARMERS' FRIEND TRACTOR COMPANY
MAKERS OF EARTHWORM TRACTORS
EARTHWORM CITY, ILL.
October 9, 1924
Mr. David Crockett Suggs
Dry River Junction, Tex.
DEAR SIR: This will acknowledge your valued letter of October 6, stating that you desire a gear for your tractor, but are unable to give us the parts number of same owing to the fact that you have no parts book. We have carefully gone over your description of the gear, but we regret that we have been unable positively to identify what gear it is that you desire. We note that you state the gear has 44 teeth and we feel sure that some mistake has been made, as there is no 44-tooth gear in the tractor.

We are therefore mailing you under separate cover a parts book for the Model 45 Earthworm Tractor, year 1915, and would suggest that you look up the gear in this book, and let us know the part number so that we can fill the order.

Unfortunately we are not able to supply you a parts book printed in English.

Nearly all of the old-style Model 45 tractors were sold to the French Government in 1915 to be used in pulling artillery on the western front. As only a few of these tractors were sold in America, the edition of English parts books was very limited and has been exhausted. We are, however, sending you one of the French parts books.

We regret exceedingly that we are obliged to give you a parts book printed in a foreign language; and we realize, of course, that possibly you may be unable to understand it. However, you should be able to find the gear in the picture.

Kindly give us the part number which is given under the picture of the gear, and we will make immediate shipment.

Very truly yours,
FREDERICK R. OVERTON
Parts Department

Dry River Junction, Texas
October 12, 1924
To the Farmers Friend Tractor Company
Earthworm City, Illinois
DEAR SIR: Your letter has come your book has come you was right when you said I might not understand it. I cant understand the French printing and I been looking at the pictures all evening and I cant understand the pictures they dont look like nothing I ever seen. So I cant give you no part number, but I'm in a hurry so please send the gear anyway. It is the one way at the back. You cant miss it. Its not the one that lays down its the one that sets up on edge and has 44 teeth and meshes with the little one with 12 teeth. The little one goes round and round and drives the big one. And the big one is keyed on the main shaft and goes round and round and drive the tractor. Or I should say used to go round and round, but now has six teeth busted out and wont go round—only makes a funny noise when it gets to the place where the teeth are busted out.

I'm in a hurry and to show you that I need this gear quick, I will explain that the tractor is laid up right in the middle of an important job I'm doing for Mr. Rogers of this city. I'm a young man, age 24 years,

and new at the house moving business and I want to make a good impression and also expect to get married soon.

When Mr. Rogers of this city decided to move his house from down by the depot up to the north end of town, and give me the job, I thought it was a fine chance to get started in business and make a good impression. I got the house jacked up, and I put heavy timbers underneath and trucks with solid wheels that I bought from a contractor at Llano. And I bought this second-hand tractor from Joe Banks at Llano at the auction after he died, and all my money is tied up in this equipment and on October 1, at 3 P.M. we had the house moved half way to where they want it, when the tractor made a funny noise and quit. And if I don't get a new gear pretty soon and move the house the rest of the way I'll be a blowed up sucker.

I'm just starting in business and want to make a good impression and I'm expecting to get married so please hurry with the gear. Excuse paper as my regular business paper has not come yet and oblige,

DAVID CROCKETT SUGGS

FARMERS' FRIEND TRACTOR COMPANY
MAKERS OF EARTHWORM TRACTORS
EARTHWORM CITY, ILL.
October 14, 1924
Mr. David Crockett Suggs
Dry River Junction, Tex.
DEAR SIR: This will acknowledge your valued favor of October 12, and we regret exceedingly that you have been unable to locate the part which you desire in the parts book, and that consequently you have been subject to annoying delay. As it is always our desire to render the greatest possible service to Earthworm Tractor owners, we have gone into this matter with the greatest care; and after checking very thoroughly the description given in your latest

letter and also in former letters, we have come to the conclusion that the gear you desire is the 45-tooth intermediate spur gear, symbol number 6843, as illustrated on page 16 of the parts book. We note that you state the gear has 44 teeth, but as there is no such gear in your model tractor, and as No. 6843 gear fits the description in other particulars, we can only assume that you made a mistake in counting the number of teeth in the gear.

Accordingly we are shipping you by express this afternoon one No. 6843 gear, which we trust will prove to be the part desired. Assuring you of our constant desire to render you every possible service, efficiently and promptly, I remain,

Very truly yours,
FREDERICK R. OVERTON
Parts Department

Dry River Junction, Texas
October 18, 1924
To the Farmers Friend Tractor Company
Earthworm City, Illinois
DEAR SIR: Your letter come yesterday your gear come today C.O.D. $41.26 and not only that, but it is no good and it wont fit. It is not like the old gear. It looks like a well made gear but there is nothing like it on my tractor so it is no good to me it is too big it wont go on it won't fit on the shaft. And if it did fit on the shaft, it would not work because it is too big and the teeth would not mesh with the teeth on the little gear, and it ought to have 44 teeth like I said, *not* 45.

So will you look this up again more carefully and send me the right gear and send it as quick as possible? I'm in a hurry, and I will explain to you how things stand so you can see I am no liar when I say I got to have this gear right off or I am a blowed up sucker.

I am new in the house moving business

and I am moving a house for Mr. Rogers of this city, and Mr. Rogers is a very stubborn old cus and he insisted that the house be moved all together—which includes the main part which is two stories high and built very strong and solid, and also the front porch which sticks out in front and is built pretty weak, and also the one-story kitchen which sticks out behind. The kitchen is very frail.

But Mr. Rogers did not listen to me when I wanted to move the kitchen and front porch separate from the house. So, as I am a young man and new at the house moving business and anxious to make a good impression, I tried to do it like he wanted. I jacked up the whole works all together, and put timbers underneath, and heavy trucks that I bought from a contractor at Llano, and came up from the depot fine—the tractor pulling good and the little old house rolling along smooth and quiet and beautiful. But at 3 P.M. October 1, just as we was going past Jim Ferguson's Drug Store on the main street of this city, there come a funny noise in the tractor, and we have been stuck ever since waiting for a new gear because the tractor will not run with six teeth busted out of the old gear.

So you can see that it is no lie that I am in a hurry, and I will explain that for 2 and ½ weeks, no traffic has been able to go past Jim Ferguson's Drug Store. All traffic on the main street of this city has been detoured—turning to the right through the field next to Johnson's Garage, following the back lane past the shed where Harvey Jenkins keeps his cow, and then around Wilson's Hardware Store and back to the main street, and all this owing to the stubbornness of old man Rogers making me take the porch and the kitchen along at the same time.

The porch is now resting two feet from

the drug store and the kitchen just three feet from the post office on the other side of the street. If old man Rogers had listened to me and we had taken the kitchen off, there would have been room for traffic to get past, but now we can't take the kitchen off on account of being so jammed up against the post office, but people don't figger on that and everybody in town blames it on me that traffic is held up, which is very wrong as I am doing the best I can.

And now old man Rogers says that I contracted to move his house, and I had better hurry up, and he says why don't I hire some horses but I say horses would be unsafe, because when they get to pulling something very heavy they get to jerking and they would be liable to jerk the house and injure it, owing to the fact that Mr. Rogers was so stubborn as to make me leave the kitchen and the porch on the house, thus weakening it. And besides I got no money to waste hiring horses when I got a tractor already, so you can see why

I'm in a hurry being anxious to make a good impression and get married.

Please send at once the right gear which has FORTY-FOUR TEETH (44), because the old gear has 38 good teeth, and 6 busted off, making 44 like I said, *not* 45. And the right gear is an inch narrower than the one you sent, and the hole through the middle is smaller. I am making a picture so you can see just what gear it is, so please send it at once and oblige,

DAVID CROCKETT SUGGS

FARMERS' FRIEND TRACTOR COMPANY
MAKERS OF EARTHWORM TRACTORS
EARTHWORM CITY, ILL.
October 21, 1924
Mr. David Crockett Suggs
Dry River Junction, Tex.
DEAR SIR: This will acknowledge receipt of your letter of October 18, from which we note that you are having trouble in installing in your tractor gear No. 6843, which we shipped you on October 14.

We regret exceedingly that you have had this trouble, and to the end that the basis of the difficulty might be discovered, we have carefully checked over your former correspondence and have at length come to the conclusion that gear No. 6843, which we sent you, is the proper gear. We are therefore at a loss to understand why you have been unable to use it, and can only suggest that you may possibly have made some error in installing it.

To obviate this difficulty we are today mailing you, under separate cover, a copy of our latest instruction book on the care, operation, and repair of Earthworm Tractors. We regret that this book was prepared for the new-style tractors, but as the method of installing transmission gears is essentially the same in both old and new-style tractors, we feel sure that you will have no trouble in applying the instructions to your old-style tractor. Please study carefully the pictures and full descriptions on page 34, and if you proceed as directed we feel sure you will experience no further difficulty in installing the gear.

In case, however, there still remains some minor trouble to interfere with the perfect operation of the tractor, we shall appreciate it if you will notify us, as we are always anxious to give owners of Earthworm Tractors the fullest possible coöperation.

Very truly yours,
FREDERICK R. OVERTON
Parts Department

Dry River Junction, Texas
October 25, 1924
To the Farmers Friend Tractor Company
Earthworm City, Illinois
DEAR SIR: Your letter come yesterday your book come today they are no good to me. It takes more than a book for a new tractor to put onto an entirely different old tractor a gear wheel that don't belong to it. I tell

you again—you have sent me the wrong gear.

What I want is the big bull gear on the back that has 44 teeth. FORTY-FOUR. Not 45. And it goes round and round and makes the tractor go. It is the great big cog wheel that meshes with the little cog wheel. I bet you have sent me a gear for one of your new-style tractors—how do I know? You told me you had looked it up what model tractor I got, so why don't you send me the gear that will fit?

If you people knew what I was up against, you would get busy, and you would send me that gear in a hurry. The whole town is sore at me. And I will explain that this is a big place with trolley cars and everything.

The trolleys here run on a track, but they are not electric, they run by gasoline motors inside, and are very modern and up-to-date like everything else in this city. And for over three weeks now the trolley from the depot has been coming up almost as far as Jim Ferguson's Drug Store, and then it has to stop and the conductor will give the people transfers. And they will get out and squeeze past old man Rogers' house, and get on the other trolley and ride on. And it is lucky they have two cars. A few years ago they only had one.

And old man Rogers says if I don't get action by the first of the week, he is going to hire horses himself, and pull the house where he wants it. And if I expect to get a cent for it I can just sue him, and he says he is tired of living in a house sitting in the middle of the street with the front porch poking into the drug store window and the people kidding him all the time. But it's all on account of his own foolishness and stubbornness, because I told him he had better go live with his brother in Llano while the house was being moved, but he is a guy that you can't tell him nothing and so he is living there with Mrs. Rogers and daughter Mildred. So you can see I'm in a hurry and everybody is sore because the traffic is detoured and me having to hang red lanterns on the house every night so people won't run into it, and the Police Department has served notice on me that I got until next Thursday to move the house or get pinched. And they had given me a permit to move the house. But they say a permit ain't no 99-year lease. And that just shows how it is—they all try to make mean cracks like that.

And this afternoon, old Mr. Rogers came up to me and he said, "Dave, I hope you ain't still thinking of getting married?"

And I said, "I sure am," because, as I told you in another letter, I'm expecting to get married.

Then Mr. Rogers said, "I may have something to say about that, young man." And I will explain that it is possible that old Mr. Rogers—whose house I am moving with my tractor—may have some influence in the matter, owing to the fact that the girl I expect to marry is named Mildred Rogers, and unfortunately happens to be the daughter of old Mr. Rogers.

So you see, I want that gear, and I want it quick. I am sending back the new gear please credit me with the $41.26 I paid on the C.O.D. I am also sending you the old busted gear and send me one just like it, only with the six teeth not busted out. Please hurry and remember FORTY-FOUR TEETH, and oblige yours truly,

DAVID CROCKETT SUGGS

P.S. *Not* 45 teeth.

FARMERS' FRIEND TRACTOR COMPANY
MAKERS OF EARTHWORM TRACTORS
EARTHWORM CITY, ILL.
October 29, 1924
Mr. David Crockett Suggs
Dry River Junction, Tex.

DEAR SIR: This will acknowledge your valued favor of October 26 in reference to the trouble you are having with your tractor. We regret exceedingly that the misunderstanding in regard to the gear which you need has caused you the annoying delay which you mention.

As soon as your old gear arrives, it will be checked up and every possible effort will be made to supply you promptly with a duplicate of it.

Very truly yours,
FREDERICK R. OVERTON
Parts Department

DAVID CROCKETT SUGGS
CONTRACTOR
HOUSES MOVED SAFELY, SPEEDILY,
AND SURELY
DRY RIVER JUNCTION, TEXAS
October 31, 1924
To the Farmers Friend Tractor Company
Earthworm City, Illinois
DEAR SIR: My new letter paper has come your letter has come please send me the gear as quick as possible. I'm in a hurry more than at any time before and unless I can get this mess straightened out I'll be more of a blowed up sucker than anybody you ever seen, and in order that you may see what a rush I am in and send the gear as quick as possible, I will explain 2 very unfortunate events which has took place since my last letter. The first was last night. Being Thursday night and my regular night to call, I went around to see Miss Mildred Rogers, how, as I have explained before, I had expected to marry very soon, and who used to live down by the depot, but is now located temporarily on Main Street just in front of Ferguson's Drug Store. It is not as much fun as it used to be to call at the Rogers' house. Formerly it was possible to sit in the hammock on the front porch, and as the house set back

from the street and there was trees around and no street lights, a very pleasant evening could be had.

But at present the front porch is located in a most unfortunate way just two feet from the windows of Ferguson's Drug Store, which is all lighted up—you know how drug store windows is—lots of big white lights, and all kinds of jars full of colored water with more lights shining through. And people squeezing past between the porch and the drug store and going in to get ice cream sodas or stopping to crack bum jokes about me, which I will not repeat. So you can see that it would not be any fun for me and Mildred to sit in the hammock in the evening, even if it was possible to sit in the hammock which it is not, owing to the fact that the porch pillar to which the hammock is fastened has become so weakened by the jacking up of the house that it would take very little to pull it over and let the whole porch roof down with a bang.

So we decided that we better sit in the parlor and we had no sooner entered and I was not doing any harm in any way when old Mr. Rogers came in and there was a very painful scene which I won't describe only to say that he used such expressions as "Get the heck out of here," and "I don't want my daughter keeping company with any moron," which is a word he got out of the Dallas *News*.

So after he had hollered around and Mildred had cried, I left the house in a dignified manner. Being a gentleman and always respectful to old age, I did not talk back to him, the dirty crook. But you can see why it is I am in a hurry for the gear.

The other unfortunate event was just this A.M., when old man Rogers went out and hired twelve horses from all over town and also one small size flivver tractor to move his house up to where he wants it.

He tried to get a big tractor, but there is none in town or nearby except mine which is broke down. But there is plenty of horses and this little flivver tractor that would not be big enough to pull the house by itself.

So this morning they wheeled my poor old tractor out of the way, and they hooked up to the house and there was about a hundred people from the town and from round about that was helping with advice and hollering and yelling and telling Mr. Rogers how to do it. And there was I—the only practical and professional house-mover in the whole city—and none of them asked my advice about anything and so it is not my fault what happened.

When they was all ready, Mr. Rogers he stands up and hollers out, "All ready—Go!" And the six drivers yelled at the twelve horses, and all the people standing around began to cheer and shout. And the feller on the little flivver tractor started up the motor so quick it made a big noise and scared the horses and all the horses began jumping and heaving and they jerked the house sidewise, and some of the timbers slipped, and the kitchen that I told you about—it gave a little lurch and fell off the house.

Just let go, and fell off.

So that scared them, and they unhooked the horses and the flivver tractor, and didn't try no more moving, and the house is still there except the kitchen which was busted up so bad that they finished the job and knocked it to pieces and took it away in wheel barrows.

One good thing is that now the traffic can get in between the house and the Post Office so they don't have to detour any more. But one very unfortunate thing was that Mrs. Rogers happened to be in the kitchen when it fell off being shaken up considerable but not seriously injured so you can see that I got to have the tractor running again so I can move the house and I hope you will send the gear at once yours truly and oblige,

DAVID CROCKETT SUGGS

FARMERS' FRIEND TRACTOR COMPANY
MAKERS OF EARTHWORM TRACTORS
EARTHWORM CITY, ILL.
November 2, 1924
Mr. David Crockett Suggs
Dry River Junction, Tex.
DEAR SIR: This will acknowledge your valued favor of October 31 requesting that we use all possible haste in sending you a gear which you need to repair your tractor. We are also pleased to report the receipt of one No. 6843 gear which we shipped you on October 14 and which you returned unused owing to the fact that it will not fit your tractor. We are crediting your account with $41.26 C.O.D. which you paid on this shipment.

The broken gear which you sent has been carefully checked over by our Engineering Department. We are at a loss to understand how this gear ever came to be in your tractor. We do not make gears similar to the one you have sent in, and it will therefore be impossible for us to supply you with one.

We would suggest that the best thing to do in the circumstances would be for one of our service mechanics to inspect your machine.

Mr. Luke Torkle, one of our service men, will be at Dry River Junction in a few days to unload a tractor. If you desire, we will have Mr. Torkle stop off and inspect your machine.

Kindly let us know what you wish us to do in this matter.

Very truly yours,
FREDERICK R. OVERTON
Parts Department

TELEGRAM

DRY RIVER JUNC TEX NOV 4 1924
FARMERS FRIEND TRACTOR CO
EARTHWORM CY ILLS
HAVE THE GUY COME QUICK IN A HURRY.

DAVID CROCKETT SUGGS

FARMERS' FRIEND TRACTOR COMPANY
SERVICE MAN'S REPORT
WRITTEN AT: Dry River Junction, Tex.
DATE: November 7, 1924.
WRITTEN BY: Luke Torkle, Serviceman.
SUBJECT: Tractor belonging to D. C. Suggs.

Reached here 7 A.M. Unloaded tractor for Canyon Ranch, and will drive it over tomorrow.

Before I had a chance to look up D. C. Suggs, the mayor and prominent citizens urgently requested me to use the new tractor to move a house that was blocking the main street. This looked like good advertising for us, especially as the county commissioner here is expecting to buy a tractor for road work. Accordingly, I spent the morning moving the house to where they wanted it, and then looked up Mr. Suggs.

Found he has left town. It was reported that he was shot at three times yesterday by a man called Rogers, but escaped. Last night he sold his entire property, consisting of a second-hand tractor, an old fliv, one radio set, and the good-will in a house-moving business for $450. He then took the train north with a girl called Mildred Rogers of this place.

I inspected the tractor formerly owned by Mr. Suggs. No wonder we couldn't supply him with repairs for it. It is not one of our tractors. It has no name plate, but I was able to identify it as a 1920 Model, Steel Elephant Tractor, made by the S. E. Tractor Company of Indianapolis. I talked on the phone with Mrs. Joseph Banks, whose husband formerly owned the tractor. She says her husband sold the old Earthworm Tractor three years ago to a man in Dallas. Mr. Banks owned four or five different kinds of tractors. Mrs. Banks remembered he had once bought tractor parts from the Farmers' Friend Tractor Company.

In regard to your suggestion that Mr. Suggs might be persuaded to buy a new tractor, I think this is hardly possible.

It is reported that before he left, Mr. Suggs stated that he and Miss Rogers would be married and would locate in Chicago.

He was uncertain what business he would take up, but said it would be nothing in any way connected with housemoving, or with tractors, or any kind of machinery.

The man who wrote this story

WILLIAM HAZLETT UPSON   1891–

A graduate of Cornell University's Agricultural College, Mr. Upson started his career as a farmer. He abandoned farming for a stint in the Army and then took a job as mechanic with a tractor company. In 1923 he discovered that he could write—and sell—short stories. Since then he has written several books, one play, and over 100 stories for the *Saturday Evening Post*.

Mr. Upson enjoys traveling and has visited every state in the Union, many European countries, and various regions of Canada.

Let's consider . . .

1. Why was Suggs in such a hurry to get a new gear for his tractor?

2. How could he have avoided having so much trouble with his correspondence?

3. In what ways did Suggs disrupt the entire town?

4. Why didn't Suggs want to use horses for moving the house? When horses were used, what was the result?

5. What finally happened to the house? What finally happened to Suggs?

6. Explain how a girl was basically responsible for Suggs' difficulties.

7. Have you ever had difficulty in getting an item you ordered by mail? What caused the confusion?

The writer's craft . . .

1. What is your opinion of the author's use of letters to tell his story? What did the story gain through the use of this technique? What did it lose?

2. Although Suggs used poor grammar, his letters had a warm quality that seemed to reflect his personality. Write a brief character sketch of Suggs as you came to know him through his letters.

The Rich Man

FRANKLIN P. ADAMS

The rich man has his motorcar,
    His country and his town estate.
He smokes a fifty-cent cigar
        And jeers at Fate.

He frivols through the livelong day,
    He knows not Poverty her pinch.
His lot seems light, his heart seems gay,
        He has a cinch.

Yet though my lamp burns low and dim,
    Though I must slave for livelihood—
Think you that I would change with him?
        You bet I would!

The man who wrote this poem

FRANKLIN PIERCE ADAMS 1881–

Franklin P. Adams got his start as a journalist by failing to sell insurance. This failure led him to try a job with the newspapers, and soon he was writing a popular column in Chicago. Later he moved to New York City to write for several large daily papers.

Adams became famous as "F. P. A.," the creator of the very successful column called "The Conning Tower." His column was so well written and so interesting that excerpts from it have been collected and published in book form.

Adams has also written humorous, clever poems, like "The Rich Man." In his spare time he has made several translations of the early Latin poets which have been praised as the best of their kind. However, most of us remember him as a permanent member of the panel of experts on the radio program, "Information Please."

The poet's art . . .

1. Were you surprised at the last line of "The Rich Man"? How had Mr. Adams prepared you for a different ending?

2. You learned how Mr. Adams felt about changing places with the rich man. How would you like to make the change?

3. According to the poem, what are the advantages in being rich? Does money always bring happiness?

4. Do you think Mr. Adams was completely sincere? Why?

Fragonard

There was an old miser named Clarence,
Who simonized both of his parents.
"The initial expense,"
He remarked, "is immense,
But I'll save it on wearance and tearance."

Ogden Nash

Ah Love! Ah Me!

MAX STEELE

Dave wanted everything to go just right on his first date with Sara. Little did he suspect that by the end of the evening he would be fizzing like a bottle of soda water.

It happened six years ago—when I was in my junior year at high school—that I saw Sara Nell Workman for the first time and—not to be sentimental—I liked the girl. I liked her so much, in fact, that I would go to the library and read the cards in the back of the books to find the ones she had borrowed. I would take these out and read them carefully, including one called *Needlepoint and Needlecraft*.

"It's for my sister," I said hoarsely to the librarian who was looking at me curiously. There were some penciled notes in the margin about hemstitching, and whether Sara made these notes or not, I don't know. At the time I liked to imagine that she did, and I read them over and over: "Two skeins of black, two orange, one yellow, and the tulip stencil. Mother's Day, 17 days."

But when you're sixteen, you can't keep reading marginal notes over and over. At least I couldn't. And so the time came that I decided to ask Sara for a date. That day at school I couldn't find her by herself, and juniors in high school don't just up and ask a girl for a date in front of everybody.

At home that night I went out into the hall where the phone was and shut the door behind me. I wrote Sara's number on the pad and then one sentence: "Sara— *Jezebel* is on Friday night and I was just wondering if you'd like to see it with me."

That sounded casual and easy enough to say, but when I heard the operator ringing the number, I got excited and crumpled the paper in my hand. For a second I considered hanging up, but then someone said, "Hello."

"Oh," I said. "May I speak to Sara Workman?"

"This is she," she said, rather impatiently it seemed.

"Uh, Sara," I said, "uh, this is Dave. . . ."

"Yes," she said.

"Do you know what our history assignment is for tomorrow?" I asked hopelessly.

"Just a minute," she said. She got her book and gave me the assignment. I thanked her and hung up. Then I untwisted the phone wire and went back to my room to brood.

About an hour later I decided that the thing to do was to jump up suddenly without thinking, rush into the hall, and phone her before I had a chance to become flustered. I jumped up quickly, but then I turned back to the dresser and brushed my hair before rushing out of the room.

When Sara answered the phone, I blurted out, "Would you like to go to the show with me Friday night? This is Dave."

"Well, I don't know," Sara said very slowly and coolly. "What's on?"

"I don't know," I said. "I thought maybe we'd just go mess around uptown."

"What?" she asked.

"I mean I don't know," I said. *"Lucy Belle* or something like that." I really couldn't remember.

"Jezebel!" she said. "Bette Davis. Yeah! I'd love to see it."

"Okay," I said. "Good-by."

The next day I avoided meeting Sara alone. In the line at cafeteria she leaned around two people and said to me, "That was you last night, wasn't it?"

"Yeah," I said.

She smiled and for a moment I was afraid that she was going to laugh, but she didn't.

Friday night at eight o'clock when we were leaving Sara's house, Mr. Workman, who looked like John L. Lewis, asked, "Who's driving?"

"I am," I said.

"You got a license?"

"Yes, sir."

"Well," he hollered, as we went down the walk, "just see to it that you get Sara back here safe. And before eleven o'clock."

"Yes, sir," I said.

"Eleven o'clock, Sara," he screamed.

She was embarrassed, but she hollered back, "Yes, sir."

At the theater we had to stand in line, and when finally we did get seats they were in the third row. My neck was hurting before the newsreel was over, but Sara didn't seem to mind looking straight up at the screen.

When the picture was almost over, she caught me looking at her. "Whatsa matter?" she whispered.

"Headache," I said. "I think it's from looking straight . . . ."

"Shhh . . ." she whispered. On the screen Bette Davis was risking death by yellow fever to be with her man and nurse him.

Sara was very quiet when we came out of the show. As we walked down Main Street, I said, "Do you think she should have stayed with him? She probably caught yellow fever, too."

"It's not a matter of what you should or shouldn't do," Sara said. "For when you love a man, nothing can tear you away."

"Good gosh!" I said. Above us a neon light flickered off and on and buzzed as though it would explode.

We stood in front of Shaeffer's drugstore for a minute. It was 10:15 then, and Sara was worried about getting home.

"Just something to drink," she said, "we haven't time to eat."

She ordered a chocolate milk, and I wanted one, too, but I thought it would look kind of sophisticated to order something for my headache. I couldn't remember ammonia and Coke, and so I asked the waiter what he had for a headache.

"Aspirin, epsom salts, litho-bromide, anything you want," he said.

"Bring me a litho-bromide," I said, trying to sound weary, "and a Coke."

"Still hurts?" Sara asked softly.

I smiled at her without answering.

John Bowerman and two other seniors came in and took the booth next to ours. All of the booths and tables were filling with the crowd from the movie.

The waiter brought the order. My Coke was in one glass, two litho-bromide tablets were in the bottom of an empty glass, and there was a big glass of water.

I'd never taken a litho-bromide, and I

didn't know that the tablets were supposed to be dropped into a glass of water where they would fizz while dissolving. I just shook the tablets out into my hand, popped them in my mouth, and swallowed them one at a time as though they were aspirin. Then I drank half the Coke while Sara tasted her milk shake.

Before I had time to say anything, the litho-bromide started bubbling noisily in my stomach.

I drank the rest of the Coke and tried to pretend that nothing was happening. Sara put down her glass and stared at me, terrified. I sounded like somebody gargling under a barrel.

"It always does this," I said bravely. But by then the rumblings from the mixture were too ominous to be ignored by me or the people in the other booths. Everyone was staring at my stomach.

"Everybody's looking at you," Sara whispered. She was so red that I was afraid she was going to cry.

"Sounds like somebody churning buttermilk," John Bowerman said, coming around to our booth.

"He's effervescing!" the waiter announced happily to the astonished customers. "Just listen to him fizz!"

"Sara," I said, and I was going to tell her to get me out of there, but I was afraid to open my mouth to say anything else. The rumbling just sounded deeper when I did, like drumming on a hollow log.

"Doc Shaeffer!" John Bowerman called out when Sara told him what I had done.

Doc Shaeffer climbed over the prescription counter. "Stand back!" he said to the crowd that was gathering around our booth.

They stepped back as though they expected me to explode.

"It's nothing serious," Doc Shaeffer said. "Get his head lower than his stomach. Give me a hand with him."

"He says it always does this," Sara said.

"That's pretty hard to believe," Doc said, as John Bowerman and the two seniors picked me up and carried me to the prescription counter. They stretched me out and let my head hang off with my mouth open. A dogfight couldn't have attracted more attention. Doc Shaeffer brought a

wet towel from the back of the drugstore. Sara stood beside me and rubbed my forehead with it.

"Sara," I said, and I suppose now I must have sounded rather melodramatic to the other people, "you won't leave me, will you?"

"Oh, my goodness!" Sara said. "What time is it?"

"Ten till eleven," John Bowerman said.

Sara dropped the wet towel in my face. "I've got to be home by eleven!" she said.

"I'll take you," John said.

I took the towel off my face in time to see them stopping by the booth for Sara's pocketbook. She didn't even look back at me.

The four or five people who were standing by me went back to their tables. I lay quietly on the counter and watched the light above swaying gently in the noisy room.

Gradually, two by two, the people left, and the noise of the dishes being stacked grew quieter and quieter. I watched the waiter turn the chairs upside down on the tables and felt sorry for him and for myself and for the whole pitiful world.

The man who wrote this story

MAX STEELE 1922–

Born in Greenville, South Carolina, Max Steele attended college in the Deep South and on the West Coast before he was graduated from the University of North Carolina.

After three years' service with the Army Air Force as a meteorologist, he began to publish short stories in *Harper's,* the *Atlantic Monthly,* and other magazines.

His skill in writing won him a fellowship in 1947 to work on a novel which later won the Harper Prize novel contest and the Mayflower Award.

Let's consider . . .

1. When Dave decided to call Sara, he wrote the following sentence on a piece of paper: "Sara—*Jezebel* is on Friday night and I was just wondering if you'd like to see it with me." Why do you suppose he put this in writing?

2. As Dave and Sara were leaving for the movies, Mr. Workman began questioning Dave about his driving. Do you think this is typical of most parents? Are parents justified in being concerned about teen-age drivers?

3. In Shaeffer's drugstore, Dave wanted a chocolate milk. Why didn't he order one?

4. What happened to Dave after he swallowed the litho-bromide?

5. In what ways is Dave like most teen-age boys? In what ways is he different?

6. Usually you don't think of suffering as being funny. Yet Dave suffered physically as well as mentally. Did you laugh at him? If so, why?

The writer's craft . . .

Throughout most of "Ah Love! Ah Me!" you saw the humorous side of Dave's problems. But look again at the ending of the story.

1. How did the tone of the story change at this point?

2. Why wasn't the ending funny?

3. When you finished the story, did you feel sympathetic towards Dave? Why?

My Kingdom for Jones

WILBUR SCHRAMM

You may have heard certain rumors about the Brooklyn baseball team. Of course, no one would ever publicly admit they were true. But now the secret is out and the whole story can be told: A horse played third base for Brooklyn.

The first day Jones played third base for Brooklyn was like the day Galileo turned his telescope on the planets or Columbus sailed back to Spain. First, people said it couldn't be true; then they said things will never be the same.

Timothy McGuire, of the Brooklyn *Eagle,* told me how he felt the first time he saw Jones. He said that if a bird had stepped out of a cuckoo clock that day and asked him what time it was, he wouldn't have been surprised enough to blink an Irish eye. And still he knew that the whole future of baseball hung that day by a cotton thread.

Don't ask Judge Kenesaw Mountain Landis [1] about this. He has never yet admitted publicly that Jones ever played for Brooklyn. He has good reason not to. But ask an old-time sports writer. Ask Tim McGuire.

It happened so long ago it was even be-

fore Mr. Roosevelt became President. It was a lazy Georgia-spring afternoon, the first time McGuire and I saw Jones. There was a light-footed little breeze and just enough haze to keep the sun from burning. The air was full of fresh-cut grass and wisteria and fruit blossoms and the ping of baseballs on well-oiled mitts. Everyone in Georgia knows that the only sensible thing to do on an afternoon like that is sleep. If you can't do that, if you are a baseball writer down from New York to cover Brooklyn's spring-training camp, you can stretch out on the grass and raise yourself every hour or so on one elbow to steal a glance at fielding practice. That was what we were doing—meanwhile amusing ourselves halfheartedly with a game involving small cubes and numbers—when we first saw Jones.

The *Times* wasn't there. Even in those days they were keeping their sports staff at home to study for Information Please. But four of us were down from the New York papers—the *World,* the *Herald,* Tim, and I. I can even remember what we were talking about.

I was asking the *World,* "How do they look to you?"

"Pitchers and no punch," the *World* said. "No big bats. No great fielders. No Honus Wagner. No Hal Chase. No Ty Cobb."

"No Tinker to Evers to Chance," said the *Herald.* "Seven come to Susy," he added soothingly, blowing on his hands.

"What's your angle today?" the *World* asked Tim.

Tim doesn't remember exactly how he answered that. To the best of my knowledge, he merely said, "Ulk." It occurred to me that the Brooklyn *Eagle* was usually more eloquent than that, but the Southern weather must have slowed up my reaction.

The *World* said, "What?"

"There's a sorsh," Tim said in a weak, strangled sort of voice—"a horse . . . on third . . . base."

"Why don't they chase it off?" said the *Herald* impatiently. "Your dice."

"They don't . . . want to," Tim said in that funny voice.

I glanced up at Tim then. Now Tim, as you probably remember, was built from the same blueprints as a truck, with a magnificent red nose for a headlight. But when I looked at him, all the color was draining out of that nose slowly, from top to bottom, like turning off a gas mantle. I should estimate Tim was, at the moment, the whitest McGuire in four generations.

Then I looked over my shoulder to see where Tim was staring. He was the only one of us facing the ball diamond. I looked for some time. Then I tapped the *World* on the back.

"Pardon me," I asked politely, "do you notice anything unusual?"

"If you refer to my luck," said the *World,* "it's the same pitiful kind I've had since Christmas."

"Look at the infield," I suggested.

"Hey," said the *Herald,* "if you don't want the dice, give them to me."

"I know this can't be true," mused the *World,* "but I could swear I see a horse on third base."

The *Herald* climbed to his feet with some effort. He was built in the days when there was no shortage of materials.

"If the only way to get you guys to put your minds on this game is to chase that horse off the field," he said testily, "I'll do it myself."

He started toward the infield, rubbed his eyes and fainted dead away.

"I had the queerest dream," he said, when we revived him. "I dreamed there was a horse playing third base. My gosh!" he shouted, glancing toward the diamond. "I'm still asleep!"

That is, word for word, what happened the first day Jones played third base for Brooklyn. Ask McGuire.

When we felt able, we hunted up the Brooklyn manager, who was a chunky, red-haired individual with a whisper like a foghorn. A foghorn with a Brooklyn accent. His name was Pop O'Donnell.

"I see you've noticed," Pop boomed defensively.

"What do you mean," the *Herald* said severely, "by not notifying us you had a horse playing third base?"

"I didn't guess you'd believe it," Pop said.

Pop was still a little bewildered himself. He said the horse had wandered on the field that morning during practice. Someone tried to chase it off by hitting a baseball toward it. The horse calmly opened its mouth and caught the ball. Nothing could be neater.

While they were still marveling over

that, the horse galloped thirty yards and took a ball almost out of the hands of an outfielder who was poised for the catch. They said Willie Keeler couldn't have done it better. So they spent an hour hitting fungo flies—or, as some wit called them, horse flies—to the horse. Short ones, long ones, high ones, grass cutters, line drives—it made no difference; the animal covered Dixie like the dew.

They tried the horse at second and short, but he was a little slow on the pivot when compared with men like Napoleon Lajoie. Then they tried him at third base, and knew that was the right, the inevitable place. He was a great wall of China. He was a flash of brown lightning. In fact, he covered half the shortstop's territory and two-thirds of left field, and even came behind the plate to help the catcher with foul

tips. The catcher got pretty sore about it. He said that anybody who was going to steal his easy put-outs would have to wear an umpire's uniform like the other thieves.

"Can he hit?" asked the *World*.

"See for yourself," Pop O'Donnell invited.

The Superbas—they hadn't begun calling them the Dodgers yet—were just starting batting practice. Nap Rucker was tossing them in with that beautiful smooth motion of his, and the horse was at bat. He met the first ball on the nose and smashed it into left field. He laid down a bunt that waddled like a turtle along the base line. He sizzled a liner over second like a clothesline.

"What a story!" said the *World*.

"I wonder," said the *Herald*—"I wonder how good it is."

We stared at him.

"I wouldn't say it is quite as good as the sinking of the *Maine,* if you mean that," said Tim.

"I wonder how many people are going to believe it," said the *Herald*.

"I'll race you to the phone," Tim said.

Tim won. He admits he had a long start. Twenty minutes later he came back, walking slowly.

"I wish to announce," he said, "that I have been insulted by my editor and am no longer connected with the Brooklyn *Eagle*. If I can prove that I am sober tomorrow, they may hire me back," he added.

"You see what I mean," said the *Herald*.

We all filed telegraph stories about the horse. We swore that every word was true. We said it was a turning point in baseball. Two of us mentioned Columbus; and one, Galileo. In return, we got advice.

THESE TROUBLED TIMES, NEWSPAPERS NO SPACE FOR FICTION, EXPENSE ACCOUNT NO PROVISION DRUNKEN LEVITY, the *Herald's* wire read. The *World* read, ACCURACY, AC-

CURACY, ACCURACY, followed by three exclamation points, and signed "Joseph
Pulitzer." CHARGING YOUR TELEGRAM RE
BROOKLYN HORSE TO YOUR SALARY, my wire
said. THAT'S A HORSE ON YOU!

Have you ever thought what you would
do with a purple cow if you had one? I
know. You would paint it over. We had
a horse that could play third base, and all
we could do was sit in the middle of
Georgia and cuss our editors. I blame the
editors. It is their fault that for the last
thirty years you have had to go to smoking
rooms or Pullman cars to hear about Jones.

But I don't entirely blame them either.
My first question would have been: How
on earth can a horse possibly bat and
throw? That's what the editors wondered.
It's hard to explain. It's something you
have to see to believe—like dogfish and
political conventions.

And I've got to admit that the next
morning we sat around and asked one another whether we really had seen a horse
playing third base. Pop O'Donnell confessed that when he woke up he said to
himself, *It must be shrimp that makes me
dream about horses.* Then all of us went
down to the park, not really knowing
whether we would see a horse there or not.

We asked Pop was he going to use the
horse in games.

"I don't know," he thundered musingly.
"I wonder. There are many angles. I don't
know," he said, pulling at his chin.

That afternoon the Cubs, the world
champs, came for an exhibition game. A
chap from Pennsylvania—I forget his name
—played third base for Brooklyn, and the
horse grazed quietly beside the dugout.
Going into the eighth, the Cubs were
ahead, 2–0, and Three-Finger Brown was
tying Brooklyn in knots. A curve would
come over, then a fast one inside, and then
the drop, and the Superbas would beat the

air or hit puny little rollers to the infield
which Tinker or Evers would grab up and
toss like a beanbag to Frank Chance. It
was sickening. But in the eighth, Maloney
got on base on an error, and Jordan walked.
Then Lumley went down swinging, and
Lewis watched three perfect ones sail past
him. The horse still was grazing over by
the Brooklyn dugout.

"Put in the horse!" Frank Chance yelled.
The Cubs laughed themselves sick.

Pop O'Donnell looked at Chance, and
then at the horse, and back at Chance, as

though he had made up his mind about something. "Go in there, son, and get a hit," he said. "Watch out for the curve." "Coive," Pop said.

The horse picked up a bat and cantered out to the plate.

"Pinch-hitting for Batch," announced the umpire dreamily, "this horse." A second later he shook himself violently. "What am I saying?" he shouted.

On the Cubs' bench every jaw had dropped somewhere around the owner's waist. Chance jumped to his feet, his face muscles worked like a coffee grinder, but nothing came out. It was the only time in baseball history, so far as I can find out, that Frank Chance was ever without words.

When he finally pulled himself together he argued, with a good deal of punctuation, that there was no rule saying you could play a horse in the big leagues. Pop roared quietly that there was no rule saying you couldn't, either. They stood there nose to nose, Pop firing methodically like a cannon, and Chance crackling like a machine gun. Chance gave up too easily. He was probably a little stunned. He said that he was used to seeing queer things in Brooklyn, anyway. Pop O'Donnell just smiled grimly.

Well, that was Jones' first game for Brooklyn. It could have been a reel out of a movie. There was that great infield— Steinfeldt, Tinker, Evers, and Chance—so precise, so much a machine, that any ball hit on the ground was like an apple into a sorter. The infield was so famous that not many people remember Sheckard and Slagle and Schulte in the outfield, but the teams of that day knew them. Behind the plate was Johnny Kling, who could rifle a ball to second like an 88-mm. cannon. And on the mound stood Three-Finger Brown, whose drop faded away as though someone were pulling it back with a string.

Brown took a long time getting ready. His hand shook a little, and the first one he threw was ten feet over Kling's head into the grandstand. Maloney and Jordan advanced to second and third. Brown threw the next one in the dirt. Then he calmed down, grooved one, and whistled a curve in around the withers.

"The glue works for you, Dobbin!" yelled Chance, feeling more like himself. Pop O'Donnell was mopping his forehead.

The next pitch came in fast, over the outside corner. The horse was waiting. He leaned into it. The ball whined all the way to the fence. Ted Williams was the only player I ever saw hit one like it. When Slagle finally got to the ball, the two runners had scored and the horse was on third. Brown's next pitch got away from Kling a few yards, and the horse stole home in a cloud of dust, all four feet flying. He got up, dusted himself off, looked at Chance and gave a horselaugh.

If this sounds queer, remember that queerer things happen in Brooklyn every day.

"How do we write this one up?" asked the *Herald*. "We can't put just 'a horse' in the box score."

That was when the horse got his name. We named him Jones, after Jones, the caretaker who had left the gate open so he could wander onto the field. We wrote about "Horse" Jones.

Next day we all chuckled at a banner headline in one of the metropolitan papers. It read: JONES PUTS NEW KICK IN BROOKLYN.

Look in the old box scores. Jones got two hits off Rube Waddell, of Philadelphia, and three off Cy Young, of Boston. He pounded Eddie Plank and Iron Man McGinnity and Wild Bill Donovan. He robbed Honus Wagner of a hit that would have been a double against any other third baseman in the league. On the base paths he was a bullet.

Our papers began to wire us, WHERE DOES JONES COME FROM? SEND BACKGROUND, HUMAN INTEREST, INTERVIEW. That was a harder assignment than New York knew. We decided by a gentlemen's agreement that Jones must have come from Kentucky and got his first experience in a Blue Grass league. That sounded reasonable enough. We said he was long-faced, long-legged, dark, a vegetarian, and a nonsmoker. That was true. We said he was a horse for work, and ate like a horse. That was self-evident. Interviewing was a little harder.

Poor Pop O'Donnell for ten years had wanted a third baseman who could hit hard enough to dent a cream puff. Now that he had one he wasn't quite sure what to do with it. Purple-cow trouble. "Poiple," Pop would have said.

One of his first worries was paying for Jones. A strapping big farmer appeared at the clubhouse, saying he wanted either his horse or fifty thousand dollars.

Pop excused himself, checked the team's bank balance, then came back.

"What color is your horse?" he asked.

The farmer thought a minute. "Dapple gray," he said.

"Good afternoon, my man," Pop boomed unctuously, holding open the door. "That's a horse of another color." Jones was brown.

There were some audience incidents too. Jonathan Daniels, of Raleigh, North Carolina, told me that as a small boy that season he saw a whole row of elderly ladies bustle into their box seats, take one look toward third base, look questioningly at one another, twitter about the sun being hot, and walk out. Georgia police records show that at least five citizens, cold sober, came to the ball park and were afraid to drive their own cars home. The American medical journals

of that year discovered a new psychoneurosis which they said was doubtless caused by a feeling of insecurity resulting from the replacement of the horse by the horseless carriage. It usually took the form of hallucination—the sensation of seeing a horse sitting on a baseball player's bench. Perhaps that was the reason a famous pitcher, who shall here go nameless, came to town with his team, took one incredulous look at Brooklyn fielding practice, and went to his manager, offering to pay a fine.

But the real trouble was over whether horses should be allowed to play baseball. After the first shock, teams were generally amused at the idea of playing against a horse. But after Jones had batted their star pitchers out of the box, they said the Humane Society ought to protect the poor Brooklyn horse.

The storm that brewed in the South that spring was like nothing except the storm that gathered in 1860. Every hotel that housed baseball players housed a potential civil war. The better orators argued that the right to play baseball should not be separated from the right to vote or the responsibility of fighting for one's country. The more practical ones said a few more horses like Jones and they wouldn't have any jobs left. Still others said that this was probably just another bureaucratic trick on the part of the Administration.

Even the Brooklyn players protested. A committee of them came to see old Pop O'Donnell. They said wasn't baseball a game for human beings? Pop said he had always had doubts as to whether some major-league players were human or not. They said touché, and this is all right so long as it is a one-horse business, so to speak. But if it goes on, before long won't a man have to grow two more legs and a tail before he can get in? They asked Pop how he would like to manage the Brooklyn

Percherons, instead of the Brooklyn Superbas? They said, what would happen to
baseball if it became a game for animals—
say, giraffes on one team, trained seals on
a second, and monkeys on a third? They
pointed out that monkeys had already got
a foot in the door by being used to dodge
baseballs in carnivals. How would Pop like
to manage a team of monkeys called the
Brooklyn Dodgers, they asked.

Pop said heaven help anyone who has to
manage a team called the Brooklyn Dodgers. Then he pointed out that Brooklyn
hadn't lost an exhibition game, and that
the horse was leading the league in batting
with a solid .516. He asked whether they
would rather have a world series or a two-
legged third baseman. They went away
muttering.

But his chief worry was Jones himself.

"That horse hasn't got his mind on the
game," he told us one night on the hotel
veranda.

"Ah, Pop, it's just horseplay," said the
World, winking.

"Nope, he hasn't got his heart in it," said
Pop, his voice echoing lightly off the distant mountains. "He comes just in time for
practice and runs the minute it's over.
There's something on that horse's mind."

We laughed, but had to admit that Jones
was about the saddest horse we had ever
seen. His eyes were great brown pools of
liquid sorrow. His ears drooped. And still
he hit well over .500 and covered third
base like a rug.

One day he missed the game entirely. It
was the day the Giants were in town, and
fifteen thousand people were there to watch
Jones bat against the great Matty. Brooklyn lost the game, and Pop O'Donnell almost lost his hair at the hands of the disappointed crowd.

"Who would have thought," Pop mused,
in the clubhouse after the game, "that that

(here some words are omitted) horse would
turn out to be a prima donna? It's all right
for a major-league ball player to act like a
horse, but that horse is trying to act like
a major-league ball player."

It was almost by accident that Tim and I
found out what was really bothering Jones.
We followed him one day when he left
the ball park. We followed him nearly two
miles to a race track.

Jones stood beside the fence a long time,
turning his head to watch the thorough-
breds gallop by on exercise runs and time
trials. Then a little stable boy opened the
gate for him.

"Po' ol' hoss," the boy said. "Yo' wants
a little runnin'?"

"Happens every day," a groom explained
to us. "This horse wanders up here from
who knows where, and acts like he wants
to run, and some boy rides him a while,
bareback, pretending he's a race horse."

Jones was like a different horse out there
on the track; not drooping any more—ears
up, eyes bright, tail like a plume. It was
pitiful how much he wanted to look like
a race horse.

"That horse," Tim asked the groom, "is
he any good for racing?"

"Not here, anyway," the groom said.
"Might win a county-fair race or two."

He asked us whether we had any idea
who owned the horse.

"Sir," said Tim, like Edwin M. Stanton,
"that horse belongs to the ages."

"Well, mister," said the groom, "the ages
had better get some different shoes on that
horse. Why, you could hold a baseball in
those shoes he has there."

"It's very clear," I said as we walked
back, "what we have here is a badly frustrated horse."

"It's clear as beer," Tim said sadly.

That afternoon Jones hit a home run
and absent-mindedly trotted around the

bases. As soon as the game was over, he disappeared in the direction of the race track. Tim looked at me and shook his head. Pop O'Donnell held his chin in his hands.

"I'll be boiled in oil," he said. "Berled in erl," he said.

Nothing cheered up poor Pop until someone came in with a story about the absentee owner of a big-league baseball club who had inherited the club along with the family fortune. This individual had just fired the manager of his baseball farm system, because the farms had not turned out horses like Jones. "What are farms for if they don't raise horses?" the absentee owner had asked indignantly.

Jones was becoming a national problem second only to the Panama Canal and considerably more important than whether Mr. Taft got to be President.

There were rumors that the Highlanders —people were just beginning to call them the Yankees—would withdraw and form a new league if Jones was allowed to play. It was reported that a team of kangaroos from Australia was on its way to play a series of exhibition games in America, and President Ban Johnson of the American League was quoted as saying that he would never have kangaroos in the American League because they were too likely to jump their contracts. There was talk of a constitutional amendment concerning horses in baseball.

The· thing that impressed me, down there in the South, was that all this was putting the cart before the horse, so to speak. Jones simply didn't want to play baseball. He wanted to be a race horse. I don't know why life is that way.

Jones made an unassisted triple play, and Ty Cobb accused Brooklyn of furnishing fire ladders to its infielders. He said that no third baseman could have caught the drive that started the play. At the end of the training season, Jones was batting .538, and fielding .997, had stolen twenty bases and hit seven home runs. He was the greatest third baseman in the history of baseball, and didn't want to be!

Joseph Pulitzer, William Randolph Hearst, Arthur Brisbane and the rest of the big shots got together and decided that if anyone didn't know by this time that Jones was a horse, the newspapers wouldn't tell him. He could find it out.

Folks seemed to find it out. People began gathering from all parts of the country to see Brooklyn open against the Giants— Matty against Jones. Even a tribe of Sioux Indians camped beside the Gowanus and had war dances on Flatbush Avenue, waiting for the park to open. And Pop O'Donnell kept his squad in the South as long as he could, laying plans to arrive in Brooklyn only on the morning of the opening game.

The wire said that night that 200,000 people had come to Brooklyn for the game, and 190,000 of them were in an ugly mood over the report that the league might not let Jones play. The Governor of New York sent two regiments of the National Guard. The Giants were said to be caucusing to decide whether they would play against Jones.

By game time, people were packed for six blocks, fighting to get into the park. The Sioux sent a young buck after their tomahawks, just in case. Telephone poles a quarter of a mile from the field were selling for a hundred dollars. Every baseball writer in the country was in the Brooklyn press box; the other teams played before cub reporters and society editors. Just before game time I managed to push into Pop O'Donnell's little office with the presidents of the two major leagues, the Mayor of New York, a half dozen other reporters, and a delegation from the Giants.

"There's just one thing we want to know," the spokesman for the Giants was asking Pop. "Are you going to play Jones?"

"Gentlemen," said Pop in that soft-spoken, firm way of his that rattled the window blinds, "our duty is to give the public what it wants. And the public wants Jones."

Like an echo, a chant began to rise from the bleachers, "We want Jones!"

"There is one other little thing," said Pop. "Jones has disappeared."

There were about ten seconds of the awful silence that comes when your nerves are paralyzed, but your mind keeps on thrashing.

"He got out of his boxcar somewhere between Georgia and Brooklyn," Pop said. "We don't know where. We're looking."

A Western Union boy dashed in. "Hold on!" said Pop. "This may be news!"

He tore the envelope with a shaky hand. The message was from Norfolk, Virginia. HAVE FOUND ELEPHANT THAT CAN BALANCE MEDICINE BALL ON TRUNK, it read. WILL HE DO? If Pop had said what he said then into a telephone, it would have burned out all the insulators in New York.

Down at the field, the President of the United States himself was poised to throw out the first ball. "Is this Jones?" he asked. He was a little nearsighted.

"This is the Mayor of New York," Pop said patiently. "Jones is gone. Run away."

The President's biographers disagree as to whether he said at that moment, "Oh, well, who would stay in Brooklyn if he could run?" or "I sympathize with you for having to change horses in midstream."

That was the saddest game ever covered by the entire press corps of the nation. Brooklyn was all thumbs in the field, all windmills at bat. There was no Jones to

whistle hits into the outfield and make sensational stops at third. By the sixth inning, when they had to call the game with the score 18–1, the field was ankle-deep in pop bottles and the Sioux were waving their tomahawks and singing the scalp song.

You know the rest of the story. Brooklyn didn't win a game until the third week of the season, and no team ever tried a horse again, except a few dark horses every season. Pittsburgh, I believe, tried trained seals in the outfield. They were deadly at catching the ball, but couldn't cover enough ground. San Francisco has an entire team of Seals, but I have never seen them play. Boston tried an octopus at second base, but had to give him up. What happened to two rookies who disappeared trying to steal second base against Boston that spring is another subject baseball doesn't talk about.

There has been considerable speculation as to what happened to Jones. Most of us believed the report that the Brooklyn players had unfastened the latch on the door of his boxcar, until Pop O'Donnell's Confidential Memoirs came out, admitting that he himself had taken the hinges off the door because he couldn't face the blame for making baseball a game for horses. But I have been a little confused since Tim McGuire came to me once and said he might as well confess. He couldn't stand to think of that horse standing wistfully beside the track, waiting for someone to let him pretend he was a race horse. That haunted Tim. When he went down to the boxcar he found the door unlatched and the hinges off, so he gave the door a little push outward. He judged it was the will of the majority.

And that is why baseball is played by men today instead of by horses. But don't think that the shadow of Jones doesn't still lie heavy on the game. Have you ever noticed how retiring and silent and hang-dog major-league ball players are, how they cringe before the umpire? They never know when another Jones may break away from a beer wagon or a circus or a plow, wander through an unlocked gate, and begin batting .538 to their .290. The worry is terrible. You can see it in the crowds too. That is why Brooklyn fans are so aloof and disinterested, why they never raise their voices above a whisper at Ebbets Field. They know perfectly well that this is only

minor-league ball they are seeing, that horses could play it twice as well if they had a chance.

That is the secret we sports writers have kept all these years; that is why we have never written about Jones. And the Brooklyn fans still try to keep it secret, but every once in a while the sorrow eats like lye into one of them until he can hold it back no longer, and then he sobs quietly and says, "Dem bums, if dey only had a little horse sense!"

The man who wrote this story

WILBUR LANG SCHRAMM 1907–

After reading "My Kingdom for Jones" you might expect the author to be a baseball player, a reporter, or, perhaps, a horse like the one in the story. However, Mr. Schramm says that he is "not wholly a horse" and that he is "getting too old and stiff to play third base" as he did during his high-school and college days. But he was a reporter for the Associated Press after he was graduated from college.

With this experience in practical reporting, Mr. Schramm took a position as the director of the School of Journalism at the University of Iowa. He is now a dean of the University of Illinois.

Mr. Schramm has written a number of short stories. In his *Windwagon Smith and Other Yarns,* he has a fine time presenting the impossible as though it were true. There are stories about a train that hopped the tracks in order to see the country and a cider that was powerful enough to serve as fuel for B-29's. He has also written several serious books and has frequently served as an advisor to the government on communication problems.

Let's consider . . .

1. Much of the humor in this story came from people's reactions to a horse playing baseball. What was the reporters' reaction when they first saw the horse playing third base?

2. After the reporters had wired their stories about the horse, what advice did they get from their editors?

3. Why didn't Wilbur Schramm blame the editors for not believing the story?

4. What information about Jones were the reporters safe in sending to their papers?

5. What arguments were used against having a horse on the team? Which of these did you think was funniest?

6. What amused you most in the description of the Brooklyn ball park on opening day?

7. Wilbur Schramm wrote that the shadow of Jones still lies heavy on the game. What effect did Schramm say Jones still has on the behavior of the players and the fans? Actually none of these comments on the players and fans is true. Point out the inaccuracies. How did these tongue-in-cheek comments add to the humor of the story?

The writer's craft . . .

"My Kingdom for Jones" is a good illustration of the **tall tale.** The writer of tall tales must get his readers to believe the basic idea of his story—no matter how absurd that idea may be. In fact, the more far-fetched the idea is, the funnier the story. Once the reader has accepted the main idea, he is all set to enjoy whatever follows.

1. What absurd idea was the basis for "My Kingdom for Jones"?

2. At the beginning of the story, the reporters refused to believe that the horse was playing ball. You were with them as they gradually accepted the idea. How did their acceptance help *you* to believe in a ball-playing horse?

3. Wilbur Schramm included the names of real ball players and big league teams. Why did this make his tall tale seem more believable?

4. How is Jones similar to other heroes of tall tales, like Paul Bunyan and Pecos Bill?

Knowing words . . .

How good is your vocabulary of baseball terms? Be sure you know the meaning of each of the italicized words in the sentences below. Then use the italicized words in a sentence of your own.

1. "Look at the *infield,*" I suggested.

2. He laid down a *bunt* that waddled like a turtle along the base line.

3. They tried the horse at second and short, but he was a little slow on the *pivot* when compared with men like Napoleon Lajoie.

4. That afternoon the Cubs, the world champs, came for an *exhibition* game.

5. *"Pinch-hitting* for Batch," announced the umpire dreamily, "this horse."

A Fellow That Hasn't Seen Much

A fellow that hasn't seen much
Is easily astonished;
He looks at a camel and says
"A horse with a swollen back!"

*Edwin Thomason after the Chinese
of Meo Yung*

Adventures of Isabel

OGDEN NASH

Isabel met an enormous bear;
Isabel, Isabel, didn't care.
The bear was hungry, the bear was ravenous,
The bear's big mouth was cruel and cavernous.
The bear said, Isabel, glad to meet you,
How do, Isabel, now I'll eat you!
Isabel, Isabel, didn't worry;
Isabel didn't scream or scurry.
She washed her hands and she straightened her hair up,
Then Isabel quietly ate the bear up.

Once in a night as black as pitch
Isabel met a wicked old witch.
The witch's face was cross and wrinkled,
The witch's gums with teeth were sprinkled.
Ho, ho, Isabel! the old witch crowed,
I'll turn you into an ugly toad!
Isabel, Isabel, didn't worry;
Isabel didn't scream or scurry.
She showed no rage and she showed no rancor,
But she turned the witch into milk and drank her.

Isabel met a hideous giant,
Isabel continued self-reliant.
The giant was hairy, the giant was horrid,
He had one eye in the middle of his forehead.
Good morning, Isabel, the giant said,
I'll grind your bones to make my bread.
Isabel, Isabel, didn't worry;
Isabel didn't scream or scurry.
She nibbled the zwieback that she always fed off,
And when it was gone, she cut the giant's head off.

Isabel met a troublesome doctor,
He punched and poked till he really shocked her.
The doctor's talk was of coughs and chills,
And the doctor's satchel bulged with pills.
The doctor said unto Isabel,
Swallow this, it will make you well.
Isabel, Isabel, didn't worry;
Isabel didn't scream or scurry.
She took those pills from the pill-concocter,
And Isabel calmly cured the doctor.

The poet's art . . .

1. Isabel's adventures were certainly on the fantastic side. Why couldn't these "adventures" have really happened?

2. Did the fantastic nonsense of the poem add to, or lessen, your enjoyment? Explain why.

3. What seems to be Isabel's outstanding characteristic? Point to lines in the poem that support your answer.

4. Read your favorite stanza to the class.

The Night the Ghost Got In

JAMES THURBER

The boys thought they heard a ghost, but Mother knew it was burglars.
And Grandfather believed the house was filled with deserters from the
army. The police decided the whole family was just a little crazy.

The ghost that got into our house on the
night of November 17, 1915, raised such a
hullabaloo of misunderstandings that I am
sorry I didn't just let it keep on walking,
and go to bed. Its advent caused my
mother to throw a shoe through a window
of the house next door and end up with my

grandfather shooting a patrolman. I am
sorry, therefore, as I have said, that I ever
paid any attention to the footsteps.

They began about a quarter past one
o'clock in the morning, a rhythmic, quick-
cadenced walking around the dining-room
table. My mother was asleep in one room

upstairs, my brother Herman in another; grandfather was in the attic, in the old walnut bed which, as you will remember, once fell on my father. I had just stepped out of the bathtub and was busily rubbing myself with a towel when I heard the steps. They were the steps of a man walking rapidly around the dining-room table downstairs. The light from the bathroom shone down the back steps, which dropped directly into the dining-room; I could see the faint shine of plates on the plate-rail; I couldn't see the table. The steps kept going round and round the table; at regular intervals a board creaked, when it was trod upon. I supposed at first that it was my father or my brother Roy, who had gone to Indianapolis but were expected home at any time. I suspected next that it was a burglar. It did not enter my mind until later that it was a ghost.

After the walking had gone on for perhaps three minutes, I tiptoed to Herman's room. "Psst!" I hissed, in the dark, shaking him. "Awp," he said, in the low, hopeless tone of a despondent beagle—he always half suspected that something would "get him" in the night. I told him who I was. "There's something downstairs!" I said. He got up and followed me to the head of the back staircase. We listened together. There was no sound. The steps had ceased. Herman looked at me in some alarm: I had only the bath towel around my waist. He wanted to go back to bed, but I gripped his arm. "There's something down there!" I said. Instantly the steps began again, circled the dining-room table like a man running, and started up the stairs toward us, heavily, two at a time. The light still shone palely down the stairs; we saw nothing coming; we only heard the steps. Herman rushed to his room and slammed the door. I slammed shut the door at the stairs' top and held my knee against it. After a long

minute, I slowly opened it again. There was nothing there. There was no sound. None of us ever heard the ghost again.

The slamming of the doors had aroused mother: she peered out of her room. "What on earth are you boys doing?" she demanded. Herman ventured out of his room. "Nothing," he said, gruffly, but he was, in color, a light green. "What was all that running around downstairs?" said mother. So she had heard the steps, too! We just looked at her. "Burglars!" she shouted, intuitively. I tried to quiet her by starting lightly downstairs.

"Come on, Herman," I said.

"I'll stay with mother," he said. "She's all excited."

I stepped back onto the landing.

"Don't either of you go a step," said mother. "We'll call the police." Since the phone was downstairs, I didn't see how we were going to call the police—nor did I want the police—but mother made one of her quick, incomparable decisions. She flung up a window of her bedroom which faced the bedroom windows of the house of a neighbor, picked up a shoe, and whammed it through a pane of glass across the narrow space that separated the two houses. Glass tinkled into the bedroom occupied by a retired engraver named Bodwell and his wife. Bodwell had been for some years in rather a bad way and was subject to mild "attacks." Most everybody we knew or lived near had *some* kind of attacks.

It was now about two o'clock of a moonless night; clouds hung black and low. Bodwell was at the window in a minute, shouting, frothing a little, shaking his fist. "We'll sell the house and go back to Peoria," we could hear Mrs. Bodwell saying. It was some time before Mother "got through" to Bodwell. "Burglars!" she shouted. "Burglars in the house!" Herman

and I hadn't dared to tell her that it was not burglars but ghosts, for she was even more afraid of ghosts than of burglars. Bodwell at first thought that she meant there were burglars in his house, but finally he quieted down and called the police for us over an extension phone by his bed. After he had disappeared from the window, mother suddenly made as if to throw another shoe, not because there was further need of it but, as she later explained, because the thrill of heaving a shoe through a window glass had enormously taken her fancy. I prevented her.

The police were on hand in a commendably short time: a Ford sedan full of them, two on motorcycles, and a patrol wagon with about eight in it and a few reporters. They began banging at our front door. Flashlights shot streaks of gleam up and down the walls, across the yard, down the walk between our house and Bodwell's. "Open up!" cried a hoarse voice. "We're men from Headquarters!" I wanted to go down and let them in, since there they were, but mother wouldn't hear of it. "You haven't a stitch on," she pointed out. "You'd catch your death." I wound the towel around me again. Finally the cops put their shoulders to our big heavy front door with its thick beveled glass and broke it in: I could hear a rending of wood and a splash of glass on the floor of the hall. Their lights played all over the living-room and crisscrossed nervously in the dining-room, stabbed into hallways, shot up the front stairs and finally up the back. They caught me standing in my towel at the top. A heavy policeman bounded up the steps. "Who are you?" he demanded. "I live here," I said. "Well, whattsa matta, ya hot?" he asked. It was, as a matter of fact, cold; I went to my room and pulled on some trousers. On my way out, a cop stuck a gun into my ribs. "Whatta you doin' here?" he demanded. "I live here," I said.

The officer in charge reported to mother. "No sign of nobody, lady," he said. "Musta got away—whatt'd he look like?" "There were two or three of them," mother said, "whooping and carrying on and slamming doors." "Funny," said the cop. "All ya windows and doors was locked on the inside tight as a tick."

Downstairs, we could hear the tromping of the other police. Police were all over the place; doors were yanked open, drawers were yanked open, windows were shot up and pulled down, furniture fell with dull thumps. A half-dozen policemen emerged out of the darkness of the front hallway upstairs. They began to ransack the floor: pulled beds away from walls, tore clothes off hooks in the closets, pulled suitcases and boxes off shelves. One of them found an old zither that Roy had won in a pool tournament. "Looky here, Joe," he said, strumming it with a big paw. The cop named Joe took it and turned it over. "What is it?" he asked me. "It's an old zither our guinea pig used to sleep on," I said. It was true that a pet guinea pig we once had would never sleep anywhere except on the zither, but I should never have said so. Joe and the other cop looked at me a long time. They put the zither back on a shelf.

"No sign o' nuthin'," said the cop who had first spoken to mother. "This guy," he explained to the others, jerking a thumb at me, "was nekked. The lady seems historical." They all nodded, but said nothing; just looked at me. In the small silence we all heard a creaking in the attic. Grandfather was turning over in bed. "What's 'at?" snapped Joe. Five or six cops sprang for the attic door before I could intervene or explain. I realized that it would be bad if they burst in on grandfather unannounced, or even announced. He was going through a phase in which he believed that General Meade's men, under steady hammering by Stonewall Jackson, were beginning to retreat and even desert.

When I got to the attic, things were pretty confused. Grandfather had evidently jumped to the conclusion that the police were deserters from Meade's army, trying to hide away in his attic. He bounded out of bed wearing a long flannel nightgown over long woolen underwear, a nightcap, and a leather jacket around his chest. The cops must have realized at once that the indignant white-haired old man belonged in the house, but they had no chance to say so. "Back, ye cowardly dogs!" roared grandfather. "Back t' the lines, ye lily-livered cattle!" With that, he fetched the officer who found the zither a flat-handed smack alongside his head that sent him sprawling. The others beat a retreat, but not fast enough; grandfather grabbed Zither's gun from its holster and let fly. The report seemed to crack the rafters; smoke filled the attic. A cop cursed and shot his hand to his shoulder. Somehow, we all finally got downstairs again and locked the door against the old gentleman. He fired once or twice more in the darkness and then went back to bed. "That was grandfather," I explained to Joe, out of breath. "He thinks you're deserters." "I'll say he does," said Joe.

The cops were reluctant to leave without getting their hands on somebody besides grandfather; the night had been distinctly a defeat for them. Furthermore, they obviously didn't like the "layout"; something looked—and I can see their viewpoint—phony. They began to poke into things again. A reporter, a thin-faced, wispy man, came up to me. I had put on one of mother's blouses, not being able to find anything else. The reporter looked at me with mingled suspicion and interest. "Just what is the real lowdown here, Bud?"

he asked. I decided to be frank with him. "We had ghosts," I said. He gazed at me a long time as if I were a slot machine into which he had, without results, dropped a nickel. Then he walked away. The cops followed him, the one grandfather shot holding his now-bandaged arm, cursing and blaspheming. "I'm gonna get my gun back from that old bird," said the zither-cop. "Yeh," said Joe. "You—and who else?" I told them I would bring it to the station house the next day.

"What was the matter with that one policeman?" mother asked, after they had gone. "Grandfather shot him," I said. "What for?" she demanded. I told her he was a deserter. "Of all things!" said mother. "He was such a nice-looking young man."

Grandfather was fresh as a daisy and full of jokes at breakfast next morning. We thought at first he had forgotten all about what had happened, but he hadn't. Over his third cup of coffee, he glared at Herman and me. "What was the idee of all them cops tarryhootin' round the house last night?" he demanded. He had us there.

The man who wrote this selection

JAMES THURBER   1894–

James Thurber was raised in a family that had an unusual knack for getting into humorous situations. The selection you have just read was taken from Thurber's autobiography, *My Life and Hard Times.* Although this book may overdo things a bit, there is no doubt that something is always happening to Thurber. Whether it is a ghost stalking around the dining table or a unicorn munching flowers in the garden, Thurber delights in presenting the ridiculous side of the situation.

Like many other modern writers, Thurber began his career by working on a newspaper. For many years he served with *The New Yorker* as a feature writer and even, for a short time, as the managing editor. He now lives on the earnings from his stories and books.

Thurber is able to create stories that are easy and fun to read because he is an extremely careful writer. Often he will rewrite a story ten times or more before it satisfies him.

Thurber began to draw long before he started writing, and he has illustrated his own books and several others as well. Many of you have seen his drawings: just a few lines which make a huge dog, a domineering woman, or a little plump man who looks as if he were in a state of continuous timid surprise. When Thurber's drawings appear together with his writings, his humor is irresistible. These talents have made him one of America's most popular humorists.

Let's consider . . .

1. The police seemed to think that the Thurbers were a rather strange family. What things helped to create this impression?

2. What happened when the police tried to search the attic? Do you think grandfather knew the intruders were really policemen? Explain your answer.

3. What is your opinion of Mother's quick decision to arouse the neighbors by whamming a shoe through their window?

4. Although most ghost stories aren't

as funny as James Thurber's, almost everyone enjoys hearing good ghost stories. How can you account for their popularity?

5. Do you have a family ghost story? If so, tell it to the class.

The writer's craft . . .

From his own experience, James Thurber created a story with a single impression. The plot, characters, dialogue, setting—all contribute to the unity of the story. Look again at the opening paragraph of "The Night the Ghost Got In." James Thurber wrote that the ghost raised a "hullabaloo of misunderstanding." This one phrase summed up all the complications of the story. Everything in the story in some way or other added to that hilarious "hullabaloo of misunderstanding."

Select one of the following ingredients of the story and explain how it added to the "hullabaloo of misunderstanding":

| plot | dialogue |
| characters | setting |

The Height of the Ridiculous

I wrote some lines once on a time
  In wondrous merry mood,
And thought, as usual, men would say
  They were exceeding good.

They were so queer, so very queer,
  I laughed as I would die;
Albeit, in the general way,
  A sober man am I.

I called my servant, and he came;
  How kind it was of him
To mind a slender man like me,
  He of the mighty limb.

"These to the printer," I exclaimed,
  And, in my humorous way,
I added (as a trifling jest,)
  "There'll be the devil to pay."

He took the paper, and I watched,
  And saw him peep within;
At the first line he read, his face
  Was all upon the grin.

He read the next; his grin grew broad,
  And shot from ear to ear;
He read the third; a chuckling noise
  I now began to hear.

The fourth; he broke into a roar;
  The fifth; his waistband split;
The sixth; he burst five buttons off,
  And tumbled in a fit.

Ten days and nights, with sleepless eye,
  I watched that wretched man,
And since, I never dare to write
  As funny as I can.

Oliver Wendell Holmes

NOW THINK BACK

THINK FOR YOURSELF

1. All readers enjoy humor. But they may differ in what makes them laugh. What makes *you* laugh? What stories, characters, or situations did you think the funniest in ON THE LIGHTER SIDE? Explain why.

2. Some humorous stories "date" very quickly. At the time they were written, the people and situations seemed funny, but in a very short time they were so old-fashioned that the humor was lost. Did any of the stories in ON THE LIGHTER SIDE refer to things which are no longer humorous? If so, explain why the humor now seems dated.

3. Even though the events in "The Night the Ghost Got In" took place many years ago, they are still amusing. Explain why.

4. You have probably known a few rare people who could enjoy a joke on themselves. Which people in this part were able to laugh at themselves?

5. All humorous stories and poems are written to be enjoyed. Some of them also contain an underlying thread of wisdom. Were there any selections in ON THE LIGHTER SIDE which contained wisdom as well as humor?

SHARE YOUR IDEAS

1. Why do you suppose "comic" books are given that name? How many of them are truly funny?

2. A few people think that reading hu-morous literature is a waste of time. Do you agree? What value—if any—does this kind of reading have?

3. Why do you enjoy being with people who have a good sense of humor?

4. How can humor help you keep a sense of balance? Describe an experience in which a tense situation was "saved" as a result of someone's sense of humor.

5. Who are your favorite radio and television comedians? How do these comedians differ in their ways of getting laughs?

6. A few years ago, you thought certain stories were very funny. As you think of them now, they seem childish. How can you account for your changed point of view?

WIDEN YOUR EXPERIENCE

Things to do . . .

1. Prepare a "Reading Is Fun" book exhibit. If you don't have room in your classroom, ask your school librarian to set aside a table in the library for your exhibit of humorous books. The artistic members of your class can make posters and illustrations for the exhibit.

2. Prepare a brief book-talk on one of the books in the exhibit. Be sure to include the following information:

   a. The title and author

   b. The things you liked about the book

   c. A description of an episode from the book which you found particularly amusing

   d. The kind of person who you think would like to read the book

3. Make a scrapbook of your favorite humorous poems. Look through poetry collections and current magazines. You'll find a wealth of material.

More to read . . .

Tall Tale America by WALTER BLAIR. You will meet twelve American folk heroes in this humorous book. Coward-Mc-Cann Inc., 1944.

Paul Bunyan by ESTHER SHEPHARD. Paul Bunyan was the greatest lumberjack of them all. Here are really tall tales about a famous American folk character. Harcourt, Brace and Company, Inc., 1941.

Pecos Bill, Texas Cowpuncher by HAROLD W. FELTON. The rodeo, cattle branding, and the perpetual motion ranch—Pecos Bill started them all. Alfred A. Knopf, Inc., 1949.

Just for Fun by ELIA S. SMITH and ALICE I. HAZELTINE. This is another collection of humorous tales, poems, tall tales and unnatural history. Lothrop, Lee & Shepard Co., Inc., 1948.

Innocent Merriment by FRANKLIN P. ADAMS. In this volume Mr. Adams has gathered together his favorite humorous verse. McGraw-Hill Book Company, Inc., 1942.

Brave Laughter by ARTHUR GUITERMAN. A collection of whimsical, wonderfully humorous poems is always good reading. Here are some of Mr. Guiterman's best. E. P. Dutton & Company, Inc., 1943.

Parents Keep Out; Elderly Poems for Youngerly Readers by OGDEN NASH. Light-hearted verse with something to say is Mr. Nash's special gift. Little, Brown and Company, 1951.

The Casting Away of Mrs. Lecks and Mrs. Aleshine by FRANK STOCKTON. Perhaps you can imagine two proper New England ladies shipwrecked on a tropical island, but you couldn't guess the strange and humorous results. Appleton-Century-Crofts, Inc., 1933.

Laugh with Leacock by STEPHEN LEACOCK. The great Canadian humorist is particularly funny in this collection of essays. Dodd, Mead and Company, Inc., 1930.

Chucklebait and *More Chucklebait* by MARGARET C. SCOGGIN (ed.). These two books contain some of the best humorous stories in our language. There are illustrations too. Alfred A. Knopf, Inc., 1945 and 1949.

Our Hearts Were Young and Gay by CORNELIA OTIS SKINNER and EMILY KIMBROUGH. Two American girls spend a summer in Europe and find both adventures and hilarious misadventures. Dodd, Mead & Company, 1942.

Get Thee Behind Me by HARTZELL SPENCE. The life of a minister's son can sometimes get more involved than other boys' lives. At least this was true of one minister's son. McGraw-Hill Book Company, Inc., 1942.

Penrod by BOOTH TARKINGTON. Penrod is a boy with a natural gift for getting himself into mischief. Doubleday & Company, Inc., 1931.

Alice in Wonderland by LEWIS CARROLL. Although this book was written to entertain one girl, it has brought pleasure to many generations. *Through the Looking Glass* continues Alice's adventures. The Macmillan Company, 1923.

The Remarkable Exploits of Lancelot Biggs by NELSON BOND. Lancelot Biggs, a gangly mate on the space ship, *Saturn,* leaps gaily from one trouble to another. Doubleday & Company, Inc., 1950.

My Life and Hard Times by JAMES THURBER. This book includes "The Night the Ghost Got In." The rest of the stories are just as funny. Harcourt, Brace and Company, Inc., 1933.

THE THINGS THAT COUNT

Whenever you are allowed to make a decision, you usually decide in favor of the things that count for you. If a basketball game is more important than a sundae, you will simply choose to spend your last quarter on the game. But suppose you found yourself unable to answer a test question, and the person next to you had the answer. You know that getting a good mark is important, but you also know that your honesty is at stake. This kind of a decision is not only more difficult, it is also more important. The intangibles, like honesty, courage, or generosity determine the kind of person you are. They affect the course of your entire life.

All the people in this unit have made important decisions. As you read, ask yourself whether they really decided in favor of THE THINGS THAT COUNT.

PART NINE

THE THINGS THAT COUNT

Doc Mellhorn and the Pearly Gates

STEPHEN VINCENT BENÉT

What is *your* idea of Heaven? Doc Mellhorn was surprised and a little disappointed when he discovered what it was like, but that was because he had driven his old Model T in through the wrong entrance.

Doc Mellhorn had never expected to go anywhere at all when he died. So, when he found himself on the road again, it surprised him. But perhaps I'd better explain a little about Doc Mellhorn first. He was seventy-odd when he left our town; but when he came, he was as young as Bates or Filsinger or any of the boys at the hospital. Only there wasn't any hospital when he came. He came with a young man's beard and a brand-new bag and a lot of new-fangled ideas about medicine that we didn't take to much. And he left, forty-odd years later, with a first-class county health record and a lot of people alive that wouldn't have been alive if he hadn't been there. Yes, a country doctor. And nobody ever called him a man in white or a death grappler that I know of, though they did think of giving him a degree at Pewauket College once. But then the board met again and decided they needed a new gymnasium, so they gave the degree to J. Prentiss Parmalee instead.

They say he was a thin young man when he first came, a thin young man with an Eastern accent who'd wanted to study in Vienna. But most of us remember him chunky and solid, with white hair and a little bald spot that always got burned bright red in the first hot weather. He had about four card tricks that he'd do for you, if you were a youngster—they were always the same ones—and now and then, if he felt like it, he'd take a silver half dollar out of the back of your neck. And that worked as well with the youngsters who were going to build rocket ships as it had with the youngsters who were going to be railway engineers. It always worked. I guess it was Doc Mellhorn more than the trick.

But there wasn't anything unusual about him, except maybe the card tricks. Or, anyway, he didn't think so. He was just a good doctor and he knew us inside out. I've heard people call him a pigheaded, obstinate old mule—that was in the fight about the water supply. And I've heard a weepy

533

old lady call him a saint. I took the tale to him once, and he looked at me over his glasses and said, "Well, I've always respected a mule. Got ten times the sense of a—horse." Then he took a silver half dollar out of my ear.

Well, how do you describe a man like that? You don't—you call him up at three in the morning. And when he sends in his bill, you think it's a little steep.

All the same, when it came to it, there were people who drove a hundred and fifty miles to the funeral. And the Masons came down from Bluff City, and the Poles came from across the tracks, with a wreath the size of a house, and you saw cars in town that you didn't often see there. But it was after the funeral that the queer things began for Doc Mellhorn.

The last thing he remembered, he'd been lying in bed, feeling pretty sick, on the whole, but glad for the rest. And now he was driving his Model T down a long straight road between rolling, misty prairies that seemed to go from nowhere to nowhere.

It didn't seem funny to him to be driving the Model T again. That was the car he'd learned on, and he kept to it till his family made him change. And it didn't seem funny to him not to be sick any more. He hadn't had much time to be sick in his life —the patients usually attended to that. He looked around for his bag, first thing, but it was there on the seat beside him. It was the old bag, not the presentation one they'd given him at the hospital, but that was all right too. It meant he was out on a call and, if he couldn't quite recollect at the moment just where the call was, it was certain to come to him. He'd wakened up often enough in his buggy, in the old days, and found the horse was taking him home, without his doing much about it. A doctor gets used to things like that.

All the same, when he'd driven and driven for some time without raising so much as a traffic light, just the same rolling prairies on either hand, he began to get a little suspicious. He thought, for a while, of stopping the car and getting out, just to take a look around, but he'd always hated to lose time on a call. Then he noticed something else. He was driving without his glasses. And yet he hadn't driven without his glasses in fifteen years.

"H'm," said Doc Mellhorn. "I'm crazy as a June bug. Or else— Well, it might be so, I suppose."

But this time he did stop the car. He opened his bag and looked inside it, but everything seemed to be in order. He opened his wallet and looked at that, but there were his own initials, half rubbed away, and he recognized them. He took his pulse, but it felt perfectly steady.

"H'm," said Doc Mellhorn. "Well."

Then, just to prove that everything was perfectly normal, he took a silver half dollar out of the steering wheel of the car.

"Never did it smoother," said Doc Mellhorn. "Well, all the same, if this is the new highway, it's longer than I remember it."

But just then a motorcycle came roaring down the road and stopped with a flourish, the way motor cops do.

"Any trouble?" said the motor cop. Doc Mellhorn couldn't see his face for his goggles, but the goggles looked normal.

"I am a physician," said Doc Mellhorn, as he'd said a thousand times before to all sorts of people, "on my way to an urgent case." He passed his hand across his forehead. "Is this the right road?" he said.

"Straight ahead to the traffic light," said the cop. "They're expecting you, Doctor Mellhorn. Shall I give you an escort?"

"No; thanks all the same," said Doc Mellhorn, and the motor cop roared away. The Model T ground as Doc Mellhorn gassed her. "Well, they've got a new breed of traffic cop," said Doc Mellhorn, "or else—"

But when he got to the light, it was just like any light at a crossroads. He waited till it changed and the officer waved him on. There seemed to be a good deal of traffic going the other way, but he didn't get a chance to notice it much, because Lizzie bucked a little, as she usually did when you kept her waiting. Still, the sight of traffic relieved him, though he hadn't passed anybody on his own road yet.

Pretty soon he noticed the look of the country had changed. It was parkway now and very nicely landscaped. There was dogwood in bloom on the little hills, white and pink against the green; though, as Doc Mellhorn remembered it, it had been August when he left his house. And every now and then there'd be a nice little white-painted sign that said TO THE GATES.

"H'm," said Doc Mellhorn. "New State Parkway, I guess. Well, they've fixed it up pretty. But I wonder where they got the dogwood. Haven't seen it bloom like that since I was East."

Then he drove along in a sort of dream for a while, for the dogwood reminded him of the days when he was a young man in an Eastern college. He remembered the look of that college and the girls who'd come to dances, the girls who wore white gloves and had rolls of hair. They were pretty girls, too, and he wondered what had become of them. "Had babies, I guess," thought Doc Mellhorn. "Or some of them, anyway." But he liked to think of them as they had been when they were just pretty and excited at being at a dance.

He remembered other things too—the hacked desks in the lecture rooms, and the trees on the campus, and the first pipe he'd ever broken in, and a fellow called Paisley Grew that he hadn't thought of in years—

a rawboned fellow with a gift for tall stories and playing the jew's-harp.

"Ought to have looked up Paisley," he said. "Yes, I ought. Didn't amount to a hill of beans, I guess, but I always liked him. I wonder if he still plays the jew's-harp. Pshaw, I know he's been dead twenty years."

He was passing other cars now and other cars were passing him, but he didn't pay much attention, except when he happened to notice a license you didn't often see in the state, like Rhode Island or Mississippi. He was too full of his own thoughts. There were foot passengers, too, plenty of them—and once he passed a man driving a load of hay. He wondered what the man would do with the hay when he got to the Gates. But probably there were arrangements for that.

"Not that I believe a word of it," he said, "but it'll surprise Father Kelly. Or maybe it won't. I used to have some handsome arguments with that man, but I always knew I could count on him, in spite of me being a heretic."

Then he saw the Wall and the Gates, right across the valley. He saw them, and they reached to the top of the sky. He rubbed his eyes for a while, but they kept on being there.

"Quite a sight," said Doc Mellhorn.

No one told him just where to go or how to act, but it seemed to him that he knew. If he'd thought about it, he'd have said that you waited in line, but there wasn't any waiting in line. He just went where he was expected to go and the reception clerk knew his name right away.

"Yes, Doctor Mellhorn," he said. "And now, what would you like to do first?"

"I think I'd like to sit down," said Doc Mellhorn. So he sat, and it was a comfortable chair. He even bounced the springs once or twice, till he caught the reception clerk's eye on him.

"Is there anything I can get you?" said the reception clerk. He was young and brisk and neat as a pin, and you could see he aimed to give service and studied about it. Doc Mellhorn thought, "He's the kind that wipes off your windshield no matter how clean it is."

"No," said Doc Mellhorn. "You see, I don't believe this. I don't believe any of it. I'm sorry if that sounds cranky, but I don't."

"That's quite all right, sir," said the reception clerk. "It often takes a while." And he smiled as if Doc Mellhorn had done him a favor.

"Young man, I'm a physician," said Doc Mellhorn, "and do you mean to tell me—"

Then he stopped, for he suddenly saw there was no use arguing. He was either there or he wasn't. And it felt as if he were there.

"Well," said Doc Mellhorn, with a sigh, "how do I begin?"

"That's entirely at your own volition, sir," said the reception clerk briskly. "Any meetings with relatives, of course. Or if you would prefer to get yourself settled first. Or take a tour, alone or conducted. Perhaps these will offer suggestions," and he started to hand over a handful of leaflets. But Doc Mellhorn put them aside.

"Wait a minute," he said. "I want to think. Well, naturally, there's Mother and Dad. But I couldn't see them just yet. I wouldn't believe it. And Grandma—well, now, if I saw Grandma—and me older than she is—was—used to be—well, I don't know what it would do to me. You've got to let me get my breath. Well, of course, there's Uncle Frank—he'd be easier." He paused. "Is he here?" he said.

The reception clerk looked in a file. "I am happy to say that Mr. Francis V. Mell-

horn arrived July 12, 1907," he said. He smiled winningly.

"Well!" said Doc Mellhorn. "Uncle Frank! Well, I'll be—well! But it must have been a great consolation to Mother. We heard—well, never mind what we heard—I guess it wasn't so. . . . No, don't reach for that phone just yet, or whatever it is. I'm still thinking."

"We sometimes find," said the reception clerk eagerly, "that a person not a relative may be the best introduction. Even a stranger sometimes—a distinguished stranger connected with one's own profession—"

"Well, now, that's an idea," said Doc Mellhorn heartily, trying to keep his mind off how much he disliked the reception clerk. He couldn't just say why he disliked him, but he knew he did.

It reminded him of the time he'd had to have his gall bladder out in the city hospital and the young, brisk interns had come to see him and called him "Doctor" every other word.

"Yes, that's an idea," he said. He reflected. "Well, of course, I'd like to see Koch," he said. "And Semmelweiss. Not to speak of Walter Reed. But, shucks, they'd be busy men. But there is one fellow—only he lived pretty far back—"

"Hippocrates, please," said the reception clerk into the telephone or whatever it was. "H for horse—"

"No!" said Doc Mellhorn quite violently. "Excuse me, but you just wait a minute. I mean if you can wait. I mean, if Hippocrates wants to come, I've no objection. But I never took much of a fancy to him, in spite of his oath. It's Aesculapius [1] I'm thinking about. George W. Oh, glory!" he said. "But he won't talk English. I forgot."

"I shall be happy to act as interpreter,"

[1] *Aesculapius,* the god of medicine in Greek mythology

said the reception clerk, smiling brilliantly.

"I haven't a doubt," said Doc Mellhorn. "But just wait a shake." In a minute, by the way the clerk was acting, he was going to be talking to Aesculapius. "And what in time am I going to say to the man?" he thought. "It's too much." He gazed wildly about the neat reception room—distempered, as he noticed, in a warm shade of golden tan. Then his eyes fell on the worn black bag at his feet and a sudden warm wave of relief flooded over him.

"Wait a minute," he said, and his voice gathered force and authority. "Where's my patient?"

"Patient?" said the reception clerk, looking puzzled for the first time.

"Patient," said Doc Mellhorn. "P for phlebitis." He tapped his bag.

"I'm afraid you don't quite understand, sir," said the reception clerk.

"I understand this," said Doc Mellhorn. "I was called here. And if I wasn't called professionally, why have I got my bag?"

"But, my dear Doctor Mellhorn—" said the reception clerk.

"I'm not your dear doctor," said Doc Mellhorn. "I was called here, I tell you. I'm sorry not to give you the patient's name, but the call must have come in my absence and the girl doesn't spell very well. But in any well-regulated hospital—"

"But I tell you," said the reception clerk, and his hair wasn't slick any more, "nobody's ill here. Nobody can be ill. If they could, it wouldn't be He—"

"Humph," said Doc Mellhorn. He thought it over, and felt worse. "Then what does a fellow like Koch do?" he said. "Or Pasteur?" He raised a hand. "Oh, don't tell me," he said. "I can see they'd be busy. Yes, I guess it'd be all right for a research man. But I never was . . . Oh, well, shucks, I've published a few papers. And there's that clamp of mine—always

meant to do something about it. But they've got better ones now. Mean to say there isn't so much as a case of mumps in the whole place?"

"I assure you," said the reception clerk, in a weary voice. "And now, once you see Doctor Aesculapius—"

"Funny," said Doc Mellhorn. "Lord knows there's plenty of times you'd be glad to be quit of the whole thing. And don't talk to me about the healer's art of grateful patients. Well, I've known a few . . . a few. But I've known others. All the same, it's different, being told there isn't any need for what you can do."

"A for Ararát," said the reception clerk into his instrument. "E for Eden."

"Should think you'd have a dial," said Doc Mellhorn desperately. "We've got 'em down below." He thought hard and frantically. "Wait a shake. It's coming back to me," he said. "Got anybody named Grew here? Paisley Grew?"

"S for serpent . . ." said the reception clerk. "What was that?"

"Fellow that called me," said Doc Mellhorn. "G-r-e-w. First name, Paisley."

"I will consult the index," said the reception clerk.

He did so, and Doc Mellhorn waited, hoping against hope.

"We have 94,183 Grews, including 83 Prescotts and one Penobscot," the reception clerk said at last. "But I fail to find Paisley Grew. Are you quite sure of the name?"

"Of course," said Doc Mellhorn briskly. "Paisley Grew. Chronic indigestion. Might be appendix—can't say—have to see. But anyhow, he's called." He picked up his bag. "Well, thanks for the information," he said, liking the reception clerk better than he had yet. "Not your fault, anyway."

"But—but where are you going?" said the reception clerk.

"Well, there's another establishment, isn't there?" said Doc Mellhorn. "Always heard there was. Call probably came from there. Crossed wires, I expect."

"But you can't go there!" said the reception clerk. "I mean—"

"Can't go?" said Doc Mellhorn. "I'm a physician. A patient's called me."

"But if you'll only wait and see Aesculapius!" said the reception clerk, running his hands wildly through his hair. "He'll be here almost any moment."

"Please give him my apologies," said Doc Mellhorn. "He's a doctor. He'll understand. And if any messages come for me, just stick them on the spike. Do I need a road map? Noticed the road I came was all one way."

"There is, I believe, a back road in rather bad repair," said the reception clerk icily. "I can call Information if you wish."

"Oh, don't bother," said Doc Mellhorn. "I'll find it. And I never saw a road beat Lizzie yet." He took a silver half dollar from the doorknob of the door. "See that?" he said. "Slick as a whistle. Well, good-by, young man."

But it wasn't till he'd cranked up Lizzie and was on his way that Doc Mellhorn really felt safe. He found the back road and it was all the reception clerk had said it was and more. But he didn't mind—in fact, after one particularly bad rut, he grinned.

"I suppose I ought to have seen the folks," he said. "Yes, I know I ought. But —not so much as a case of mumps in the whole abiding dominion! Well, it's lucky I took a chance on Paisley Grew."

After another mile or so, he grinned again.

"And I'd like to see old Aesculapius' face. Probably rang him in the middle of dinner—they always do. But shucks, it's happened to all of us."

Well, the road got worse and worse and the sky above it darker and darker, and what with one thing and another, Doc Mellhorn was glad enough when he got to the other gates. They were pretty impressive gates, too, though of course in a different way, and reminded Doc Mellhorn a little of the furnaces outside Steeltown, where he'd practiced for a year when he was young.

This time Doc Mellhorn wasn't going to take any advice from reception clerks and he had his story all ready. All the same, he wasn't either registered or expected, so there was a little fuss. Finally they tried to scare him by saying he came at his own risk and that there were some pretty tough characters about. But Doc Mellhorn remarked that he'd practiced in Steeltown. So, after he'd told them what seemed to him a million times that he was a physician on a case, they finally let him in and directed him to Paisley Grew. Paisley was on Level 346 in Pit 68,953, and Doc Mellhorn recognized him the minute he saw him. He even had the jew's-harp stuck in the back of his overalls.

"Well, Doc," said Paisley finally, when the first greetings were over, "you certainly are a sight for sore eyes! Though, of course, I'm sorry to see you here," and he grinned.

"Well, I can't see that it's so different from a lot of places," said Doc Mellhorn, wiping his forehead. "Warmish, though."

"It's the humidity, really," said Paisley Grew. "That's what it really is."

"Yes, I know," said Doc Mellhorn. "And now tell me, Paisley; how's that indigestion of yours?"

"Well, I'll tell you, Doc," said Paisley. "When I first came here, I thought the climate was doing it good. I did for a fact. But now I'm not so sure. I've tried all sorts of things for it—I've even tried being transferred to the boiling asphalt lakes. But it just seems to hang on, and every now and then, when I least expect it, it catches me. Take last night. I didn't have a thing to eat that I don't generally eat—well, maybe I did have one little snort of hot sulphur, but it wasn't the sulphur that did it. All the same, I woke up at four, and it was just like a knife. Now . . ."

He went on from there and it took him some time. And Doc Mellhorn listened, happy as a clam. He never thought he'd be glad to listen to a hypochondriac, but he was. And when Paisley was all through, he examined him and prescribed for him. It was just a little soda bicarb and pepsin, but Paisley said it took hold something wonderful. And they had a fine time that evening, talking over the old days.

Finally, of course, the talk got around to how Paisley liked it where he was. And Paisley was honest enough about that.

"Well, Doc," he said, "of course this isn't the place for you, and I can see you're just visiting. But I haven't many real complaints. It's hot, to be sure, and they work you, and some of the boys here are rough. But they've had some pretty interesting experiences, too, when you get them talking—yes, sir. And anyhow, it isn't Peabodyville, New Jersey," he said with vehemence. "I spent five years in Peabodyville, trying to work up in the leather business. After that I bust out, and I guess that's what landed me here. But it's an improvement on Peabodyville." He looked at Doc Mellhorn sidewise. "Say, Doc," he said, "I know this is a vacation for you, but all the same there's a couple of the boys—nothing really wrong with them of course—but—well, if you could just look them over—"

"I was thinking the office hours would be nine to one," said Doc Mellhorn.

So Paisley took him around and they found a nice little place for an office in one of the abandoned mine galleries, and Doc Mellhorn hung out his shingle. And right away patients started coming around. They didn't get many doctors there, in the first place, and the ones they did get weren't exactly the cream of the profession, so Doc Mellhorn had it all to himself. It was mostly sprains, fractures, bruises and dislocations, of course, with occasional burns and scalds—and, on the whole, it reminded Doc Mellhorn a good deal of his practice in Steeltown, especially when it came to foreign bodies in the eye. Now and then Doc Mellhorn ran into a more unusual case —for instance, there was one of the guards that got part of himself pretty badly damaged in a rock slide. Well, Doc Mellhorn had never set a tail before, but he managed it all right, and got a beautiful primary union, too, in spite of the fact that he had no X-ray facilities. He thought of writing up the case for the State Medical Journal, but then he couldn't figure out any way to send it to them, so he had to let it slide. And then there was an advanced carcinoma of the liver—a Greek named Papadoupolous or Prometheus [2] or something. Doc Mellhorn couldn't do much for him, considering the circumstances, but he did what he could, and he and the Greek used to have long conversations. The rest was just everyday practice—run of the mine—but he enjoyed it.

Now and then it would cross his mind that he ought to get out Lizzie and run back to the other place for a visit with the folks. But that was just like going back East had been on earth—he'd think he had everything pretty well cleared up, and then a new flock of patients would come in. And it wasn't that he didn't miss his wife

---

[2] *Prometheus,* a Greek mythological figure; a Titan who was punished for bringing fire to man; the first rebel against the gods

and children and grandchildren—he did. But there wasn't any way to get back to them, and he knew it. And there was the work in front of him and the office crowded every day. So he just went along, hardly noticing the time.

Now and then, to be sure, he'd get a suspicion that he wasn't too popular with the authorities of the place. But he was used to not being popular with authorities and he didn't pay much attention. But finally they sent an inspector around. The minute Doc Mellhorn saw him, he knew there was going to be trouble.

Not that the inspector was uncivil. In fact, he was a pretty high-up official—you could tell by his antlers. And Doc Mellhorn was just as polite, showing him around. He showed him the free dispensary and the clinic and the nurse—Scotch girl named Smith, she was—and the dental chair he'd rigged up with the help of a fellow named Ferguson, who used to be an engineer before he was sentenced. And the inspector looked them all over, and finally he came back to Doc Mellhorn's office. The girl named Smith had put up curtains in the office, and with that and a couple of potted gas plants it looked more homelike than it had. The inspector looked around it and sighed.

"I'm sorry, Doctor Mellhorn," he said at last, "but you can see for yourself, it won't do."

"What won't do?" said Doc Mellhorn, stoutly. But, all the same, he felt afraid.

"Any of it," said the inspector. "We could overlook the alleviation of minor suffering—I'd be inclined to do so myself— though these people are here to suffer, and there's no changing that. But you're playing merry Hades with the whole system."

"I'm a physician in practice," said Doc Mellhorn.

"Yes," said the inspector. "That's just the trouble. Now, take these reports you've been sending," and he took out a sheaf of papers. "What have you to say about that?"

"Well, seeing as there's no county health officer, or at least I couldn't find one—" said Doc Mellhorn.

"Precisely," said the inspector. "And what have you done? You've condemned fourteen levels of this pit as unsanitary nuisances. You've recommended 2136 lost souls for special diet, remedial exercise, hospitalization—Well—I won't go through the list."

"I'll stand back of every one of those recommendations," said Doc Mellhorn. "And now we've got the chair working, we can handle most of the dental work on the spot. Only Ferguson needs more amalgam."

"I know," said the inspector patiently, "but the money has to come from somewhere—you must realize that. We're not a rich community, in spite of what people think. And these unauthorized requests— oh, we fill them, of course, but—"

"Ferguson needs more amalgam," said Doc Mellhorn. "And that last batch wasn't standard. I wouldn't use it on a dog."

"He's always needing more amalgam!" said the inspector bitterly, making a note. "Is he going to fill every tooth in Hades? By the way, my wife tells me I need a little work done myself—but we won't go into that. We'll take just one thing—your entirely unauthorized employment of Miss Smith. Miss Smith has no business working for you. She's supposed to be gnawed by a never-dying worm every Monday, Wednesday and Friday."

"Sounds silly to me," said Doc Mellhorn.

"I don't care how silly it sounds," said the inspector. "It's regulations. And, besides, she isn't even a registered nurse."

"She's a practical one," said Doc Mellhorn. "Of course, back on earth a lot of her patients died. But that was because when she didn't like a patient, she poisoned him. Well, she can't poison anybody here and I've kind of got her out of the notion of it anyway. She's been doing A-1 work for me and I'd like to recommend her for—"

"Please!" said the inspector. "Please! And as if that wasn't enough, you've even been meddling with the staff. I've a note here on young Asmodeus—Asmodeus XIV—"

"Oh, you mean Mickey!" said Doc Mellhorn, with a chuckle. "Short for Mickey Mouse. We call him that in the clinic. And he's a young imp if I ever saw one."

"The original Asmodeus [3] is one of our most prominent citizens," said the inspector severely. "How do you suppose he felt when we got your report that his fourteenth great-grandson had rickets?"

"Well," said Doc Mellhorn, "I know rickets. And he had 'em. And you're going to have rickets in these youngsters as long as you keep feeding them low-grade coke.

[3] *Asmodeus,* the "king of demons" in Jewish tradition

I put Mickey on the best Pennsylvania anthracite, and look at him now!"

"I admit the success of your treatment," said the inspector, "but, naturally—well, since then we've been deluged with demands for anthracite from as far south as Sheol. We'll have to float a new bond issue. And what will the taxpayers say?"

"He was just cutting his first horns when he came to us," said Doc Mellhorn reminiscently, "and they were coming in crooked. Now, I ask you, did you ever see a straighter pair? Of course, if I'd had cod liver oil—My gracious, you ought to have somebody here that can fill a prescription; I can't do it all."

The inspector shut his papers together with a snap. "I'm sorry, Doctor Mellhorn," he said, "but this is final. You have no right here, in the first place; no local license to practice in the second—"

"Yes, that's a little irregular," said Doc Mellhorn, "but I'm a registered member of four different medical associations—you might take that into account. And I'll take any examination that's required."

"No!" said the inspector violently. "No, no, no! You can't stay here! You've got to go away! It isn't possible!"

Doc Mellhorn drew a long breath. "Well," he said, "there wasn't any work for me at the other place. And here you won't let me practice. So what's a man to do?"

The inspector was silent.

"Tell me," said Doc Mellhorn presently. "Suppose you do throw me out? What happens to Miss Smith and Paisley and the rest of them?"

"Oh, what's done is done," said the inspector impatiently, "here as well as anywhere else. We'll have to keep on with the anthracite and the rest of it. And Hades only knows what'll happen in the future. If it's any satisfaction to you, you've started something."

"Well, I guess Smith and Ferguson between them can handle the practice," said Doc Mellhorn. "But that's got to be a promise."

"It's a promise," said the inspector.

"Then there's Mickey—I mean Asmodeus," said Doc Mellhorn. "He's a smart youngster—smart as a whip—if he is a hellion. Well, you know how a youngster gets. Well, it seems he wants to be a doctor. But I don't know what sort of training he'd get—"

"He'll get it," said the inspector feverishly. "We'll found the finest medical college you ever saw, right here in West Baal. We'll build a hospital that'll knock your eye out. You'll be satisfied. But now, if you don't mind—"

"All right," said Doc Mellhorn, and rose.

The inspector looked surprised. "But don't you want to—" he said. "I mean my instructions are we're to give you a banquet, if necessary—after all, the community appreciates—"

"Thanks," said Doc Mellhorn, with a shudder, "but if I've got to go, I'd rather get out of town. You hang around and announce your retirement, and pretty soon folks start thinking they ought to give you a testimonial. And I never did like testimonials."

All the same, before he left he took a silver half dollar out of Mickey Asmodeus' chin.

When he was back on the road again and the lights of the gates had faded into a low ruddy glow behind him, Doc Mellhorn felt alone for the first time. He'd been lonely at times during his life, but he'd never felt alone like this before. Because, as far as he could see, there was only him and Lizzie now.

"Now, maybe if I'd talked to Aesculapius—" he said. "But pshaw, I always was pigheaded."

He didn't pay much attention to the way he was driving and it seemed to him that the road wasn't quite the same. But he felt tired for a wonder—bone-tired and beaten—and he didn't much care about the road. He hadn't felt tired since he left earth, but now the loneliness tired him.

"Active—always been active," he said to himself. "I can't just lay down on the job. But what's a man to do?

"What's a man to do?" he said. "I'm a doctor. I can't work miracles."

Then the black fit came over him and he remembered all the times he'd been wrong and all the people he couldn't do anything for. "Never was much of a doctor, I guess," he said. "Maybe, if I'd gone to Vienna. Well, the right kind of man would have gone. And about that Bigelow kid," he said. "How was I to know he'd hemorrhage? But I should have known.

"I've diagnosed walking typhoid as appendicitis. Just the once, but that's enough. And I still don't know what held me back when I was all ready to operate. I used to wake up in a sweat, six months afterward, thinking I had.

"I could have saved those premature twins, if I'd known as much then as I do now. I guess that guy Dafoe would have done it anyway—look at what he had to work with. But I didn't. And that finished the Gorhams' having children. That's a dandy doctor, isn't it? Makes you feel fine.

"I could have pulled Old Man Halsey through. And Edna Biggs. And the little Lauriat girl. No, I couldn't have done it with her. That was before insulin. I couldn't have cured Ted Allen. No, I'm clear on that. But I've never been satisfied about the Collins woman. Bates is all right —good as they come. But I knew her, inside and out—ought to, too—she was the biggest nuisance that ever came into the office. And if I hadn't been down with the flu . . .

"Then there's the flu epidemic. I didn't take my clothes off, four days and nights. But what's the good of that, when you lose them? Oh, sure, the statistics looked good. You can have the statistics.

"Should have started raising hell about the water supply two years before I did.

"Oh, yes, it makes you feel fine, pulling babies into the world. Makes you feel you're doing something. And just fine when you see a few of them, twenty-thirty years later, not worth two toots on a cow's horn. Can't say I ever delivered a Dillinger. But there's one or two in state's prison. And more that ought to be. Don't mind even that so much as a few of the fools. Makes you wonder.

"And then, there's incurable cancer. That's a daisy. What can you do about it, Doctor? Well, Doctor, we can alleviate the pain in the last stages. Some. Ever been in a cancer ward, Doctor? Yes, Doctor, I have.

"What do you do for the common cold, Doctor? Two dozen clean linen handkerchiefs. Yes, it's a good joke—I'll laugh. And what do you do for a boy when you know he's dying, Doctor? Take a silver half dollar out of his ear. But it kept the Lane kid quiet and his fever went down that night. I took the credit, but I don't know why it went down.

"I've only got one brain. And one pair of hands.

"I could have saved. I could have done. I could have.

"Guess it's just as well you can't live forever. You make fewer mistakes. And sometimes I'd see Bates looking at me as if he wondered why I ever thought I could practice.

"Pigheaded, opinionated, ineffective old imbecile! And yet, Lord, Lord, I'd do it all over again."

He lifted his eyes from the pattern of the road in front of him. There were white markers on it now and Lizzie seemed to be bouncing down a residential street. There were trees in the street and it reminded him of town. He rubbed his eyes for a second and Lizzie rolled on by herself—she often did. It didn't seem strange to him to stop at the right house.

"Well, Mother," he said rather gruffly to the group on the lawn. "Well, Dad. . . . Well, Uncle Frank." He beheld a small, stern figure, advancing, hands outstretched. "Well, Grandma," he said meekly.

Later on he was walking up and down in the grape arbor with Uncle Frank. Now and then he picked a grape and ate it. They'd always been good grapes, those Catawbas, as he remembered them.

"What beats me," he said, not for the first time, "is why I didn't notice the Gates. The second time, I mean."

"Oh, that Gate," said Uncle Frank, with

the easy, unctuous roll in his voice that
Doc Mellhorn so well remembered. He
smoothed his handle-bar mustaches. "That
Gate, my dear Edward—well, of course it
has to be there in the first place. Literature,
you know. And then, it's a choice," he
said richly.

"I'll draw cards," said Doc Mellhorn.
He ate another grape.

"Fact is," said Uncle Frank, "that Gate's
for one kind of person. You pass it and
then you can rest for all eternity. Just fold
your hands. It suits some."

"I can see that it would," said Doc Mellhorn.

"Yes," said Uncle Frank, "but it wouldn't
suit a Mellhorn. I'm happy to say that very
few of our family remain permanently on
that side. I spent some time there myself."
He said, rather self-consciously, "Well, my
last years had been somewhat stormy. So
few people cared for refined impersonations
of our feathered songsters, including lightning sketches. I felt that I'd earned a rest.
But after a while—well, I got tired of being
at liberty."

"And what happens when you get tired?"
said Doc Mellhorn.

"You find out what you want to do,"
said Uncle Frank.

"My kind of work?" said Doc Mellhorn.

"Your kind of work," said his uncle.
"Been busy, haven't you?"

"Well," said Doc Mellhorn. "But here.
If there isn't so much as a case of mumps
in—"

"Would it have to be mumps?" said his
uncle. "Of course, if you're aching for
mumps, I guess it could be arranged. But
how many new souls do you suppose we
get here a day?"

"Sizable lot, I expect."

"And how many of them get here in first-
class condition?" asked Uncle Frank triumphantly. "Why, I've seen Doctor Rush

—Benjamin Rush—come back so tired
from a day's round he could hardly flap one
pinion against the other. Oh, if it's work
you want— And then, of course, there's
the earth."

"Hold on," said Doc Mellhorn. "I'm not
going to appear to any young intern in
wings and a harp. Not at my time of life.
And anyway, he'd laugh himself sick."

" 'Tain't that," said Uncle Frank. "Look
here. You've left children and grandchildren behind you, haven't you? And they're
going on?"

"Yes," said Doc Mellhorn.

"Same with what you did," said Uncle
Frank. "I mean the inside part of it—that
stays. I don't mean any funny business—
voices in your ear and all that. But haven't
you ever got clean tuckered out, and been
able to draw on something you didn't know
was there?"

"Pshaw, any man's done that," said Doc
Mellhorn. "But you take the adrenal—"

"Take anything you like," said Uncle
Frank placidly. "I'm not going to argue
with you. Not my department. But you'll
find it isn't all adrenalin. Like it here?"
he said abruptly. "Feel satisfied?"

"Why, yes," said Doc Mellhorn sur-
prisedly, "I do." He looked around the
grape arbor and suddenly realized that he
felt happy.

"No, they wouldn't all arrive in first-
class shape," he said to himself. "So there'd
be a place." He turned to Uncle Frank.
"By the way," he said diffidently, "I mean,
I got back so quick—there wouldn't be a
chance of my visiting the other establishment now and then? Where I just came
from? Smith and Ferguson are all right,
but I'd like to keep in touch."

"Well," said Uncle Frank, "you can take
that up with the delegation." He arranged
the handkerchief in his breast pocket.
"They ought to be along any minute now,"

he said. "Sister's been in a stew about it all day. She says there won't be enough chairs, but she always says that."

"Delegation?" said Doc Mellhorn. "But—"

"You don't realize," said Uncle Frank, with his rich chuckle. "You're a famous man. You've broken pretty near every regulation, except the fire laws, and refused the Gate first crack. They've got to do something about it."

"But—" said Doc Mellhorn, looking wildly around for a place to escape.

"Sh-h!" hissed Uncle Frank. "Hold up your head and look as though money were bid for you. It won't take long—just a welcome." He shaded his eyes with his hand. "My," he said with frank admiration, "you've certainly brought them out. There's Rush, by the way."

"Where?" said Doc Mellhorn.

"Second from the left, third row, in a wig," said Uncle Frank. "And there's—"

Then he stopped, and stepped aside. A tall grave figure was advancing down the grape arbor—a bearded man with a wise, majestic face who wore robes as if they belonged to him, not as Doc Mellhorn had seen them worn in college commencements. There was a small fillet of gold about his head and in his left hand, Doc Mellhorn noticed without astonishment, was a winged staff entwined with two fangless serpents. Behind him were many others. Doc Mellhorn stood straighter.

The bearded figure stopped in front of Doc Mellhorn. "Welcome, Brother," said Aesculapius.

"It's an honor to meet you, Doctor," said Doc Mellhorn. He shook the outstretched hand. Then he took a silver half dollar from the mouth of the left-hand snake.

Let's consider . . .

1. Almost everyone seemed to like and trust Doc Mellhorn. Can you explain why? If you were ill, would you like to have him treat you? Give several reasons for your answer.

2. Everything the reception clerk said and did seemed to rub Doc Mellhorn the wrong way. Doc couldn't just say why he disliked him, but he knew that he did. Describe the clerk's personality. Why would such a person irritate Doc Mellhorn? How do *you* feel about people like the clerk?

3. As Doc was driving back toward the Gates, he began to reflect on his life as a doctor. How did he feel about the work he had done? Do you think he was being fair with himself? Explain.

4. Uncle Frank mentioned the visit of a delegation. Why did they come to welcome Doc Mellhorn? In what way was Doc's behavior at this time just what you expected of him?

5. Write a paragraph in which you sum up the things which Doc Mellhorn valued. Do you think that his values helped to make him a better doctor? Explain why.

6. Old-fashioned family doctors like Doc Mellhorn are gradually becoming extinct. What are the gains and losses in the present system of specialization?

The writer's craft . . .

The setting for this story was unusual to say the least. Yet Stephen Vincent Benét made the story believable by including common, everyday details.

1. Look again at the part in which Doc Mellhorn talked with the reception clerk. What details helped to make this scene seem real?

2. The characters, too, made the story believable. Even though everyone was dead, each person behaved in a natural, lifelike way and had a distinct personality. Select one character and explain how his personality made the story believable.

3. Did you enjoy the story more because Benét made the characters and setting seem true-to-life? Give several reasons to support your answer.

Knowing words . . .

To get the most enjoyment from Doc Mellhorn's personality you have to understand the words which Stephen Vincent Benét used to describe him. When Benét wrote, "I've heard people call him a pigheaded, obstinate old mule," did you know the meaning of *obstinate*? What clues to its meaning did the context supply? Explain the meaning of *obstinate*. Do you think that Doc Mellhorn was obstinate? Why, or why not?

At one point in the story Doc Mellhorn referred to himself as a "pigheaded, opinionated, ineffective old imbecile." What does each of these words mean? Was Doc really all these things? Why do you think he referred to himself in this particular way?

Abou Ben Adhem

Abou Ben Adhem (may his tribe increase!)
Awoke one night from a deep dream of peace,
And saw, within the moonlight in his room,
Making it rich, and like a lily in bloom,
An angel writing in a book of gold:—
Exceeding peace had made Ben Adhem bold,
And to the Presence in the room he said,
"What writest thou?"—The vision raised its head,
And with a look made of all sweet accord,
Answered, "The names of those who love the Lord."
"And is mine one?" said Abou. "Nay, not so,"
Replied the Angel. Abou spoke more low,
But cheerly still; and said, "I pray thee, then,
Write me as one that loves his fellow-men."

The angel wrote, and vanished. The next night
It came again with a great wakening light,
And showed the names whom love of God had blessed,
And lo! Ben Adhem's name led all the rest.

Leigh Hunt

Terror at Daybreak

PAUL HORGAN

No family in town was better known or better liked than the Pollocks.
It was hard to imagine they could ever change. Then, early one morning,
a tragic accident broke the quiet security of their family life.

East of town about a dozen miles ran the river. To a place near its edge before dawn on Saturday came Mr. Pollock and his younger son, Madison, accompanied by their dog, Punch. It was a cold morning in autumn. The boy was hardly awake yet. His father had to nudge him to get a move on and climb out of the car when they stopped in a clump of rust-brown salt cedar at the end of the sandy road Mr. Pollock knew about. For years it had brought him from the paved highway and through the low dunes of sand and clay to his favorite spot for duck hunting.

Madison left the car, carrying his own new shotgun. Over his bony little shoulder was slung his canvas bag for shells. In the darkness the air tasted like snow. As they moved forward to walk beside the river to Mr. Pollock's favorite blind, the father did not have to tell Madison to be as quiet as possible. He wasted no words, but merely gave by example a lesson in the caution and delicacy of how to move when there were surely ducks out on the river. Punch, an elderly rat-tailed spaniel, went heavily but silently on the sand, pausing at intervals to be sure the others were following.

As they came between two huge clumps of salt cedar that rattled in the faint cold wind before daylight, Mr. Pollock halted and held his freezing fist by his ear. Madison could just see him. The gesture said, "Listen!"

Madison turned his head and held his breath.

Then, yes, how could his father ever have heard it, it was so faint, but now he could hear it too—the reedy, murmurous sound of ducks disturbed and talking over there, out of sight under the high carved clay banks of the red Pecos River earth.

The boy's heart began to pound. He loved his father for this experience. They stood shivering in the graying dark until there was no more sleepy music from the hidden water. Then they walked carefully up the river, keeping away from the bank until Mr. Pollock found the shallow dirt canyon which led to his favorite blind. They entered into it, a miniature wilderness choked with brittle weeds which grew from dry alkaline earth. Nearing the river, they began to walk in mud and marshy water. The bank rose before them a little, making a small peninsula screened at the

547

edge by a spare rank of young willows. Here was the place. They knelt down on the cold sand and allowed the day to come.

It was now not far off.

Though nobody knew it, Mr. Pollock came for this as much as for anything else. In the spectacle of the natural world he found his poetry, his music, his art gallery. This was his culture, and what it meant to him he had no way to tell, except through example, for the benefit of his sons. All his feelings were buried, anyhow. He was a short, heavy man who walked leaning backward, to carry his weight evenly. He was a director of the local bank and the manager of a building-and-loan association. During business hours he was a leading citizen of Main Street. Many people felt about him as they would about a doctor, for he knew and helped with serious problems in their families which had to do with the possession and safety of their homes. Under his low hat brim his large light eyes saw everything and betrayed nothing. His mouth was small in his big face, and habitually he said little, but when he spoke, he was believed.

Wherever the town showed its composite mind or strength, you'd see a Pollock. If Mr. Pollock would sit on platforms as a silent endorsement of civic desires or ambitions, his wife was likely to be one of the speakers. She did not speak with skill, for her voice was loud and harsh, somehow inappropriate to her small size; but everyone was always impressed as she struggled to bend the public will to her personal belief. She governed her family in much the same way, overwhelming them with her anxious vitality, which was a happy joke among them all until in some issue she yielded to the tears that always seemed to lie in waiting behind her pinch-nose eyeglasses which trembled before her face. But she was as apt to weep for happiness and her good for-

tune in such a kind, sober husband and in two such wonderful boys, as she was out of vexation or "just nerves."

The parents embraced so completely their station in middle life that it was hard to imagine either of them as ever having been boy and girl. Especially was this impossible for their sons to do. It was as though Mr. and Mrs. Pollock had ceded to their young all graces of person and fiber, and were content to lose those beauties which had once served their mindless purpose in the founding of the family, whose sons now contained the future's desires.

Living life again through their sons, Mr. and Mrs. Pollock knew the elders' eternal wonderment about their children: *They may be bright, but are they good?*

Edwin was eighteen, his brother Madison twelve. Both were already taller than their parents, and far more communicative than the father. Give either of the boys something to take part in, and, according to their ages, they would fling themselves into it, and pretty soon end up in charge of it. Edwin was a great local athlete. He was also an honor man in high-school studies. Boys and girls alike admired him as a terrible cynic, and the yearbook in his senior year said that if you ever wanted a shock, just ask Edwin Pollock for his honest opinion of anything. But it added that he always grinned when he gave it, which accounted for all the "broken hearts" he left scattered around him. So tribute was already paid in pathetic and heartfelt ways to Edwin's powers of comeliness, strength and warmth in life. He was a junior public figure in the small city, and was loved most of all because he never seemed to know it.

Now, before going to college, he was taking a year to learn the value of a dollar —his father's favorite words—by selling farm-implement machinery up and down Pecos Valley, which lay fertile and prosperous in the wilderness of dry plains all around, graced by the far-distant lift, loom and daylong change of the southernmost Rocky Mountains.

Madison Pollock at twelve had the energy and the laughable daring of a half-grown cat. Of all the Pollocks, he was the funniest and the most high-spirited. He loved to show off, knowing exactly how to make people take delight in his antics. He, too, was a good student, and he had a few pygmy enemies because he seemed to have been born with all the schoolbooks in his head, for he never studied, or said he didn't. He probably didn't. He was as excitable as his mother, but, unlike her, he made more than evasions come of his excitements, whether in play, work or mischief. He was the only blond Pollock. His eyes were dark blue, his cheeks a furious dusty pink, and his whole self, no matter what he did, seemed always to look dry and clean.

The last member of the Pollock Family was Punch, the spaniel, who was an actual character because they had all put their characters into him ever since his puppy-dom. Now, in his privileged later life, Punch was a leading citizen of the alleys of town, and with his mornings to himself, he made his daily tour of inspection and gluttony along the back yards of countless friends. They would hear him coming, with his collar chain and tags tinkling to his heavy trot, and would know that this day, like all the others, would pursue its reassuring course, under the great sky whose light, beating upon houses, and streets, and highways squared to the points of the compass, and plains, and the long river, could show everything except what the future would bring.

2.

Waiting for daylight by the river, Mr.

Pollock and Madison shivered companionably. Behind them rose the escarpment [1] of the river's eastern bluffs in cold shadow. But they could see the edge of the sky line now, outlined by a faint lift of pearly light.

Before them across the river reached the great plain still held in night. A few far lights showed sweetly and steadily where the town was, and every half minute the faraway beacon of the airport swept suddenly out of the darkness, showing now a white light, and next time a jeweled green. Madison knew exactly where it was, twelve miles away. He admired it and in half-thought wished it were his, for it was pretty, and perhaps it did belong to him, if he said so.

As still as the rest of the river world, they waited. But they waited in growing excitement, for over and about them proceeded the immense arrival of the day. It seemed to start slowly, but vast events as they watched, happened more quickly, and the light gained behind them, and turned to the color of embers, and in the dome of the sky came a smoky blue, and then the western sky showed a pale rose against which the curved shadow of the sleeping earth swept a dying image. Little clouds that were lost in the dark now came to show like wisps of flame in the east. What was that now, on the endless western horizon? The rosy light came down, dispelling the blue earth shadow, and struck the tips of the mountains which so remotely faced the coming sun.

How was this? Before the sun was up, its light rested across the world on the rocky faces of the mountains and made them show great sweeps of stone, as though heat and light were within them. A green glow filtered into the sky and far-off irrigation canals picked up the reflection and made ribbons of silver and green in the

---
[1] *escarpment,* cliff

hazy ground. It suddenly seemed colder. Madison hugged himself around his gun. The grand vision before them arose in their spirits, too, and their faces were open with the wonder and promise of this splendor. All this was what Mr. Pollock meant and said nothing about. His greatest moment was still to come, and nothing must destroy it.

Down the distant mountains crept the growing light, until soon there was a blade of golden light cutting across the whole plain at the mountain base, and behind the escarpment to the east blazed visible rays of glory as the sun showed itself at last, tearing the long quiet horizon clouds into silken rags of fire.

Just then another sense than sight joined in the tremendous arrival, and the air was filled from everywhere with sound as startling as the vision which grew and grew and spilled over the world. Up from the black lazy water rose the birds in salute to the sunrise. Their wings beat and beat until they seemed to beat on the very ear itself. Their calls made a chorus that veered and varied like the wind. The hard stout birds seemed to hurl themselves at the day. They wheeled and shuttered, stirring like a strike of life itself, and went off to taste the sky.

Madison was half standing in the big commotion of all nature. His empty gun was raised. His father reached up and pulled him down again. They could now see everything. Mr. Pollock's face betrayed nothing of the high achievement of feeling which the dawn flight had brought him.

"They'll come back and settle down again," he said in his mild, grainy voice, "if we keep still."

Madison subsided. He swallowed. As thoughtlessly as a duck, he himself had saluted the day, out of an excitement older than memory, and a recognition of glory as near as his impassive father.

The light was now drawing eastward across the plains, and the airport beacon seemed to dwindle. Farmhouses began to show, little cubicles poured with gold. Trees stood plain. Green fields of winter wheat looked out of the receding twilight. In a few moments there would be no mystery, no startling grandeur, but only daytime, and a forgotten sun climbing overhead showing, common, the red rocks of the cliffs, the endless sweep of the plains, the smoke-defined town, and the mountains with their faint hovering clouds.

3.

The ducks returned. Madison saw them before he heard them, little twinkling specks of black that moved together against the dove-wing colors of the northern sky. Then came their sound again, from everywhere, as though a cloud could be heard.

Mr. Pollock nodded and silently thrust two shells into his gun and then closed it.

Madison copied him, watching his father now, instead of the flight, which came staggering yet orderly on the beaten air. Punch quivered, his nose lifted to the sky.

Mr. Pollock gave Madison a half look and raised his gun in a trial sight. Then he indicated that if the birds came over them and started to settle on the river beyond the willows, they would shoot.

The river was chocolate brown, shallow, snaking its way around mudbanks of the same color which gave off a rich smell.

Here they came, growing specks along the silver reflection of the gun barrels, with silver streaks in the sky beyond. The air drummed. All sound vanished and only sight was left, tense, as the guns made their arcs with the circle and swift descent of the ducks.

Then, by a common power of agreement, they both fired. The shots broke the whole adventure in stunning strike, and dawn, and boy, and father, and sky life, and river world, blazed into an instant of ringing silence.

The flight struck upward again from the waiting water, and were gone beyond speed. But three fell, and they saw them, and they knew where—heavy black bullets with ragged wings from which a few feathers drifted separately so long after.

Madison jumped to his feet. He was charged with love for the birds he had helped to kill. All huntsmen from before his own small lifetime stirred in him. His teeth chattered with mindless power and memory.

But his father showed him in silent example how to break his gun and lay it for safety's sake on the ground, and lovingly, because of its exciting oily smell, its sweet smooth wood, its power of compressed dominion over living things. With a hand on Punch, Mr. Pollock led the way through the little willow brake to the shallow water and beyond, where their game lay on the long mudbank in midstream.

Madison's belly felt full to bursting with joy. He ached with longing for even more happiness. He wished his brother Edwin could see him now. He wanted to be like Edwin in every way—his body, his style, his mind and his famous cynicism. He felt like Edwin right now, having killed some ducks out of the sky, and as he walked he spread his legs somewhat as Edwin did, walking, and made a rather hard-boiled expression on his face, looking ahead. This was more like it. None of that childish excitement. Madison retrenched his spirit, and did his best to seem offhand; the master of his gun, and of his power to kill, and provide.

4.

Later they moved downstream. They had chances to shoot three more times, and did their best, before Mr. Pollock said that they'd better think about getting back, as he intended to be at his office by ten o'clock, where there was other quarry to size up and bring to terms. He had his canvas pouch pockets full of birds whose blood smelled like marsh weeds, and whose inert weight bumped against his stride with the majestic bother of all trophies.

Madison carried three ducks by hand. They were, it was agreed, his first three. There was still enough baby in him to want to hold them forever, just as they were, just as he had made them, with their tiny head and neck feathering of green and blue fire, their stripes of white, black and brown, their leathery bills, their dear death. Punch was allowed to carry one bird in his important jaws. He almost pranced in slow dignity as they all returned down the river to the hidden car. All three of them felt the same feelings.

Mr. Pollock unlocked the car and opened the back door on the left side. The back seat was covered by heavy brown wrapping paper—Mrs. Pollock's contribution to the good sense and economy of the expedition. There they put down their bleeding ducks.

This was about nine o'clock. There were no mysteries left in the day. True, it was turning a little colder, for low gray clouds were unfolding from the east. But everything stood clear and simple, so far just like another day.

"Mad, you take the guns and put them in the car," said Mr. Pollock. "I counted one more duck that we knocked down last time. I'll take Punch and go back and find him. You wait here, so's I won't have to lock up the car all over again."

All of this seemed reasonable to Madison except the claim of another duck. He hadn't seen an extra one fall. He'd have seen it, he'd been watching, he said to himself.

But one thing that was never done was to question the father—aloud anyhow. He took Mr. Pollock's gun, which was left open at the break, and empty of shells. He saw the man and the dog trudge off. He went around the car to the other side and opened the front door. There he hurriedly put the two shotguns on the seat, side by side, making the same angle with their open chambers and barrels, muzzles outward. He shut the door on them with a vague feeling of forgetting something, but it seemed more desirable at the moment to get around to the other side of the car in a hurry, in order to watch the progress of the retrievers. He could tell where they were. Mr. Pollock and Punch rattled and cracked through the tall reeds up the river. There were a few pauses, way up there, while the father would halt and reconstruct the angles of flight, sight, fire and fall. Then the search would continue. Finally Punch gave out his wheezing bark, at the very instant Madison was saying to himself, *They'll never find it, because there isn't one.*

Presently the two others reappeared from the blurred brown ranks of weeds and walked patiently back toward the car. Punch carried in his proudly lifted jaws one more dead duck.

Well, sure enough.

But Mr. Pollock was short about his triumph. He had a good eye, a faithful sense of numbers, and a lifelong principle of collecting what was due to him. He simply trusted these faculties. Impervious to compliments, he took the duck from Punch, and leaning somewhat backward, walked heavily around the car to the right side and opened the front door to see where the shotguns were.

So it was that everybody else came to find out where Madison had put the guns, and how. Madison's gun was released by the opening of the car door, and slid along the mohair covering of the seat toward the floor of the car. It struck with force. The breech closed as the butt thumped on the floor, and what Madison had half-forgotten then took effect. He had not removed the shells from his gun. The impact of the gun stock on the floor jarred the gun sharply.

One barrel fired.

Madison was right there, for he had come around the car to watch, and finally to take his place on the front seat.

That flash of color and sound—what did it do—go off?

The duck fell from Mr. Pollock's hand. It trailed a trifle of slimy blood on the dried mud earth. Mr. Pollock bent forward and made a long agonized sound of groan on the word, "Oh-h-h," and fell down, bleeding, too, slowly, until he was humped leaning against the car with his arms around his middle, his head forced back and his eyes closing from the lower lids up, slowly, shutting out the light of the sky and the mind, both.

5.

He was alone with his younger son and his weight of authority now passed to the boy. Madison, as if he were being watched by a host of people, pursed his lips and pinched them with his fingers, and said, nearly aloud, "Now let's see."

But his heart was banging with sick hurry in him, and choking him in the throat. He wanted to talk to his father, but his father was gone, for the time being—he could see that—and he was afraid to reach him, for he knew whose fault it was that Mr. Pollock lay there like something else, after that ringing explosion and the sudden strike of dream.

He knelt down and put his stalky arms under Mr. Pollock's shoulders, thinking to lift him into the car. He could not budge him.

Maybe it would kill him to move him, anyway—echoing the Red Cross lessons in first aid they had learned in school during the war.

Plans occurred to him. Perhaps if he waited a little while, Mr. Pollock would wake up refreshed from a little nap, and they would get into the car and go back to town, and he and Edwin would clean the ducks in the back yard, and, yum-yum, mom would cook them, with an apple and onion inside each one. Or perhaps Dr. Dave Sessions would come by here duck hunting, and operate at once, with the heroic assistance of young Madison Pollock, who also happened to be there.

Or perhaps he, too, would simply die. He closed his eyes to feel how this would be. When he opened them again, he was crying and fully aware of what he had done.

As reality returned to him, he came into himself and saw what he must do. He managed inch by inch to move his father down to earth from the side of the car. Mr. Pollock was breathing wetly. He seemed to shake his head blindly at Madison as the boy moved him. Now the car was free.

Madison put Punch on guard. The dog looked hungrily after the boy, but stayed where he was meant to be, beside his still master. Madison got into the car, and remembered the few times he had stolen rides alone in it, against every law of the household: no boy of twelve should be allowed to drive, think what could happen— and all the rest of Mrs. Pollock's timeless obedience to the whimpering gods of worry.

He pinched his lips and again said, "Now let's see," as he rehearsed the technique of driving. He started the engine, put the gear into reverse and let the clutch go, but too suddenly. The car leaped backward and then stopped, for he stalled the engine with too much gas. He started over again, this time swinging in a wide arc to turn around and head for the highway over the sand dunes, whose profiles were now blurred by the play of a low hard wind which had come up. Just before he drove forward, Madison glanced back fearfully to see if perhaps his father would sharply call to him, asking, "Where do you think you're going with that car? You know you are not supposed to drive it."

But there was no such threat, and he whined along in second gear, swaying with the lift and boggle of the car over the uneven road. On the back seat, the inert necks and heads of the dead ducks rolled from side to side in little arcs. Mrs. Pollock's brown paper was moist and stained in places.

When he reached the highway, he stopped the car just off the paving on the shoulder of the road. He sat there, numb, for a little while, as three or four cars went flashing by.

Now let's see. What would he have to say if he stopped someone? How could he ever say it? He hoped nobody would stop.

He looked both ways. The highway was now empty as far as he could see. His heart fell with pity and relief, even as he licked his dry mouth in a panic of disgust over his great betrayal.

But here came a car, way up at the crest of the cliff, where, in a deep cut, the highway took its course toward the sky, and found its level to cross the great wilderness which led to West Texas and beyond. The car came fast down the long slope toward the bridge.

Inviting his own doom, Madison got out and stepped into the near lane. Long before he could see the driver he began to wave his arms. He ended by leaping off the ground a few times. He never realized that he did this.

The driver began to slacken his speed, and when he saw that this was a boy, he slammed on the brakes, as he said afterward, and did not overshoot the mark very far. Something told him before he stopped that here was bad trouble, which spoke so

powerfully through that young, jumping figure alone in that big spread of country. The boy did not come to him, so he left his own car and walked back to find young Madison Pollock, with his teeth chattering and his right arm pointing off up the river and trying to tell.

"What's it, son?" asked the driver. He was Tim Motherwell, of the Soil Conservation Service. It was lucky he came along. He was a young man in whom the outdoors had reposed its secrets and its ways during all his life. At ease with the natural world, Tim was one of those who could wring an essential note of goodness, or hope, or respect out of people at their worst. He squatted down before Madison and began to chew on a match, not looking at him, but musing in his presence as though they were two men with all the time in the world to decide or exchange something important. He had noticed blood on the boy's field jacket. What might have put it there he was already imagining, when Madison managed to tell him what lay up the sandy road by the river, and what was needed.

Tim nodded mildly, but he lost no time. He pulled his weathered green Government pickup truck well off the highway, where it was a familiar sight, and returned to Mr. Pollock's car. He drove Madison back up the river. As they went, Madison tried to tell him how it had happened.

"I did it," he kept repeating.

"We'll see," Tim replied, and wondered, like so many people in the next few days, what could ever reclaim this boy from this morning.

Madison was awry in every possible way. His thick yellow hair was tangled and upright, resembling the strawlike weeds by the river. His face was white generally, but even so, square patches of dusky-peach red tried to show on his cheekbones. His

eyes were wild. He kept trying to put his hands on his round young thighs in composure, but they would not stay there, but would spring up in the air as though moved by counterweights.

"About there?" asked Tim, pointing to the terminal clumps of salt cedar which at last they could see.

Madison nodded.

In a moment they came to a halt and got out of the car. Punch was there, trembling with fear and strangeness, and stood up to greet them with a high, stifled yawp. He cringed in an agony of humble love, but did not leave his post. They came forward and Tim bent down. Almost at once he saw that the father was dead.

They got to town as soon as they could manage, and in ten minutes the news was everywhere.

6.

If people did not say it aloud, they spoke plainly with their eyes. "Oh, that poor boy! He will never get over this for the rest of his life!"

In everybody's face, Madison read, "That is the boy who killed his father," and somehow a buried mythic purpose stirred in those who looked at him or talked about him; and awe was mingled with their pity, and guilt with their forgiveness.

After the three days—the rest of Saturday, all day Sunday, until Monday afternoon, when the funeral was held—Madison Pollock was in danger. Edwin knew it. The boy's teeth would chatter suddenly and for no immediate reason. By turns he longed to be with his mother, and could not bear facing her. "My baby," she would sob, smothering him with crushing sympathy. And then again, she would have hours during which she would exile him in silent grief and widowhood. He was afraid most of all that Edwin would not like him any more for what he had done. He spent hours awake at night breaking his will on terrible schemes to make everything up to everybody. But an imp of maturity abided in him, and told him how useless were these waking dreams. He must shrink even from them.

Tuesday morning he did not want to go back to school, giving as his reason that someone had let the air out of his bicycle tires. Edwin went to see, and it was true. The brothers looked at each other, both knowing who had done it. They did not discuss it. Instead, Edwin drove Madison over to school in the car, but he could not make him get out of the car and fall in with the tumbling boys who played touch football on the pale Bermuda grass of the playfield.

"One of these days, you know, Mad," said Edwin, meaning that he'd have to start school again sooner or later.

Madison shook his head. "Never. I can't."

"You can't?"

"Nope."

"Why not?"

Madison shrugged. He didn't know.

"How about trying, say just the first period?" asked Edwin. "I'll promise to be here when the bell rings after the first period, and if you still want to then, I'll let you out of it."

Madison shook his head.

"Well, then, what do you want to do?"

"Nothing."

The brothers sat in silence, staring straight ahead through the windshield while Edwin played a little jazzy tune on his teeth with his thumbnail. A couple of boys spotted the car and ran over to get Madison, calling his name.

Madison crouched down and said hoarsely, "Come on, come on. Let's go, let's go."

Edwin drove off. The other boys watched after them, and then one of them went loose on his legs, pointed a forefinger at the crown of his own head, made his eyes cross, and hung out his tongue, enacting the goofiness of what had just happened. Then they went back to the game of touch football.

Without further discussion, Edwin simply let Maddy stay with him that day, in the front seat of the car, as he went on his business calls down the valley in the interest of selling farm implements and checking up on servicing those already sold. This made an idle and drowsy day for Madison, and when it was over, and they were home for supper, he was ready to go to bed early.

It was barely half past seven when someone drifted with heavily shod steps up on the wooden porch and, unable to find the bell button in the dark, knocked once or twice on the beveled plate-glass pane of the front door.

Mrs. Pollock pressed her cheeks with both hands and silently gasped that she could not stand another trial of any sort. Edwin caressed her shoulder and went to see. He put on the porch light and could see through the white net curtain inside the glass that a familiar figure stood there, slowly spinning his fawn-colored felt hat on his forefinger. It was Tim Motherwell, offhand and mild, but a champion of life in its possible small daily acts.

He came in and shook hands, saying that he just happened to be driving up this street, and thought of looking in for a second, to see if there was anything he could do, and to tell Mrs. Pollock that he certainly felt for her. At this, she raised her head with a hazy social smile conforming to the best of manners, as though to say that people like her should not inflict their misfortunes upon others, but the imposture lasted only a moment before her little face with its passionately trembling eye lenses appeared to dissolve like molten glass changing to another set of shapes, and she lay back in her chair, subject to the grief that pounded upon her from without, and made her say in a choked treble like a child's, that she did not know how she could go on living.

Edwin asked Tim to sit down, which he declined to do. In a minute or two, Mrs. Pollock recovered enough to ask Edwin to show Tim the messages of sympathy they had received, and the long list of those who had sent flowers. Tim examined these gravely, still standing, while the widow watched him hungrily for signs of dolorous pride in the tribute paid to the stricken family. With his mouth shaped for silent, musing whistling, Tim read what people thought and said about Mr. Pollock, and gave the papers back to Edwin without a word, but with a black sparkling look in his eyes which was like thought itself made manifest. It satisfied Mrs. Pollock. She covered her eyes and wept again. Edwin felt ashamed of her, and then, for feeling so, ashamed of himself.

Well, he had to be going, said Tim. Edwin went out to the pickup truck with him, and the real purpose of the call became clear. They talked for about fifteen minutes, Tim at the wheel, Edwin leaning his chin on his fists on the open window sill of the car. Their conversation was muted and serious. Tim felt younger, Edwin felt older, and both felt like good men, assembled in honor of what needed to be done for someone—in this case, Madison Pollock.

Edwin said, yes, his brother was in a bad way, and said something had to be worked out. Tim said he suspected as much, and with modesty and diffidence

told what he would do about it if it were his kid brother. Their conversation had many gaps of words, but not of thought.

When the essential matter was finished, there was a long terminal pause, after which Tim, where he sat, jumped comically, as though he felt an electric shock, and said, "I'd better get a move on or my little woman won't act so little, time I get there. See you, Ed."

"See you, Tim. Sure do thank you."

Tim switched on his car lights and drove off. Edwin watched him round the next corner. The red tail light on the SCS truck spoke for Tim as long as Edwin could see it, admire it and covet the goodly strength it stood for.

7.

The next morning, Mrs. Pollock, in the name of what dad would have wanted, declared that this time Madison must go to school, and ordered Edwin to drive him there again.

Madison turned white. "No. I can't."

"Yes, you can. Oh, what have I done to deserve— You know how your father slaved to give you boys a good education, and now, here you sit, and won't—"

Madison left the table and went to the back yard. There he was violently sick at his stomach. Edwin found him there, shuddering on the back steps like a starving cat.

"Come on, Maddy," he said, and practically dragged the boy to the car. They drove off, heading south toward the school. Madison set his jaws and braced his feet against the floor boards the closer they came to the red-bricked school building, but Edwin, without a glance, drove right on past the teeming block of the school and its winter-blanched playing field, and continued on south and out of town down the valley.

"I'd gain his confidence," Tim had said. "I wouldn't hurry."

So once again—this time defying the suffering authority at home—Edwin took his brother with him, and did the same all the rest of the week. The brothers were together all day long. They visited farms in the broad flat valley, and while Edwin talked business, Madison was let alone just to fool around. They spent one afternoon tinkering with an ailing tractor. One evening they lingered with a little crowd of itinerant cotton pickers who had a bonfire going under some cottonwoods by an irrigation ditch; and to guitar music, clapped hands and country song, the illimitable twilight came down like forgiveness—for a little while—over Madison and everyone in the world. Sometimes Edwin took him along to have a glass of beer, though Mad drank only soda. Another time they called on a girl Edwin knew in the little town of Dexter, and the conversation, full of evocative memories and half-suggested plans for the creation of more such, brought Madison a wondering sense of more trouble, sweeter than his awful kind.

And then on Saturday—one week after Madison's first time out hunting—Edwin, having made a few preparations in private, got up at four in the morning and went in his shivering nakedness to Maddy's sleeping porch and woke him up, turning on the light and picking up scattered garments off the floor.

"Come on, get up," he said.

Madison was stunned with sleep. "What for?"

"Never mind what for. Get up. Come on. I've got your clothes. We can dress in the living room, where it's warm. Be quiet. Don't wake mom. Turn out the light."

The boy followed his brother. In the front room they got dressed stealthily. It was exciting.

"Where're we going?"

"Never you mind. Come on. We'll get some breakfast downtown."

Edwin was dressed first. Waiting for Maddy, he sat down at the dining-room table, which bore marks on its brown oak surface of a strenuous life, and wrote a note which Mrs. Pollock told everybody later she would keep forever.

"Dear mom," it said, "don't worry. Mad and I have gone off on a job. Back during the day. Taking Punch along for the buggy ride. Be a good girl and don't worry. Love and kisses. E."

He propped it up against the crystal fruit bowl in the center of the table, where she would easily find it, for the bowl held her darning materials and her glasses. He knew, too, that when she came to his fond, impudent advice to be a good girl, she, in whom there remained no degree of girl whatever, would weep over it with famished pride, to see that the power of the family had passed to him, the first-born, now escaped into his own life. It was not cruel to make her weep. It was almost a kindness, for she enjoyed it so, and in these days it gave her solace to feel anything but the main dream of her shocking loss.

The boys went gently out the front door, and around to the back yard to Punch's house, which they had built together so long ago. One of the family mysteries was that they had never caught Punch asleep out there. He knew them now as they approached, and mildly banged his ugly rat tail on the floor of his residence.

"Come on, Punch, old boy, old boy," said Edwin softly. The self-important old dog got up slowly and stretched himself, sagging luxuriously, first fore and then aft. And then with a prankish lunge he assumed the gaiety of a puppy, but could not sustain it, and soberly followed his masters to their car, which was parked in the alley. Edwin unlocked it, they all got in, and Edwin drove off. The night was black and empty in the cold streets of town.

They had coffee, canned orange juice and ham and eggs in Charlie the Greek's, without conversation, though not without communication, for Edwin could feel Maddy throbbing beside him with doubtful wonder. Edwin once turned on his swiveled stool to face Madison and cuff him near the ear—an action which said that he was not to worry, or be afraid, or in doubt, for this was still the family, doing its best for him, no matter how things might look; indeed, if they became too much for anyone to bear, never mind; there was someone right here who would stop everything before that point was reached.

It was still pitch dark when they went out and drove off again. They crossed Main Street, whose neon signs and traffic lights were dead, and headed out toward the east, where the road forked to go either down the valley or out to the river over the bluffs to West Texas.

Madison looked sidewise to question his brother, who drove. Edwin, though he felt the look, did not acknowledge it, but merely drove on in general confidence and repose.

At the crossroads they were slowed down by a traffic light which blinked all night long. Madison looked to the right, along the highway which would take them on one of their familiar days of salesmanship at the valley farms. But Edwin, resuming high gear, drove straight ahead on the other highway, which led to the river. Maddy's teeth began to chatter.

The first pale strips of day now showed ahead of them in the east. Suddenly, as though between looks, it was there. With it came a colder feeling. Edwin speeded up as though to race the dawn.

Maddy saw the highway unreel before

and under him. Where were they going? He put his hand on the door handle beside him with an unformed notion that he might open the door and, speed or no speed, get out right now. Why not? Edwin caught this out of the corner of his eye in the half-light of the instrument panel. He began to whistle a little tune inside his teeth, leaned over and snapped the door handle up to a locked position. Again it was an action which said more than it appeared to.

By the time they saw the river, its slow sparse waters were reflecting the early light in the midst of heavy shade over the earth. The watery course in the black nearing distance lay like shining silver knives, curved and jagged. They were driving fast.

Maddy, in terror, both did and did not believe it when the family car slowed down at the far end of the Pecos River bridge and took the sandy turnoff of the road that ran over the dunes, in the same darkness, by the same willows, in the same cold, to the same screen of salt cedars as a week ago this morning.

8.

Edwin stopped the car and got out. He opened the rear door for Punch, who scrambled forth with his head lifted amid the marshy smells on the faintly stirring air. At the luggage compartment, Edwin unlocked the handle and flung open the lid. He took out two shotguns, a canvas musette bag full of shells, and two pairs of rubber boots.

"Come on, Mad!" he called.

The front door opened and Madison stepped out, against his wish.

Edwin threw Maddy's boots to him. "Put them on."

"What for?"

"Put them on."

Everything was greater than Maddy. He

was overwhelmed. He was numb, inside and out. He put the boots on.

Edwin handed him his own gun.

"No."

"Take it. Go on. We're going to get some ducks."

Madison took it. He could hardly feel it in his grasp.

Edwin led the way up the river to the blind where, long ago, he, too, had come with his father. The day was nearing. Again, sky, mountain, plain and earth's own curve evolved toward the moment of glory and revelation.

Once again not only all light but all sound and all space beat upon the senses when the sun rose. The ducks were there again. They fled the shadows and streaked noisily into the lofty light. Like his father, Edwin stayed their fire at the dawn flight. The birds would return. To be ready—

"Load," said Edwin.

Madison fumbled with his gun. He could not handle it. Edwin took it from him and loaded it, closed it, which cocked it, and handed it back.

"You take the first one, Mad."

They waited. The older brother set his jaws. He knew what he was doing, and the pain he was causing.

Presently the birds were coming over again. Edwin pointed. Madison saw only a dazzle of flying black specks in the yellowing day.

"Now," whispered Edwin.

Madison raised his gun and tried to sight, leading the flight, which seemed everywhere. He was shaking. He fired alone. Nothing fell. He brought down his gun. His head was ringing. He looked at Edwin.

"Tough," said Edwin.

Madison thrust his gun at Edwin for him to take. "Let me go," he said in pitiful modesty.

Edwin shook his head and pushed the gun back in his brother's grasp. "You'll do better next time."

"I will?"

"Sure."

Edwin, whistling silently, turned his gaze over the sky.

What? thought Madison. And then this was astounding: powerfully like a wind, free and lofting, the idea blew through him, and he thought, *Of course I will.* He looked at Edwin to find an explanation of the excitement which spread so fast in his being. But Edwin was immovable, watching the lower reaches of the sky.

"I will get some next time," whispered Madison. "I got three last Saturday, and I'll get more today."

Edwin nodded briefly. His heart began to thump with relief. Maddy's excitement could not be hidden. He could never have said so, but Edwin knew they had come here to put death in its place, and were going to succeed.

9.

They stayed two hours. Punch was busy retrieving. They got nearly the limit in ducks. Seven of them were Madison's.

It was another high gold-and-blue morning when they returned to the car.

"Do you want to drive?" asked Edwin.

"You think I can?"

"Sure."

"O.K."

"Hop in."

Madison drove all the way. His right ear was ringing from the repeated sound of the gun. He turned his head now and then to listen to the sound, as if it came from beyond him. He liked it. He forgot it.

Though nobody was aware of it, they entered their streets in triumph and drove across town and got home in safety.

Mrs. Pollock was waiting for them.

When she heard where they'd been, she steadied herself by a chair, and said to Madison, with a shudder, that she did not know how he could ever again hold a gun in his hand.

He flushed with feeling, but he grinned. Edwin wanted to shake her with fury. But he remembered what had befallen her, and he just went and held her hand, and she cried and got over it.

When he could, Edwin called up Tim Motherwell.

"How'd it go?"

"Fine. We're all O.K."

"I thought it would. But then, you never know. Glad you called me."

"Sure. I wanted to. It was pretty rough at first."

"Yes. Poor kid. Well, it was worth it."

"Surely was. Well, thanks again, Tim."

"Forget it. See you."

"O.K."

"Good-by now."

"So long."

On Monday morning, Madison Pollock went back to school on his bicycle, as usual.

The man who wrote this story

PAUL HORGAN 1903–

When Paul Horgan was eleven, he left private school in Buffalo and moved to Albuquerque, New Mexico, with his family. There he found a new and interesting world in which "the country" was always near. The main street ended in desert.

When his father died, and the family moved back to New York State, Paul Horgan kept "the country" in the back of his mind. He began to study singing, but instead of practicing, he spent his time at the Eastman Theatre. What he learned in those three intense years later proved very useful in his playwriting.

When he was offered the position of librarian at the New Mexico Military Institute, he was glad to return to Albuquerque and has lived there ever since. He wrote his first novels while working in the library and had written six before one was finally published. Today he is known primarily for his descriptions of the Southwest. His latest work, *Great River, the Rio Grande in North American History,* won a Pulitzer Prize in 1955.

Let's consider . . .

1. In the opening section of the story, Paul Horgan introduced you to each member of the Pollock family. Write a brief character sketch of each person as you knew him before the disaster.

2. After Madison put the guns in the car, he had a vague feeling of forgetting something. Explain how his forgetfulness caused the accident.

3. What thoughts and plans passed through Madison's mind after the shooting? When he gained control of himself, what steps did he take to help his father?

4. When the townspeople heard the news, they thought, "Oh, the poor boy!" Why do you think they felt pity rather than anger?

5. After the shooting, Madison refused to return to school. Why did school seem unbearable?

6. When Edwin asked Madison what he wanted to do, Madison replied, "Nothing." How does this answer reflect the boy's state of mind?

7. The Pollocks had always helped others. Now that they were in need, how did an outsider come to their aid?

8. Edwin not only took Madison back to the scene of the accident, he also made him shoot at the ducks. Explain how this experience, which seemed to be so cruel, helped Madison to overcome his fear and depression.

9. Even though Madison was responsible for his father's tragic death, why was it important that he resume the life of an ordinary twelve-year-old boy?

10. How do you know that Madison *did* become himself again?

11. Each member of the family felt a deep loss when the father died. But sorrow was not the only result of the tragedy. Explain how Mother, Edwin, and Madison were able to withstand and rise above the disaster.

The writer's craft . . .

When people talk about different writers, you often hear them say, "I like that writer's style" or "Is his style difficult to read?" **Style** is nothing more than the writer's own particular way of expressing himself.

A characteristic of Paul Horgan's style in "Terror At Daybreak" is his skill in writing vivid, colorful descriptions. Rather than merely writing that Madison and his father entered a patch of undergrowth, Paul Horgan wrote, "They entered into it, a miniature wilderness choked with brittle weeds which grew from dry alkaline earth."

1. Why is "miniature wilderness" a sharper descriptive phrase than just the word *undergrowth?*

2. What does the word *choked* suggest? In your own words describe a place that is "choked with brittle weeds."

3. What does the word *brittle* mean? How did the addition of this word help you to visualize the scene more clearly?

4. Find other illustrations of Paul Horgan's descriptive style. Read one example aloud to the class.

5. Think of a scene from your own experience which made a deep impression on you. It may have been the hills at twilight, or a city street, or the sky just before a storm. Write a description of this scene using as many vivid details as you can.

Knowing words . . .

Below are several sentences taken from the selection. Each of the sentences has one word written in italics. After you are sure of the meaning of the italicized word, use it in a sentence of your own.

1. If Mr. Pollock would sit on platforms as a silent *endorsement* of civic desires or ambitions, his wife was likely to be one of the speakers.

2. She did not speak with skill, for her voice was loud and harsh, somehow *inappropriate* to her small size.

3. Their conversation was *muted* and serious.

4. One evening they lingered with a little crowd of *itinerant* cotton pickers who had a bonfire going under some cottonwoods by an irrigation ditch.

5. And then with a prankish lunge he assumed the gaiety of a puppy, but could not *sustain* it.

The Wish Books

NEILL C. WILSON

For years, the mail-order catalogue had been only a wish book. Now Corie
could make some of those wishes come true.

A quilt for Ellie and her husband was
the first one finished. Its center was a
"Star of Bethlehem" of eight points and
many colors, with smaller stars set in the
corners. Granny was pleased to see that
the underside was stitched as neatly as the
top. Never would coverlet be prettier, or
more welcome up on Old Dad Knob where
the winds blew and Ellie and John had
their little home.

But while the quilt was still taking
shape, there was more to be heard from a
Beckett. "Corie," the needleworkers prod-
ded, "remember the party at your house
after Ellie returned from the fair?"

Yes, Corie remembered. It had brought
her vast pleasure.

"Tell us how you thought that party up."

"But it just happened."

"Well, tell how it happened."

So Corie dug back.

Corie knew that her sister was coming
home with tidings incredible and exciting.
She could hear Ellie singing and laughing
on the trail above the Beckett house—
laughing crazily, for sheer jubilee and racing downward.

Here was Ellie.

And here, after an urging and a pulling,
was the tall, shy boy. His name was John
Lee.

The way John kept worshipful eye on
Ellie, while he stood in the presence of
Mrs. Beckett and Corie, told Corie all she
needed to know. He certainly didn't think
Ellie's hair was a grab of tow,[1] or her nose
a nub, or her girl flesh a strip of thong
leather from chasing shoats up and down
hillsides. Like Corie, he considered Ellie
the most wonderful person in the world.

But when healthy, happy, home-longing,
child-craving Ellie twisted halfway around
in her skin to get at a shirt tail, and undid
the knot with trembling fingers, Corie
learned how successful the business part
of the journey also had been. One by one
Ellie laid the greenbacks on the blue and
white coverlet of Corie's bed. Seven vic-
torious oblongs of crumpled paper, with
curly Washingtons and black-bearded
Lincolns frowning out of oval frames. Ellie
explained all. How she'd won the prize,
and then sold the carving.

[1] *grab of tow*, handful of unfinished flax or hemp

Twenty-seven dollars! It was even more ready money than the Beckett household had ever seen.

Then Ellie fetched the wish book. Laid it on the coverlet beside the greenbacks.

It was almost as if she'd told Corie that she could get up and run.

That thick, frayed mail-order catalogue had been Corie's ever since she was ten, and at the moment Corie was sixteen. The book had been left behind by the Peelers when they moved west. Spangled with two thousand pictures, it was the pumpkin coach that had taken Corie on countless Cinderella journeys. Never a day but she had pored over its gray-white pages, and by their magic skimming on shining skates, swirling in taffeta, sitting before parlor organs, or doing her hair with jeweled combs and brushes.

"Now you shall pick out whatever you want, clear up to twenty-seven dollars, and it will really be yours," Ellie told her in that brand-new wood-thrush voice, and kissed Corie on the forehead.

As soon as there could be a wedding, Ellie and John Lee went away. The brave old wish book and Corie settled down to practical business. To the last musty whiff of the five-hundredth brown-edged page, Corie knew the treasures contained in that two-pound stack. But until now, Corie had been only a wisher. Now she was to be a *haver*. It thrilled and scared her. She'd studied until she knew the heft and feel of every article pictured in the book. And here she was, doing it all over again, but this time with the purchase price in her grasp. It was so important—so vastly important—to be right and to have no regrets. And it stretched out the fun.

Sometimes Ma helped. Ma took the book in her hands, which work had never managed to make unpretty, and with eyes not used to reading she looked mighty hard at the splendid glitter. She saw so much for a body to hanker for that she always ended by shutting the book with a clap. Apple corers and astrakhans [2] and arch supports, and Smyrna rugs and steel ranges! The things one could buy, if greenbacks grew on hemlocks! But the thing that counted, she vowed, and the only thing, was the fulfilling of Corie's want and wishing. That was what Ellie had whittled her fox and made her journey for. Such fortune wouldn't knock on the Becketts' door again.

Uncle Bide was another whose advice Corie sought. He came in from his grimy forge and took the book in his paws. He did his best to sort out something for Corie while keeping his eye off anvils, hoof knives and spring wagons. He liked the lady tacking down eight fluffy pads of cotton into an elastic mattress, and was strongly taken with the woven wire springs. He'd made Corie's rope and feather bed himself and knew its shortcomings.

And there was Grandsir. He stomped into the little bedroom with swamp mud on his shins and took the book onto his knee. He went past the corsets, bust pads, petticoats and hair switches as if they were porcupines getting ready to quill him, but he slowed down at the breech-loading hammerless shotguns. Grandsir had been knocking crows out of the corn with a muzzle-loader all his life. Since most of the merchandise was for people who were up and doing, like himself, he wasn't much help to Corie, but he finally lit on a magic lantern and a kit of slides of the Klondike Gold Rush and Far West, including grizzly bears and big trees. He thought she might find a peck of enjoyment in owning that.

There were the neighbors, whose opinions Corie invited whenever they dropped in. The Vaseys of Little Piney, who num-

---
[2] *astrakhans,* wool-covered skins of young lambs

bered seventeen and lived on parsnips. The fourteen Annables, up the mountain, who lived on buck and beans and anything they could borrow. The ridge-running Hardees, father and three sons, . . . The eight Cornetts, deep in the laurel, who lived on practically nothing. And Amos Toler, keeper of the Mountain Store, and his grandson Kyle. Few of these neighbors could move through the type, but not a one yielded to anybody at reading pictures.

"That's what I would git if I was you, Corie," urged Aunt Arretha Annable, pointing to a truss guaranteed to help one to sit up, if not actually walk. Levicy Vasey, tall and spare, squealed over the smooth dainty nainsook nightgowns. "If I had skin as soft as yours, Corie," said Levicy, "I'd purely want something nicer below the neck than flour sacking." And Uncle Ep Tiddany put in a powerful word for a beautiful Rest Easy fringed hammock with lay-back pillow. From end to end of the Holler, everyone rejoiced in the jackpot of pleasure and comfort that had come to Corie Beckett.

Corie worked on her list until it figured out to twenty-six dollars and ninety cents, counting shipping costs. She added seven cents for candy, allowed three for the stamp, and made out the ruled form at the back of the book. Uncle Bide, who was stretched out extra long from ax-swinging but walked with a lurch because the ax had come down wrong one time, gimped the two miles to the post office at Toler's Mountain Store. Corie hadn't figured on a money order, but old Amos Toler insisted on supplying that. It was one of the privileges of representing the United States Government at Toler's Corner, he said, and he'd be responsible for the fifteen cents himself till Congress refunded him the money.

Corie asked Uncle Bide anxiously, "How long will it take for my package to come?"

Warned Bide, "It's likely to be a right wearying spell, Corie." He knew how long it took to make a watertight bucket or a pair of gate hinges, and whatever Corie had checked off out of that wishing book would probably keep the people in Chicago a-grinding. His tone implied centuries.

It was to take even longer. It was to take until never. A letter came, addressed to Miss Corinda Beckett.

Dear Madam:

This acknowledges your recent order. There appears to be a misunderstanding. We do not stock any of the articles you mention. Is it possible you have consulted an obsolete catalogue? We are sending you our latest edition under separate cover, and enclose our check herewith for $26.97.

According to our older employees, the goods you ordered are quoted in our catalogues of approximately the McKinley era. As we have occasional calls for these old volumes for libraries, universities and motion picture studios, and our own files were destroyed in the Clark Street fire of 1904, we are willing to pay liberally for such historic relics. In exchange for your present catalogue we shall be pleased to credit you with three dollars, and we offer a reasonable sum, depending upon age and condition, for any other old issues in your possession. Assuring you of our eager desire to serve.

CHICAGO MAIL ORDER CORPORATION

"Three dollars for that old book!" exclaimed Uncle Bide. "Why, Corie, there's more of them things in the Peeler's tumbledown haymow. Maybe a dozen. I'll fotch an armful in, first thing tomorrow."

Some of the books were under a ton of rotted hay, and there were many more than he'd remembered. With cover pictures of plump-armed goddesses spilling cornucopias[3] of Turkish couches, banjos, and

---

[3] *cornucopias,* horns filled to overflowing; symbols of plenty

three-bottle breakfast casters, they ran back to the World's Fair year of 1893, and there were some in plain covers that reached to the day of the Philadelphia Centennial and the high-wheel bicycle. Bide promised to tote them to Marianboro and express them off as soon as he got a hog brined down and his apples in.

The new wish book arrived. It was a gorgeous book, and it made Corie's head whirl. Polo coats and checked velour knickers and coal-scuttle hats and pajamas and elastic girdles—the world had moved several notches. Not that those things fitted into Corie's usings. But there was a tilt-up bed with a coil-spring mattress which Uncle Bide, as soon as he'd taken in the details, grew almost church-reverent over; and a chair on wheels that the sitter could propel by a push of her own hands, only the Holler didn't have much in the way of paths to run it on; and a walking machine, made out of lightweight tubing.

So Corie studied the new book and licked her stumpy pencil. Once more, folks dropped in aplenty to give advice. They tracked Ma Beckett's sand-scrubbed floor and they helped wear out the pages.

It was a lengthy business, consuming most of the summer and fall, but Corie finally got to the end of it. Not knowing what the old books would bring exactly, she made her order list a little bulgy, and marked the extra or maybe-things with question marks. Bide filled a bushel basket with the books the Peelers had abandoned, and lashed it to his mule, and struck off for Marianboro. Corie waved good-by, with a special wave to the wish book she cherished all her girlhood. She lay back to wait.

It was the Toler boy, Kyle, who spread the word that Corie's grand return tote of mail was in sight, because for what else would a wagon be jouncing up mud on the Coal Mountain road from Marianboro? Most Holler letters, and they weren't many, came in by saddlebag.

It was the tidings the neighbors had been waiting for. They set aside fish pole and heaved aside hoe and tracked for the Beckett house, beaming their pleasure at Corie's luck and eager to see her new bed and new walking machine. They said their howdies and squeezed into the neat clapboard house, bringing tang of glen and hilltop, of clover field and cow yard. Ellie and John were there, too. They came straight down off Old Dad Knob the minute John, whose eyesights were sharp, spied all the movement around the Beckett house. Kyle Toler came in breathless and wanted to know, since Corie couldn't go to the store, could the postmaster borrow Bide's mule for the last leg of the delivery.

Corie was sitting up. She never had looked so pretty or excited. She had on a sugar-sack nightgown that smelled of sun and ironing, and she thrust a spray of rose geranium in her hair.

"Here they come!" reported Beech Trevitt from the fork of the quince tree by the gate.

The official party was advancing, sure enough. Bide had washed his mule and put a circle of yellow witch hazel blossoms around its neck. Amos Toler strode at Bide's elbow and his beard blew wide. He had his split-tail coat on, the one he'd once helped nominate Teddy Roosevelt in.

The mule slipped and slid down the leaves. He wasn't loaded near as lofty as folks had expected. The pile of him was nothing like what a wheel chair and a wove-spring bed would make. There was only a pair of barrels atop of him. When Grandsir saw those stained old barrels, he yelped some. They were his barrels. . . .

But Amos said, "Hush you fuff, Nathan," and beckoned to Felt Annable and

other strongbacks to help Bide fetch the barrels into Corie's little room.

Corie looked as pleased as a robin with a six-inch worm.

Amos, drawing his whiskers into two banners, launched himself a speech.

"Corinda Beckett," he pronounced, like he was addressing the multitudes from the steps of the Capitol at Washington, "in the name of the United States Government, whose representative I am in these parts, and in joyful defiance of postal rules and regulations, I hereby declare the Cat Track Hollow post office open for business in this room. Corie, your mail has arrove."

"I'm sorry to be so much trouble," said Corie.

"Bide, lift off the barrel heads."

They came right off.

Amos thrust a hand down. He brought out a package, small and square.

"This here matter, postmarked Chicago, has been entrusted for conveyance and delivery to Miss Levicia Vasey. Levicy, you in the room? Come forward and be identified."

Exclaimed Levicy, "Who in the Holler doesn't know me? But who in Chicago does?"

Amos fished again. "Windy Bill Vasey!"

"I served my time!" shouted Uncle Bill. "If it's papers, I ain't here!"

"Nathan Beckett."

Grandsir's jaw dropped, the way it did whenever Amos flung a ringer that knocked off his two leaners.

"Miss Aster Tiddany! . . . Catch her, boys. . . . Aster, honey, shove right under that old roarer's legs."

By this time Levicy Vasey, after inspecting all six sides of her flat parcel, smelling it, shaking it, and listening to it, had slid the string off. She prized up one corner of the wrapping and squealed.

Aster Tiddany, who was nine, wasn't making a sound. She couldn't.

"Miss Deborah Cornett!"

A young lady of Miss Aster's age wriggled through and halted, unbelieving.

"Here you are, Debbie, sweetheart. Take it away, and see if you can find your tongue when Aster does. . . . Lee Maclise!"

The floor became littered with torn paper. It lay like leaves of fall and it reached out to the side porch. People were in a stir, and cries were shrill. Among them were Lark Beckett's, Corie and Ellie's mother. She'd been handed a real big parcel with her name on it, and in it were Persian-pattern dress material, a roll of camisole lace, six pair of black stockings and twelve china dishes.

Levicy Vasey stood rigid, dumbfoundment and rapture on her plain face and a tiny nainsook bloomer combination, with elastic knees and lace bodice top, scrunched out of sight in her hands. Aster and Flax and Alyssum and Myrtle Tiddany and Debbie and Katie-Jo and Vernice and Ona Cornett hugged dolls so tightly that they almost mashed the living squeaks out of them. Aunt Effie Tiddany stood regarding a baby peach tree that had come in a pasteboard tube, and Aunt Zelda Podlaski had five or six paper packets with pictures on them of the prettiest sweet peas, violets, spice pinks and candytufts that ever snuggled a fence. And still old Amos plunged arm into barrel and brought packets out. A reel of baby dress flouncing for Aunt Poppy Maclise. A skinning knife for Kyle Toler. A sequin-covered beanie for Silvermoon Annable. An ankle brace for Granny Hite. An ocarina for Ararat Annable, who could charm the sow bugs out of a stump with his jug tootling, but had never got over an early fall on his head. And there was more, much more. A hearing tube for Uncle Tom Swisher, who was always cross because he never knew what folks were saying. A bright little silver-bead necklace for Kedron Hardee, who'd never had anything pretty in her born days. A family medicine case for Aunt Arretha Vasey that was all set for colic, colds, burns, pleurisy, nervous troubles and pimples. A bottle of something new—vitamin pills—for Aunt Belle Gunderson up on her mountain. Belle was too huge and ailing to make the long trudge down, but somebody would take it to her. A baseball for Beech Trevitt and a bat for Norv Cornett; an Ivorette comb and brush for Travis Swisher, and a pair of sparkling side combs for Esther Podlaski.

For Uncle Bide there was nothing but an envelope with a bill of lading. But the lading notice was of a three-horsepower gasoline engine waiting for him at the Marianboro freight depot.

A ten-power, thirteen-inch telescope for John Lee, and a set of carving chisels.

For Ellie, who'd tramped through rain and over mountains to the fair to start all this, a red wool-flannel jacket, whipcord knickers, two pairs of thick gray stockings, and a folding knife with four blades.

For others there were paint boxes, mouth organs, hair clips. There were turkey bells, team bells, dehorning clippers, hog-ringing tools, oxhorn balls, and hoof trimmers. For Postmaster Toler there was a porch thermometer and a cold weather cap. Sixty-one packages in all, including one for Bide's mule. He got a sweat pad.

"Bust my bones," breathed Grandsir, standing in his new Storm King rubber boots and h'isting and lowering his double-barreled blue-steel hammerless shotgun and rubbing his hand over the sleek stock.

There was still another package for Grandsir. It contained a warm woolen union suit. "Horse-high, pig-tight, and bull-strong!" admired Amos when Grandsir broke it out and held it up.

Pa Hardee kept staring at his corn planter.

Stated Amos, straightening, "The bottom of the barrels have arrove."

Cried Mrs. Beckett, "But, Corie! There's nothing for you!"

"Oh, yes, there is," said Corie, her cheeks bright as rhododendrons. "I have the new wish book." Every time she'd open it, the memory of this day would return.

Uncle Bide whispered, "Pick out anything you want in that book, Corie. Just about any durn thing, so it's wood or iron or feathers or leather—I bet I kin make it. I'll start right in with a tilt-up bed, and next with a chair on wheels, and I'll turn out every man in the Holler to see there's a good wide path brushed out for it. We'll shove a path clear to Toler's store, won't we, folks?"

The pain hadn't come on, thought Corie blissfully. It was nearly nightfall. But the pain hadn't come on as it usually did at this hour. Perhaps it was never going to again. If it did, she would bury her nose in the new wish book. There must be at least ten thousand pictures in it, and six hundred close-packed pages to read and read.

The man who wrote this story

NEILL C. WILSON 1899–

When Mr. Wilson was four, he wrote his first poem:

"Higgledy piggledy my black hen,
She lays eggs for Jesus' sake amen."

When he was eight, he wrote another poem entitled "Pickett's Charge at Gettysburg." By the time he was twelve, he was a published author, and he has been a professional writer ever since.

While a newspaperman, Mr. Wilson gained some distinction by being the city editor of two different city newspapers at the same time. On this job he learned to write compactly. Each evening he had to send a radio message to Honolulu containing all the day's news in only 166 words. About this time an ambitious young lady asked his advice on how to become a successful writer. He took her for a short drive to the city dumps. "Yesterday I tossed thirty stories and two novels in there," he said. The young lady decided to try another field.

Among his literary materials, Mr. Wilson has a collection of mail order catalogues running back to 1899. He finds them valuable for story ideas and for getting an exact picture of what people were wearing and using at a certain time. With material like this, he created his most popular book, *The Nine Brides and Granny Hite*. The story you have just read was taken from this novel.

Let's consider . . .

1. Corie called the mail-order catalogue her wish book. Why do you suppose she gave it this name?

2. Why wasn't Corie's first order filled? How did this failure turn out to be a stroke of good fortune?

3. Explain why the new wish book made Corie's head whirl.

4. Instead of ordering things for herself, Corie bought gifts for her family and friends. Why do you think she did this?

5. Do you think Corie chose her gifts wisely? Why or why not?

6. Would you like Corie as a friend? Give several reasons for your answer.

7. Do you believe the saying, "It is better to give than to receive"? What pleas-

ures are there in giving? Why is the thought behind a gift more important than the gift itself?

Knowing words . . .

Below are several sentences taken from the selection. Each of the sentences has one word written in italics. After you are sure of the meaning of the italicized word, use it in a sentence of your own.

1. Corie knew that her sister was coming home with tidings *incredible* and exciting.

2. For what else would a wagon be *jouncing* up mud on the Coal Mountain road from Marianboro?

3. The pain hadn't come on, thought Corie *blissfully*.

These Things I Love

These things I love:
Trees on a hillside
Masked in purple haze,
Dottings of dwellings
On a prairie plain,
Full moon and stars up high,
And the sun at noonday
Blazing in blue sky.

A baby's dimpled cheek,
A young girl's smile,
And stalwart young manhood
Beaming at her side.
A lullaby,
Family dinner hour,
Evenings of renewal,
Old house,
Pink rose-bower,
And thunder storm's
Wild lash and power.

These things I love:
A dewy morn
And twilight's close,
A time of reverie,
Old books, old shoes,
And friends to come
And visit some—
These things I love!
                                    Annette Wildman

Cargoes

JOHN MASEFIELD

Quinquereme of Nineveh from distant Ophir,
Rowing home to haven in sunny Palestine,
With a cargo of ivory,
And apes and peacocks,
Sandalwood, cedarwood, and sweet white wine.

Stately Spanish galleon coming from the Isthmus,
Dipping through the Tropics by the palm-green shores,
With a cargo of diamonds,
Emeralds, amethysts,
Topazes, and cinnamon, and gold moidores.

Dirty British coaster with a salt-caked smokestack,
Butting through the Channel in the mad March days,
With a cargo of Tyne coal,
Road-rails, pig lead,
Firewood, ironware, and cheap tin trays.

The man who wrote this poem

JOHN MASEFIELD 1874–

As a boy, John Masefield cared more for adventure than study, and he roamed the woods near his home in search of excitement. His adventurous spirit led his family to apprentice him to the merchant marine when he was thirteen. He sailed about the world but tired of the life at sea. In New York City he left his ship with five dollars in his pocket, took an apartment in Greenwich Village, and found a job with a baker. As he shifted from one humble job to another, he spent all his spare time reading.

When Masefield returned to England, his first book of poems, *Salt Water Ballads,* was published. In this book he refers to himself as a champion of "the dust and scum of the earth." Because of his wide experience as a workman and a sailor, his love and friendship for the worker and the humble man, Masefield is considered a poet of democracy.

Masefield has written many novels, stories, dramas, and essays; more than one hundred books have been published under his name. But he is best known as a poet, and received the highest honor ever paid an English poet. He was named the Poet Laureate of England.

The poet's art . . .

1. Can you describe the three types of ships mentioned?

2. How do their cargoes vary? How does each cargo represent "the things that count" at different times and in different ways of life?

3. On which ship would you prefer to travel? Which do you think John Masefield liked best? Justify your answer.

4. This poem has been described as a thumbnail sketch of the history of civilization. According to the poem, how does present-day civilization differ from civilizations of the past? Do you think the poem paints a true picture of the present? Why?

Old Holy Joe

JAMES STREET

Chaplain Joe Colcutt knew that the time had come for "the meek, the terrible meek, the agonizing meek, to go out and fight for their inheritance." It was up to him to decide what his weapon would be.

It was easy for Lieutenant Joseph Colcutt, Chaplain, to spot the paratroopers and armored-force men in his congregation, because they all bore evidence of their weekly free-for-all. He knew they had been fighting again, and was aware that most of them were attending his service in tribute to his brother, Greg, the paratrooper on the rear bench.

Tankmen recognized no closed season on paratroopers, and vice versa. They had met in town the night before, and a tank sergeant had sung a ditty about Holy Joe, the natural nickname for the chaplain. It wasn't meant as an insult to Joe, but as a come-on to Greg and his comrades. So Greg had backed against a bar and said, "All right, tin soldiers. But after we beat you, I want you to drop around tomorrow and hear my brother. He won't dish the bunk."

And Joe didn't. He didn't wave flags or jerk tears. His congregation had been small back home in Ohio, and was even smaller at camp when he arrived a year before.

Things changed, however, when Greg was sent to camp with his paratroop battalion. Greg was everything that Joe wasn't. The younger brother fought and joked his way to leadership among his comrades, and because the paratroopers liked Greg they went to hear Joe preach. Joe became the most popular chaplain in camp and was so proud of Greg that the mere mention of his kid brother's name caused his chest to tighten.

There was a deep, pulsating pride within him as he looked at his congregation, at the name-tags on the troopers—Kappas, King, Kosvoci, Daly, Downs, Donald—a slice right out of the backbone of America.

The next day he was enjoying his pipe and a book, when Major Gordon White dropped by and invited the chaplain to accompany him to the field where the battalion's Number One unit was ready to jump.

"Picked this unit myself," Major White said. "I want them to be the first to jump, and sort of show the way to the others."

"Is Greg among them?" Joe asked quickly.

"Sure. Didn't he tell you?"

"I haven't had a chance to talk to him for several days." Joe was reaching for his cap. He didn't want to go. The sight of boys tumbling out of planes, staking their lives on a bit of silk, always frightened him. But, thinking that Greg might want him to be there, he got his cap.

The battalion was already assembled when he and Major White arrived in the command car and parked. Twenty-four men stepped from ranks and walked toward the transport plane.

As they neared the plane, a paratrooper, still in ranks, forgot himself, and tilted his head and screamed, "Geronimo-o-o!"

It was their salute to the twenty-four. Then the first man of the Number One unit stared for a second at the command car, and waved; a careless, reckless wave. Joe knew that was Greg. He was the first in the ship and would be the first to jump.

The plane lumbered off, and the battalion took its ease, but Joe was tense. He watched the plane disappear over the rim of the world, then return. The Major said, "They'll jump now."

The whole battalion seemed to hold its breath as the plane leveled off. Joe fastened his eyes on the jump door and saw the figure poised there. Then he saw the paratrooper leap, and Joe closed his eyes and looked away. When he looked up again, the chute was open, and his heart resumed its beating.

They jumped in teams of three. One, two, three—one, two, three—Joe counted them. Whitecaps on a sea of blue, billowing down. The battalion was cheering. Then suddenly, the battalion was hushed, and every paratrooper was counting the chutes.

"Major!" Joe gripped his arm.

"Yes, I know. Only twenty-three jumped. Some poor devil caved in."

The plane landed at another field, far away from where the battalion was waiting. The jumpmaster must see to it that none of the other paratroopers ever saw the boy who had refused to jump. Joe, waiting in the command car, was thinking of the boy, wishing he might talk to him or write his parents.

And then a premonition almost overwhelmed him. He tried to shake it off, but it stuck. His mouth suddenly was dry. But he got a grip on himself and sat very still.

"Let's have a cup of coffee, Chaplain," Major White said, returning after talking with a courier.

"It was my brother." Joe was surprised at his own calmness.

Major White nodded and looked away.

"Regulations say that in training a man can have another chance if he wants it. But this para—this man doesn't want another chance."

"He folded completely?" Joe measured his words.

"Completely." Major White almost whispered it.

He knew he couldn't see his brother and knew his brother didn't want to see him. He knew that even then Greg probably was en route to another camp, the paratrooper emblems stripped from his clothing. That's the way they did. The battalion was in disgrace; but Joe wasn't giving the battalion a thought. He was thinking only of the agony that his brother's proud spirit was suffering.

Joe's services were scheduled for 11 A.M. in the chapel, and when he arrived for his sermon the following Sunday only four men were present. Joe looked at the soldiers and they looked at him. He tried to preach but his words echoed in the hall. He forced himself to call for a song and it was a miserable failure. The next Sunday only five men appeared.

That night Joe sat before his desk just staring at his notes. He wished Greg would write. He had learned from the grapevine that Greg was over at Shelby, a foot soldier again.

The battalion had progressed to mass jumping, twelve men in six seconds, when Major White sent for Joe. The Major went straight to the point: "Chaplain, you must understand that my men have nothing against you. But when they see you they think of your brother, and they don't want to think of your brother. And I don't want them to. He represents something that no paratrooper can afford to remember. I have arranged for your transfer."

Even that didn't surprise Joe. He answered: "I've been trying to see you, sir. I understand what morale means to this outfit. You know that I am a detached chaplain. I have come to request that I be made chaplain of your battalion. I want to jump with the outfit. I am within the age and height limit. I can meet the requirements."

The major smoked in silence. Then he said, "I can understand your desire to vindicate your brother."

Joe said, "It's more than that, sir. Much more."

Major White got up and walked to a window. "You have put your request in such a way that I can't refuse it. There is only one thing . . ."

"Yes, sir."

"This outfit's morale has been bent, but not broken. The men are about over it. However, if an officer should fail anywhere along the line, especially a chaplain, and *particularly* another man named Colcutt—well it would hurt; bad."

Joe was on the Trainasium when the battalion was assembled and got the order that Lieutenant Joseph Colcutt had been made chaplain of the outfit. They didn't dare grumble at assembly, but they were sullen.

"He's out on the Trainasium," said Sergeant Odell McRae. "He won't last long."

The sergeant was born on a Mississippi shantyboat and was as tough as baling wire.

Everything that Joe did was met by silence from the paratroopers. He began jumping from the platforms to strengthen his ankles. He was issued a pair of paratrooper's boots, the insteps reinforced by steel. He was so tired after the first day's training that he didn't report for mess. He worked in the harnessroom and learned about chutes and how to make a chute slip ahead. Soon he was able to run the five miles daily that is part of the routine. He took off weight so fast that often he was ill, and his muscles cried out in agony.

He finally was allowed to jump from a 250-foot tower, using a chute attached to cables. And he was frightened. The sensation of falling through space frightened him so much that he was rigid when his chute landed. Sergeant McRae took one look at him and walked away.

"Holy Joe thinks that makes him a jumper," the sergeant told one of the men.

Joe realized that he didn't belong. He hadn't expected his training to melt the men's antagonism, but he hadn't expected it to increase the feeling. Then came the Sunday when Joe had only one person in his congregation, a selectee who had arrived the night before.

The battalion had advanced to radio operation and demolition by the time Joe was ready for the obstacle course. The course ran up a ridge, thence through a swamp and across a creek. It was a network of slit trenches, barriers, and barbed wire. Sergeant McRae, on orders from the major, handled the watch while Joe ran the course, scaling the barriers and swinging hand over hand across the creek. His time was fair, and the sergeant grunted.

At the silent signal from a platoon leader, the paratroopers began slithering along the ground, under barbed wire that ripped their flesh. Stationary machine guns poured bullets just above their heads. They crawled into a trench and Joe's reflexes simply gave way. He moved his head an inch or so, and a sniper put a steel jacket within a foot of his nose. Sergeant McRae grabbed him. "Keep down, sir." Joe wondered if his imagination was tricking him. He thought there was something kind about the sergeant's words.

The chaplain took everything the course had to offer, and the ordeal left him weak. Then the major ordered the battalion on a twenty-mile hike. It had begun raining.

Joe took his place beside Sergeant McRae and sloshed away, his head drooping.

"Excuse me, sir," the sergeant said. "But you've flattened out and sort of toughened up."

"Thanks, Sergeant. And thanks, also, for holding me down back there. I almost blew up."

"You ain't admittin' you were scared, are you, sir?"

"Yes, I was frightened. Don't you ever get frightened?"

Sergeant McRae laughed. "Ever'time I jump I get scared, too. We all do."

That night the major called Joe to headquarters and told him that the outfit would soon be fighting.

"I'll be ready," Joe said, "as soon as I make my first jump."

The major ground out his cigarette. "The next jumping day will be Friday."

It was Thursday before the reaction really set in on Joe, and he spent that day in his quarters. He was almost too weak to walk, and the idea of food made him ill. He couldn't read. His body was hot, then cold. He had heard that all paratroopers "sweated it out" the day before their first jump, and now he understood. And he kept thinking, "So this is what Greg went through."

It was a cloudy, gloomy day and the battalion was on the parade ground, waiting for transportation to the field.

"Look at Holy Joe," one man whispered. "Looks like he's been through a wringer."

"He's scared to death," whispered another. "He's still sweating."

Each paratrooper carried four grenades, maps, a compass, a knife, two boxes of T.N.T., a rope, and a first-aid kit. Each also had a carbine, and some had parts of machine guns and mortars. Joe had no weapons, however. His pack contained extra food to bring it to maximum weight.

Sergeant McRae sauntered over to Joe.

"So you aim to jump with us, Chaplain?" the sergeant asked.

"Yes," said Joe, adjusting his emergency chute.

McRae grinned. "You needn't worry about that emergency gear. It's okay at high altitudes, but you'll never have a chance to open it at low altitude. So when you go out, Chaplain, count, 'One thousand, two thousand, three thousand.' If your regular chute ain't open by then, well, you better start tending to business."

"Business?"

"You're in the praying business, ain't you?"

Joe's laugh was hollow. He literally was green around the lips. However, he had quit sweating.

They rode over to the field, and as they hurried out to the C-47 transport the jumpmaster told Joe, "You'll be in Number One seat, the first man in and the first man out."

That was laying it on a bit too thick, Joe thought. He remembered that Greg had had the Number One position. Actually, the jumpmaster was following the correct procedure. An officer should always be the first out.

Joe got in the ship and walked up to his position and sat down. He was glad the

seat was there, for his legs were giving in
at the knees. When the plane took off, his
stomach seemed to squirm up into his
chest.

The light over the doorway was red.
This was the pilot's signal that he wasn't
ready for the men to jump.

Joe watched the light, fascinated. It
would soon turn green, the go-ahead. Joe
tried not to think of that. He began sweating again and felt the sweat collect under
his wide chinstrap.

Joe felt the plane descending. The
jumpmaster, standing by the door, shouted,
"Adjust static lines."

The veterans quickly hooked their para-
chute lines onto the cable that ran the
length of the ship. Joe fumbled with his
line, and nobody volunteered to help him.

"Inspect gear," the jumpmaster shouted.
Joe clawed at his chute and pack.

"Count off."

The pilot leveled off, and the green light
showed above the jump door.

The jumpmaster nodded to Joe, and the
chaplain pushed against the side of the
ship, forcing himself to his feet. He took
a deep breath and stepped to the door.
Suddenly there was an urge to jump, to
leap into space, to get it over with. Still he
braced himself.

"Jump!"

Joe closed his eyes and pitched forward.
It was a bad take-off, a clumsy thing.

The jumpmaster put his arm across the
door and stopped Number Two man. "I'll
be—," said the jumpmaster. "He did it."

"He didn't do nothing else but," said
Sergeant McRae and, cupping his hands,
screamed out of the opening—"Geronimo-o-o!"

Joe didn't hear him. He was saying,
"One thousand, two . . ."

The static line jerked open his chute,
and the jolt shook him. He felt as though

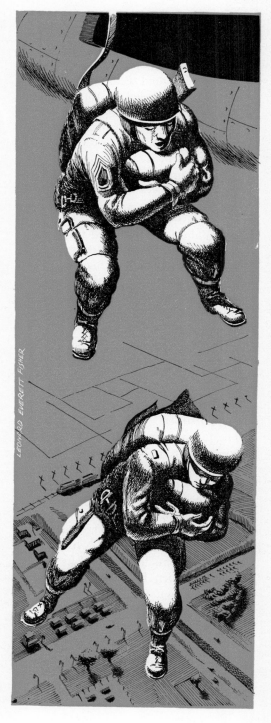

he were suspended between heaven and earth, and the sensation was exhilarating. He wanted to shout. The earth seemed to rush up to meet him, for he had jumped from a few hundred feet. He landed in a heap, then scrambled to his feet and tripped his chute, collapsing it.

The major sent a jeep for him, and he sat very erect as he rode back to camp. He was a proud man.

"Well, you didn't bounce, anyway," said Major White. "Let's have a cup of coffee."

"Thanks," said Joe.

They went to the Officer's Club, and Major White leaned forward to say something. Then without further ado, he pulled a message out of his pocket and handed it to the chaplain.

Another premonition came to Joe then. He saw only a part of one line: "The War Department regrets . . ."

Greg! Joe's eyes swept through the message. A landing barge, a beach in Africa. "I know a few more details," Major White said. "He was among the first ashore. Machine-gun fire cut him in two. He didn't suffer."

The human mind can't swallow tragedy at one gulp; it must take it in sips. It took hours for the events to find their proper places in Joe's mind. He wrote home.

Then he tried to study, and went to sleep in his chair. When he woke up the camp seemed deserted. The guard was changing and he was lonely. It was then that the righteous hatred that often comes to righteous men began to seep into his being and fasten itself on his spirit, and grow. He knew what he would do. He would leave the ministry and get a gun and avenge his brother. The very thought made him feel better.

He wished some of the paratroopers would drop by. They were going to be his real comrades. He didn't know that the jumpers were in town swaggering through the streets, looking for tankmen, and screaming their cry of "Geronimo-o-o!"

All the next day Joe memorized what he would say in his last sermon. He wouldn't mention Greg. He would simply say that he was leaving the ministry to fight. Make it simple, direct. . . .

The chapel was filled with soldiers. Tankmen, foot soldiers, artillerymen, and sky troops. And directly in front of the pulpit were paratroopers. Some had black eyes and their faces were grim as they looked up at him. Suddenly he realized that this was where he belonged . . . in the pulpit. This was where he could help the men the most.

He couldn't remember his text. For the first time in his life he forgot the verse of Scripture that he had planned to quote.

He put his hands on the pulpit and leaned forward, and in a clear voice, so restrained that it rang with emotion, said: "The time has come for the humble to hate the forces of evil. The time has come for the meek, the terrible meek, the agonizing meek, to go out and fight for their inheritance."

Joe turned and walked away from the pulpit, out the back door and over to his quarters. He must pack his gear, his notes, and his Bibles. He knew that he and the paratroopers would soon go forth, and he would need them.

Back in the chapel, the men sat in silence for a second, then got up and filed out. One tankman said, "That sermon was short and snappy. Old Holy Joe is all right."

Sergeant McRae poked his finger against the tankman's chest. "From here on out, he's Holy Jumping Joe."

The man who wrote this story

JAMES STREET 1903–1954

When James Street was born, Lumberton, Mississippi, was a raw frontier-like town. In some ways, James Street was as wild as his birthplace. His mother was named William Thompson Scott Street, and young James loved to confuse unwary people who asked about his family. He threw away his schoolbooks when he was seventeen and became a reporter. Then, although he had been raised as a Catholic, he became a Baptist minister. Two years later he was again a reporter.

James Street worked for newspapers all over the South. Finally, with a dime and a borrowed overcoat, he came to New York City to work for a paper.

He sold his first story to pay the rent, and it was so successful he quit the paper. Mr. Street only wrote when he needed to. When his pockets were empty, he sat down and wrote another story. In this way he wrote a number of short stories and many books. *Oh, Promised Land* and *Tap Roots* are two of his books about early life in the South that have been very popular.

Let's consider . . .

1. Joe had been the most popular chaplain in camp. After Greg failed to jump, how did things change? Do you think the men were right in changing as they did?

2. What were the Major's reasons for wanting to transfer Joe?

3. When Joe told the Major that he wanted to jump with the outfit, the Major said, "I can understand your desire to vindicate your brother." Joe answered, "It's more than that, sir. Much more." What do you think Joe had in mind?

4. After Joe learned of his brother's death, he almost decided to leave the ministry. Why? What made him change his mind?

5. Often a man's beliefs are stronger after they have been tested in some way. Do you think Joe's faith in his work was strengthened as a result of his experiences? Why, or why not?

6. At one point, the sergeant said, "Ever' time I jump I get scared, too. We all do." Have you ever been in a situation where even though you were frightened you went ahead with whatever you were doing? Write a description of your experience. Be sure to explain why you acted bravely in spite of your fears.

7. Why does it require greater bravery to do something when you are afraid than when you have self-confidence?

The writer's craft . . .

You recall that **characterization** is a "word picture" which the author paints of someone in the story. It is through characterization that you come to know the characters as real people.

1. Why do you feel that you *know* Joe as a real person?

2. What specific things did James Street tell you about Joe that made him come alive?

3. The entire story revolved around Joe. Suppose James Street had failed to make Joe a believable person. Explain how this would have affected your interest in the story.

Knowing words . . .

Often just one word can carry descriptive quality that would otherwise require several sentences of explanation. Look carefully at the following sentence: "Joe took his place beside Sergeant McRae and *sloshed* away, his head drooping."

The word *sloshed* is especially appropriate for painting a word picture of the scene. The very sound of the word suggests what it means. Rewrite the quoted sentence, substituting another word—or words—for *sloshed*. Read your rewritten sentence to the class. After the entire class has read their sentences, decide which one was the most expressive. Were any of them more descriptive than the original sentence? If not, why?

The italicized word in each of the following sentences is particularly effective. Explain why.

1. He didn't know that the jumpers were in town *swaggering* through the streets, looking for tankmen, and screaming their cry of "Geronimo-o-o!"

2. At the silent signal from a platoon leader, the paratroopers began *slithering* along the ground, under barbed wire that ripped their flesh.

Integer Vitae

The man of life upright,
 Whose guiltless heart is free
From all dishonest deeds,
 Or thought of vanity;

The man whose silent days
 In harmless joys are spent,
Whom hopes cannot delude,
 Nor sorrow discontent;

That man needs neither towers
 Nor armour for defense,
Nor secret vaults to fly
 From thunder's violence:

He only can behold
 With unaffrighted eyes
The horrors of the deep
 And terrors of the skies.

Thus, scorning all the cares
 That fate or fortune brings,
He makes the heaven his book,
 His wisdom heavenly things;

Good thoughts his only friends,
 His wealth a well-spent age,
The earth his sober inn
 And quiet pilgrimage.
                                        Thomas Campian

Richard Cory

EDWIN ARLINGTON ROBINSON

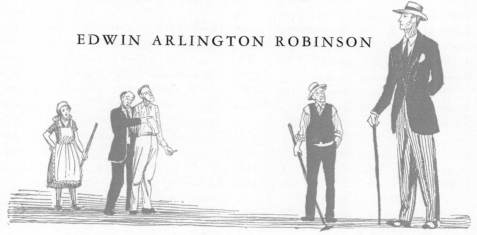

Whenever Richard Cory went down town,
    We people on the pavement looked at him:
He was a gentleman from sole to crown,
    Clean favored, and imperially slim.

And he was always quietly arrayed,
    And he was always human when he talked;
But still he fluttered pulses when he said,
    "Good-morning," and he glittered when he walked.

And he was rich—yes, richer than a king—
    And admirably schooled in every grace:
In fine, we thought that he was everything
    To make us wish that we were in his place.

So on we worked, and waited for the light,
    And went without the meat, and cursed the bread;
And Richard Cory, one calm summer night,
    Went home and put a bullet through his head.

The man who wrote this poem

EDWIN ARLINGTON ROBINSON
1869–1935

Born in a little town in Maine, Edwin Robinson was raised like many other New England boys. He went through school and attended Harvard for two years before he had to drop out because of his father's illness.

Although he was already writing poems, he had to wait many years before they were known to more than a few people. He once said that in fifteen years he had fifteen readers. In the dedication for a book of poems in 1896, he wrote, "This book is dedicated to any man, woman, or critic who will cut the edges of it."

After Robinson moved to New York City, he worked at many odd jobs, but none of them held any interest for him. They were necessary so that he could live and write.

A reserved, quiet man who was completely devoted to his art, Robinson never advertised himself or his poetry. He wrote in every free moment, and eventually his devotion and talent won him no less than three Pulitzer Prizes. Frequently he wrote about people who seemed to have failed—perhaps because he, too, felt he was a failure by the common standards of his day. Many of his poems voice his criticism of the conventional American idea of success.

The poet's art . . .

1. In the first three stanzas the poet described Richard Cory as the townspeople saw him. What was there about him that made them wish they were in his place?

2. The last line of the poem shatters the entire picture which the poet had painted of Richard Cory. What effect did Robinson achieve by waiting until the last line to tell you of Cory's unpleasant end?

3. You recall that in poetry a world of meaning is often condensed into one or two lines. Explain what Robinson meant when he wrote:

"So on we worked, and waited for the light,
And went without the meat, and cursed the bread."

4. The people of the town "went without the meat and cursed the bread." What do you think Richard Cory "went without"?

5. How does this poem help illustrate the saying, "The grass always looks greener on the other side of the fence"?

The Bottle Imp

ROBERT LOUIS STEVENSON

Just a little less than fifty dollars—that's all Keawe paid for the miraculous bottle guaranteed to bring him wealth beyond measure. The bottle worked its magic well, too. Why, then, was he so eager to sell it at a loss, and why did he have such a hard time finding a customer?

There was a man of the island of Hawaii, whom I shall call Keawe; for the truth is, he still lives, and his name must be kept secret; but the place of his birth was not far from Honaunau, where the bones of Keawe the Great lie hidden in a cave. This man was poor, brave, and active; he could read and write like a schoolmaster; he was a first-rate mariner besides, sailed for some time in the island steamers, and steered a whaleboat on the Hamakua coast. At length it came in Keawe's mind to have a sight of the great world and foreign cities, and he shipped on a vessel bound to San Francisco.

This is a fine town, with a fine harbor, and rich people uncountable; and, in particular, there is one hill which is covered with palaces. Upon this hill Keawe was one day taking a walk, with his pocket full of money, viewing the great houses upon either hand with pleasure. "What fine houses they are!" he was thinking, "and how happy must these people be who dwell in them, and take no care for the morrow!" The thought was in his mind when he came abreast of a house that was smaller than some others, but all finished and beautiful like a toy; the steps of that house shone like silver, and the borders of the garden bloomed like garlands, and the windows were bright like diamonds; and Keawe stopped and wondered at the excellence of all he saw. So stopping, he was aware of a man that looked forth upon him through a window, so clear, that Keawe could see him as you see a fish in a pool upon the reef. The man was elderly, with a bald head and a black beard; and his face was heavy with sorrow, and he bitterly sighed. And the truth of it is, that as Keawe looked in upon the man, and the man looked out upon Keawe, each envied the other.

All of a sudden the man smiled and nodded, and beckoned Keawe to enter, and met him at the door of the house.

"This is a fine house of mine," said the man, and bitterly sighed. "Would you not care to view the chambers?"

So he led Keawe all over it, from the cellar to the roof, and there was nothing there that was not perfect of its kind, and Keawe was astonished.

"Truly," said Keawe, "this is a beautiful house; if I lived in the like of it, I should be laughing all day long. How comes it, then, that you should be sighing?"

"There is no reason," said the man, "why you should not have a house in all points similar to this, and finer, if you wish. You have some money, I suppose?"

"I have fifty dollars," said Keawe; "but a house like this will cost more than fifty dollars."

The man made a computation. "I am sorry you have no more," said he, "for it may raise you trouble in the future; but it shall be yours at fifty dollars."

"The house?" asked Keawe.

"No, not the house," replied the man; "but the bottle. For, I must tell you, although I appear to you so rich and fortunate, all my fortune, and this house itself and its garden, came out of a bottle not much bigger than a pint. This is it."

And he opened a lockfast place, and took out a round-bellied bottle with a long neck; the glass of it was white like milk, with changing rainbow colors in the grain. Withinsides something obscurely moved, like a shadow and a fire.

"This is the bottle," said the man; and, when Keawe laughed, "You do not believe me?" he added. "Try, then, for yourself. See if you can break it."

So Keawe took the bottle up and dashed it on the floor till he was weary; but it jumped on the floor like a child's ball, and was not injured.

"This is a strange thing," said Keawe. "For by the touch of it, as well as by the look, the bottle should be of glass."

"Of glass it is," replied the man, sighing more heavily than ever; "but the glass of it was tempered in the flames of hell. An imp lives in it, and that is the shadow we behold there moving; or, so I suppose. If any man buy this bottle the imp is at his command; all that he desires—love, fame, money, houses like this house, ay, or a city like this city—all are his at the word uttered. Napoleon had this bottle, and by it he grew to be the king of the world; but he sold it at the last and fell. Captain Cook had this bottle, and by it he found his way to so many islands; but he, too, sold it, and was slain upon Hawaii. For, once it is sold, the power goes and the protection; and unless a man remain content with what he has, ill will befall him."

"And yet you talk of selling it yourself?" Keawe said.

"I have all I wish, and I am growing elderly," replied the man. "There is one thing the imp cannot do—he cannot prolong life; and it would not be fair to conceal from you there is a drawback to the bottle; for if a man die before he sells it, he must burn in hell forever."

"To be sure, that is a drawback and no mistake," cried Keawe. "I would not meddle with the thing. I can do without a house, thank God; but there is one thing I could not be doing with one particle, and that is to be damned."

"Dear me, you must not run away with things," returned the man. "All you have to do is to use the power of the imp in moderation, and then sell it to someone else, as I do to you, and finish your life in comfort."

"Well, I observe two things," said Keawe. "All the time you keep sighing like a maid in love, that is one; and, for the other, you sell this bottle very cheap."

"I have told you already why I sigh," said the man. "It is because I fear my health is breaking up; and, as you said yourself, to die and go to the devil is a pity for anyone. As for why I sell so cheap, I must explain to you there is a peculiarity about the bottle. Long ago, when the devil brought it first upon earth, it was extremely expensive, and was sold first of all to Prester John for many millions of dollars; but it cannot be sold at all, unless sold at a loss. If you sell it for as much as you paid for it, back it comes to you again like a homing pigeon. It follows that the price has kept falling in these centuries, and the bottle is now remarkably cheap. I bought it myself from one of my neighbors on this hill, and the price I paid was only ninety dollars. I could sell it for as high as eighty-nine dollars and ninety-nine cents, but not a penny dearer, or back the thing must come to me. Now, about this there are two bothers. First, when you offer a bottle so singular for eighty-odd dollars, people suppose you to be jesting. And second— but there is no hurry about that—and I need not go into it. Only remember it must be coined money that you sell it for."

"How am I to know that this is all true?" asked Keawe.

"Some of it you can try at once," replied the man. "Give me your fifty dollars, take the bottle, and wish your fifty dollars back into your pocket. If that does not happen, I pledge you my honor I will cry off the bargain and restore your money."

"You are not deceiving me?" said Keawe.

The man bound himself with a great oath.

"Well, I will risk that much," said Keawe, "for that can do no harm," and he paid over his money to the man, and the man handed him the bottle.

"Imp of the bottle," said Keawe, "I want my fifty dollars back." And sure enough, he had scarce said the word before his pocket was as heavy as ever.

"To be sure this is a wonderful bottle," said Keawe.

"And now good-morning to you, my fine fellow, and the devil go with you for me," said the man.

"Hold on," said Keawe, "I don't want any more of this fun. Here, take your bottle back."

"You have bought it for less than I paid for it," replied the man, rubbing his hands. "It is yours now; and, for my part, I am only concerned to see the back of you." And with that he rang for his Chinese servant, and had Keawe shown out of the house.

Now, when Keawe was in the street, with the bottle under his arm, he began to think. "If all is true about this bottle, I may have made a losing bargain," thinks he. "But, perhaps the man was only fooling me." The first thing he did was to count his money; the sum was exact—forty-nine dollars American money; and one Chili piece. "That looks like the truth," said Keawe. "Now I will try another part."

The streets in that part of the city were as clean as a ship's deck, and though it was noon, there were no passengers. Keawe set the bottle in the gutter and walked away. Twice he looked back, and there was the milky, round-bellied bottle where he left it. A third time he looked back, and turned a corner; but he had scarce done so when something knocked upon his elbow, and behold! It was the long neck sticking up; and as for the round belly, it was jammed into the pocket of his pilot-coat.

"And that looks like the truth," said Keawe.

The next thing he did was to buy a corkscrew in a shop, and go apart into a secret place in the fields. And there he tried to draw the cork, but as often as he put the screw in, out it came again, and the cork as whole as ever.

"This is some new sort of cork," said Keawe, and all at once he began to shake and sweat, for he was afraid of that bottle.

On his way back to port-side he saw a shop where a man sold shells and clubs from the wild islands, old heathen deities, old coined money, pictures from China and Japan, and all manner of things that sailors bring in their sea-chests. And here he had an idea. So he went in and offered the bottle for a hundred dollars. The man of the shop laughed at him at first, and offered him five; but, indeed, it was a curious bottle, such glass was never blown in any human glassworks, so prettily the colors shone under the milky white, and so strangely the shadow hovered in the midst; so, after he had disputed awhile after the manner of his kind, the shopman gave Keawe sixty silver dollars for the thing and set it on a shelf in the midst of his window.

"Now," said Keawe, "I have sold that for sixty which I bought for fifty—or, to say truth, a little less, because one of my dollars was from Chili. Now I shall know the truth upon another point."

So he went back on board his ship, and when he opened his chest, there was the bottle, and had come more quickly than himself. Now Keawe had a mate on board whose name was Lopaka.

"What ails you," said Lopaka, "that you stare in your chest?"

They were alone in the ship's forecastle, and Keawe bound him to secrecy, and told all.

"This is a very strange affair," said Lopaka; "and I fear you will be in trouble about this bottle. But there is one point very clear—that you are sure of the trouble, and you had better have the profit in the bargain. Make up your mind what you want with it; give the order, and if it is done as you desire, I will buy the bottle myself; for I have an idea of my own to get a schooner, and go trading through the islands."

"That is not my idea," said Keawe; "but to have a beautiful house and garden on the Kona Coast, where I was born, the sun shining in at the door, flowers in the garden, glass in the windows, pictures on the walls, and toys and fine carpets on the tables, for all the world like the house I was in this day—only a story higher, and with balconies all about like the King's palace; and to live there without care and make merry with my friends and relatives."

"Well," said Lopaka, "let us carry it back with us to Hawaii, and if all comes true, as you suppose, I will buy the bottle, as I said, and ask a schooner."

Upon that they were agreed, and it was not long before the ship returned to Honolulu, carrying Keawe and Lopaka and the bottle. They were scarce come ashore when they met a friend upon the beach, who began at once to condole with Keawe.

"I do not know what I am to be condoled about," said Keawe.

"Is it possible you have not heard," said the friend, "your uncle—that good old man —is dead, and your cousin—that beautiful boy—was drowned at sea?"

Keawe was filled with sorrow, and, beginning to weep and to lament, he forgot about the bottle. But Lopaka was thinking to himself, and presently, when Keawe's grief was a little abated, "I have been thinking," said Lopaka, "had not your uncle lands in Hawaii, in the district of Kau?"

"No," said Keawe, "not in Kau; they are on the mountain-side—a little be-south Hookena."

"These lands will now be yours?" asked Lopaka.

"And so they will," says Keawe, and began again to lament for his relatives.

"No," said Lopaka, "do not lament at present. I have a thought in my mind. How if this should be the doing of the bottle? For here is the place ready for your house."

"If this be so," cried Keawe, "it is a very

ill way to serve me by killing my relatives. But it may be, indeed; for it was in just such a station that I saw the house with my mind's eye."

"The house, however, is not yet built," said Lopaka.

"No, nor like to be!" said Keawe; "for though my uncle has some coffee and ava and bananas, it will not be more than will keep me in comfort; and the rest of that land is the black lava."

"Let us go to the lawyer," said Lopaka; "I have still this idea in mind."

Now when they came to the lawyer's, it appeared Keawe's uncle had grown monstrous rich in the last days, and there was a fund of money.

"And here is the money for the house!" cried Lopaka.

"If you are thinking of a new house," said the lawyer, "here is the card of a new architect, of whom they tell me great things."

"Better and better!" cried Lopaka. "Here is all made plain for us. Let us continue to obey orders."

So they went to the architect, and he had drawings of houses on his table.

"You want something out of the way," said the architect. "How do you like this?" and he handed a drawing to Keawe.

Now, when Keawe set eyes on the drawing, he cried aloud, for it was the picture of his thought exactly drawn.

"I am in for this house," thought he. "Little as I like the way it comes to me, I am in for it now, and I may as well take the good along with the evil."

So he told the architect all that he wished, and how he would have that house furnished, and about the pictures on the wall and the knick-knacks on the tables; and he asked the man plainly for how much he would undertake the whole affair.

The architect put many questions, and took his pen and made a computation; and when he had done he named the very sum that Keawe had inherited.

Lopaka and Keawe looked at one another and nodded.

"It is quite clear," thought Keawe, "that I am to have this house, whether or no. It comes from the devil and I fear I will get little good by that; and of one thing I am sure, I will make no more wishes as long as I have this bottle. But with the house I am saddled, and I may as well take the good along with the evil."

So he made his terms with the architect, and they signed a paper; and Keawe and Lopaka took ship again and sailed to Australia; for it was concluded between them they should not interfere at all, but leave the architect and the bottle imp to build and to adorn that house at their own pleasure.

The voyage was a good voyage, only all the time Keawe was holding in his breath for he had sworn he would utter no more wishes, and take no more favors, from the devil. The time was up when they got back, and Keawe and Lopaka took a passage in the *Hall,* and went down Kona way to view the house, and see if all had been done fitly according to the thought that was in Keawe's mind.

Now, the house stood on the mountainside, visible to ships. Above, the forest ran up into the clouds of rain; below, the black lava lay in cliffs, where the kings of old lay buried. A garden bloomed about that house with every hue of flowers; and there was an orchard of papaia on the one hand and an orchard of herdprint on the other, and right in front, toward the sea, a ship's mast had been rigged up and bore a flag. As for the house, it was three stories high, with great chambers and broad balconies on each. The windows were of glass, so excellent that it was as clear as water and as bright as day. All manner of furniture adorned the chambers. Pictures hung upon the wall in golden frames—pictures of ships, and men fighting, and of the most beautiful women, and of singular places; nowhere in the world are there pictures of so bright a color as those Keawe found hanging in his house. As for the knick-knacks they were extraordinarily fine: chiming clocks and musical boxes, little men with nodding heads, books filled with pictures, weapons of price from all quarters of the world, and the most elegant puzzles to entertain the leisure of a solitary man. And as no one would care to live in such chambers, only to walk through and view them, the balconies were made so broad that a whole town might have lived upon them in delight; and Keawe knew not which to prefer, whether the back porch, where you got the land-breeze, and looked upon the orchards and the flowers, or the front balcony, where you could drink the wind of the sea, and look down the steep wall of the mountain and see the *Hall* going by once a week or so between Hookena and the hills of Pele, or the schooners plying up the coast for wood and ava and bananas.

When they had viewed all, Keawe and Lopaka sat on the porch.

"Well," asked Lopaka, "is it all as you designed?"

"Words cannot utter it," said Keawe. "It is better than I dreamed, and I am sick with satisfaction."

"There is but one thing to consider," said Lopaka, "all this may be quite natural, and the bottle imp have nothing whatever to say to it. If I were to buy the bottle, and got no schooner after all, I should have put my hand in the fire for nothing. I gave you my word, I know; but yet I think you would not grudge me one more proof."

"I have sworn I would take no more

favors," said Keawe. "I have gone already deep enough."

"This is no favor I am thinking of," replied Lopaka. "It is only to see the imp himself. There is nothing to be gained by that, and so nothing to be ashamed of, and yet, if I once saw him, I should be sure of the whole matter. So indulge me so far, and let me see the imp; and, after that, here is the money in my hand, and I will buy it."

"There is only one thing I am afraid of," said Keawe. "The imp may be very ugly to view, and if you once set eyes upon him you might be very undesirous of the bottle."

"I am a man of my word," said Lopaka. "And here is the money betwixt us."

"Very well," replied Keawe, "I have a curiosity myself. So come, let us have one look at you, Mr. Imp."

Now as soon as that was said, the imp looked out of the bottle, and in again, swift as a lizard; and there sat Keawe and Lopaka turned to stone. The night had quite come before either found a thought to say or voice to say it with; and then Lopaka pushed the money over and took the bottle.

"I am a man of my word," said he, "and had need to be so, or I would not touch this bottle with my foot. Well, I shall get my schooner and a dollar or two for my pocket; and then I will be rid of this devil as fast as I can. For to tell you the plain truth, the look of him has cast me down."

"Lopaka," said Keawe, "do not you think any worse of me than you can help; I know it is night, and the roads bad, and the pass by the tombs an ill place to go by so late, but I declare since I have seen that little face, I cannot eat or sleep or pray till it is gone from me. I will give you a lantern, and a basket to put the bottle in, and any picture or fine thing in all my house that takes your fancy; and be gone at once, and go sleep at Hookena with Nahinu."

"Keawe," said Lopaka, "many a man would take this ill; above all, when I am doing you a turn so friendly, as to keep my word and buy the bottle; and for that matter, the night and the dark, and the way by the tombs, must be all tenfold more dangerous to a man with such a sin upon his conscience, and such a bottle under his arm. But for my part, I am so extremely terrified myself, I have not the heart to blame you. Here I go, then; and I pray God you may be happy in your house and I fortunate with my schooner, and both get to heaven in the end in spite of the devil and his bottle."

So Lopaka went down the mountain; and Keawe stood in his front balcony, and listened to the clink of the horse's shoes, and watched the lantern go shining down the path, and along the cliff of caves where the old dead are buried; and all the time he trembled and clasped his hands, and prayed for his friend, and gave glory to God that he himself was escaped out of that trouble.

But the next day came very brightly, and that new house of his was so delightful to behold that he forgot his terrors. One day followed another, and Keawe dwelt there in perpetual joy. He had his place on the back porch; it was there he ate and lived, and read the stories in the Honolulu newspapers; but when anyone came by they would go in and view the chambers and the pictures. And the fame of the house went far and wide; it was called Ka-Hale-Nui— the Great House—in all Kona; and sometimes the Bright House, for Keawe kept a Chinaman, who was all day dusting and furbishing; and the glass, and the gilt, and the fine stuffs, and the pictures, shone as bright as the morning. As for Keawe himself, he could not walk in the chambers without singing, his heart was so enlarged; and when ships sailed by upon the sea, he would fly his colors on the mast.

So time went by, until one day Keawe went upon a visit as far as Kailua to certain of his friends. There he was well feasted; and left as soon as he could the next morning, and rode hard, for he was impatient to behold his beautiful house; and, besides, the night then coming on was the night in which the dead of old days go abroad in the sides of Kona; and having already meddled with the devil, he was the more chary of meeting with the dead. A little beyond Honaunau he was aware of a woman bathing in the edge of the sea. Now Keawe no sooner beheld her than he drew rein.

"I thought I knew everyone in this country," said he. "How comes it that I do not know you?"

"I am Kokua, daughter of Kiano," said the girl, "and I have just returned from Oahu. Who are you?"

"I will tell you who I am in a little," said Keawe, dismounting from his horse, "but not now. For I have a thought in my mind, and if you knew who I was you might have heard of me, and would not give me a true answer. But tell me, first of all, one thing: are you married?"

At this Kokua laughed out loud. "It is you who ask questions," she said. "Are you married yourself?"

"Indeed, Kokua, I am not," replied Keawe, "and never thought to be until this hour. But here is the plain truth. I have met you here at the roadside, and I saw your eyes, which are like the stars, and my heart went to you as swift as a bird. And so now, if you want none of me, say so, and I will go on to my own place; but if you think me no worse than any other young man, say so, too, and I will turn aside to your father's for the night, and tomorrow I will talk with the good man."

Kokua said never a word, but she looked at the sea and laughed.

"Kokua," said Keawe, "if you say nothing, I will take that for the good answer; so let us be stepping to your father's door."

She went on ahead of him, still without speech; only sometimes she glanced back and glanced away again, and she kept the strings of her hat in her mouth.

Now, when they had come to the door, Kiano came out on his veranda, and cried out and welcomed Keawe by name. At that the girl looked over, for the fame of the great house had come to her ears; and, to be sure, it was a great temptation. All that evening they were very merry together; and the girl was as bold as brass under the eyes of her parents, and made a mark of Keawe, for she had a quick wit. The next day he had a word with Kiano, and found the girl alone.

"Kokua," said he, "you made a mark of me all the evening; and it is still time to bid me go. I would not tell you who I was, because I have so fine a house, and I feared you would think too much of that house and too little of the man that loves you. Now you know all, and if you wish to have seen the last of me, say so at once."

"No," said Kokua, but this time she did not laugh, nor did Keawe ask for more.

This was the wooing of Keawe; things had gone quickly; but so an arrow goes, and the ball of a rifle swifter still, and yet both may strike the target. Things had gone fast, but they had gone far also, and the thought of Keawe rang in the maiden's head; she heard his voice in the breach of the surf upon the lava, and for this young man that she had seen but twice she would have left father and mother and her native islands. As for Keawe himself, his horse flew up the path of the mountain under the cliff of tombs, and the sound of the hoofs, and the sound of Keawe singing to himself for pleasure echoed in the caverns of the dead. He came to the Bright House, and he was still singing. He sat and ate in the broad balcony, and the Chinaman wondered at his master, to hear how he sang between the mouthfuls. The sun went down into the sea, and the night came; and Keawe walked the balconies by lamplight, high on the mountains, and the voice of his singing startled men on ships.

"Here am I now upon my high place," he said to himself. "Life may be no better; this is the mountain top; and all shelves about me toward the worse. For the first time I will light up the chambers, and bathe in my fine bath with the hot water and the cold, and sleep above in the bed of my bridal chamber."

So the Chinaman had word, and he must rise from sleep and light the furnaces; and as he walked below, beside the boilers, he heard his master singing and rejoicing above him in the lighted chambers. When the water began to be hot the Chinaman cried to his master; and Keawe went into the bath-room; and the Chinaman heard him sing as he filled the marble basin; and heard him sing, and the singing broken, as he undressed; until of a sudden, the song ceased. The Chinaman listened, and listened; he called up the house to Keawe to ask if all were well, and Keawe answered him "Yes," and bade him go to bed; but there was no more singing in the Bright House; and all night long the Chinaman heard his master's feet go round and round the balconies without repose.

Now, the truth of it was this: as Keawe undressed for his bath, he spied upon his flesh a patch like a patch of lichen on a rock, and it was then that he stopped singing. For he knew the likeness of that patch, and knew that he was fallen in the Chinese Evil.

Now, it is a sad thing for any man to fall into this sickness. And it would be a sad thing for anyone to leave a house so beautiful and so commodious, and depart from all his friends to the north coast of Molokai, between the mighty cliff and the sea-breakers. But what was that to the case of the man Keawe, he who had met his love but yesterday, and won her but that morning, and now saw all his hopes break, in a moment, like a piece of glass?

Awhile he sat upon the edge of the bath, then sprang, with a cry, and ran outside; and to and fro, to and fro, along the balcony, like one despairing.

"Very willingly could I leave Hawaii, the home of my fathers," Keawe was thinking. "Very lightly could I leave my house, the high-placed, the many-windowed, here upon the mountains. Very bravely could I go to Molokai, to Kalaupapa by the cliffs, to live with the smitten and to sleep there, far from my fathers. But what wrong have I done, what sin lies upon my soul, that I should have encountered Kokua coming cool from the sea-water in the evening? Kokua, the soul ensnarer! Kokua, the light of my life! Her may I never wed, her may I look upon no longer, her may I no more handle with my loving hand; and it is for this, it is for you, O Kokua! that I pour my lamentations!"

Now you are to observe what sort of a man Keawe was, for he might have dwelt there in the Bright House for years, and no one been the wiser of his sickness; but he reckoned nothing of that, if he must lose Kokua. And again he might have wed Kokua even as he was; and so many would have done, because they have the souls of pigs; but Keawe loved the maid manfully, and he would do her no hurt and bring her in no danger.

A little beyond the midst of the night, there came in his mind the recollection of that bottle. He went around to the back porch, and called to memory the day when the devil had looked forth; and at the thought ice ran in his veins.

"A dreadful thing is the bottle," thought Keawe, "and dreadful is the imp, and it is a dreadful thing to risk the flames of hell. But what other hope have I to cure my sickness or to wed Kokua? What!" he thought, "would I beard the devil once, only to get me a house, and not face him again to win Kokua?"

Thereupon he called to mind it was the next day the *Hall* went by on her return to Honolulu. "There must I go first," he thought, "and see Lopaka. For the best hope that I have now is to find that same bottle I was so pleased to get rid of."

Never a wink could he sleep; the food stuck in his throat; but he sent a letter to Kiano, and about the time when the steamer would be coming, rode down beside the cliff of the tombs. It rained; his horse went heavily; he looked up at the black mouths of the caves, and he envied the dead that slept there and were done with trouble; and called to mind how he had galloped by the day before, and was astonished. So he came down to Hookena, and there was all the country gathered for the steamer as usual. In the shed before the store they sat and jested and passed the news; but there was no matter of speech in Keawe's bosom, and he sat in their midst and looked without on the rain falling on the houses, and the surf beating among the rocks, and the sighs arose in his throat.

"Keawe of the Bright House is out of spirits," said one to another. Indeed, and so he was, and little wonder.

Then the *Hall* came, and the whale-boat carried him on board. The afterpart of the ship was full of Haoles—whites—who had been to visit the volcano, as their custom is; and the midst was crowded with Kanakas, and the fore-part with wild bulls from Hilo and horses from Kau: but Keawe sat apart from all in his sorrow, and watched for the house of Kiano. There it sat low upon the shore in the black rocks, and shaded by the cocoa-palms, and there by the door was a red holoku, no greater than a fly, and going to and fro, with a fly's busyness. "Ah, queen of my heart," he cried, "I'll venture my dear soul to win you!"

Soon after, darkness fell and the cabins were lit up, and the Haoles sat and played at the cards and drank whisky as their custom is; but Keawe walked the deck all night; and all the next day, as they steamed under the lee of Maui or of Molokai, he was still pacing to and fro like a wild animal in a menagerie.

Toward evening they passed Diamond Head, and came to the pier of Honolulu. Keawe stepped out among the crowd and began to ask for Lopaka. It seemed he had become the owner of a schooner—none better in the islands—and was gone upon an adventure as far as Pola-Pola or Kakhiki; so there was no help to be looked for from Lopaka. Keawe called to mind a friend of his, a lawyer in the town (I must not tell his name), and inquired of him. They said he was grown suddenly rich, and had a fine new house upon Waikiki shore; and this put a thought in Keawe's head, and he called a hack and drove to the lawyer's house. The house was all brand new, and the trees in the garden no greater than walking-sticks, and the lawyer, when he came, had the air of a man well pleased.

"What can I do to serve you?" said the lawyer.

"You are a friend of Lopaka's," replied Keawe, "and Lopaka purchased from me a certain piece of goods that I thought you might enable me to trace."

The lawyer's face became very dark. "I do not profess to misunderstand you, Mr. Keawe," said he, "though this is an ugly business to be stirring in. You may be sure I know nothing, but yet I have a guess, and if you would apply in a certain quarter I think you might have news."

And he named the name of a man, which, again, I had better not repeat. So it was for days, and Keawe went from one to another, finding everywhere new clothes and carriages, and fine new houses and men everywhere in great contentment, although, to be sure, when he hinted at his business their faces would cloud over.

"No doubt I am upon the track," thought Keawe. "These new clothes and carriages are all the gifts of the little imp, and these glad faces are the faces of men who have taken their profit and got rid of the accursed thing in safety. When I see pale cheeks and hear sighing, I shall know that I am near the bottle."

So it befell at last he was recommended to a Haole in Beritania Street. When he came to the door, about the hour of the evening meal, there were the usual marks of the new house, and the young garden, and the electric light shining in the windows; but when the owner came, a shock of hope and fear ran through Keawe; for here was a young man, white as a corpse, and black about the eyes, the hair shedding from his head, and such a look in his countenance as a man may have when he is waiting for the gallows.

"Here it is, to be sure," thought Keawe, and so with this man he noways veiled his errand. "I am come to buy the bottle," said he.

At the word, the young Haole of Beritania Street reeled against the wall.

"The bottle!" he gasped. "To buy the bottle!" Then he seemed to choke, and seizing Keawe by the arm, carried him into a room and poured out wine in two glasses.

"Here is my respects," said Keawe, who had been much about Haoles in his time. "Yes," he added, "I am come to buy the bottle. What is the price by now?"

At the word the young man let his glass slip through his fingers, and looked upon Keawe like a ghost.

"The price," says he, "the price! You do not know the price?"

"It is for that I am asking you," returned Keawe. "But why are you so much concerned? Is there anything wrong about the price?"

"It has dropped a great deal in value since your time, Mr. Keawe," said the young man, stammering.

"Well, well, I shall have the less to pay for it," says Keawe. "How much did it cost you?"

The young man was as white as a sheet. "Two cents," said he.

"What?" cried Keawe, "two cents? Why, then, you can only sell it for one. And he who buys it—" The words died upon Keawe's tongue; he who bought could never sell it again, the bottle and the bottle imp must abide with him until he died, and when he died must carry him to the red end of hell.

The young man of Beritania Street fell upon his knees. "For God's sake, buy it!" he cried. "You can have all my fortune in the bargain. I was mad when I bought it at that price. I had embezzled money at my store; I was lost else; I must have gone to jail."

"Poor creature," said Keawe, "you would risk your soul upon so desperate an adventure, and to avoid the proper punishment of your own disgrace, and you think I could hesitate with love in front of me. Give me the bottle, and the change which I make sure you have all ready. Here is a five-cent piece."

It was as Keawe supposed; the young man had the change ready in a drawer; the bottle changed hands, and Keawe's fingers were no sooner clasped upon the stalk than he had breathed his wish to be a clean man. And, sure enough, when he got home to his room, and stripped himself before a glass, his flesh was as whole as an infant's. And here was the strange thing: he had no sooner seen this miracle than his mind was changed with him, and he cared naught for the Chinese Evil, and little enough for Kokua; and had no better hope but to be a cinder forever in the flames of hell. Away ahead of him he saw them blaze with his mind's eye, and his soul shrank, and darkness fell upon the light.

When Keawe came to himself a little, he was aware it was the night when the band played at the hotel. Thither he went, because he feared to be alone; and there, among happy faces, walked to and fro, and heard the tunes go up and down, and saw Berger beat the measure, and all the while he heard the flames crackle, and saw the red fire burning in the bottomless pit. Of a sudden the band played Hiki-ao-ao; that was a song that he had sung with Kokua, and at the strain courage returned to him.

"It is done now," he thought, "and once more let me take the good along with the evil."

So it befell that he returned to Hawaii by the first steamer, and as soon as it could be managed he was wedded to Kokua, and carried her up the mountainside to the Bright House.

Now it was so with these two, that when they were together Keawe's heart was stilled; but as soon as he was alone he fell into a brooding horror, and heard the flames crackle, and saw the red fire burn in the bottomless pit. The girl, indeed, had come to him wholly; her heart leaped in her side at sight of him, her hand clung to his; and she was so fashioned, from the hair upon her head to the nails upon her toes, that none could see her without joy. She was pleasant in her nature. She had the good word always. Full of song she was, and went to and fro in the Bright House, the brightest thing in its three stories, carolling like the birds. And Keawe beheld and heard her with delight, and then must shrink upon one side, and weep and groan to think upon the price that he had paid for her; and then he must dry his eyes, and wash his face, and go and sit with her on the broad balconies, joining in her songs, and, with a sick spirit, answering her smiles.

There came a day when her feet began to be heavy and her songs more rare; and now it was not Keawe only that would weep apart, but each would sunder from the other and sit in opposite balconies with the whole width of the Bright House betwixt. Keawe was so sunk in his despair, he scarce observed the change, and was only glad he had more hours to sit alone and brood upon his destiny, and was not so frequently condemned to pull a smiling face on a sick heart. But one day, coming softly through the house, he heard the sound of a child sobbing, and there was Kokua rolling her face upon the balcony floor and weeping like the lost.

"You do well to weep in this house, Kokua," he said. "And yet I would give the head off my body that you (at least) might have been happy."

"Happy!" she cried. "Keawe, when you lived alone in your Bright House you were the word of the island for a happy man; laughter and song were in your mouth, and your face was as bright as the sunrise. Then you wedded poor Kokua; and the good God knows what is amiss in her—but from that day you have not smiled. Oh!" she cried, "what ails me? I thought I was pretty, and I knew I loved him. What ails me, that I throw this cloud upon my husband?"

"Poor Kokua," said Keawe. He sat down by her side, and sought to take her hand; but that she plucked away. "Poor Kokua," he said, again. "My poor child—my pretty. And I had thought all this while to spare you! Well, you shall know all. Then, at least, you will pity poor Keawe; then you will understand how much he loved you in the past—that he dared hell for your possession—and how much he loves you still (the poor condemned one), that he can yet call up a smile when he beholds you."

With that, he told her all, even from the beginning.

"You have done this for me?" she cried. "Ah, well, then what do I care!" and she clasped and wept upon him.

"Ah, child!" said Keawe, "and yet, when I consider of the fire of hell, I care a good deal!"

"Never tell me," said she, "no man can be lost because he loved Kokua, and no other fault. I tell you, Keawe, I shall have you with these hands, or perish in your company. What! you loved me and gave your soul, and you think I will not die to save you in return?"

"Ah, my dear, you might die a hundred times, and what difference would that make," he cried, "except to leave me lonely till the time comes of my damnation?"

"You know nothing," said she. "I was educated in a school in Honolulu; I am no common girl. And I tell you I shall save my lover. What is this you say about a cent? But all the world is not American. In England they have a piece they call a farthing, which is about half a cent. Ah! sorrow!" she cried, "that makes it scarcely better for the buyer must be lost, and we shall find none so brave as my Keawe! But then, there is France; they have a small coin there which they call a centime, and these go five to the cent or thereabout. We could not do better. Come, Keawe, let us go to the French islands; let us go to four centimes, three centimes, two centimes, one centime; four possible sales to come and go on; and two of us to push the bargain. Come, my Keawe! kiss me, and banish care. Kokua will defend you."

"Gift of God!" he cried. "I cannot think that God will punish me for desiring aught so good! Be it as you will, then, take me where you please; I put my life and my salvation in your hands."

Early the next day Kokua was about her preparations. She took Keawe's chest that he went with sailoring; and first she put the bottle in a corner, and then packed it with the richest of their clothes and the bravest of the knick-knacks in the house. "For," said she, "we must seem to be rich folks, or who will believe in the bottle!" All the time of her preparation she was as gay as a bird; only when she looked upon Keawe the tears would spring in her eye, and she must run and kiss him. As for Keawe, a weight was off his soul; now that he had his secret shared, and some hope in front of him, he seemed like a new man, his feet went lightly on the earth, and his breath was good to him again. Yet was terror still at his elbow; and ever and again, as the wind blows out a taper, hope died in him, and he saw the flames toss and the red fire burn in hell.

It was given out in the country they were gone pleasuring to the States, which was thought a strange thing, and yet not so strange as the truth, if any could have guessed it. So they went to Honolulu in the *Hall,* and thence in the *Umatilla* to San Francisco with a crowd of Haoles, and at San Francisco took their passage by mail brigantine, the *Tropic Bird,* for Papeete, the chief place of the French in the south islands. Thither they came, after a pleasant voyage, on a fair day of the Trade wind, and saw the reef with the surf breaking and Motuiti with its palms, and the schooner riding withinside, and the white houses of the town low down along the shore among green trees, and overhead the mountains and the clouds of Tahiti, the wise island.

It was judged the most wise to hire a house, which they did accordingly, opposite the British Consul's, to make a great parade of money, and themselves conspicuous with carriages and horses. This it was very easy to do, so long as they had the bottle in their possession; for Kokua was more bold than Keawe, and, whenever she had a mind, called on the imp for twenty or a hundred dollars. At this rate they soon grew to be remarked in the town; and the strangers from Hawaii, their riding and their driving, the fine holokus, and the rich lace of Kokua, became the matter of much talk.

They got on well after the first with the Tahitian language, which is indeed like to the Hawaiian, with a change of certain letters; and as soon as they had any freedom of speech, began to push the bottle. You are to consider it was not an easy subject to introduce; it was not easy to persuade people you are in earnest, when you offer to sell them for four centimes the spring of health and riches inexhaustible. It was

necessary besides to explain the dangers of the bottle; and either people disbelieved the whole thing and laughed, or they thought the more of the darker part, became overcast with gravity, and drew away from Keawe and Kokua, as from persons who had dealings with the devil. So far from gaining ground, these two began to find they were avoided in the town; the children ran away from them screaming, a thing intolerable to Kokua; Catholics crossed themselves as they went by; and all persons began with one accord to disengage themselves from their advances.

Depression fell upon their spirits. They would sit at night in their house, after a day's weariness, and not exchange a word, or the silence would be broken by Kokua bursting suddenly into sobs. Sometimes they would pray together; sometimes they would have the bottle out upon the floor, and sit all evening watching how the shadow hovered in the midst. At such times they would be afraid to go to rest. It was long ere slumber came to them, and, if either dozed off, it would be to wake and find the other silently weeping in the dark, or perhaps to wake alone, the other having fled from the house and the neighborhood of that bottle, to pace under the bananas in the little garden, or to wander on the beach by moonlight.

One night it was so when Kokua awoke. Keawe was gone. She felt in the bed and his place was cold. Then fear fell upon her, and she sat up in bed. A little moonshine filtered through the shutters. The room was bright, and she could spy the bottle on the floor. Outside it blew high, the great trees of the avenue cried aloud, and the fallen leaves rattled in the veranda. In the midst of this Kokua was aware of another sound; whether of a beast or of a man she could scarce tell, but it was as sad as death, and cut her to the soul. Softly, she arose, set the door ajar, and looked forth into the moonlit yard. There, under the bananas, lay Keawe, his mouth in the dust, and as he lay he moaned.

It was Kokua's first thought to run forward and console him; her second potently withheld her. Keawe had borne himself before his wife like a brave man; it became her little in the hour of weakness to intrude upon his shame. With the thought she drew back into the house.

"Heaven," she thought, "how careless have I been—how weak! It is he, not I, that stands in this eternal peril; it was he, not I, that took the curse upon his soul. It is for my sake, and for the love of a creature of so little worth and such poor help, that he now beholds so close to him the flames of hell—ay, and smells the smoke of it, lying without there in the wind and moonlight. Am I so dull of spirit that never till now have I surmised my duty, or have I seen it before and turned aside? But now, at least, I take up my soul in both the hands of my affection; now I say farewell to the white steps of heaven and the waiting faces of my friends. A love for a love, and let mine be equalled with Keawe's. A soul for a soul, and be it mine to perish!"

She was a deft woman with her hands, and was soon apparelled. She took in her hands the change—the precious centimes they kept ever at their side; for this coin is little used, and they had made provision at a government office. When she was forth in the avenue clouds came on the wind, and the moon was blackened. The town slept, and she knew not whither to turn till she heard one coughing in the shadow of the trees.

"Old man," said Kokua, "what do you here abroad in the cold night?"

The old man could scarce express himself for coughing, but she made out that he was old and poor, and a stranger in the island.

"Will you do me a service?" said Kokua. "As one stranger to another, and as an old man to a young woman, will you help a daughter of Hawaii?"

"Ah," said the old man. "So you are the witch from the Eight Islands, and even my old soul you seek to entangle. But I have heard of you, and defy your wickedness."

"Sit down here," said Kokua, "and let me tell you a tale." And she told him the story of Keawe from the beginning to the end.

"And now," said she, "I am his wife, whom he bought with his soul's welfare. And what should I do? If I went to him myself and offered to buy it, he would refuse. But if you go, he will sell it eagerly; I will await you here; you will buy it for four centimes, and I will buy it again for three. And the Lord strengthen a poor girl!"

"If you meant falsely," said the old man, "I think God would strike you dead."

"He would!" cried Kokua. "Be sure he would. I could not be so treacherous, God would not suffer it."

"Give me four centimes and await me here," said the old man.

Now, when Kokua stood alone in the street, her spirit died. The wind roared in the trees, and it seemed to her the rushing flames of hell; the shadows towered in the light of the street lamp, and they seemed to her the snatching hands of evil ones. If she had had the strength, she must have run away, and if she had had the breath, she must have screamed aloud; but, in truth, she could do neither, and stood and trembled in the avenue, like an affrighted child.

Then she saw the old man returning, and he had the bottle in his hand.

"I have done your bidding," said he, "I left your husband weeping like a child; tonight he will sleep easy." And he held the bottle forth.

"Before you give it to me," Kokua panted, "take the good with the evil—ask to be delivered from your cough."

"I am an old man," replied the other, "and too near the gate of the grave to take a favor from the devil. But what is this? Why do you not take the bottle? Do you hesitate?"

"Not hesitate!" cried Kokua. "I am only weak. Give me a moment. It is my hand resists, my flesh shrinks back from the accursed thing. One moment only!"

The old man looked upon Kokua kindly. "Poor child!" said he, "you fear; your soul misgives you. Well, let me keep it. I am old, and can never more be happy in this world, and as for the next—"

"Give it to me!" gasped Kokua. "There is your money. Do you think I am so base as that? Give me the bottle."

"God bless you, child," said the old man.

Kokua concealed the bottle under her holoku, said farewell to the old man, and walked off along the avenue, she cared not whither. For all roads were now all the same to her, and led equally to hell. Sometimes she walked, and sometimes ran; sometimes she screamed out loud in the night, and sometimes lay by the wayside in the dust and wept. All that she had heard of hell came back to her; she saw the flames blaze, and she smelled the smoke, and her flesh withered on the coals.

Near day she came to her mind again, and returned to the house. It was even as the old man said—Keawe slumbered like a child. Kokua stood and gazed upon his face.

"Now, my husband," said she, "it is your turn to sleep. When you wake it will be your turn to sing and laugh. But for poor Kokua, alas! that meant no evil—for poor Kokua no more sleep, no more singing, no

more delight, whether in earth or Heaven."

With that she lay down in the bed by his side, and her misery was so extreme that she fell into a deep slumber instantly.

Late in the morning her husband woke her and gave her the good news. It seemed he was silly with delight, for he paid no heed to her distress, ill though she dissembled it. The words stuck in her mouth, it mattered not; Keawe did the speaking. She ate not a bite, but who was to observe it? For Keawe cleared the dish. Kokua saw and heard him, like some strange thing in a dream; there were times when she forgot or doubted, and put her hands to her brow; to know herself doomed and hear her husband babble seemed so monstrous.

All the while Keawe was eating and talking, and planning the time of their return, and thanking her for saving him, and fondling her, and calling her the true helper after all. He laughed at the old man that was fool enough to buy that bottle.

"A worthy old man he seemed," Keawe said. "But no one can judge by appearances. For why did the old reprobate require the bottle?"

"My husband," said Kokua, humbly, "his purpose may have been good."

Keawe laughed like an angry man.

"Fiddle-de-dee!" cried Keawe. "An old rogue, I tell you; and an old ass to boot. For the bottle was hard enough to sell at four centimes; and at three it will be quite impossible. The margin is not broad enough, the thing begins to smell of scorching—brr!" said he, and shuddered. "It is true I bought it myself at a cent, when I knew not there were smaller coins. I was a fool for my pains; there will never be found another, and whoever has that bottle now will carry it to the pit."

"Oh, my husband!" said Kokua. "Is it not a terrible thing to save oneself by the eternal ruin of another? It seems to me I could not laugh. I would be humbled. I would be filled with melancholy. I would pray for the poor holder."

Then Keawe, because he felt the truth of what she said, grew the more angry. "Hoity-toity!" cried he. "You may be filled with melancholy if you please. It is not the mind of a good wife. If you thought at all of me, you would sit shamed."

Thereupon he went out, and Kokua was alone.

What chance had she to sell that bottle at two centimes? None, she perceived. And if she had any, here was her husband hurrying her away to a country where there was nothing lower than a cent. And here—on the morrow of her sacrifice—was her husband leaving her and blaming her.

She would not even try to profit by what time she had, but sat in the house, and now had the bottle out and viewed it with unutterable fear, and now, with loathing, hid it out of sight.

By and by, Keawe came back, and would have her take a drive.

"My husband, I am ill," she said. "I am out of heart. Excuse me, I can take no pleasure."

Then was Keawe more wroth than ever. With her, because he thought she was brooding over the case of the old man; and with himself, because he thought she was right, and was ashamed to be so happy.

"This is your truth," cried he, "and this your affection! Your husband is just saved from eternal ruin, which he encountered for the love of you—and you can take no pleasure! Kokua, you have a disloyal heart!"

He went forth again furious, and wandered in the town all day. He met friends, and drank with them; they hired a carriage and drove into the country, and there drank again. All the time Keawe was ill at ease, because he was taking this pastime while his wife was sad, and because he knew in his heart that she was more right than he; and the knowledge made him drink the deeper.

Now, there was an old brutal Haole drinking with him, one that had been a boatswain of a whaler—a runaway, a digger in gold mines, a convict in prisons. He had a low mind and a foul mouth; he loved to drink and to see others drunken; and he pressed the glass upon Keawe. Soon there was no more money in the company.

"Here, you!" said the boatswain, "you are rich, you have been always saying. You have a bottle or some foolishness."

"Yes," said Keawe, "I am rich; I will go back and get some money from my wife, who keeps it."

"That's a bad idea, mate," said the boatswain. "Never you trust a petticoat with dollars. They're all as false as water; you keep an eye on her."

Now, this word struck in Keawe's mind; for he was muddled with what he had been drinking.

"I should not wonder but she was false, indeed," thought he. "Why else should she be so cast down at my release? But I will show her I am not the man to be fooled. I will catch her in the act."

Accordingly, when they were back in town, Keawe bade the boatswain wait for him at the corner, by the old calaboose, and went forward up the avenue alone to the door of his house. The night had come again; there was a light within, but never a sound; and Keawe crept about the corner, opened the back door softly, and looked in.

There was Kokua on the floor, the lamp at her side; before her was a milk-white bottle, with a round belly and a long neck; and as she viewed it, Kokua wrung her hands.

A long time Keawe stood and looked in the doorway. At first he was struck stupid;

corner where they kept the bottle, and
there was no bottle there.

At that the chest heaved upon the floor
like a sea-billow, and the house span about
him like a wreath of smoke, for he saw she
was lost now, and there was no escape.
"It is what I feared," he thought. "It is
she who has bought it."

And then he came to himself a little and
rose up; but the sweat streamed on his
face as thick as the rain and as cold as the
well-water.

"Kokua," said he, "I said to you today
what ill became me. Now I return to house
with my jolly companions," and at that he
laughed a little quietly. "I will take more
pleasure in the cup if you forgive me."

She clasped his knees in a moment; she
kissed his knees with flowing tears.

"Oh," she cried, "I ask but a kind word!"

"Let us never think hardly of the other,"
said Keawe, and was gone out of the house.

Now, the money that Keawe had taken
was only some of that store of centime
pieces they had laid in at their arrival. It
was very sure he had no mind to be drinking. His wife had given her soul for him,
now he must give his for hers; no other
thought was in the world with him.

At the corner, by the old calaboose, there
was the boatswain waiting.

"My wife has the bottle," said Keawe,
"and unless you help me to recover it, there
can be no more money and no more liquor
tonight."

"You do not mean to say you are serious
about that bottle?" cried the boatswain.

"There is the lamp," said Keawe. "Do I
look as if I was jesting?"

"That is so," said the boatswain. "You
look as serious as a ghost."

"Well, then," said Keawe, "here are two
centimes; you must go to my wife in the
house, and offer her these for the bottle,
which (if I am not much mistaken) she

and then fear fell upon him that the bargain had been made amiss, and the bottle
had come back to him as it came at San
Francisco; and at that his knees were
loosened, and the fumes of the wine departed from his head like mists off a river
in the morning. And then he had another
thought; and it was a strange one, that
made his cheeks to burn.

"I must make sure of this," thought he.

So he closed the door, and went softly
round the corner again, and then came
noisily in, as though he were but now returned. And, lo! by the time he opened the
front door no bottle was to be seen; and
Kokua sat in a chair and started up like
one awakened out of sleep.

"I have been drinking all day and making merry," said Keawe. "I have been with
good companions, and now I only come
back for money, and return to drink and
carouse with them again."

Both his face and voice were as stern as
judgment, but Kokua was too troubled to
observe.

"You do well to use your own, my husband," said she, and her words trembled.

"Oh, I do well in all things," said Keawe,
and he went straight to the chest and took
out money. But he looked besides in the

will give to you instantly. Bring it to me here, and I will buy it back from you for one; for that is the law with this bottle, that it still must be sold for a less sum. But whatever you do, never breathe a word to her that you have come from me."

"Mate, I wonder are you making a fool of me?" asked the boatswain.

"It will do you no harm if I am," returned Keawe.

"That is so, mate," said the boatswain.

"And if you doubt me," added Keawe, "you can try. As soon as you are clear of the house, wish to have your pocket full of money, or a bottle of the best rum, or what you please, and you will see the virtue of the thing."

"Very well, Kanaka," says the boatswain. "I will try; but if you are having your fun out of me I will take my fun out of you with a belaying-pin."

So the whaler-man went off up the avenue; and Keawe stood and waited. It was near the same spot where Kokua had waited the night before; but Keawe was more resolved, and never faltered in his purpose; only his soul was bitter with despair.

It seemed a long time he had to wait before he heard a voice singing in the darkness of the avenue. He knew the voice to be the boatswain's; but it was strange how drunken it appeared upon a sudden.

Next the man himself came stumbling into the light of the lamp. He had the devil's bottle buttoned in his coat; another bottle was in his hand; and even as he came in view he raised it to his mouth and drank.

"You have it," said Keawe. "I see that."

"Hands off!" cried the boatswain, jumping back. "Take a step near me, and I'll smash your mouth. You thought you could make a cat's paw of me, did you?"

"What do you mean?" cried Keawe.

"Mean?" cried the boatswain. "This is a pretty good bottle, this is; that's what I mean. How I got it for two centimes I can't make out; but I am sure you sha'n't have it for one."

"You mean you won't sell?" gasped Keawe.

"No, sir," cried the boatswain. "But I'll give you a drink of the rum, if you like."

"I tell you," said Keawe, "the man who has that bottle goes to hell."

"I reckon I'm going anyway," returned the sailor, "and this bottle's the best thing to go with I've struck yet. No, sir!" he cried again, "this is my bottle now, and you can go and fish for another."

"Can this be true?" Keawe cried. "For your own sake, I beseech you, sell it me!"

"I don't value any of your talk," replied the boatswain. "You thought I was a flat, now you see I'm not; and there's an end. If you won't have a swallow of the rum, I'll have one myself. Here's your health, and good-night to you!"

So off he went down the avenue toward town, and there goes the bottle out of the story.

But Keawe ran to Kokua light as the wind; and great was their joy that night; and great, since then, has been the peace of all their days in the Bright House.

Let's consider . . .

1. Whoever owned the bottle could have almost anything he desired. Why then did every owner of the bottle want to get rid of it?

2. At one point Keawe seemed to have everything. He owned a beautiful house filled with treasures, he had Kokua's love, and he had gotten rid of the bottle. Why did he wish to buy the bottle back again? How was he able to trace it?

3. Was the bottle merely a source of evil? What benefits came to Keawe and Kokua from its possession?

4. How did Kokua prove her love for Keawe?

5. Why didn't she let the sick old stranger keep the bottle? What did this action tell you about the kind of person she was?

6. Why didn't Stevenson describe the imp in any detail? What do you think it looked like? Can you draw a picture of it?

7. If someone offered to sell you the bottle at a cost of *more* than five cents, would you buy it? Give several reasons to support your answer.

Knowing words . . .

During the story, Keawe developed a mysterious illness. What do you think this illness was? (The reference to the island of Molokai is a clue.)

1. Why did Keawe, a Hawaiian, call the disease "the *Chinese* Evil"?

2. Why didn't he call it by its true name?

3. What other diseases do you know of that are called by roundabout names? How can you account for this hedging?

4. There are many different ways of referring to death without ever mentioning the word. List as many as you can think of.

Dream Pedlary

If there were dreams to sell,
     What would you buy?
Some cost a passing bell;
     Some a light sigh,
That shakes from Life's fresh crown
Only a rose-leaf down.

If there were dreams to sell,
Merry and sad to tell,
And the crier rang the bell,
     What would you buy?
                    Thomas Lovell Beddoes

How Much Land Does a Man Need?

LEO TOLSTOY

Pahom, perched on top of the oven, listened to the women as they chattered. He nodded in silent agreement with his wife. The lot of the peasants was not so bad—if only they had more land. With plenty of land, one need not fear anything, not even the Devil himself. As it turned out, Pahom would have been better off if the Devil hadn't been eavesdropping, too.

An elder sister came to visit her younger sister in the country. The elder was married to a tradesman in town, the younger to a peasant in the village. As the sisters sat over their tea talking, the elder began to boast of the advantages of town life; saying how comfortably they lived there, how well they dressed, what fine clothes her children wore, what good things they ate and drank, and how she went to the theatre, promenades, and entertainments.

The younger sister was piqued, and in turn disparaged the life of a tradesman, and stood up for that of a peasant.

"I would not change my way of life for yours," said she. "We may live roughly but at least we are free from anxiety. You live in better style than we do, but though you often earn more than you need, you are very likely to lose all you have. You know the proverb, 'Loss and gain are brothers twain.' It often happens that people who are wealthy one day are begging their bread the next. Our way is safer. Though a peasant's life is not a fat one, it is a long one. We shall never grow rich, but we shall always have enough to eat."

The elder sister said sneeringly:

"Enough? Yes, if you like to share with the pigs and the calves! What do you know of elegance or manners! However much your goodman may slave, you will die as you are living—on a dung heap—and your children the same."

"Well, what of that?" replied the younger. "Of course our work is rough and coarse. But, on the other hand, it is sure; and we need not bow to any one. But you, in your towns, are surrounded by temptations; today all may be right, but to-morrow the Evil One may tempt your husband with cards, wine, or women, and all will go to ruin. Don't such things happen often enough?"

Pahom, the master of the house, was lying on top of the oven, and he listened to the women's chatter.

"It is perfectly true," thought he. "Busy

603

as we are from childhood tilling mother earth, we peasants have no time to let any nonsense settle in our heads. Our only trouble is that we haven't land enough. If I had plenty of land, I shouldn't fear the Devil himself!"

The women finished their tea, chatted a while about dress, and then cleared away the tea-things and lay down to sleep.

But the Devil had been sitting behind the oven, and had heard all that was said. He was pleased that the peasant's wife had led her husband into boasting, and that he had said that if he had plenty of land he would not fear the Devil himself.

"All right," thought the Devil. "We will have a tussle. I'll give you land enough; and by means of that land I will get you into my power."

2.

Close to the village there lived a lady, a small land owner, who had an estate of about three hundred acres. She had always lived on good terms with the peasants, until she engaged as her steward an old soldier, who took to burdening the people with fines. However careful Pahom tried to be, it happened again and again that now a horse of his got among the lady's oats, now a cow strayed into her garden, now his calves found their way into her meadows— and he always had to pay a fine.

Pahom paid up, but grumbled, and, going home in a temper, was rough with his family. All through that summer, Pahom had much trouble because of this steward; and he was even glad when winter came and the cattle had to be stabled. Though he grudged the fodder when they could no longer graze on the pastureland, at least he was free from anxiety about them.

In the winter the news got about that the lady was going to sell her land, and that the keeper of the inn on the high road was bargaining for it. When the peasants heard this they were very much alarmed.

"Well," thought they, "if the innkeeper gets the land, he will worry us with fines worse than the lady's steward. We all depend on the estate."

So the peasants went on behalf of their Commune, and asked the lady not to sell the land to the innkeeper; offering her a better price for it themselves. The lady agreed to let them have it. Then the peasants tried to arrange for the Commune to buy the whole estate, so that it might be held by them all in common. They met twice to discuss it, but could not settle the matter; the Evil One sowed discord among them, and they could not agree. So they decided to buy the land individually, each according to his means; and the lady agreed to this plan as she had to the other.

Presently Pahom heard that a neighbour of his was buying fifty acres, and that the lady had consented to accept one half in cash and wait a year for the other half. Pahom felt envious.

"Look at that," thought he, "the land is all being sold, and I shall get none of it." So he spoke to his wife.

"Other people are buying," said he, "and we must also buy twenty acres or so. Life is becoming impossible. That steward is simply crushing us with his fines."

So they put their heads together and considered how they could manage to buy it. They had one hundred roubles laid by. They sold a colt, and one half of their bees; hired out one of their sons as a labourer, and took his wages in advance; borrowed the rest from a brother-in-law and so scraped together half the purchase money.

Having done this, Pahom chose out a farm of forty acres, some of it wooded, and went to the lady to bargain for it. They came to an agreement, and he shook hands with her upon it, and paid her a deposit in advance. Then they went to town and signed the deeds; he paying half the price down, and undertaking to pay the remainder within two years.

So now Pahom had land of his own. He borrowed seed, and sowed it on the land he had bought. The harvest was a good one, and within a year he had managed to pay off his debts both to the lady and to his brother-in-law. So he became a landowner, ploughing and sowing his own land, making hay on his own land, cutting his own trees, and feeding his cattle on his own pasture. When he went out to plough his fields, or to look at his growing corn, or at his grass-meadows, his heart would fill with joy. The grass that grew and the flowers that bloomed there, seemed to him unlike any that grew elsewhere. Formerly, when he had passed by that land, it had appeared the same as any other land, but now it seemed quite different.

3.

So Pahom was well-contented, and everything would have been right if the neighbouring peasants would only not have trespassed on his cornfields and meadows. He appealed to them most civilly, but they still went on; now the Communal herdsmen would let the village cows stray into his meadows; then horses from the night pasture would get among his corn. Pahom turned them out again and again, and forgave their owners, and for a long time he forbore from prosecuting any one. But at last he lost patience and complained to the District Court. He knew it was the peasants' want of land, and no evil intent on their part, that caused the trouble; but he thought:

"I cannot go on overlooking it, or they will destroy all I have. They must be taught a lesson."

So he had them up, gave them one lesson, and then another, and two or three of the peasants were fined. After a time Pahom's neighbours began to bear him a grudge for this, and would now and then let their cattle on to his land on purpose. One peasant even got into Pahom's wood at night and cut down five young lime trees for their bark. Pahom passing through the wood one day noticed something white. He came nearer, and saw the stripped trunks lying on the ground, and close by stood the stumps, where the trees had been. Pahom was furious.

"If he had only cut one here and there it would have been bad enough," thought Pahom, "but the rascal has actually cut down a whole clump. If I could only find out who did this, I would pay him out."

He racked his brains as to who it could be. Finally he decided: "It must be Simon —no one else could have done it." So he went to Simon's homestead to have a look round, but he found nothing, and only had an angry scene. However, he now felt more certain than ever that Simon had done it, and he lodged a complaint. Simon was summoned. The case was tried, and retried, and at the end of it all Simon was acquitted, there being no evidence against him. Pahom felt still more aggrieved, and let his anger loose upon the Elder and the Judges.

"You let thieves grease your palms," said he. "If you were honest folk yourselves, you would not let a thief go free."

So Pahom quarrelled with the Judges and with his neighbours. Threats to burn his building began to be uttered. So though Pahom had more land, his place in the Commune was much worse than before.

About this time a rumour got about that many people were moving to new parts.

"There's no need for me to leave my land," thought Pahom. "But some of the others might leave our village, and then there would be more room for us. I would take over their land myself, and make my estate a bit bigger. I could live more at ease. As it is, I am still too cramped to be comfortable."

One day Pahom was sitting at home, when a peasant, passing through the village, happened to call in. He was allowed to stay the night, and supper was given him. Pahom had a talk with this peasant and asked him where he came from. The stranger answered that he came from beyond the Volga, where he had been working. One word led to another, and the man went on to say that many people were settling in those parts. He told how some people from his village had settled there. They had joined the Commune, and had had twenty-five acres per man granted them. The land was so good, he said, that the rye sown on it grew as high as a horse, and so thick that five cuts of a sickle made a sheaf. One peasant, he said, had brought nothing with him but his bare hands, and now he had six horses and two cows of his own.

Pahom's heart kindled with desire. He thought:

"Why should I suffer in this narrow hole if one can live so well elsewhere? I will sell my land and my homestead here, and with the money I will start afresh over there and get everything new. In this crowded place one is always having trouble. But I must first go and find out all about it myself."

Towards summer he got ready and started. He went down the Volga on a steamer to Samara, then walked another three hundred miles on foot, and at last reached the place. It was just as the stranger had said. The peasants had plenty of land: every man had twenty-five acres of Communal land given him for his use, and

anyone who had money could buy, besides, at two shillings an acre as much good freehold land as he wanted.

Having found out all he wished to know, Pahom returned home as autumn came on, and began selling off his belongings. He sold his land at a profit, sold his homestead and all his cattle, and withdrew from membership of the Commune. He only waited till the spring, and then started with his family for the new settlement.

4.

As soon as Pahom and his family arrived at their new abode, he applied for admission into the Commune of a large village. He stood treat to the Elders, and obtained the necessary documents. Five shares of Communal land were given him for his own and his sons' use: that is to say—125 acres (not all together, but in different fields) besides the use of the Communal pasture. Pahom put up the buildings he needed, and bought cattle. Of the Communal land alone he had three times as much as at his former home, and the land was good cornland. He was ten times better off than he had been. He had plenty of arable land and pasturage, and could keep as many head of cattle as he liked.

At first, in the bustle of building and settling down, Pahom was pleased with it all, but when he got used to it he began to think that even here he had not enough land. The first year, he sowed wheat on his share of the Communal land, and had a good crop. He wanted to go on sowing wheat, but had not enough Communal land for the purpose, and what he had already used was not available; for in those parts wheat is only sown on virgin soil or on fallow land. It is sown for one or two years, and then the land lies fallow till it is again overgrown with prairie grass. There were many who wanted such land, and there was not enough for all; so that people quarrelled about it. Those who were better off, wanted it for growing wheat, and those who were poor, wanted it to let to dealers, so that they might raise money to pay their taxes. Pahom wanted to sow more wheat; so he rented land from a dealer for a year. He sowed much wheat and had a fine crop, but the land was too far from the village—the wheat had to be carted more than ten miles. After a time Pahom noticed that some peasant-dealers were living on separate farms, and were growing wealthy; and he thought:

"If I were to buy some freehold land,[1] and have a homestead on it, it would be a different thing altogether. Then it would all be nice and compact."

The question of buying freehold land recurred to him again and again.

He went on in the same way for three years: renting land and sowing wheat. The seasons turned out well and the crops were good, so that he began to lay money by. He might have gone on living contentedly, but he grew tired of having to rent other people's land every year, and having to scramble for it. Wherever there was good land to be had, the peasants would rush for it and it was taken up at once, so that unless you were sharp about it you got none. It happened in the third year that he and a dealer together rented a piece of pasture land from some peasants; and they had already ploughed it up, when there was some dispute, and the peasants went to law about it, and things fell out so that the labour was all lost.

"If it were my own land," thought Pahom, "I should be independent, and there would not be all this unpleasantness."

[1] *freehold land,* land that can be held for life and passed on to one's children

5.

So Pahom began looking out for land which he could buy; and he came across a peasant who had bought thirteen hundred acres, but having got into difficulties was willing to sell again cheap. Pahom bargained and haggled with him, and at last they settled the price at 1,500 roubles, part in cash and part to be paid later. They had all but clinched the matter, when a passing dealer happened to stop at Pahom's one day to get a feed for his horses. He drank tea with Pahom, and they had a talk. The dealer said that he was just returning from the land of the Bashkirs far away, where he had bought thirteen thousand acres of land, all for 1,000 roubles. Pahom questioned him further, and the tradesman said:

"All one need do is to make friends with the chiefs. I gave away about one hundred roubles' worth of dressing-gowns and carpets, besides a case of tea, and I gave wine to those who would drink it; and I got the land for less than twopence an acre." And he showed Pahom the title-deeds, saying:

"The land lies near a river, and the whole prairie is virgin soil."

Pahom plied him with questions, and the tradesman said:

"There is more land there than you could cover if you walked a year, and it all belongs to the Bashkirs. They are as simple as sheep, and land can be got almost for nothing."

"There now," thought Pahom, "with my one thousand roubles, why should I get only thirteen hundred acres, and saddle myself with a debt besides? If I take it out there, I can get more than ten times as much for the money."

Pahom inquired how to get to the place, and as soon as the tradesman had left him, he prepared to go there himself. He left his wife to look after the homestead, and started on his journey taking his man with him. They stopped at a town on their way, and bought a case of tea, some wine, and other presents, as the tradesman had advised. On and on they went until they had gone more than three hundred miles, and on the seventh day they came to a place where the Bashkirs had pitched their tents. It was all just as the tradesman had said. The people lived on the steppes, by a river, in felt-covered tents. They neither tilled the ground, nor ate bread. Their cattle and horses grazed in herds on the steppe. The colts were tethered behind the tents, and the mares were driven to them twice a day. The mares were milked and from the milk kumiss [2] was made. It was the women who prepared kumiss, and they also made cheese. As far as the men were concerned, drinking kumiss and tea, eating mutton, and playing on their pipes was all they cared about. They were all stout and merry, and all the summer long they never thought of doing any work. They were quite ignorant, and knew no Russian, but were good-natured enough.

As soon as they saw Pahom, they came out of their tents and gathered round their visitor. An interpreter was found, and Pahom told them he had come about some land. The Bashkirs seemed very glad; they took Pahom and led him into one of the best tents, where they made him sit on some down cushions placed on a carpet, while they sat round him. They gave him tea and kumiss, and had a sheep killed, and gave him mutton to eat. Pahom took presents out of his cart and distributed them among the Bashkirs, and divided amongst them the tea. The Bashkirs were delighted. They talked a great deal among themselves, and then told the interpreter to translate.

---

[2] *kumiss,* a liquor made from fermented mare's milk

"They wish to tell you," said the interpreter, "that they like you, and that it is our custom to do all we can to please a guest and to repay him for his gifts. You have given us presents, now tell us which of the things we possess please you best, that we may present them to you."

"What pleases me best here," answered Pahom, "is your land. Our land is crowded, and the soil is exhausted; but you have plenty of land and it is good land. I never saw the like of it."

The interpreter translated. The Bashkirs talked among themselves for a while. Pahom could not understand what they were saying, but saw that they were much amused, and that they shouted and laughed. Then they were silent and looked at Pahom while the interpreter said:

"They wish me to tell you that in return for your presents they will gladly give you as much land as you want. You have only to point it out with your hand and it is yours."

The Bashkirs talked again for a while and began to dispute. Pahom asked what they were disputing about, and the interpreter told him that some of them thought they ought to ask their chief about the land and not act in his absence, while others thought there was no need to wait for his return.

6.

While the Bashkirs were disputing, a man in a large fox-fur cap appeared on the scene. They all became silent and rose to their feet. The interpreter said: "This is our Chief himself."

Pahom immediately fetched the best dressing-gown and five pounds of tea, and offered these to the Chief. The Chief accepted them, and seated himself in the place of honour. The Bashkirs at once began telling him something. The Chief listened for a while, then made a sign with his hand for them to be silent, and addressing himself to Pahom, said in Russian:

"Well, let it be so. Choose whatever piece of land you like; we have plenty of it."

"How can I take as much as I like?" thought Pahom. "I must get a deed to make it secure, or else they may say, 'It is yours,' and afterward may take it away again."

"Thank you for your kind words," he said aloud. "You have much land and I only want a little. But I should like to be sure which bit is mine. Could it not be measured and made over to me? Life and death are in God's hands. You good people give it to me, but your children might wish to take it away again."

"You are quite right," said the Chief. "We will make it over to you."

"I heard that a dealer had been here," continued Pahom, "and that you gave him a little land, too, and signed title-deeds to that effect. I should like to have it done in the same way."

The Chief understood.

"Yes," replied he, "that can be done quite easily. We have a scribe, and we will go to town with you and have the deed properly sealed."

"And what will be the price?" asked Pahom.

"Our price is always the same: one thousand roubles a day."

Pahom did not understand.

"A day? What measure is that? How many acres would that be?"

"We do not know how to reckon it out," said the Chief. "We sell it by the day. As much as you can go round on your feet in a day is yours, and the price is one thousand roubles a day." Pahom was surprised.

"But in a day you can get round a large tract of land," he said.

The Chief laughed.

"It will all be yours!" said he. "But there is one condition: If you don't return on the same day to the spot whence you started, your money is lost."

"But how am I to mark the way that I have gone?"

"Why, we shall go to any spot you like, and stay there. You must start from that spot and make your round, taking a spade with you. Wherever you think necessary, make a mark. At every turning, dig a hole and pile up the turf; then afterwards we will go round with a plough from hole to hole. You may make as large a circuit as you please, but before the sun sets you must return to the place you started from. All the land you cover will be yours."

Pahom was delighted. It was decided to start early next morning. They talked a while, and after drinking some more kumiss and eating some more mutton, they had tea again, and then the night came on. They gave Pahom a feather bed to sleep on, and the Bashkirs dispersed for the night, promising to assemble the next morning at daybreak and ride out before sunrise to the appointed spot.

7.

Pahom lay on the feather bed, but could not sleep. He kept thinking about the land.

"What a large tract I will mark off!" thought he. "I can easily do thirty-five miles in a day. The days are long now, and within a circuit of thirty-five miles what a lot of land there will be! I will sell the poorer land, or let it to the peasants, but I'll pick out the best and farm it. I will buy two ox-teams, and hire two more labourers. About a hundred and fifty acres shall be plough-land, and I will pasture cattle on the rest."

Pahom lay awake all night, and dozed off only just before dawn. Hardly were his eyes closed when he had a dream. He thought he was lying in that same tent, and heard somebody chuckling outside. He wondered who it could be, and rose and went out, and he saw the Bashkir Chief sitting in front of the tent holding his sides and rolling about with laughter. Going nearer to the Chief, Pahom asked: "What are you laughing at?" But he saw that it was no longer the Chief, but the dealer who had recently stopped at his house and had told him about the land. Just as Pahom was going to ask, "Have you been here long?" he saw that it was not the dealer, but the peasant who had come up from the Volga, long ago, to Pahom's old home. Then he saw that it was not the peasant either, but the Devil himself with hoofs and horns, sitting there and chuckling, and before him lay a man barefoot, prostrate on the ground, with only trousers and a shirt on. And Pahom dreamt that he looked more attentively to see what sort of man it was that was lying there, and he saw that the man was dead, and that it was himself!

He woke horror-struck.

"What things one does dream," thought he.

Looking round he saw through the open door that the dawn was breaking.

"It's time to wake them up," thought he. "We ought to be starting."

He got up, roused his man (who was sleeping in his cart), bade him harness; and went to call the Bashkirs.

"It's time to go to the steppe [3] to measure the land," he said.

The Bashkirs rose and assembled, and the Chief came too. Then they began drinking kumiss again, and offered Pahom some tea, but he would not wait.

"If we are to go, let us go. It is high time," said he.

_____
[3] *steppe,* flat, treeless, vast area of land

8.

The Bashkirs got ready and they all started; some mounted on horses, and some in carts. Pahom drove in his own small cart with his servant, and took a spade with him. When they reached the steppe, the morning red was beginning to kindle. They ascended a hillock (called by the Bashkirs a *shikhan*) and, dismounting from their carts and their horses, gathered in one spot. The Chief came up to Pahom and stretching out his arm towards the plain:

"See," said he, "all this, as far as your eye can reach, is ours. You may have any part of it you like."

Pahom's eyes glistened: it was all virgin soil, as flat as the palm of your hand, as black as the seed of a poppy, and in the hollows different kinds of grasses grew breast high.

The Chief took off his fox-fur cap, placed it on the ground and said:

"This will be the mark. Start from here, and return here again. All the land you go round shall be yours."

Pahom took out his money and put it on the cap. Then he took off his outer coat, remaining in his sleeveless undercoat. He unfastened his girdle and tied it tight below his stomach, put a little bag of bread into the breast of his coat, and tying a flask of water to his girdle, he drew up the tops of his boots, took the spade from his man, and stood ready to start. He considered for some moments which way he had better go —it was tempting everywhere.

"No matter," he concluded, "I will go towards the rising sun."

He turned his face to the east, stretched himself, and waited for the sun to appear above the rim.

"I must lose no time," he thought, "and it is easier walking while it is still cool."

The sun's rays had hardly flashed above

the horizon, before Pahom, carrying the spade over his shoulder, went down into the steppe.

Pahom started walking neither slowly nor quickly. After having gone a thousand yards he stopped, dug a hole, and placed pieces of turf one on another to make it more visible. Then he went on; and now that he had walked off his stiffness he quickened his pace. After a while he dug another hole.

Pahom looked back. The hillock could be distinctly seen in the sunlight, and the glittering tires of the cart-wheels. At a rough guess Pahom concluded that he had walked three miles. It was growing warmer; he took off his under-coat, flung it across his shoulder, and went on again. It had grown quite warm now; he looked at the sun, it was time to think of breakfast.

"The first shift is done, but there are four in a day, and it is too soon yet to turn. But I will just take off my boots," said he to himself.

He sat down, took off his boots, stuck them into his girdle, and went on. It was easy walking now.

"I will go on for another three miles," thought he, "and then turn to the left. This spot is so fine, that it would be a pity to lose it. The further one goes, the better the land seems."

He went straight on for a while, and when he looked round, the hillock was scarcely visible and the people on it looked like black ants, and he could just see something glistening in the sun.

"Ah," thought Pahom, "I have gone far enough in this direction, it is time to turn. Besides I am in a regular sweat, and very thirsty."

He stopped, dug a large hole, and heaped up pieces of turf. Next he untied his flask, had a drink, and then turned sharply to the left. He went on and on; the grass was high, and it was very hot.

Pahom began to grow tired: he looked at the sun and saw that it was noon.

"Well," he thought, "I must have a rest."

He sat down, and ate some bread and drank some water; but he did not lie down, thinking that if he did he might fall asleep. After sitting a little while, he went on again. At first he walked easily: the food had strengthened him; but it had become terribly hot, and he felt sleepy; still he went on, thinking: "An hour to suffer, a life-time to live."

He went a long way in this direction also, and was about to turn to the left again, when he perceived a damp hollow: "It would be a pity to leave that out," he thought. "Flax would do well there." So he went on past the hollow, and dug a hole on the other side of it before he turned the corner. Pahom looked toward the hillock. The heat made the air hazy: it seemed to be quivering, and through the haze the people on the hillock could scarcely be seen.

"Oh!" thought Pahom, "I have made the sides too long; I must make this one shorter." And he went along the third side, stepping faster. He looked at the sun: it was nearly half way to the horizon, and he had not yet done two miles of the third side of the square. He was still ten miles from the goal.

"No," he thought, "though it will make my land lopsided, I must hurry back in a straight line now. I might go too far, and as it is I have a great deal of land."

So Pahom hurriedly dug a hole, and turned straight towards the hillock.

9.

Pahom went straight towards the hillock, but he now walked with difficulty. He was done up with the heat, his bare feet were cut and bruised, and his legs began to fail.

He longed to rest, but it was impossible if he meant to get back before sunset. The sun waits for no man, and it was sinking lower and lower.

"Oh dear," he thought, "if only I have not blundered trying for too much! What if I am too late?"

He looked towards the hillock and at the sun. He was still far from his goal, and the sun was already near the rim.

Pahom walked on and on; it was very hard walking, but he went quicker and quicker. He pressed on, but was still far from the place. He began running, threw away his coat, his boots, his flask, and his cap, and kept only the spade which he used as a support.

"What shall I do," he thought again, "I have grasped too much, and ruined the whole affair. I can't get there before the sun sets."

And this fear made him still more breathless. Pahom went on running, his soaking shirt and trousers stuck to him, and his mouth was parched. His breast was working like a blacksmith's bellows, his heart was beating like a hammer, and his legs were giving way as if they did not belong to him. Pahom was seized with terror lest he should die of the strain.

Though afraid of death, he could not stop. "After having run all that way they will call me a fool if I stop now," thought he. And he ran on and on, inflamed his heart still more. He gathered his last strength and ran on.

The sun was close to the rim, and cloaked in mist looked large, and red as blood. Now, yes now, it was about to set! The sun was quite low, but he was also quite near his aim. Pahom could already see the people on the hillock waving their arms to hurry him up. He could see the fox-fur cap on the ground, and the money on it, and the Chief sitting on the ground holding his sides. And Pahom remembered his dream.

"There is plenty of land," thought he, "but will God let me live on it? I have lost my life! I shall never reach that spot!"

Pahom looked at the sun, which had reached the earth: one side of it had already disappeared. With all his remaining strength he rushed on, bending his body forward so that his legs could hardly follow fast enough to keep him from falling. Just as he reached the hillock it suddenly grew dark. He looked up—the sun had already set! He gave a cry: "All my labour has been in vain," thought he, and was about to stop, but he heard the Bashkirs still shouting, and remembered that though to him, from below, the sun seemed to have set, they on the hillock could still see it. He took a long breath and ran up the hillock. It was still light there. He reached the top and saw the cap. Before it sat the Chief laughing and holding his sides. Again Pahom remembered his dream, and he uttered a cry: his legs gave way beneath him; he fell forward and reached the cap with his hands.

"Ah, that's a fine fellow!" exclaimed the Chief. "He has gained much land."

Pahom's servant came running up and tried to raise him, but he saw that blood was flowing from his mouth. Pahom was dead!

The Bashkirs clicked their tongues to show their pity.

His servant picked up the spade and dug a grave long enough for Pahom to lie in, and buried him in it. Six feet from his head to his heels was all he needed.

The man who wrote this story

LEO TOLSTOY   1828–1910

After his father and mother died, Leo Tolstoy was brought up on his father's country estate by his elderly female relatives. Although he had French tutors and later attended the university, he was never really interested in study. He quit the university when he was nineteen and joined in the wild life that was common then for young men of his rank, but his conscience was uneasy. He joined the army, hoping to find a meaning to his existence. As he worked with his gun crew during the long siege of Sevastopol, he felt the hollowness and terror of war. He expressed these feelings in a collection of stories entitled *Sevastopol Tales.*

After traveling in Western Europe, Tolstoy returned to his estate. There he wrote the two books which are famous throughout the world: *War and Peace* and *Anna Karenina.* For a time he seemed content. His estate was thriving and his books were well received. Yet his conscience was again uneasy. He couldn't forget the plight of the Russian peasant and was disturbed by the useless and vain lives of the aristocrats. Because he believed in the good, simple life, he made his own shoes, plowed his fields, and wore a peasant blouse. He founded a school for peasants and wrote articles about the principles of education. But his family did not accept his views. The friction that developed between Tolstoy and his wife and children was the cause of much unhappiness.

He finally left his family, gave up all his worldly possessions, and moved into a small cabin to finish his life. He had little faith that laws and rules would improve society. He preached that society would only be better when people became better.

Let's consider . . .

1. When Pahom finally was able to get some land of his own, what trouble did it cause him?

2. How did you interpret Pahom's dream? What should he have learned from it?

3. How was the question asked in the title answered in the story? Which sentence answered it? Do you think that the idea expressed in this sentence applies to all men?

4. Was the Devil really responsible for Pahom's troubles? If not, who was?

5. Pahom's wife told her sister that country life was better than city life because there were fewer temptations in the country. How did the story prove that temptation does not depend on *where* you are?

6. Have you known people like Pahom? What advice would you give them?

The writer's craft . . .

The **setting** of a story is the location in which the action and events take place.

1. In what ways did Tolstoy make the reader aware of the Russian setting? How many details can you find that identify the location of the story?

2. The setting in some stories is of such importance that you could not change it without losing the whole point of the story. Could the setting of "How Much Land Does a Man Need?" be altered without distorting the story? Why, or why not?

Knowing words . . .

Below are several sentences taken from the selection. Each of the sentences has one or two words written in italics. After you are sure of the meaning of the italicized word, use it in a sentence of your own.

1. The younger sister was *piqued,* and in turn *disparaged* the life of a tradesman, and stood up for that of a peasant.

2. "All right," thought the Devil. "We will have a *tussle.*"

3. He appealed to them most *civilly,* but they still went on.

4. As soon as Pahom and his family arrived at their new *abode,* he applied for admission into the Commune of a large village.

5. Pahom felt still more *aggrieved,* and let his anger loose upon the Elder and the Judges.

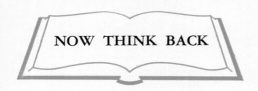

NOW THINK BACK

THINK FOR YOURSELF

It's entertaining to read about someone who gets everything his heart desires. Sometimes, though, a daydream turns into a kind of nightmare—remember Keawe, or Pahom.

Maybe you read the stories in this part of your book just for the fun, the entertainment in them. But perhaps you also asked yourself: "What does the story reveal about the things that count in life?" If you did, you were interested not only in *what* happened, but also in *why* it happened just that way. Thinking for yourself, you gain extras from your reading.

Choose any one of the stories in THE THINGS THAT COUNT. Discuss your answers to the questions below with the members of your committee or class.

1. What was the author's aim in telling this story? This doesn't mean that the story has a moral, as in some of the fables you have read. However, if you clearly understood and enjoyed the story, you should have seen the author's purpose. What was he trying to make you see? Did he succeed in conveying his idea?

2. Do you agree with the author's ideas on the things that count in life? Why, or why not?

3. Was there anything strange about the setting of the story (the time and place of the action)? Did this strangeness of setting help, or spoil, your interest in the story? Why?

4. What are the things in life that really count with you?

SHARE YOUR IDEAS

Have you made up your mind about the things that count in life? Do other people agree with your ideas? The way to find out is through friendly and frank discussion.

After you have read the stories and poems in THE THINGS THAT COUNT, you will want to share your ideas with your classmates. Keep an open mind; be willing to change your beliefs when someone else's ideas seem more convincing than yours. During your discussions, refer to your reading as well as to the personal experiences you have had.

1. What are the things in life that money can buy?

2. What are the things in life that money cannot buy?

3. Which of these are most important to you?

4. Did any of the selections in this part change your ideas about the things that count in life? How?

5. Do older people's ideas about life differ from yours? In what ways? How do you explain the changes that come over people in their views about life? In your opinion, are older people wiser in their attitudes toward successful living? Explain.

6. The stories in this part of your book are all similar in at least one respect. In what way are they alike? In what ways are they different?

7. Where did you come across these quotations?

　　a. "Loss and gain are brothers twain."

　　b. "Is it not a terrible thing to save oneself by the eternal ruin of another?"

　　c. "The time has come for the humble to hate the forces of evil."

Can you find other quotations in THE THINGS THAT COUNT which make an important comment about life in a few words?

WIDEN YOUR EXPERIENCE

Things to do . . .

1. Look critically at the advertisements in magazines and newspapers. How do they help to influence our thinking in determining what *counts*? Bring sample ads to class. Discuss them. What tricks have the advertisers used to get us to *think* a product is important and that *their* product is more important than other similar products?

2. What do older people say in answer to some of the questions that have come up in class during this part? Interview older members of your family and other adults in your community. Plan your interviews so that you will get the reactions of adults of varying ages. Try to learn *why* they have come to believe as they do.

3. Bring to class favorite poems and short quotations on the things that count with you. Plan a period when these selections can be shared with your classmates. Introduce your oral reading of any quotations with an explanation of why you chose them.

4. The chances are that by now you have read most of the selections in this book. Think back over all the stories, and with your classmates vote upon the ten most unforgettable characters you have met. Try to decide what counted for each of these ten people. What effect did their major interests have upon their own lives? Upon the lives of others in the stories? Upon your class?

5. Surely by this time you are more than ready to write something for yourself. Class discussions are all very well, but courtesy demands that you give the other fellow a chance. Only on paper can you have your say without fear of being talked down. Choose from the list below a topic which has possibilities for you. Once more, if you think of a better one—connected, of course, with the general topic of this part—use it.

Money Talks
If I Had a Personal Genie
What Counts with Me
The Happiest Person I Know
My Hardest Decision

More to Read . . .

Albert Schweitzer, Genius in the Jungle by JOSEPH GOLLOMB. This man of many and great talents uses his abilities to establish a medical mission for the natives of Africa. Vanguard Press, Inc., 1949.

The Diary of a Young Girl by ANNE FRANK. Anne Frank was a young German-Jewish girl who was forced to hide in a warehouse in Holland with her family during the Nazi occupation. Her diary describes these years. Doubleday & Company, Inc., 1952.

The Man Without a Country by EVERETT HALE. This man learned the value of citizenship the hard way—by being forbidden ever to enter his country again. Random House, Inc., 1940. (First published about 1863.)

Lost Horizon by JAMES HILTON. Four men are kidnapped in an airplane and crash in the mountains of Tibet. In a secret valley they discover people two hundred years old who seem young and beautiful. William Morrow & Company, Inc., 1933.

Ramona by HELEN HUNT JACKSON. Miss Jackson describes life in old California in the days of the missions, and the tragedy suffered by an Indian through the white man's injustice. Little, Brown and Company, 1939. (First published 1884.)

Sea Wolf by JACK LONDON. Rough treatment by Wolf Larson, rugged skipper of the *Ghost,* helps a rich man discover his own strength. The Macmillan Company, 1904.

A City of Bells by ELIZABETH GOUDGE. Jocelyn Irwin returns from the Boer War to a quiet English cathedral town to recover from his wounds. When he opens a small book shop, he finds friends and unravels a mystery. Coward-McCann Inc., 1936.

The Little World of Don Camillo by GIOVANNI GUARESCHI. In a small Italian town, the issue of Christianity versus Communism is humorously fought out between the mayor and the village priest (who has a mortar somewhere beneath the church). Pellegrini and Cudahy, Inc., 1950.

Here I Stay by ELIZABETH COATSWORTH. When all her neighbors leave the small Maine settlement to move to newly opened land, Margaret Winslow refuses to leave the farm she has helped to clear. Coward-McCann Inc., 1938.

The Snow Goose by PAUL GALLICO. A Canadian snow goose becomes the symbol of British courage at Dunkirk. Alfred A. Knopf, Inc., 1940.

Animal Farm by GEORGE ORWELL. Something is bound to happen when the animals take over the farm so they can live together in peace and harmony. For one thing, the pigs decide to raise the watch dogs in secret. Harcourt, Brace and Company, Inc., 1954.

Fahrenheit 451 by RAY BRADBURY. The hero of this book is a fireman who starts fires instead of putting them out. This science-fiction book has important things to say about freedom of communications. Houghton Mifflin Company, 1953.

The Prince and the Pauper by MARK TWAIN. By a strange mistake, a young king and a poor boy change places. The adventures that follow teach both boys a great deal about each other's lives. Harper & Brothers, 1931. (First published 1881.)

A Christmas Carol by CHARLES DICKENS. It took a ghost to make Mr. Scrooge realize that there was more to Christmas than losing a day of work. In this well-loved story Dickens brings out the true spirit of Christmas. J. B. Lippincott, 1952. (First published 1843.)

Peter Pan and Wendy by SIR JAMES M. BARRIE. A crocodile with a ticking clock in his stomach, treacherous Captain Hook, a magic island, and Peter Pan have made this book popular with young people. It has its serious side, too, because Peter Pan never wants to grow up. Charles Scribner's Sons, 1940. (First published 1911.)

Portrait of Jennie by ROBERT NATHAN. A young artist is inspired by his friendship with a girl from another time and place. This gentle story will leave you wondering. Alfred A. Knopf, Inc., 1939.

Goodby, My Lady by JAMES STREET. The author of "Old Holy Joe" has written this full-length novel about a dog who could laugh and the boy who found her. The boy is faced with a difficult decision—whether or not he should return the dog to its rightful owner. J. B. Lippincott Company, 1954.

Deep Flowing Brook by MADELEINE B. GOSS. This is a well-written biography about one of the greatest composers of all time, Johann Sebastian Bach. It explains how Bach found in his own religious experience the inspiration for creating great music. Henry Holt and Company, Inc., 1938.

Maggie by VIVIAN BRECK. Maggie must make a choice between a life of ease and a life of love and hardship. Doubleday and Company, Inc., 1954.

Trish by MARGARET CRAIG. When she falls in love for the first time, Trish Ingram finds that there are standards of living other than her own. Thomas Y. Crowell Company, 1951.

The Bridges at Toko-ri by JAMES MICHENER. A jet pilot wins his battle during the Korean War by losing his life. Random House, Inc., 1953.

The Pearl by JOHN STEINBECK. A poor Mexican family finds the world's largest pearl but soon learns that wealth cannot bring happiness. The Viking Press, 1947.

GLOSSARY

The purpose of this glossary is to provide a simple definition or synonym for each word, based on the meaning of that word in the context of a selection or in a vocabulary exercise. For a fuller definition or for other meanings of a word, students should consult a standard dictionary.

The system of indicating pronunciation is used by permission of the publishers of *Webster's New International Dictionary,* Second Edition, copyright, 1934, 1939, 1945, 1950, 1953, by G. & C. Merriam Co.

āle, chăotic, câre, ădd, *ȧ*ccount, ärm, ȧsk, sof*ȧ*; ēve, hẹre, ĕvent, ĕnd, silĕnt, makẽr; īce, ĭll, charĭty; ōld, ǒbey, ôrb, ŏdd, sǒft, cǒnnect; fōōd, fŏŏt; out, oil; cūbe, ŭnite, ûrn, ŭp, circ*ŭ*s, menü; chair; go; sing; then, thin; natụre, verdụre; yet; zh = z in azure.

A

abating (*ȧ*·bāt'ĭng). Going down.

abbot (ăb'ŭt). Head of an abbey of monks.

abeam (*ȧ*·bēm'). Directly opposite.

abode (*ȧ*·bōd'). Home.

absconder (ăb·skŏnd'ẽr). One who runs away and hides, usually after a misdeed.

absolved (ăb·sŏlv'd). Excused; released.

abstract (ăb·străkt'). Not concrete.

abstractions (ăb·străk'sh*ŭ*nz). General types, not individuals.

abundance (*ȧ*·bŭn'dăns). A great deal; more than enough.

acceded (ăk·sēd'ĕd). Agreed.

access (ăk'sĕs). Permission to enter.

accustomed (*ȧ*·kŭs't*ŭ*md). Usual.

acknowledge (ăk·nŏl'ĕj). Report receipt of.

adamant (ăd'*ȧ*·mănt). Unyielding.

admirable (ăd'mĭ·rȧ·b'l). Very good.

affliction (*ȧ*·flĭk'sh*ŭ*n). Trouble.

aft (ȧft). To the stern of the ship.

agape (*ȧ*·gāp'). Wide open.

aggrieved (*ȧ*·grēvd'). Injured; put upon.

agility (*ȧ*·jĭl'ĭ·tĭ). Quickness.

agitate (ăj'ĭ·tāt). Stir up; disturb; excite.

airs (ârz). Melodies, tunes.

alert (*ȧ*·lûrt). Wide-awake.

alien (āl'yĕn). Strange.

alimentary (ăl·ĭ·mĕn'tȧ·rĭ). Digestive.

allurement (*ȧ*·lūr'mĕnt). Attraction.

aloft (*ȧ*·lǒft'). Up to the higher yards above the deck.

alternate (ôl'tẽr·nāt). One after the other.

altimeter (ăl·tĭm'ê·tẽr). Instrument for measuring height above sea level.

altitude (ăl'tĭ·tūd). Height.

amalgam (*ȧ*·măl'găm). Mercury mixture used in dentistry.

ambrosia (ăm·brō'zhĭ·*ȧ*). **1.** In Greek mythology: food of the gods. **2.** Modern dessert: cut-up oranges and bananas sprinkled with shredded cocoanut.

amenities (*ȧ*·mĕn'ĭ·tĭz). Niceties; pleasant ways.

amidships (*ȧ*·mĭd'shĭps). In the middle of a ship.

ample subsistence (ăm'p'l s*ŭ*b·sĭs'tĕns). Plenty to live on.

anemones (*ȧ*·nĕm'ǒ·nēz). Wildflowers.

anguish (ăng'gwĭsh). Pain; despair.

animate (ăn'ĭ·māt). **1.** Living. **2.** Make lively; stimulate.

anthracite (ăn'thrȧ·sīt). Hard coal.

anticipation (ăn·tĭs'ĭ·pā'sh*ŭ*n). Looking forward to.

anti-Welsh questions (ăn'tĭ-wĕlsh' kwĕs'ch*ŭ*nz). Subjects involving criticism of the Welsh.

appraise (*ȧ*·prāz'). Set a value on.

appraising (*ȧ*·prāz'ĭng). Evaluating.

619

apprehended effect (ăp · rĕ · hĕnd'ĕd ĕ · fĕkt'). Feared result.

apprehension (ăp · rĕ · hĕn'shŭn). Understanding; idea.

apprehensively (ăp · rĕ · hĕn'sĭv · lĭ). Fearfully.

apprentice (ă · prĕn'tĭs). Person learning a trade.

approbation (ăp'rŏ · bā'shŭn). Praise.

appropriate (ă · prō'prĭ · ĭt). Suitable.

arable (ăr'á · b'l). Fit for plowing.

aristocracy (ăr'ĭs · tŏk'ră · sĭ). Nobility; upper class.

arrears (ă · rērz'). Debts due but not paid. *In arrears:* behindhand in payments or work.

arrogant (ăr'ŏ · gănt). Overbearing.

arteries (är'tĕr · ĭz). Streets.

artful (ärt'fŏŏl). Skillful; crafty.

articulate (är · tĭk'û · lăt). Able to express oneself through words.

ascending (ă · sĕnd'ĭng). Rising.

ascent (ă · sĕnt'). Going up, rising.

ascertain (ăs'ēr · tān'). Find out.

Asmodeus (ăz'mŏ · dē'ŭs). "King of demons" in Jewish tradition.

aspen (ăs'pĕn). A kind of poplar tree.

asperity (ăs · pĕr'ĭ · tĭ). Sharpness.

assumption (ă · sŭmp'shŭn). Taking for granted.

astern (á · stûrn'). At the rear of the ship.

astrakhan (ăs'trá · kăn). Curly fur of young karakul lambs.

asylum (á · sī'lŭm). Place of safety, retreat.

atmosphere (ăt'mŏs · fēr). Air that surrounds the earth.

atmospheric (ăt'mŏs · fēr'ĭk). Having to do with the air surrounding the earth.

atolls (ăt'ŏlz). Ring-shaped coral islands.

atrocious (á · trō'shŭs). Cruel.

audible (ô'dĭ · b'l). Loud enough to be heard.

augmented (ôg · mĕnt'ĕd). Increased.

au revoir (ō'rĕ · vwár'). Good-by till we meet again. *French.*

avail (á · vāl'). Be of use; advantage.

avalanche (ăv'á · lánch). Large mass of descending ice and snow.

awry (á · rī'). Mussed up.

B

backwash (băk'wŏsh'). Water thrown back by the swells or propeller.

ball diamond (bôl' dī'á · mŭnd). Field on which baseball is played.

bark (bärk). Ship.

barnacles (bär'ná · k'lz). Small salt-water animals, with shells, that attach themselves to rocks.

barnacled (bär'ná · k'ld). Covered with barnacles.

baronial (bá · rō'nĭ · ăl). Befitting a baron.

baseless (bās'lĕs). Groundless, without reason.

bas-relief (bä'rĕ · lēf'). Raised.

Bedlam (bĕd'lăm). London hospital for lunatics.

beef-kid (bēf'-kĭd'). Small wooden tub used for sailors' meat supply.

begrudged (bĕ · grŭj'd). Envied.

beholden (bĕ · hōl'd'n). Under obligations, indebted.

belligerently (bĕ · lĭj'ēr · ĕnt · lĭ). In a fighting manner.

bellows (bĕl'ōz). Device for producing a strong current of air to make a fire burn hotter.

bequest (bĕ · kwĕst'). Gift left by will.

berth (bûrth). Bed on a ship, usually fastened to the wall on one side.

beseechingly (bĕ · sēch'ĭng · lĭ). Pleadingly.

beveled (bĕv'ĕld). With an edge cut at an angle.

bickered (bĭk'ērd). Quarreled.

billboard (bĭl'bōrd). Signboard for advertisements.

bivalves (bī'vălvz'). Water animals with a two-valved shell, like oysters or clams.

bizarre (bĭ · zär'). Odd, queer.

blind (blīnd). Artificial or natural screen behind which to hide while duck hunting.

blissfully (blĭs'fŏŏl · lĭ). Happily.

bog (bŏg). Wet spongy ground.

bolted (bōlt'ĕd). Ran away.

bounty (boun'tĭ). Reward.

bousin' your jib (bous'ĭn yŏŏr jĭb). Pulling in your sail: overestimating your powers.

bow (bou).   Forward part of a ship.
box scores (bŏks skōrs).   Official scores entered in a square ruled space known as a "box".
braces (brās'ĕz).   Ropes in the rigging.
brandish (brăn'dĭsh).   Wave.
breached (brēch'd).   Broke through the surface of the water.
bread barge (brĕd bärj).   Box for bread for the crew's use.
breaker (brāk'ēr).   Machine for breaking up coal.
bridling (brī'dlĭng).   Holding the head up in an irritated manner.
brier (brī'ēr).   1. Pipe made of brier root. 2. Thorny plant with a woody stem.
brindled (brĭn'd'ld).   Having dark streaks or spots on a gray or tawny ground.
brined (brīnd).   Pickled in a salt solution.
buckskin-clad (bŭk'skĭn'-klăd').   Dressed in garments made from the skin of a buck.
bulkheads (bŭlk'hĕdz').   Upright partitions in a ship.
bunt (bŭnt).   Lightly hit ball that goes to the ground.
burdened (bûr'd'nd).   Weighed down.
bureaucratic (bū·rŏ·krăt'ĭk).   According to narrow official routine.
burnish (bûr'nĭsh).   Polish.
burrowing (bûr'ō·ĭng).   Digging.

C

calculate (kăl'kŭ·lāt).   Reason; expect.
calculating (kăl'kŭ·lāt'ĭng).   Planning.
camisole (kăm'ĭ·sōl).   Loose-fitting underwaist.
canaille (kà·nāl'; *French:* kà'nä'y').   Lowest class of people, riffraff.
candid (kăn'dĭd).   Frank.
canvassing (kăn'văs·ĭng).   Asking for orders.
capsized (kăp·sīz'd).   Upset.
carrying coals to Newcastle (nū'kàs'l).   Doing something useless like carrying coal to Newcastle which is a coal-mining center.
carven (kär'vĕn).   Cut out, carved of stone or wood.
casque (kăsk).   Helmet.

casters (kås'tērz).   Holders for condiment bottles.
catacombs (kăt'à·kōmz).   Underground gallery with recesses for tombs; thus, dark spaces in the underbrush.
catamounts (kăt'à·mounts).   Wildcats.
cauterized (kô'tēr·īzd).   Burned with a hot iron to prevent infection.
cavally (kà·văl'ĭ).   Kind of spiny-finned fish.
celebrated (sĕl'ê·brāt·ĕd).   Famous.
centrifugal (sĕn·trĭf'ŭ·gᵃl).   (Force) impelling things outward from the center of rotation.
cessation (sĕ·sā'shᵘn).   Stopping.
chafe (chāf).   1. Rub. 2. Make sore by rubbing. 3. To be angry or irritated.
chafing-dish (chāf'ĭng-dĭsh).   Dish for cooking at table.
chamois (shăm'ĭ).   Soft leather.
changeling (chānj'lĭng).   Child secretly left in the place of another.
chanted (chånt'ĕd).   Sang.
charnel house (chär'nĕl hous).   Place where dead bodies are piled.
chawbacons (chô'bà·kᵘnz).   People who live in the country or small towns.
chemidon (shĕm'ĭ·dŏn).   Suitcase or trunk.
chilblains (chĭl'blānz).   Sores caused by cold.
Chinese Evil (chī'nēz' ē'v'l).   Popular name for leprosy.
chipyard (chĭp'yärd).   Area covered with chips from chopping wood.
chloroform (klō'rŏ·fôrm).   Kill with chloroform.
chomping (chômp'ĭng).   Chewing.
chronometer (krŏ·nŏm'ê·tēr).   Timepiece.
circuit (sûr'kĭt).   Trip around.
circumventing (sûr'kŭm·vĕnt'ĭng).   Getting around.
citrus (sĭt'rᵘs).   Having to do with citrus fruits: lemon, orange, grapefruit.
civilly (sĭv'ĭl·lĭ).   Politely.
cleft (klĕft).   Crack.
close-reefed maintopsail (klōs'-rēft' măn·tŏp'sāl).   Sail on the main mast, tied and fastened to yards so that the smallest amount of sail is exposed to the wind.

collaborated (kŏ·lăb′ŏ·rāt·ĕd). Worked together.

comeliness (kŭm′lĭ·nĕs). Attractiveness, good looks.

commenced (kŏ·mĕnst′). Began, started.

commode (kŏ·mōd′). Washstand.

communion (kŏ·mūn′yŭn). Sharing of thoughts and feelings.

companionway (kŏm·păn′yŭn·wā′). Staircase on a ship.

compelling (kŏm·pĕl′lĭng). Forceful.

compensate (kŏm′pĕn·sāt). Make up (for).

complexity (kŏm·plĕk′sĭ·tĭ). Mixture of many.

composite (kŏm·pŏz′ĭt). Combined; made up of a group.

compositions (kŏm′pŏ·zĭsh′ŭnz). Make-up, combination of materials.

comprehendingly (kŏm′prĕ·hĕnd′ĭng·lĭ). With understanding.

comprehension (kŏm′prĕ·hĕn′shŭn). Understanding.

compunction (kŏm′pŭngk′shŭn). Regret, remorse.

computation (kŏm′pŭ·tā′shŭn). Calculation, reckoning.

computer (kŏm·pūt′ēr). That which figures out, reckons.

conceded (kŏn·sēd′ĕd). Agreed, admitted.

conclusive (kŏn·klōō′sĭv). Final.

condolence (kŏn·dō′lĕns). Sympathy.

condone (kŏn·dōn′). Forgive.

confidante (kŏn′fĭ·dănt′). One to whom secrets are confided.

confinement (kŏn·fīn′mĕnt). Imprisonment.

confounding (kŏn·found′ĭng). Confusing, mixing.

conger eel (kŏng′gēr ēl′). A large ocean eel.

conjecture (kŏn·jĕk′tūr). Guess.

connived (kŏ·nīvd′). Worked at secretly.

considerable (kŏn·sĭd′ēr·ȧ·b′l). 1. Large in extent. 2. Rather, quite.

consideration (kŏn·sĭd′ēr·ā′shŭn). Careful thought.

consolation (kŏn′sŏ·lā′shŭn). Comfort.

constantly (kŏn′stănt·lĭ). All the time.

consultation (kŏn·sŭl·tā′shŭn). Talking over, discussion.

contemplation (kŏn′tĕm·plā′shŭn). 1. Plan, intention. 2. Study.

contemporaries (kŏn·tĕm′pŏ·rĕr′ĭz). Schoolmates; people of the same age.

contemptuous (kŏn·tĕmp′tū·ŭs). Scornful.

contiguous (kŏn·tĭg′ū·ŭs). Adjoining.

contorted (kŏn·tôrt′ĕd). Twisted.

contour (kŏn′tōōr′). Outline.

contrived (kŏn·trīvd′). Managed.

convey (kŏn·vā′). Carry.

convulsive (kŏn·vŭl′sĭv). Sudden.

co-ordination (kŏ·ôr·dĭ·nā′shŭn). Muscular control.

coral (kŏr′ăl). Hard red, pink or white substance made of skeletons of tiny sea animals.

coral-encrusted (kŏr′ăl-ĕn·krŭst′ĕd). Coated with coral.

corroboration (kŏ·rŏb′ŏ·rā′shŭn). Agreement, confirmation.

cosmopolite (kŏz·mŏp′ŏ·līt). One who feels at home anywhere in the world.

countenance (koun′tĕ·nȧns). Face.

coverlet (kŭv′ēr·lĕt). Bedspread.

cowering (kou′ēr·ĭng). Crouching in fear.

craftily (krȧf′tĭ·lĭ). With deceit, guile.

crannies (krăn′ĭz). Cracks.

crevice (krĕv′ĭs). Narrow opening, resulting from a split or crack, in rock.

cricket (krĭk′ĕt). Good sportsmanship.

croup (krōōp). Disease causing coughing and difficult breathing.

crucial (krōō′shăl). Critical, decisive.

cue (kū). Signal to speak.

culmination (kŭl′mĭ·nā′shŭn). Climax.

cultivators (kŭl′tĭ·vā′tērz). Earth-workers, farmers.

cultivation (kŭl′tĭ·vā′shŭn). Preparation of land for growing crops.

culvert (kŭl′vērt). Drain.

curate (kū′răt). Assistant clergyman.

curious (kū′rĭ·ŭs). Strange.

curtailed (kûr·tāl′′d). Shortened; restricted.

cuspidor (kūs′pĭ·dôr). Spittoon.

cutler's trade (kŭt′lērz trād). Making and repairing knives.

cynic (sĭn′ĭk). One who doubts goodness of human motives.

D

damnatory (dăm′nȧ · tō′rĭ). Accusing.

deceptive (dě · sĕp′tĭv). Not true.

decision (dě · sĭzh′ŭn). Judgment.

deliberately (dě · lĭb′ĕr · ĭt · lĭ). Slowly.

delusion (dě · lū′zhŭn). False belief.

demand (dě · mȧnd′). Need.

demean'd (dě · mēnd′). Debased, lowered.

demeanor (dě · mēn′ẽr). Manner.

demolition (děm′ô · lĭsh′ŭn). Destruction.

demoniac (dě · mō′nĭ · ăk). Fiendish.

depredation (děp′rě · dā′shŭn). Robbery, plundering.

desecration (děs′ě · krā′shŭn). Insult to something sacred.

designate (děz′ĭg · nāt). Show, point out.

desolate (děs′ô · lĭt). Barren; empty; lonely.

desperate (děs′pẽr · ĭt). Almost hopeless.

despondently (dě · spŏn′děnt · lĭ). Hopelessly.

despotic (děs · pŏt′ĭk). Tyrannical.

devi (dā′vē). Goddess.

dexterity (děks · tēr′ĭ · tĭ). Skill.

diatribe (dī′ȧ · trīb). Abusive speech.

diffidence (dĭf′ĭ · děns). Restraint, lack of assumption.

diffidently (dĭf′ĭ · děnt · lĭ). Shyly, without confidence.

dimity (dĭm′ĭ · tĭ). Fine cotton cloth.

dinghy (dĭng′gĭ). Small rowboat.

disability (dĭs′ȧ · bĭl′ĭ · tĭ). Lack of ability or power.

disconcerting (dĭs′kŏn · sûrt′ĭng). Disturbing.

disconsolately (dĭs · kŏn′sô · lĭt · lĭ). Sadly.

discontent (dĭs′kŏn · těnt′). Not content.

discourse (dĭs′kōrs). Talk.

disdain (dĭs · dān′). Scorn.

disintegrating (dĭs · ĭn′tě · grāt · ĭng). Breaking up.

disjoint (dĭs · joint′). Take apart, separate.

dislike (dĭs · līk′). Not like.

dislodge (dĭs · lŏj′). Move.

dismal (dĭz′mȧl). Gloomy.

dismiss (dĭs · mĭs′). Send away.

disorganize (dĭs · ŏr′găn · īz). Upset the order.

disparaged (dĭs · păr′ĭjd). Belittled.

disparagingly (dĭs · păr′ĭj · ĭng · lĭ). Slightingly.

dispatch (dĭs′păch′). Send off.

dispelled (dĭs · pĕld′). Drove away.

dispensary (dĭs · pĕn′sȧ · rĭ). Place where medicines and medical advice are given free or very cheaply.

dispersed (dĭs · pûrs′t). Separated.

displace (dĭs · plās′). Remove from the usual place.

disputes (dĭs · pūts′). Arguments.

disputations (dĭs′pŭ · tā′shŭnz). Arguments, debates.

disreputable (dĭs · rĕp′ŭ · tȧ · b′l). Shabby, untidy.

dissect (dĭ · sĕkt′). Divide into parts for examination.

dissolved (dĭ · zŏlvd′). Ended.

distinct (dĭs · tĭngkt′). Definite.

diverting (dī · vûr′tĭng). Amusing.

divinity (dĭ · vĭn′ĭ · tĭ). Goddess.

doff your tops'l (dŏf yōor tŏp′s'l). Lower your topsail: be humbled.

doleful (dōl′f′l). Full of grief.

dolorous (dŏl′ẽr · ŭs). Grievous.

dolphins (dŏl′fĭnz). Sea animals like small whales.

domestic (dô · mĕs′tĭk). Tame.

double (dŭb′′l). Sail around.

dreadful (drĕd′fŏol). Very bad.

droll (drōl). Amusing.

dubiously (dū′bĭ · ŭs · lĭ). Doubtfully.

duly (dū′lĭ). Appropriately, properly.

E

eaves (ēvz). Lower edges of a roof which stand out a little from the building.

effervescing (ĕf′ẽr · vĕs′ĭng). Bubbling and hissing.

eight bells (āt bĕlz). Shipboard term for four, eight, or twelve o'clock.

eliminated (ě · lĭm′ĭ · nāt′ĕd). Put out of competition.

elusive (ě · lū′sĭv). Hard to find.

embodiment (ĕm · bŏd′ĭ · měnt). Symbol, expression (of an idea) in physical form.

emitting (ě · mĭt′ĭng). Giving off.

emphasis (ĕm′fȧ · sĭs). Stress, importance.

encampment (ĕn·kămp'mĕnt). Soldiers' camp.

enclosure (ĕn·klō'zhẽr). Fenced-in area.

encounter (ĕn·koun'tẽr). Meet.

endeavor (ĕn·dĕv'ẽr). Try; attempt.

endorsement (ĕn·dôrs'mĕnt). Approval, support.

engulf (ĕn·gŭlf'). Swallow up.

ensuing (ĕn·sū'ĭng). Following.

enthralled (ĕn·thrôld'). Fascinated.

environment (ĕn·vī'rŭn·mĕnt). Surroundings.

epithet (ĕp'ĭ·thĕt). Descriptive expression.

equitable (ĕk'wĭ·tȧ·b'l). Equal; fair.

escarpment (ĕs·kärp'mĕnt). Cliff.

esteem'd (ĕs·tēmd'). Judged, believed.

eternal (ē·tûr'nȧl). 1. Ever-present, constant. 2. Extremely. *Colloquial.*

Eton (ē't'n). Boys' boarding school in England.

evasive (ē·vā'sĭv). Dodging; indirect.

evocative (ē·vŏk'ȧ·tĭv). Calling forth.

ewer (ū'ẽr). Jug, pitcher.

exasperated (ĕg·zăs'pẽr·āt·ĕd). Annoyed.

exclusion (ĕks·klōō'zhŭn). Shutting out.

excursion (ĕks·kûr'zhŭn). Pleasure trip.

exemplary (ĕg·zĕm'plȧ·rĭ). Deserving imitation.

exhibition (ĕk'sĭ·bĭsh'ŭn). For public show and not in the league schedule.

extensive (ĕks·tĕn'sĭv). Large.

extraordinary (ĕks·trôr'dĭ·nĕr'ĭ). Unusual, not ordinary.

extremity (ĕks·trĕm'ĭ·tĭ). Very great.

extricate (ĕks'trĭ·kāt). Take out.

exultant (ĕg·zŭl'tănt). Joyful, triumphant.

exultation (ĕk'sŭl·tā'shŭn). Joy, triumph.

F

facetious (fȧ·sē'shŭs). Full of jokes.

fallow (făl'ō). Land which has been unplanted for at least one growing season.

falteringly (fôl'tẽr·ĭng·lĭ). Waveringly.

fast (fȧst). Fastened securely.

fatalism (fā'tȧl·ĭz'm). Belief that everything is determined in advance by fate.

fathom (făth'ŭm). Measure of 6 feet, used chiefly in speaking of depth of water.

feral (fẽr·ȧl). Wild, savage.

ferocity (fē·rŏs'ĭ·tĭ). Fierceness.

fibrous moorings (fī'brŭs mōōr'ĭngz). Stringy fastenings.

flawless (flô'lĕs). Perfect.

fodder (fŏd'ẽr). Food.

forecastle (fōk's'l). Sailors' rooms in the forward part of a ship.

foretop (fōr'tŏp). Platform at the head of a foremast.

forlornly (fŏr·lôrn'lĭ). Lonely.

forlornness (fŏr·lôrn'nĕs). Feeling of being alone, deserted.

formidable (fôr'mĭ·dȧ·b'l). To be dreaded; hard to deal with.

forum (fō'rŭm). Public meeting for open discussion.

fragment (frăg'mĕnt). A small part.

fragrance (frā'grȧns). Sweet odor.

frailty (frāl'tĭ). Weakness.

frantically (frăn'tĭ·kȧl·ĭ). Excitedly, wildly.

frat (frăt). Fraternity, secret society.

freehold land (frē'hōld' lănd'). Land that can be held for life and passed on to one's children.

frescoed (frĕs'kōd). Painted.

furbish (fûr'bĭsh). Restore, freshen.

furies (fū'rĭz). Avenging spirits.

furled (fûrl'd). Rolled up.

furtive (fûr'tĭv). Sly, secret.

G

galavant (găl'ȧ·vănt'). Roam about.

galley (găl'ĭ). The kitchen of a ship.

galling (gôl'ĭng). Chafing, hurting.

game (gām). A good sport, brave.

Ganges (găn'jēz). River in India.

gargoyle (gär'goil). Grotesque stone or metal head.

gaskets (găs'kĕts). Lines used to lash a furled sail securely.

gear (gēr). Ropes and tools.

genially (jēn'yăl·lĭ). Good-naturedly.

genies (jē'nĭz). Spirits controlled by magic.

genius (jēn'yŭs). Guardian spirit.

gesticulations (jĕs·tĭk' û·lā'shŭnz). Gestures.

ghastly (gàst′lĭ). Horrible.

gloatingly (glōt′ĭng · lĭ). Watched intently and with satisfaction.

gluttony (glŭt′′n · ĭ). Overeating.

gnarled (närld). Twisted.

granite-hard (grăn′ĭt-härd′). Hard as granite—a very hard rock.

graphically (grăf′ĭ · kăl · lĭ). Vividly.

gravity (grăv′ĭ · tĭ). Natural force that pulls objects to the earth.

greenhouse (grēn′hous′). Glass-enclosed section of airplane where the bombardier sits.

grimace (grĭ · mās′). Twisting of the face.

grisly (grĭz′lĭ). Horrible.

grotesque (grŏ · tĕsk′). Odd, fantastic.

grovel (grŏv′′l). Crawl at someone's feet.

guerilla (gĕ · rĭl′à). One who fights the enemy by engaging in irregular warfare independent of the official forces.

gullies (gŭl′ĭz). Small narrow gorges excavated by running water.

gunwale (gŭn′ĕl). Upper edge of a boat's side.

guyed (gīd). Steadied by means of a rope or chain.

gyves (jīvz). Chains about the ankles.

H

habitation (hăb′ĭ · tā′shŭn). House, place in which one lives.

habitually (hà · bĭt′ù · ăl · lĭ). Always, usually.

hair switches (hâr swĭch′ĕz). Separate tresses of long hair, once fashionable to add to one's own.

half nut and half egg (häf nŭt ănd häf ĕg). "Nut" and "egg" are sizes by which coal is graded; hence, a mixture of these two.

halliards (hăl′yĕrdz). Tackle for raising a flag.

hallow'd (hăl′ōd). Shouted.

hallucination (hă · lū · sĭ · nā′shŭn). Experience of seeing things that do not exist.

hanker (hăng′kĕr). Yearn, long for.

hansom (hăn′sŭm). Light two-wheeled covered carriage with driver's seat elevated behind.

harrow (hăr′ō). Farm implement for pulverizing the soil.

hasaika (hä · zhĭ′kà). Female owner of a house or business. *Russian.*

hatchway (hăch′wā′). Opening in the ceiling.

hauled (hôld). Changed course.

hazardous (hăz′ĕr · dŭs). Dangerous.

headlong retreat (hĕd′lŏng rĕ · trēt′). Running away hurriedly.

heathen (hē′thĕn). One who does not acknowledge the God of the Bible.

heave to (hēv tōō). To bring a ship to a standstill.

helm (hĕlm). Wheel by which ship is steered.

hesitant (hĕz′ĭ · tănt). Undecided.

hideous (hĭd′ĕ · ŭs). Horribly ugly.

hillocks (hĭl′ŭks). Little hills.

hindrance (hĭn′drăns). Obstacle, interference.

hived (hīv′d). Locked up together.

hoax (hōks). Trick.

hoisted (hoist′ĕd). Raised or lifted by means of tackle.

holocaust (hŏl′ô · kôst). Complete destruction.

home-cabin (hōm′-kăb′ĭn). Log cabin for the family to live in.

horizontal (hŏr′ĭ · zŏn′tăl). Flat.

host (hōst). Army.

hostile (hŏs′tĭl). Unfriendly.

hove-to (hōv-tōō). Without forward motion.

humiliating (hŭ · mĭl′ĭ · āt′ĭng). Humbling; embarrassing.

hydraulic (hī · drô′lĭk). Concerned with or operated by water.

hypochondriac (hī · pô · kŏn′drĭ · ăk). One who imagines he is ill when he is not.

I

idioms (ĭd′ĭ · ŭmz). Phrases with special meanings.

ignoramus (ĭg′nô · rā′mŭs). Dunce.

ignored (ĭg · nōrd′). Paid no attention to.

imbecile (ĭm′bĕ · sĭl). Fool; stupid person.

immeasurable (ĭ · mĕzh′ĕr · à · b′l). Beyond measuring.

immense (ĭ · mĕns′). Very thick, huge.

imminent collision (ĭm'ĭ · nĕnt kŏ · lĭzh'ŭn). Being about to run into each other.

immobile (ĭm · mō'bĭl). Still, motionless.

impassive (ĭm · păs'ĭv). Unmoved, showing no emotion.

impede (ĭm · pēd'). Interfere with, hinder.

imperil (ĭm · pĕr'ĭl). Endanger.

impertinence (ĭm · pûr'tĭ · nĕns). Rudeness.

imperturbability (ĭm'pēr · tûr'bȧ · bĭl'ĭ · tĭ). Calmness.

impervious (ĭm · pûr'vĭ · ŭs). Not influenced by.

impetuously (ĭm · pĕt'ṵ · ŭs · lĭ). Quickly, vehemently.

implacably (ĭm · plā'kȧ · b'lĭ). Unyieldingly.

implements (ĭm'plĕ · mĕnts). Tools.

implicitly (ĭm · plĭs'ĭt · lĭ). Absolutely.

imposture (ĭm · pŏs'tûr). Deception.

impressive (ĭm · prĕs'ĭv). Outstanding.

inadequate (ĭn · ăd'ē · kwĭt). Not sufficient.

inanimate (ĭn · ăn'ĭ · māt). Without life.

inappropriate (ĭn'ȧ · prō'prĭ · ĭt). Not suitable.

inarticulate (ĭn'är · tĭk'ṵ · lȧt). Unable to express oneself through words.

inarticulateness (ĭn'är · tĭk'ṵ · lȧt · nĕs). Inability to speak.

incapable (ĭn · kā'pȧ · b'l). Not capable.

incapacitate (ĭn'kȧ · păs'ĭ · tāt). Make incapable or unfit.

incomprehensible (ĭn'kŏm · prĕ · hĕn'sĭ · b'l). Impossible to understand.

incontinently (ĭn · kŏn'tĭ · nĕnt · lĭ). Without restraint.

incorporated (ĭn · kôr'pŏ · rāt'ĕd). Merged with, united.

incredible (ĭn · krĕd'ĭ · b'l). Unbelievable.

incubator (ĭn'kṵ · bā'tēr). Apparatus for hatching eggs artificially.

indecisively (ĭn'dē · sī'sĭv · lĭ). Uncertainly.

indefinitely (ĭn · dĕf'ĭ · nĭt · lĭ). For a long time.

indenture (ĭn · dĕn'tṵr). Contract for service.

indicating (ĭn'dĭ · kāt · ĭng). Pointing out.

indiscriminately (ĭn · dĭs · krĭm'ĭ · nĭt · lĭ). Carelessly; anywhere at all.

indistinct (ĭn'dĭs · tĭngkt'). Not clear.

indolently (ĭn'dŏ · lĕnt · lĭ). Lazily.

indulgence (ĭn · dŭl'jĕns). Tolerance; favor.

indulgently (ĭn · dŭl'jĕnt · lĭ). Tolerantly, giving in.

ineffable (ĭn · ĕf'ȧ · b'l). Indescribable.

ineffective (ĭn'ĕ · fĕk'tĭv). Of little use.

ineligible (ĭn · ĕl'ĭ · jĭ · b'l). Not eligible, not qualified.

inevitable (ĭn · ĕv'ĭ · tȧ · b'l). Certain, sure, unavoidable.

inexplicable (ĭn · ĕks'plĭ · kȧ · b'l). That cannot be explained.

infected (ĭn · fĕkt'ĕd). Influenced.

infield (ĭn'fēld). Baseball diamond.

infinitesimal (ĭn'fĭn · ĭ · tĕs'ĭ · măl). Very tiny.

infinity (ĭn · fĭn'ĭ · tĭ). Space without bounds.

infirmities (ĭn · fûr' · mĭ · tĭz). Weaknesses.

ingenious (ĭn · jēn'yŭs). Clever.

ingenuity (ĭn'jē · nū'ĭ · tĭ). Cleverness.

ingratiatingly (ĭn · grā'shĭ · āt'ĭng · lĭ). Seeking approval.

inimical (ĭn · ĭm'ĭ · kăl). Unfriendly.

initiative (ĭ · nĭsh'ĭ · ȧ'tĭv). Leadership.

insensate (ĭn · sĕn'sȧt). Inhuman.

insensibly (ĭn · sĕn'sĭ · b'lĭ). Unconsciously.

instinctively (ĭn · stĭngk'tĭv · lĭ). Without stopping to think.

insulators (ĭn'sṵ · lā'tērz). Porcelain or glass devices to prevent passage of heat or electricity.

intact (ĭn · tăkt'). Untouched.

intelligible (ĭn · tĕl'ĭ · jĭ · b'l). Understandable.

interminably (ĭn · tûr'mĭ · nȧ · b'lĭ). Endlessly.

intervene (ĭn'tēr · vēn). Come between.

intimate (ĭn'tĭ · mĭt). Close.

intimated (ĭn'tĭ · māt · ĕd). Suggested.

intricacies (ĭn'trĭ · kȧ · sĭz). Complicated details.

intricate (ĭn'trĭ · kĭt). Complicated, difficult to follow.

intuitively (ĭn · tū'ĭ · tĭv · lĭ). Without reasoning, instinctively.

invocation (ĭn · vŏ · kā'shŭn). Prayer; plea.

involuntary (ĭn · vŏl'ŭn · tĕr'ĭ). Not by one's own will.

iota (ĭ · ō'tȧ). Tiny bit.

irascibly (ĭ·răs'ĭ·blĭ). With rising temper.
irrigate (ĭr'ĭ·gāt). Water land artificially by ditches, flooding, etc.
islet (ī'lĕt). Small island.
itinerant (ī·tĭn'ēr·ănt). Going from place to place.

J

jaguar (jăg'wär). Wild animal like a leopard.
jibes (jībz). Taunts, jeers.
Job (jōb). Book of the Old Testament.
jouncing (joun'sĭng). Shaking, jolting.
journeyman's wages (jûr'nĭ·mănz wāj'ĕz). Wages paid to a man experienced in his trade.
jubilee (jōō'bĭ·lē). Joyousness.
Judge Kenesaw Mountain Landis (jŭj kĕn'ĕ·sô moun'tĕn lăn'dĭs). Commissioner of major league baseball, 1921-1944.
judicially (jōō·dĭsh'ăl·lĭ). According to law.
junction (jŭngk'shŭn). Joining place.

K

karakul (kăr'ȧ·kŭl). Soft curly black fur.
kibosh (kī'bŏsh). *To put the kibosh on—* to finish off, put an end to. *Slang.*
kin (kĭn). Relation, family.
Klondike (klŏn'dīk). Region in northwestern Canada, along the Yukon River, famous for its gold fields.
knead (nēd). To work and press with the hands.
knouter (nout'ēr). One who beats criminals with a whip, or knout.

L

£4. Four pounds (fōr poundz). English money, worth today about $11.50.
lacerated (lăs'ēr·āt'ĕd). Torn.
lagoon (lȧ·gōōn'). Water within a ring-shaped coral island.
lamentable (lăm'ĕn·tȧ·b'l). Sorrowful.
languid (lăng'gwĭd). Without energy.

languor (lăng'gēr). Dullness, sleepiness.
lapsed (lăpsd). Slipped.
larboard quarter (lär'bōrd kwôr'tĕr). Part of a ship halfway between the stern and center, on the left as one faces the bow.
larrup (lăr'ŭp). Beat.
lashed (lăsht). Bound.
lashings (lăsh'ĭngz). Places where the raft was tied.
latitude (lăt'ĭ·tūd). Measure of distance on earth'surface north or south of the Equator.
launched (lônchd). Put in the water.
lay (lā). Bet.
lead-line (lĕd'-līn'). A sounding line.
leeward (lē'wērd). Away from the wind.
levity (lĕv'ĭ·tĭ). Nonsense, frivolity.
literal (lĭt'ēr·ăl). True; exact.
literally (lĭt'ēr·ăl·lĭ). Without exaggeration.
lithe (līth). Supple.
livery (lĭv'ēr·ĭ). Concerned with the keeping of horses and carriages.
longitude (lŏn'jĭ·tūd). Measure of distance on earth's surface east and west of a line (usually Greenwich meridian) running from the North to the South Pole.
lowered (lō'ērd). Let down (from a ship).
lurched (lûrchd). Rolled.

M

madrepore (măd'rĕ·pōr). Chief reef-building corals of tropical seas.
mainsail (mān'sāl). The chief or largest sail of a ship.
mainyard (mān'yärd'). Principal cross-piece that supports a square sail.
malevolent (mȧ·lĕv'ȯ·lĕnt). Spiteful.
malice (măl'ĭs). Ill will.
malicious (mȧ·lĭsh'ŭs). Spiteful.
manacles (măn'ȧ·k'lz). Handcuffs.
maneuvring (mȧ·nōō'vēr·ĭng). Leading.
manifest (măn'ĭ·fĕst). Known, evident.
mantle (măn't'l). Cover.
manufactory (măn'ŭ·făk'tȯ·rĭ). Place where something is made.
marrow (măr'ō). Soft substance that fills hollow central part of bones.

materialized (ma·tẽr'ĭ·ăl·īzd). Appeared.

maul (môl). A heavy hammer, thus, fist.

maze (māz). Network.

meandering (mḗ·ăn'dẽr·ĭng). Winding.

meanest (mēn'ĕst). Poorest.

measure (mĕzh'ẽr). Limitations; abilities.

medley (mĕd'lĭ). Piece of music made up of parts of other pieces.

menace (mĕn'ĭs). Threat.

metallic (mḗ·tăl'ĭk). Hard in quality, like metal.

meteorites (mē'tḗ·ẽr·īts). Stony or metallic bodies that fall to the earth through space.

middling (mĭd'lĭng). Moderately, fairly.

migrate (mī'grāt). Move.

mockingly (mŏk'ĭng·lĭ). Making fun of.

moire (mwär). Watered silk.

mole (mōl). Breakwater; pier.

molten (mōl'tĕn). Melted.

monotonous (mṓ·nŏt'ṓ·nŭs). Without change, always the same.

moor (mōor). Open waste land.

moorings (mōor'ĭngz). Ropes.

morose (mṓ·rōs'). Gloomy.

mottled (mŏt'l'd). Spotted.

mottoes (mŏt'ōz). Words or brief sentences adopted as rules of conduct.

mould (mōld). Earth, humus.

moused (mouzd). Searched in a sly manner, like a mouse.

mouser (mouz'ẽr). Mouse catcher.

Moxie (mŏk'sē). A soft drink popular fifty years ago.

mullioned (mŭl'yŭnd). Divided into small panes.

multitude (mŭl'tĭ·tūd). Throng, large number of people.

musing (mūz'ĭng). Thinking, meditating.

musket-carrying (mŭs'kĕt-kăr'ĭ·ing). Carrying guns, or muskets.

musty (mŭs'tĭ). Damp and dusty odor.

muted (mūt'ĕd). Quiet.

mutton (mŭt''n). Meat from sheep.

myriad (mĭr'ĭ·ăd). Great number.

mysticism (mĭs'tĭ·sĭz'm). Doctrine of spiritual insight independent of the mind.

mythic (mĭth'ĭk). Based on ancient tradition.

N

nainsook (nān'sōok). Fine, sheer cotton cloth.

naive (nä·ēv'). Simple, innocent.

napoleon (na·pō'lḗ·ŭn). Former French gold coin of 20 francs ($3.86).

narrative (năr'a·tĭv). Story.

nationalism (năsh'ŭn·ăl·ĭz'm). Patriotism.

navigable (năv'ĭ·ga·b'l). Deep enough for boats.

navigator (năv'ĭ·gā'tẽr). Officer in charge of determining course and position of an airplane.

nectar (nĕk'tẽr). In Greek mythology, the drink of the gods.

nominal (nŏm'ĭ·năl). Very small.

nondescript (nŏn'dḗ·skrĭpt). Of no particular kind.

nonplussed (nŏn'plŭst). Baffled, puzzled.

nonsectarian (nŏn·sĕk·târ'ĭ·ăn). Open to members of any church.

novice (nŏv'ĭs). Beginner.

O

obdurate (ŏb'dù·råt). Unyielding.

obesity (ṓ·bēs'ĭ·tĭ). Fatness.

oblong (ŏb'lŏng). 1. Longer than broad. 2. A rectangular piece.

obnoxious (ŏb·nŏk'shŭs). Offensive, disagreeable.

obsession (ŏb·sĕsh'ŭn). Fixed idea.

obstinate (ŏb'stĭ·nĭt). Stubborn.

omen (ō'mĕn). A sign.

ominous (ŏm'ĭ·nŭs). Threatening, foreshadowing evil.

ominously (ŏm'ĭ·nŭs·lĭ). Threateningly.

opinionated (ṓ·pĭn'yŭn·āt'ĕd). Stubbornly sticking to one's own opinions.

opportune (ŏp'ŏr·tūn'). Favorable.

oppressive (ṓ·prĕs'ĭv). Hard to bear.

oppressively (ṓ·prĕs'ĭv·lĭ). Heavily, very.

optimistic (ŏp'tĭ·mĭs'tĭk). Cheerful.

oratorical (ŏr'a·tŏr'ĭ·kăl). Like a public speaker.

orient (ō'rĭ·ĕnt). Pearl of great luster; shine, luster.

orientation (ō'rĭ·ĕn·tā'shŭn). Sense of position in relation to places and things.

oscillate (ŏs'ĭ·lāt). Swing, move.

outcropping (out'krŏp·ĭng). Coming to the earth's surface.

outmaneuvred (out'mȧ·nōō'vērd). Outwitted, surpassed in maneuvering.

outrage (out'rāj). Offense.

outrigger (out'rĭg·ēr). Framework, ending in a float, extending from the side of a canoe to prevent upsetting.

outrigger-poles (out'rĭg·ēr-pōlz'). Part of the outrigger.

overhauled (ō'vēr·hôld'). Gone over thoroughly.

P

painstakingly (pānz'tāk'ĭng·lĭ). Very carefully.

palatable (păl'ĭt·ȧ·b'l). Agreeable.

paling (pāl'ĭng). Getting lighter.

palpitation (păl'pĭ·tā'shŭn). Rapid beating.

palsy-twitching (pôl'zĭ-twĭch'ĭng). Jerking like the uncontrolled movements of one suffering from palsy.

panne (păn). Velvet-like dress material, soft and lustrous.

papier mache (pā'pēr mȧ·shā'). Hard strong substance made of paper pulp mixed with size, rosin, etc.

parasite (păr'ȧ·sīt). An animal or plant that lives on another.

pariah dogs (pȧ·rī'ȧ). Half-wild mongrel dogs native to India.

parry (păr'ĭ). Offset, prevent.

particulars (pēr·tĭk'ů·lērz). Details, full information.

partitioned (pär·tĭsh'ŭnd). Walled off.

Paumotans (pä'ŏō·mō'tănz). Inhabitants of the Paumotu Islands, South Pacific.

pectoral fins (pĕk'tŏ·răl fĭnz). Fins on the underside of a fish, just behind the head.

pellets (pĕl'ĕts). Very small balls.

pent-up (pĕnt-ŭp). Held in, suppressed.

perambulating (pēr·ăm'bů·lāt·ing). Walking.

perception (pēr·sĕp'shŭn). Awareness.

periodic (pēr'ĭ·ŏd'ĭk). Occurring at regular intervals.

periscope (pĕr'ĭ·skōp). Vertical tube on a submarine, equipped with mirrors, affording a view of the surface.

perpetual (pēr·pĕt'ů·ăl). Constant, lasting forever.

perseverance (pûr'sĕ·vēr'ăns). Sticking to it.

pervading (pēr·vād'ĭng). Spreading throughout, present all through.

pervious (pûr'vĭ·ŭs). Allowing substances to pass through.

pessimists (pĕs'ĭ·mĭsts). Those who always expect the worst.

pestiferous (pĕs·tĭf'ēr·ŭs). Troublesome, annoying.

phial (fī'ăl). Small glass bottle.

philoprogenitiveness (fĭl'ŏ·prŏ·jĕn'ĭ·tĭv·nĕs). Love of children.

pigheaded (pĭg'hĕd'ĕd). Stubborn.

pillage (pĭl'ĭj). Loot.

pinch-hitting (pĭnch-hĭt'ĭng). Substituting, going to bat for another.

pinion (pĭn'yŭn). Wing feather.

pinnacles (pĭn'ȧ·k'lz). High peaks.

piqued (pēkd). Annoyed, hurt.

pivot (pĭv'ŭt). A turn or swing around in place.

placid (plăs'ĭd). Smooth.

placidly (plăs'ĭd·lĭ). Calmly.

plaintively (plān'tĭv·lĭ). Sadly.

plankton (plăngk'tŏn). Swimming animal and plant life of the ocean.

pleurisy (plōōr'ĭ·sĭ). Disease of lungs and throat.

plummet (plŭm'ĕt). Weight fastened to a line.

potentially (pŏ·tĕn'shăl·lĭ). Capable of being.

posterity (pŏs·tĕr'ĭ·tĭ). Descendants.

practice (prăk'tĭs). Habit, custom.

precariously (prê·kâr'ĭ·ŭs·lĭ). Insecurely.

precedent (prĕs'·ê·dĕnt). Example.

precipitous (prê·sĭp'ĭ·tŭs). Steep.

predetermined (prē'dĕ·tûr'mĭnd). Decided in advance.

preening (prēn'ĭng). Smoothing, arranging so as to look one's best.

preliminary (prĕ·lĭm'ĭ·nĕr'ĭ). First.

premises (prĕm'ĭs·ĕz). Offices, buildings.

premonition (prē'mŏ·nĭsh'ŭn). Forewarning.

presently (prĕz'ĕnt·lĭ). In a few minutes.

presumably (prĕ·zūm'à·blĭ). Supposedly, probably.

prevail (prĕ·vāl'). Conquer.

primer class (prĭm'ēr klàs). Class of young children, just beginning to read.

primly (prĭm'lĭ). Stiffly.

proclivities (prŏ·klĭv'ĭ·tĭz). Inclinations, tendencies.

procured (prŏ·kūrd'). Obtained, furnished.

proffering (prŏf'ēr·ĭng). Offering.

proficiency (prŏ·fĭsh'ĕn·sĭ). Skill.

prohibitionist (prō'ĭ·bĭsh'ŭn·ĭst). Opposed to the sale and use of liquor.

projecting (prŏ·jĕkt'ĭng). Sticking out.

promenades (prŏm'ĕ·nädz). Walks taken in a public place for pleasure or show.

propagation (prŏp'à·gā'shŭn). Breeding, giving birth to.

propositions (prŏp'ŏ·zĭsh'ŭnz). Problems to be solved.

protozoa (prō'tŏ·zō'à). Microscopic single-celled animals.

protracted (prŏ·trăkt'ĕd). Continued, drawn out.

protrude (prŏ·trōōd'). Stick out.

providential (prŏv'ĭ·dĕn'shăl). Result of God's care.

provisions (prŏ·vĭzh'ŭnz). Supply of food.

proximity (prŏks·ĭm'ĭ·tĭ). Nearness.

psychic phenomena (sī'kĭk fĕ·nŏm'ĕ·nà). Circumstances not explained by natural physical processes.

puff (pŭf). Blow with short blasts.

pugnacity (pŭg·năs'ĭ·tĭ). Readiness to fight.

pungent (pŭn'jĕnt). Sharp.

pursue (pēr·sū'). 1. Chase. 2. Continue.

Q

quarry (kwŏr'ĭ). Animal chased in a hunt.

quarterdeck (kwôr'tēr·dĕk'). The part of the upper deck between the mainmast and the stern.

quartering (kwôr'tēr·ĭng). A fourth of the way around.

quays (kēz). Docks or masonry embankments where boats may tie up.

querying (kwē̠r'ĭ·ĭng). Asking.

quietude (kwī'ĕ·tūd). Stillness.

quips (kwĭps). Clever sayings.

quivering (kwĭv'ēr·ĭng). Shaking, trembling.

quizzically (kwĭz'ĭ·kăl·lĭ). Questioningly.

quota (kwō'tà). Share of total.

R

radiation (rā'dĭ·ā'shŭn). Giving off energy.

ramrod (răm'rŏd'). Straight and stiff, like a rod.

ranker (răngk'ēr). Coarser.

rationalize (răsh'ŭn·ăl·īz). Reason out.

rattan (ră·tăn'). Wicker.

ravine (rà·vēn'). Deep, narrow valley.

reactionary (rĕ·ăk'shŭn·ĕr'·ĭ). One who looks backward, wants everything as it "used to be."

realization (rē'ăl·ĭ·zā'shŭn). Understanding.

recalculate (rē'kăl'kŭ·lāt). Figure over again.

receding (rĕ·sēd'ĭng). Backing away.

recitations (rĕs'ĭ·tā'shŭnz). Things repeated from memory.

reckoning (rĕk'ŭn·ĭng). Determining ship's position.

recollection (rĕk'ŏ·lĕk'shŭn). Memory.

reconnoiter (rĕk'ŏ·noi'tēr). Look around.

rectory (rĕk'tŏ·rĭ). Clergyman's house.

recumbent (rĕ·kŭm'bĕnt). Leaning.

regenerate (rĕ·jĕn'ēr·āt). Reestablish, restore.

reincarnation (rē'ĭn·kär·nā'shŭn). Rebirth of the soul in a new body.

remonstratingly (rĕ·mŏn'strāt·ĭng·lĭ). Protestingly, pleadingly.

rending (rĕnd'ĭng). Tearing.

rendered (rĕn'dērd). Made.

repast (rĕ·pàst'). Meal.

replenished (rĕ·plĕn'ĭsht). Populated; refilled.

reposed (rĕ·pōzd'). Placed (in trust).

reservoirs (rĕs'ẽr·vwôrz). Places where water is collected and stored in large quantity.

resignedly (rē·sīn'ĕd·lĭ). Patiently, submissively.

restive (rĕs'tĭv). Uneasy.

reticent (rĕt'ĭ·sĕnt). Reserved, unwilling to talk much.

rhetoric (rĕt'ŏ·rĭk). Art of speaking.

ridge (rĭj). Raised narrow strip of ground.

ridgepole (rĭj'pōl'). The horizontal timber along the top of a roof.

rigging (rĭg'ĭng). Ropes and chains that support and work the masts, yards, and sails of a ship.

rollicking (rŏl'ĭk·ĭng). Merry.

romance (rŏ·măns'). Fantastic stories.

rooting (rōōt'ĭng). Digging with their snouts.

roubles (rōō'b'lz). Russian coins, worth today about twenty-five cents.

rural (rōōr'ăl). Country.

rural retreat (rōōr'ăl rē·trēt'). Quiet place in the country.

ruminatively (rōō'mĭ·nā'tĭv·lĭ). Musingly, thoughtfully.

Rush (rŭsh). Dr. Benjamin Rush, 1745-1803. American physician and Revolutionary patriot.

rustle (rŭs'l). Steal, especially cattle.

rustled (rŭs'ld). Made a succession of small whispering sounds.

S

sally (săl'ĭ). Rush out.

sanctity (săngk'tĭ·tĭ). Sacredness.

sanctuary (săngk'tŭ·ĕr·ĭ). Safety.

sarcastic (sär·kăs'tĭk). Sneering.

satellite (săt'ĕ·līt). Space station.

sauntering (sôn'tẽr·ĭng). Walking aimlessly, slowly.

savage garment (săv'ĭj gär'mĕnt). Clothing worn by natives.

savve (săv'ĭ). Know. *Slang.*

scanning (skăn'ĭng). Looking over.

scornfully (skôrn'fōol·lĭ). Full of anger and disgust.

scribe (skrīb). Man who writes.

scruples (skrōō'p'lz). Principles of behavior.

scuffle (skŭf''l). Scrap, push about.

sculpin (skŭl'pĭn). Kind of fish.

scuttle (skŭt''l). Small opening or hatchway in a ship's deck with a lid for covering it.

scuttlebutt (skŭt''l·bŭt). Cask containing water for the day's use.

seams caulked (sēmz kôkd). Watertight, seaworthy; hence, ready.

secure (sē·kūr'). Tie down, fasten.

semblance (sĕm'blăns). Form, appearance.

sequence (sē'kwĕns). Series of melodic phrases (in background music, used to set a mood or indicate passage of time).

serrated (sĕr'āt·ĕd). Jagged, saw-toothed.

severity (sē·vĕr'ĭ·tĭ). Strictness.

sexton (sĕks'tŭn). Caretaker of a church.

sheened (shēnd). Bright.

shikari (shĭ·kä'rĭ). Native hunting guide.

ship chandler (shĭp chăn'dlẽr). Dealer in ship's supplies.

shoals (shōlz). Large numbers.

shroud (shroud). Cloth or garment in which a dead person is wrapped for burial.

shrouds (shroudz). Ropes from mast to sides of a ship.

siesta (sĭ·ĕs'tà). Afternoon nap.

silhouette (sĭl'ōō·ĕt'). Shadow picture.

simoleons (sĭ·mō'lĕ·ŭnz). Dollars. *Slang.*

singular (sĭng'gŭ·lẽr). Extraordinary.

sinuous (sĭn'û·ŭs). Curving.

skeins (skānz). Small hanks of embroidery thread.

skewer (skū'ẽr). Heavy pin of metal or wood to hold meat in place while cooking.

skirmish (skûr'mĭsh). Slight conflict.

slithering (slĭth'ẽr·ĭng). Sliding along the ground like a snake.

sloshed (slŏsht). Splashed.

slouched hat (sloucht hăt). Soft hat with a wide flexible brim.

sluggish (slŭg'ĭsh). Dull, slow.

slurred (slûrd). Blurred, indistinct.

smote (smōt). Hit.

snipe (snīp). A marsh bird.

snuff (snŭf). Powdered tobacco to be taken into the nose by snuffing.

sobered (sō'bẽrd).   Made serious.

soberly (sō'bẽr·lĭ).   Seriously.

solenoid (sō'lĕ·noid).   Tubular coil for production of a magnetic field.

solicitor (sŏ·lĭs'ĭ·tẽr).   Lawyer.

solicitude (sŏ·lĭs'ĭ·tūd).   Concern, anxiety.

solicitously (sŏ·lĭs'ĭ·tŭs·lĭ).   Anxiously.

solicitousness (sŏ·lĭs'ĭ·tŭs·nĕs).   Carefulness; concern.

solitary (sŏl'ĭ·tẽr'ĭ).   All alone.

somnolent (sŏm'nŏ·lĕnt).   Drowsy, inclined to sleep.

sophister (sŏf'ĭs·tẽr).   Thinker, philosopher.

sought (sôt).   Looked for.

sovereign (sŏv'ẽr·ĭn).   British gold coin worth 20 shillings or 1 pound.

spat (spăt).   Slap.

specimen (spĕs'ĭ·mĕn).   Part taken to show the quality of the whole; sample.

spectacle (spĕk'tȧ·k'l).   An unusual sight, a display.

spectral (spĕk'trăl).   Ghostly.

spectre (spĕk'tẽr).   Ghost.

speculating (spĕk'ů·lāt·ĭng).   Thinking, meditating.

speculation (spĕk'ů·lā'shŭn).   Conjecture, thought.

spindly (spĭn'dlĭ).   Skinny-legged.

splicing (splīs'ĭng).   Fastening together by interweaving the strands.

spondulix (spŏn·dū'lĭks).   Money. *Slang.*

spontaneous (spŏn·tā'nĕ·ŭs).   Natural, of itself.

staccato (stȧ·kä'tō).   Short, sharp, as of notes or beats.

stagnant (stăg'nănt).   Dull, not active.

stamina (stăm'ĭ·nȧ).   Endurance.

Starbowlines (stär'bŏ·līnz).   Men in the starboard watch.

stealthy (stĕl'thĭ).   Secret, sly.

steerage (stēr'ĭj).   The stern; cheapest, and poorest, passenger quarters.

steppe (stĕp).   Flat, treeless, vast area of land.

steward (stū'ẽrd).   Manager.

stimulus (stĭm'ů·lŭs).   Something that stirs one to action or effort.

stratagem (străt'ȧ·jĕm).   Trick, deception.

stresses (strĕs'ĕz).   Strains, pressures.

subchaser (sŭb'chās'ẽr).   Submarine chaser.

subconscious (sŭb·kŏn'shŭs).   Existing but not realized.

subdued (sŭb·dūd').   Quiet.

subjugated (sŭb'jōō·gāt·ĕd).   Subjected, forced to endure.

submerged (sŭb·mûrjd').   Under water.

subsided (sŭb·sīd'ĕd).   Became quiet.

substantial (sŭb·stăn'shăl).   Well developed.

succession (sŭk·sĕsh'ŭn).   One after another.

sufficient (sŭ·fĭsh'ĕnt).   Enough.

suffragettes (sŭf'rȧ·jĕts').   Women who sought the right to vote.

sugar-hogshead (shŏŏg'ẽr-hŏgz'hĕd).   A large sugar barrel.

"sumter" (sumpter) mule (sŭmp'tẽr mūl).   A mule for carrying baggage.

sundered (sŭn'dẽrd).   Separated.

sundries (sŭn'drĭz).   Odds and ends.

sure-footed (shŏŏr'-fŏŏt'ĕd).   Not liable to stumble.

surety (shŏŏr'tĭ).   Certainty.

surreptitiously (sûr'ĕp·tĭsh'ŭs·lĭ)   Stealthily.

suspended (sŭs·pĕnd'ĕd).   Stopped; lifted.

sustain (sŭs·tān').   Keep up, continue.

swaggering (swăg'ẽr·ĭng).   Walking with a bold swing.

swell (swĕl).   Wave.

swooshing (swōōsh'ĭng).   Whirling around.

sylvan (sĭl'văn).   Of the woods.

symmetrical (sĭ·mĕt'rĭ·kăl).   Orderly.

sympathetic (sĭm·pȧ·thĕt'ĭk).   Kind.

sympathetically (sĭm'pȧ·thĕt'ĭ·kăl·ĭ).   In a friendly manner.

synchronization (sĭng'krŏ·nĭ·zā'shŭn).   At the same time.

synthetic (sĭn·thĕt'ĭk).   Artificially made.

T

tableland (tā'b'l·lănd').   Broad elevated plateau.

tacit (tăs'ĭt).   Understood without being said.

tackles (tăk''lz). Ropes and pulleys used for handling sails.

tactful (tăkt'fŏŏl). Skilful in dealing with others.

taffeta (tăf'ĕ·tȧ). A stiff silk.

taking drift (tāk'ĭng drĭft). Determining how much an aircraft had blown off course.

tallow-chandler and sope boiler (tăl'ō-chȧn'dlēr and sōp boil'ēr). Candle and soap maker.

tang (tăng). Smell.

tangible (tăn'jĭ·b'l). That can be touched.

tapering (tā'pēr·ĭng). Getting smaller toward one end.

Tara (tä'rä). Name of the schooner.

tartar (tär'tēr). Person of violent temper.

tasselled (tăs''ld). Decorated with tassels.

tedious (tē'dĭ·ŭs). Tiresome, boring.

tenacious (tĕ·nā'shŭs). Holding fast.

tendrils (tĕn'drĭlz). Threadlike wisps.

tenfold (tĕn'fōld'). Ten times the usual amount.

terminal (tûr'mĭ·nȧl). Concluding.

testimonials (tĕs'tĭ·mō'nĭ·ȧlz). Things given or done to show esteem, admiration, or gratitude.

tethered (tĕth'ērd). Tied.

thaw (thô). Melt.

theosophy (thĕ·ŏs'ŏ·fĭ). A religious system based on mystical insight rather than knowledge of the physical world.

tholepins (thōl'pĭnz'). Wooden pegs set into the gunwale or deck to hold an oar in position.

thong (thŏng). Fastener.

thoroughfare (thûr'ŏ·fâr'). Main street.

tiered (tērd). Made in sections, one above the other.

timorously (tĭm'ēr·ŭs·lĭ). Timidly, frightened.

timothy grass (tĭm'ŏ·thĭ grȧs). A grass grown for hay.

Titan (tī'tăn). Huge, like the giant Titans of Greek mythology.

tithe (tīth). Voluntary share.

tolerable (tŏl'ēr·ȧ·b'l). Moderately.

touché (tōō'shā'). Touched, your point, in fencing; therefore "you have scored" in an argument. *French.*

tract (trăkt). 1. A religious pamphlet. 2. Area, piece of land.

traipsing (trāps'ĭng). Walking.

transformation (trăns'fôr·mā'shŭn). Complete change.

transplantation (trăns'plăn·tā'shŭn). Being moved from one place to another.

traversed (trăv'ērsd). Crossed.

treacherous (trĕch'ēr·ŭs). Not to be trusted.

trencher (trĕn'chēr). Wooden plate.

trial (trī'ȧl). Attempt.

trudging (trŭj'ĭng). Walking steadily.

truss (trŭs). Support, brace.

trustee (trŭs·tē'). Member of the town governing body.

tufted (tŭft'ĕd). With small clusters of hair.

tunnies (tŭn'ĭz). Large sea fish.

turmoil (tûr'moil). Great disturbance.

tussle (tŭs''l). Contest, rough match.

tussocky (tŭs'ŭk·ĭ). Full of bunches of grass or sedge.

two-shilling bit (tōō'-shĭl'ĭng bĭt). Piece of money worth at the time about 50 cents.

U

ultra-high (ŭl'trȧ-hī'). Extremely high.

un momento (ŭn mō·mĕnt'ō). One moment. *Spanish.*

unanimous (ŭ·năn'ĭ·mŭs). In complete agreement.

unappealing (ŭn'ȧ·pēl'ĭng). Not attractive.

uncomprehending (ŭn·kŏm'prē·hĕnd'ĭng). Not understanding.

uncompromising (ŭn·kŏm'prŏ·mīz'ĭng). Stern, not yielding.

uncongenial (ŭn·kŏn·jēn'yȧl). Unfriendly, disagreeable.

undefinable (ŭn·dē·fīn'ȧ·b'l). Indefinite.

undeleterious (ŭn·dĕl'ē·tēr'ĭ·ŭs). Harmless.

undergrowth (ŭn'dēr·grōth'). Shrubs and plants growing under taller trees.

unduly (ŭn·dū'lĭ). More than is right or proper.

unextinguishable (ŭn·ĕks·tĭng'gwĭsh·ȧ·b'l). Unyielding, not to be beaten.

universal (ū'nĭ·vûr'sȧl). General.

unperturbed (ŭn′pẽr · tûrb′′d). Untroubled.

unsentimental (ŭn · sĕn′tĭ · mĕn′tăl). Not apt to show emotion.

unusual (ŭn · ū′zhŏŏ · ăl). Not usual, not common.

unutterable (ŭn · ŭt′ẽr · ȧ · b′l). Too great for words.

utilized (ū′tĭ · līzd). Used.

V

valise (vȧ · lēs′). Traveling bag.

variations (vâr′ĭ · ā′shŭnz). Changes.

veered (vērd). Changed direction.

vegetation (vĕj′ĕ · tā′shŭn). Plant life.

vehemently (vē′ĕ · mĕnt · lĭ). Forcefully.

velour (vĕ · lŏŏr′). Velvety cotton material.

vengeful (vĕnj′fŏŏl). Wanting to punish or harm in return for harm received.

verandah (vĕ · răn′dȧ). Porch.

verbatim (vûr · bā′tĭm). Word for word.

versatile (vûr′sȧ · tĭl). Skilful in many ways.

vexation (vĕks · ā′shŭn). Annoyance.

victuals (vĭt′′lz). Food.

vigil (vĭj′ĭl). Watchful attention.

vigilance (vĭj′ĭ · lăns). Watchfulness.

vindicate (vĭn′dĭ · kāt). Make up for, justify.

vindictive (vĭn · dĭk′tĭv). Bearing a grudge.

vindictiveness (vĭn · dĭk′tĭv · nĕs). Vengeance.

visas (vē′zȧz). Endorsements on a passport permitting passage.

visionary (vĭzh′ŭn · ẽr′ĭ). Imaginary.

vociferous (vȯ · sĭf′ẽr · ŭs). Loud, noisy.

void (void). Empty, without any.

vulnerable (vŭl′nẽr · ȧ · b′l). Open to attack.

W

wainscoting (wān′skŭt · ĭng). Wooden paneling extending part way up a wall.

wan (wôn). Faint.

warrant (wŏr′ănt). Written order.

watch (wŏch). Period of duty for members of ship's crew, usually lasting four hours.

water glass (wô′tẽr glȧs′). Open box or tube with a glass bottom, used for examining objects under water.

weaver's beam (wēv′ẽrz bēm). Large rod that is part of the loom used in weaving.

well-aimed (wĕl′-āmd′). Aimed carefully, precisely.

wet (wĕt). One opposed to the Prohibition amendment.

whence (hwĕns). From where.

whimpering (hwĭm′pẽr · ĭng). Crying feebly.

wind direction trace (wĭnd dĭ · rĕk′shŭn trās). Device which records wind direction on paper.

windmills (wĭnd′mĭlz). Thrashes arms about like a windmill.

wistful (wĭst′fŏŏl). Wishing without hope.

withe (wĭth). Flexible wand, stick.

witheband (wĭth′bănd). Band of flexible withes, or hickory branches, used to tie up fodder.

wore ship (wōr shĭp). Turned around so that the wind was on the opposite side.

wrenched (rĕnchd). Pulled apart.

writhed (rīthd). Twisted.

Y

yardarm (yärd′ärm′). Either end of the beam or pole which supports a square sail.

yards (yärdz). Long spars, tapering at the ends, to support and extend sails.

Z

zither (zĭth′ẽr). Stringed musical instrument.

TABLE OF CONTENTS ACCORDING TO TYPES

Selections preceded by a † are supplementary readings and are not accompanied by an introduction or by exercises.

SHORT STORY

NOVEL

POETRY

POETRY *(Continued)*

DRAMA

BIOGRAPHY

AUTOBIOGRAPHY

PERSONAL ACCOUNT

INDEX